PEARSON CUSTOM LIBRARY

PEARSON

Pearson Learning Solutions, 501 Boylston Street, Suite 900, Boston, MA 02116
A Pearson Education Company
www.pearsoned.com

10   17

ISBN 10: 1-269-82659-X
ISBN 13: 978-1-269-82659-4

Table of Contents

Introduction to Quantitative Analysis

LEARNING OBJECTIVES

After completing this chapter, students will be able to:

1. Describe the quantitative analysis approach.
2. Understand the application of quantitative analysis in a real situation.
3. Describe the three categories of business analytics.
4. Describe the use of modeling in quantitative analysis.
5. Use computers and spreadsheet models to perform quantitative analysis.
6. Discuss possible problems in using quantitative analysis.
7. Perform a break-even analysis.

CHAPTER OUTLINE

1 Introduction
2 What Is Quantitative Analysis?
3 Business Analytics
4 The Quantitative Analysis Approach
5 How to Develop a Quantitative Analysis Model

6 The Role of Computers and Spreadsheet Models in the Quantitative Analysis Approach
7 Possible Problems in the Quantitative Analysis Approach
8 Implementation—Not Just the Final Step

Summary • Glossary • Key Equations • Self-Test • Discussion Questions and Problems • Case Study: Food and Beverages at Southwestern University Football Games • Bibliography

From Chapter 1 of *Quantitative Analysis for Management*, Twelfth Edition. Barry Render, Ralph M. Stair, Jr., Michael E. Hanna, and Trevor S. Hale. Copyright © 2015 by Pearson Education, Inc. All rights reserved.

1 Introduction

People have been using mathematical tools to help solve problems for thousands of years; however, the formal study and application of quantitative techniques to practical decision making is largely a product of the twentieth century. The techniques we study in this text have been applied successfully to an increasingly wide variety of complex problems in business, government, health care, education, and many other areas.

It isn't enough, though, just to know the mathematics of how a particular quantitative technique works; you must also be familiar with the limitations, assumptions, and specific applicability of the technique. The successful use of quantitative techniques usually results in a solution that is timely, accurate, flexible, economical, reliable, and easy to understand and use.

In this text, there are *QA (Quantitative Analysis) in Action* boxes that provide success stories on the applications of management science. They show how organizations have used quantitative techniques to make better decisions, operate more efficiently, and generate more profits. Taco Bell has reported saving over $150 million with better forecasting of demand and better scheduling of employees. NBC television increased advertising revenue by over $200 million between 1996 and 2000 by using a model to help develop sales plans for advertisers. Continental Airlines saves over $40 million per year by using mathematical models to quickly recover from disruptions caused by weather delays and other factors.

To see other examples of how companies use quantitative analysis or operations research methods to operate better and more efficiently, go to the website www.scienceofbetter.org. The success stories presented there are categorized by industry, functional area, and benefit. These success stories illustrate how operations research is truly the "science of better."

2 What Is Quantitative Analysis?

Quantitative analysis uses a scientific approach to decision making.

Quantitative analysis is the scientific approach to managerial decision making. This field of study has several different names including quantitative analysis, **management science**, and operations research. These terms are used interchangeably in this text.

Whim, emotions, and guesswork are not part of the quantitative analysis approach. The approach starts with data. Like raw material for a factory, these data are manipulated or processed into information that is valuable to people making decisions. This processing and manipulating of raw data into meaningful information is the heart of quantitative analysis. Computers have been instrumental in the increasing use of quantitative analysis.

In solving a problem, managers must consider both qualitative and quantitative factors. For example, we might consider several different investment alternatives, including certificates of deposit at a bank, investments in the stock market, and an investment in real estate. We can use quantitative analysis to determine how much our investment will be worth in the future when deposited at a bank at a given interest rate for a certain number of years. Quantitative analysis can also be used in computing financial ratios from the balance sheets for several companies whose stock we are considering. Some real estate companies have developed computer programs that use quantitative analysis to analyze cash flows and rates of return for investment property.

In addition to quantitative analysis, *qualitative* factors should also be considered. The weather, state and federal legislation, new technological breakthroughs, the outcome of an election, and so on may all be factors that are difficult to quantify.

Both qualitative and quantitative factors must be considered.

Because of the importance of qualitative factors, the role of quantitative analysis in the decision-making process can vary. When there is a lack of qualitative factors and when the problem, model, and input data remain the same, the results of quantitative analysis can *automate* the decision-making process. For example, some companies use quantitative inventory models to determine automatically *when* to order additional new materials. In most cases, however, quantitative analysis will be an *aid* to the decision-making process. The results of quantitative analysis will be combined with other (qualitative) information in making decisions.

Quantitative analysis has been particularly important in many areas of management. The field of production management, which evolved into production/operations management (POM) as society became more service oriented, uses quantitative analysis extensively. While POM focuses on internal operations of a company, the field of supply chain management takes a more complete view of the business and considers the entire process of obtaining materials from suppliers, using the materials to develop products, and distributing these products to the final consumers. Supply chain management makes extensive use of many management science models. Another area of management that could not exist without the quantitative analysis methods presented in this text, and perhaps the hottest discipline in business today, is business analytics.

3 Business Analytics

Business analytics is a data-driven approach to decision making that allows companies to make better decisions. The study of business analytics involves the use of large amounts of data, which means that information technology related to the management of the data is very important. Statistical and quantitative analysis are used to analyze the data and provide useful information to the decision maker.

Business analytics is often broken into three categories: descriptive, predictive, and prescriptive. **Descriptive analytics** involves the study and consolidation of historical data for a business and an industry. It helps a company measure how it has performed in the past and how it is performing now. **Predictive analytics** is aimed at forecasting future outcomes based on patterns in the past data. Statistical and mathematical models are used extensively for this purpose. **Prescriptive analytics** involves the use of optimization methods to provide new and better ways to operate based on specific business objectives. The optimization models presented in this text are very important to prescriptive analytics. While there are only three business analytics categories, many business decisions are made based on information obtained from two or three of these categories.

Many of the quantitative analysis techniques presented in the text are used extensively in business analytics. Table 1 highlights the three categories of business analytics, and it places many of the topics in this text in the most relevant category. Keep in mind that some topics could possibly be placed in a different category. Some of the material in this text could overlap two or even three of these categories. Nevertheless, all of these quantitative analysis techniques are very important tools in business analytics.

The three categories of business analytics are descriptive, predictive, and prescriptive.

TABLE 1

Business Analytics and Quantitative Analysis Models

BUSINESS ANALYTICS CATEGORY	QUANTITATIVE ANALYSIS TECHNIQUE
Descriptive analytics	• Statistical measures such as means and standard deviations • Statistical quality control
Predictive analytics	• Decision analysis and decision trees • Regression models • Forecasting • Project scheduling • Waiting line models • Simulation • Markov analysis
Prescriptive analytics	• Inventory models such as the economic order quantity • Linear programming • Transportation and assignment models • Integer programming, goal programming, and nonlinear programming • Network models

HISTORY The Origin of Quantitative Analysis

Quantitative analysis has been in existence since the beginning of recorded history, but it was Frederick W. Taylor who in the early 1900s pioneered the principles of the scientific approach to management. During World War II, many new scientific and quantitative techniques were developed to assist the military. These new developments were so successful that after World War II many companies started using similar techniques in managerial decision making and planning. Today, many organizations employ a staff of operations research or management science personnel or consultants to apply the principles of scientific management to problems and opportunities.

The origin of many of the techniques discussed in this text can be traced to individuals and organizations that have applied the principles of scientific management first developed by Taylor; they are discussed in *History* boxes scattered throughout the text.

4   The Quantitative Analysis Approach

Defining the problem can be the most important step.

Concentrate on only a few problems.

FIGURE 1

The Quantitative Analysis Approach

The types of models include physical, scale, schematic, and mathematical models.

The quantitative analysis approach consists of defining a problem, developing a model, acquiring input data, developing a solution, testing the solution, analyzing the results, and implementing the results (see Figure 1). One step does not have to be finished completely before the next is started; in most cases, one or more of these steps will be modified to some extent before the final results are implemented. This would cause all of the subsequent steps to be changed. In some cases, testing the solution might reveal that the model or the input data are not correct. This would mean that all steps that follow defining the problem would need to be modified.

Defining the Problem

The first step in the quantitative approach is to develop a clear, concise statement of the **problem**. This statement will give direction and meaning to the following steps.

In many cases, defining the problem is the most important and the most difficult step. It is essential to go beyond the symptoms of the problem and identify the true causes. One problem may be related to other problems; solving one problem without regard to other related problems can make the entire situation worse. Thus, it is important to analyze how the solution to one problem affects other problems or the situation in general.

It is likely that an organization will have several problems. However, a quantitative analysis group usually cannot deal with all of an organization's problems at one time. Thus, it is usually necessary to concentrate on only a few problems. For most companies, this means selecting those problems whose solutions will result in the greatest increase in profits or reduction in costs to the company. The importance of selecting the right problems to solve cannot be overemphasized. Experience has shown that bad problem definition is a major reason for failure of management science or operations research groups to serve their organizations well.

When the problem is difficult to quantify, it may be necessary to develop *specific, measurable* objectives. A problem might be inadequate health care delivery in a hospital. The objectives might be to increase the number of beds, reduce the average number of days a patient spends in the hospital, increase the physician-to-patient ratio, and so on. When objectives are used, however, the real problem should be kept in mind. It is important to avoid obtaining specific and measurable objectives that may not solve the real problem.

Developing a Model

Once we select the problem to be analyzed, the next step is to develop a **model**. Simply stated, a model is a representation (usually mathematical) of a situation.

Even though you might not have been aware of it, you have been using models most of your life. You may have developed models about people's behavior. Your model might be that friendship is based on reciprocity, an exchange of favors. If you need a favor such as a small loan, your model would suggest that you ask a good friend.

Of course, there are many other types of models. Architects sometimes make a *physical model* of a building that they will construct. Engineers develop *scale models* of chemical plants, called pilot plants. A *schematic model* is a picture, drawing, or chart of reality. Automobiles, lawn mowers, gears, fans, typewriters, and numerous other devices have schematic models (drawings and

IN ACTION — Operations Research and Oil Spills

Operations researchers and decision scientists have been investigating oil spill response and alleviation strategies since long before the BP oil spill disaster of 2010 in the Gulf of Mexico. A four-phase classification system has emerged for disaster response research: mitigation, preparedness, response, and recovery. *Mitigation* means reducing the probability that a disaster will occur and implementing robust, forward-thinking strategies to reduce the effects of a disaster that does occur. *Preparedness* is any and all organization efforts that happen *a priori* to a disaster. *Response* is the location, allocation, and overall coordination of resources and procedures during the disaster that are aimed at preserving life and property. *Recovery* is the set of actions taken to minimize the long-term impacts of a particular disaster after the immediate situation has stabilized.

Many quantitative tools have helped in areas of risk analysis, insurance, logistical preparation and supply management, evacuation planning, and development of communication systems. Recent research has shown that while many strides and discoveries have been made, much research is still needed. Certainly each of the four disaster response areas could benefit from additional research, but recovery seems to be of particular concern and perhaps the most promising for future research.

Source: Based on N. Altay and W. Green. "OR/MS Research in Disaster Operations Management," *European Journal of Operational Research* 175, 1 (2006): 475–493.

---

pictures) that reveal how these devices work. What sets quantitative analysis apart from other techniques is that the models that are used are mathematical. A **mathematical model** is a set of mathematical relationships. In most cases, these relationships are expressed in equations and inequalities, as they are in a spreadsheet model that computes sums, averages, or standard deviations.

Although there is considerable flexibility in the development of models, most of the models presented in this text contain one or more variables and parameters. A **variable**, as the name implies, is a measurable quantity that may vary or is subject to change. Variables can be *controllable* or *uncontrollable*. A controllable variable is also called a *decision variable*. An example would be how many inventory items to order. A **parameter** is a measurable quantity that is inherent in the problem. The cost of placing an order for more inventory items is an example of a parameter. In most cases, variables are unknown quantities, while parameters are known quantities. All models should be developed carefully. They should be solvable, realistic, and easy to understand and modify, and the required **input data** should be obtainable. The model developer has to be careful to include the appropriate amount of detail to be solvable yet realistic.

Acquiring Input Data

Once we have developed a model, we must obtain the data that are used in the model (*input data*). Obtaining accurate data for the model is essential; even if the model is a perfect representation of reality, improper data will result in misleading results. This situation is called *garbage in, garbage out*. For a larger problem, collecting accurate data can be one of the most difficult steps in performing quantitative analysis.

Garbage in, garbage out means that improper data will result in misleading results.

There are a number of sources that can be used in collecting data. In some cases, company reports and documents can be used to obtain the necessary data. Another source is interviews with employees or other persons related to the firm. These individuals can sometimes provide excellent information, and their experience and judgment can be invaluable. A production supervisor, for example, might be able to tell you with a great degree of accuracy the amount of time it takes to produce a particular product. Sampling and direct measurement provide other sources of data for the model. You may need to know how many pounds of raw material are used in producing a new photochemical product. This information can be obtained by going to the plant and actually measuring with scales the amount of raw material that is being used. In other cases, statistical sampling procedures can be used to obtain data.

Developing a Solution

Developing a solution involves manipulating the model to arrive at the best (optimal) solution to the problem. In some cases, this requires that an equation be solved for the best decision. In other cases, you can use a *trial and error* method, trying various approaches and picking the one that results in the best decision. For some problems, you may wish to try all possible values for the variables in the model to arrive at the best decision. This is called *complete enumeration*. This text also shows you how to solve very difficult and complex problems by repeating a few simple steps until you find the best solution. A series of steps or procedures that are repeated is called an **algorithm**, named after Algorismus, an Arabic mathematician of the ninth century.

The input data and model determine the accuracy of the solution.

The accuracy of a solution depends on the accuracy of the input data and the model. If the input data are accurate to only two significant digits, then the results can be accurate to only two significant digits. For example, the results of dividing 2.6 by 1.4 should be 1.9, not 1.857142857.

Testing the Solution

Testing the data and model is done before the results are analyzed.

Before a solution can be analyzed and implemented, it needs to be tested completely. Because the solution depends on the input data and the model, both require testing.

Testing the input data and the model includes determining the accuracy and completeness of the data used by the model. Inaccurate data will lead to an inaccurate solution. There are several ways to test input data. One method of testing the data is to collect additional data from a different source. If the original data were collected using interviews, perhaps some additional data can be collected by direct measurement or sampling. These additional data can then be compared with the original data, and statistical tests can be employed to determine whether there are differences between the original data and the additional data. If there are significant differences, more effort is required to obtain accurate input data. If the data are accurate but the results are inconsistent with the problem, the model may not be appropriate. The model can be checked to make sure that it is logical and represents the real situation.

Although most of the quantitative techniques discussed in this text have been computerized, you will probably be required to solve a number of problems by hand. To help detect both logical and computational mistakes, you should check the results to make sure that they are consistent with the structure of the problem. For example, (1.96)(301.7) is close to (2)(300), which is equal to 600. If your computations are significantly different from 600, you know you have made a mistake.

Analyzing the Results and Sensitivity Analysis

Analyzing the results starts with determining the implications of the solution. In most cases, a solution to a problem will result in some kind of action or change in the way an organization is operating. The implications of these actions or changes must be determined and analyzed before the results are implemented.

Sensitivity analysis determines how the solutions will change with a different model or input data.

Because a model is only an approximation of reality, the sensitivity of the solution to changes in the model and input data is a very important part of analyzing the results. This type of analysis is called **sensitivity analysis** or *postoptimality analysis*. It determines how much the solution will change if there were changes in the model or the input data. When the solution is sensitive to changes in the input data and the model specification, additional testing should be performed to make sure that the model and input data are accurate and valid. If the model or data are wrong, the solution could be wrong, resulting in financial losses or reduced profits.

The importance of sensitivity analysis cannot be overemphasized. Because input data may not always be accurate or model assumptions may not be completely appropriate, sensitivity analysis can become an important part of the quantitative analysis approach.

Implementing the Results

The final step is to *implement* the results. This is the process of incorporating the solution into the company. This can be much more difficult than you would imagine. Even if the solution is optimal and will result in millions of dollars in additional profits, if managers resist the new solution, all of the efforts of the analysis are of no value. Experience has shown that a large number of quantitative analysis teams have failed in their efforts because they have failed to implement a good, workable solution properly.

After the solution has been implemented, it should be closely monitored. Over time, there may be numerous changes that call for modifications of the original solution. A changing economy, fluctuating demand, and model enhancements requested by managers and decision makers are only a few examples of changes that might require the analysis to be modified.

MODELING IN THE REAL WORLD
Railroad Uses Optimization Models to Save Millions

Defining the Problem

CSX Transportation, Inc., has 35,000 employees and annual revenue of $11 billion. It provides rail freight services to 23 states east of the Mississippi River, as well as parts of Canada. CSX receives orders for rail delivery service and must send empty railcars to customer locations. Moving these empty railcars results in hundreds of thousands of empty-car miles every day. If allocations of railcars to customers is not done properly, problems arise from excess costs, wear and tear on the system, and congestion on the tracks and at rail yards.

Developing a Model

In order to provide a more efficient scheduling system, CSX spent 2 years and $5 million developing its Dynamic Car-Planning (DCP) system. This model will minimize costs, including car travel distance, car handling costs at the rail yards, car travel time, and costs for being early or late. It does this while at the same time filling all orders, making sure the right type of car is assigned to the job, and getting the car to the destination in the allowable time.

Acquiring Input Data

In developing the model, the company used historical data for testing. In running the model, the DCP uses three external sources to obtain information on the customer car orders, the available cars of the type needed, and the transit-time standards. In addition to these, two internal input sources provide information on customer priorities and preferences and on cost parameters.

Developing a Solution

This model takes about 1 minute to load but only 10 seconds to solve. Because supply and demand are constantly changing, the model is run about every 15 minutes. This allows final decisions to be delayed until absolutely necessary.

Testing the Solution

The model was validated and verified using existing data. The solutions found using the DCP were found to be very good compared to assignments made without DCP.

Analyzing the Results

Since the implementation of DCP in 1997, more than $51 million has been saved annually. Due to the improved efficiency, it is estimated that CSX avoided spending another $1.4 billion to purchase an additional 18,000 railcars that would have been needed without DCP. Other benefits include reduced congestion in the rail yards and reduced congestion on the tracks, which are major concerns. This greater efficiency means that more freight can ship by rail rather than by truck, resulting in significant public benefits. These benefits include reduced pollution and greenhouse gases, improved highway safety, and reduced road maintenance costs.

Implementing the Results

Both senior-level management who championed DCP and key car-distribution experts who supported the new approach were instrumental in gaining acceptance of the new system and overcoming problems during the implementation. The job description of the car distributors was changed from car allocators to cost technicians. They are responsible for seeing that accurate cost information is entered into DCP, and they also manage any exceptions that must be made. They were given extensive training on how DCP works so they could understand and better accept the new system. Due to the success of DCP, other railroads have implemented similar systems and achieved similar benefits. CSX continues to enhance DCP to make DCP even more customer friendly and to improve car-order forecasts.

Source: Based on M. F. Gorman, et al. "CSX Railway Uses OR to Cash in on Optimized Equipment Distribution," *Interfaces* 40, 1 (January–February 2010): 5–16.

The Quantitative Analysis Approach and Modeling in the Real World

The quantitative analysis approach is used extensively in the real world. These steps, first seen in Figure 1 and described in this section, are the building blocks of any successful use of quantitative analysis. As seen in our first *Modeling in the Real World* box, the steps of the quantitative analysis approach can be used to help a large company such as CSX plan for critical scheduling needs now and for decades into the future. Throughout this text, you will see how the steps of the quantitative analysis approach are used to help countries and companies of all sizes save millions of dollars, plan for the future, increase revenues, and provide higher-quality products and services. The *Modeling in the Real World* boxes in this text will demonstrate to you the power and importance of quantitative analysis in solving real problems for real organizations. Using the steps of quantitative analysis, however, does not guarantee success. These steps must be applied carefully.

5   How to Develop a Quantitative Analysis Model

Developing a model is an important part of the quantitative analysis approach. Let's see how we can use the following mathematical model, which represents profit:

$$\text{Profit} = \text{Revenue} - \text{Expenses}$$

Expenses include fixed and variable costs.

In many cases, we can express revenues as price per unit multiplied times the number of units sold. Expenses can often be determined by summing fixed costs and variable cost. Variable cost is often expressed as variable cost per unit multiplied times the number of units. Thus, we can also express profit in the following mathematical model:

$$\text{Profit} = \text{Revenue} - (\text{Fixed cost} + \text{Variable cost})$$
$$\text{Profit} = (\text{Selling price per unit})(\text{Number of units sold})$$
$$- [\text{Fixed cost} + (\text{Variable cost per unit})(\text{Number of units sold})]$$
$$\text{Profit} = sX - [f + vX]$$
$$\text{Profit} = sX - f - vX \tag{1}$$

where

$$s = \text{selling price per unit}$$
$$f = \text{fixed cost}$$
$$v = \text{variable cost per unit}$$
$$X = \text{number of units sold}$$

The parameters in this model are f, v, and s, as these are inputs that are inherent in the model. The number of units sold (X) is the decision variable of interest.

EXAMPLE: PRITCHETT'S PRECIOUS TIME PIECES We will use the Bill Pritchett clock repair shop example to demonstrate the use of mathematical models. Bill's company, Pritchett's Precious Time Pieces, buys, sells, and repairs old clocks and clock parts. Bill sells rebuilt springs for a price per unit of $8. The fixed cost of the equipment to build the springs is $1,000. The variable cost per unit is $3 for spring material. In this example,

$$s = 8$$
$$f = 1,000$$
$$v = 3$$

The number of springs sold is X, and our profit model becomes

$$\text{Profit} = \$8X - \$1,000 - \$3X$$

If sales are 0, Bill will realize a $1,000 loss. If sales are 1,000 units, he will realize a profit of $4,000 ($4,000 = ($8)(1,000) − $1,000 − ($3)(1,000)). See if you can determine the profit for other values of units sold.

The BEP results in $0 profits.

In addition to the profit models shown here, decision makers are often interested in the **break-even point** (BEP). The BEP is the number of units sold that will result in $0 profits. We set profits equal to $0 and solve for X, the number of units at the BEP:

$$0 = sX - f - \nu X$$

This can be written as

$$0 = (s - \nu)X - f$$

Solving for X, we have

$$f = (s - \nu)X$$
$$X = \frac{f}{s - \nu}$$

This quantity (X) that results in a profit of zero is the BEP, and we now have this model for the BEP:

$$\text{BEP} = \frac{Fixed\ cost}{(Selling\ price\ per\ unit) - (Variable\ cost\ per\ unit)}$$
$$\text{BEP} = \frac{f}{s - \nu} \tag{2}$$

For the Pritchett's Precious Time Pieces example, the BEP can be computed as follows:

$$\text{BEP} = \$1,000/(\$8 - \$3) = 200 \text{ units, or springs, at the BEP.}$$

The Advantages of Mathematical Modeling

There are a number of advantages of using mathematical models:

1. Models can accurately represent reality. If properly formulated, a model can be extremely accurate. A valid model is one that is accurate and correctly represents the problem or system under investigation. The profit model in the example is accurate and valid for many business problems.

2. Models can help a decision maker formulate problems. In the profit model, for example, a decision maker can determine the important factors or contributors to revenues and expenses, such as sales, returns, selling expenses, production costs, and transportation costs.

3. Models can give us insight and information. For example, using the profit model from the preceding section, we can see what impact changes in revenues and expenses will have on profits. As discussed in the previous section, studying the impact of changes in a model, such as a profit model, is called *sensitivity analysis*.

4. Models can save time and money in decision making and problem solving. It usually takes less time, effort, and expense to analyze a model. We can use a profit model to analyze the impact of a new marketing campaign on profits, revenues, and expenses. In most cases, using models is faster and less expensive than actually trying a new marketing campaign in a real business setting and observing the results.

5. A model may be the only way to solve some large or complex problems in a timely fashion. A large company, for example, may produce literally thousands of sizes of nuts, bolts, and fasteners. The company may want to make the highest profits possible given its manufacturing constraints. A mathematical model may be the only way to determine the highest profits the company can achieve under these circumstances.

6. A model can be used to communicate problems and solutions to others. A decision analyst can share his or her work with other decision analysts. Solutions to a mathematical model can be given to managers and executives to help them make final decisions.

Mathematical Models Categorized by Risk

Deterministic means with complete certainty.

Some mathematical models, like the profit and break-even models previously discussed, do not involve risk or chance. We assume that we know all values used in the model with complete certainty. These are called **deterministic models**. A company, for example, might want to minimize manufacturing costs while maintaining a certain quality level. If we know all these values with certainty, the model is deterministic.

Other models involve risk or chance. For example, the market for a new product might be "good" with a chance of 60% (a probability of 0.6) or "not good" with a chance of 40% (a probability of 0.4). Models that involve chance or risk, often measured as a probability value, are called **probabilistic models**.

6 The Role of Computers and Spreadsheet Models in the Quantitative Analysis Approach

Developing a solution, testing the solution, and analyzing the results are important steps in the quantitative analysis approach. Because we will be using mathematical models, these steps require mathematical calculations. Excel 2013 can be used to help with these calculations, and some spreadsheets developed in Excel. However, some of the techniques presented in this text require sophisticated spreadsheets and are quite tedious to develop. Fortunately, there are two software programs available from the Companion Website for this text that makes this much easier. These are:

1. POM-QM for Windows is an easy-to-use decision support program that was developed POM and quantitative methods (QM) courses. POM for Windows and QM for Windows were originally separate software packages for each type of course. These are now combined into one program called POM-QM for Windows. As seen in Program 1, it is possible to display all the modules, only the POM modules, or only the QM modules.

   To use QM for Windows to solve the break-even problem presented earlier, from the Module drop-down menu select Breakeven/Cost-Volume Analysis. Then select New-Breakeven Analysis to enter the problem. When the window opens, enter a name for the problem and select OK. Upon doing this, you will see the screen shown in Program 2A. The solution is shown in Program 2B. Notice the additional output available from the Window drop-down menu.

PROGRAM 1

The QM for Windows Main Menu

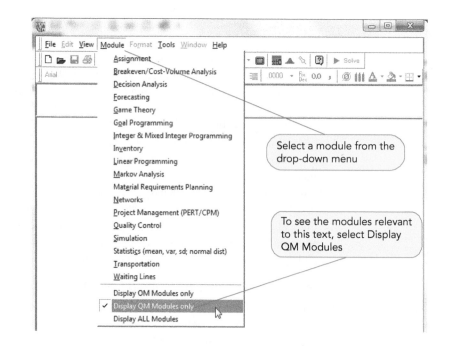

PROGRAM 2A

Entering the Data for Pritchett's Precious Time Pieces Example into QM for Windows

PROGRAM 2B

QM for Windows Solution Screen for Pritchett's Precious Time Pieces Example

Files for the QM for Windows examples can be downloaded from the Companion Website. Opening these files will demonstrate how data are input for the various modules of QM for Windows.

2. Excel QM, an add-in for Excel, can also be used to perform the mathematical calculations. When installed, in Excel 2013, Excel QM will appear as a tab on the ribbon. From this tab, the appropriate model can be selected from a menu as shown in Program 3. Excel files with the example problems shown can be downloaded from the Companion Website.

To use Excel QM in Excel 2013 to solve the break-even problem presented earlier, from the Alphabetical Menu (see Program 3) select Breakeven Analysis. When this is done, a worksheet is prepared automatically and the user simply inputs the fixed cost, variable cost, and revenue (selling price per unit) as shown in Program 4. The solution is calculated when all the inputs have been entered.

Excel 2013 contains some functions, special features, formulas, and tools that help with some of the questions that might be posed in analyzing a business problem. Once such feature, Goal Seek, is shown in Program 5 as it is applied to the break-even example. Excel 2013 also has some add-ins that must be activated before using them the first time. These include the Data Analysis add-in and the Solver add-in.

PROGRAM 3

Excel QM in Excel 2013 Ribbon and Menu of Techniques

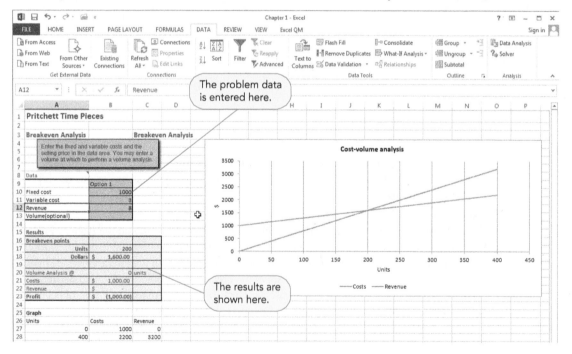

PROGRAM 4

Entering the Data for Pritchett's Precious Time Pieces Example into Excel QM in Excel 2013

PROGRAM 5
Using Goal Seek in the Break-Even Problem to Achieve a Specified Profit

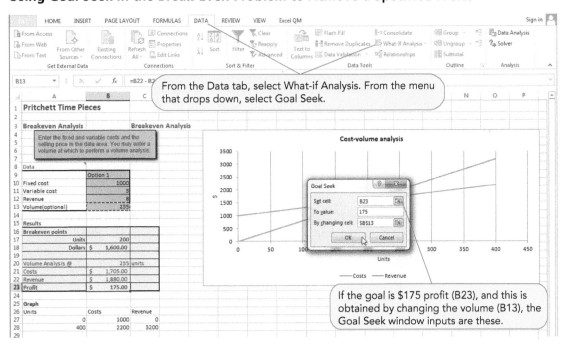

IN ACTION

Major League Operations Research at the Department of Agriculture

In 1997, the Pittsburgh Pirates signed Ross Ohlendorf because of his 95-mph sinking fastball. Little did they know that Ross possessed operations research skills also worthy of national merit. Ross Ohlendorf had graduated from Princeton University with a 3.8 GPA in operations research and financial engineering.

Indeed, after the 2009 baseball season, when Ross applied for an 8-week unpaid internship with the U.S. Department of Agriculture, he didn't need to mention his full-time employer because the Secretary of the Department of Agriculture at the time, Tom Vilsack, was born and raised in Pittsburgh and was an

avid Pittsburgh Pirates fan. Ross spent 2 months of the ensuing off-season utilizing his educational background in operations research, helping the Department of Agriculture track disease migration in livestock, a subject Ross has a vested interest in as his family runs a cattle ranch in Texas. Moreover, when ABC News asked Ross about his off-season unpaid internship experience, he replied, "This one's been, I'd say, the most exciting off-season I've had."

Source: Rick Klein, "Ross Ohlendorf: From Major League Pitcher to Unpaid Intern," ABCnews.go.com, December 15, 2009.

7 Possible Problems in the Quantitative Analysis Approach

We have presented the quantitative analysis approach as a logical, systematic means of tackling decision-making problems. Even when these steps are followed carefully, there are many difficulties that can hurt the chances of implementing solutions to real-world problems. We now take a look at what can happen during each of the steps.

Defining the Problem

One view of decision makers is that they sit at a desk all day long, waiting until a problem arises, and then stand up and attack the problem until it is solved. Once it is solved, they sit down, relax, and wait for the next big problem. In the worlds of business, government, and education, problems are, unfortunately, not easily identified. There are four potential roadblocks that quantitative analysts face in defining a problem. We use an application, inventory analysis, throughout this section as an example.

All viewpoints should be considered before formally defining the problem.

CONFLICTING VIEWPOINTS The first difficulty is that quantitative analysts must often consider conflicting viewpoints in defining the problem. For example, there are at least two views that managers take when dealing with inventory problems. Financial managers usually feel that inventory is too high, as inventory represents cash not available for other investments. Sales managers, on the other hand, often feel that inventory is too low, as high levels of inventory may be needed to fill an unexpected order. If analysts assume either one of these statements as the problem definition, they have essentially accepted one manager's perception and can expect resistance from the other manager when the "solution" emerges. So it's important to consider both points of view before stating the problem. Good mathematical models should include all pertinent information.

IMPACT ON OTHER DEPARTMENTS The next difficulty is that problems do not exist in isolation and are not owned by just one department of a firm. Inventory is closely tied with cash flows and various production problems. A change in ordering policy can seriously hurt cash flows and upset production schedules to the point that savings on inventory are more than offset by increased costs for finance and production. The problem statement should thus be as broad as possible and include input from all departments that have a stake in the solution. When a solution is found, the benefits to all areas of the organization should be identified and communicated to the people involved.

BEGINNING ASSUMPTIONS The third difficulty is that people have a tendency to state problems in terms of solutions. The statement that inventory is too low implies a solution that inventory levels should be raised. The quantitative analyst who starts off with this assumption will probably indeed find that inventory should be raised. From an implementation standpoint, a "good" solution to the *right* problem is much better than an "optimal" solution to the *wrong* problem. If a problem has been defined in terms of a desired solution, the quantitative analyst should ask questions about why this solution is desired. By probing further, the true problem will surface and can be defined properly.

An optimal solution to the wrong problem leaves the real problem unsolved.

SOLUTION OUTDATED Even with the best of problem statements, however, there is a fourth danger. The problem can change as the model is being developed. In our rapidly changing business environment, it is not unusual for problems to appear or disappear virtually overnight. The analyst who presents a solution to a problem that no longer exists can't expect credit for providing timely help. However, one of the benefits of mathematical models is that once the original model has been developed, it can be used over and over again whenever similar problems arise. This allows a solution to be found very easily in a timely manner.

Developing a Model

FITTING THE TEXTBOOK MODELS One problem in developing quantitative models is that a manager's perception of a problem won't always match the textbook approach. Most inventory models involve minimizing the total of holding and ordering costs. Some managers view these costs as unimportant; instead, they see the problem in terms of cash flow, turnover, and levels of customer satisfaction. Results of a model based on holding and ordering costs are probably not acceptable to such managers. This is why the analyst must completely understand the model and not simply use the computer as a "black box" where data are input and results are given with no understanding of the process. The analyst who understands the process can explain to the manager how the model does consider these other factors when estimating the different types of inventory costs. If other factors are important as well, the analyst can consider these and use sensitivity analysis and good judgment to modify the computer solution before it is implemented.

UNDERSTANDING THE MODEL A second major concern involves the trade-off between the complexity of the model and ease of understanding. Managers simply will not use the results of a model they do not understand. Complex problems, though, require complex models. One trade-off is to simplify assumptions in order to make the model easier to understand. The model loses some of its reality but gains some acceptance by management.

One simplifying assumption in inventory modeling is that demand is known and constant. This means that probability distributions are not needed and it allows us to build simple, easy-to-understand models. Demand, however, is rarely known and constant, so the model we build lacks some reality. Introducing probability distributions provides more realism but may put comprehension beyond all but the most mathematically sophisticated managers. One approach is for the quantitative analyst to start with the simple model and make sure that it is completely understood. Later, more complex models can be introduced slowly as managers gain more confidence in using the new approach. Explaining the impact of the more sophisticated models (e.g., carrying extra inventory called safety stock) without going into complete mathematical details is sometimes helpful. Managers can understand and identify with this concept, even if the specific mathematics used to find the appropriate quantity of safety stock is not totally understood.

Acquiring Input Data

Gathering the data to be used in the quantitative approach to problem solving is often not a simple task. One-fifth of all firms in a recent study had difficulty with data access.

Obtaining accurate input data can be very difficult.

USING ACCOUNTING DATA   One problem is that most data generated in a firm come from basic accounting reports. The accounting department collects its inventory data, for example, in terms of cash flows and turnover. But quantitative analysts tackling an inventory problem need to collect data on holding costs and ordering costs. If they ask for such data, they may be shocked to find that the data were simply never collected for those specified costs.

Professor Gene Woolsey tells a story of a young quantitative analyst sent down to accounting to get "the inventory holding cost per item per day for part 23456/AZ." The accountant asked the young man if he wanted the first-in, first-out figure, the last-in, first-out figure, the lower of cost or market figure, or the "how-we-do-it" figure. The young man replied that the inventory model required only one number. The accountant at the next desk said, "Hell, Joe, give the kid a number." The kid was given a number and departed.

VALIDITY OF DATA   A lack of "good, clean data" means that whatever data are available must often be distilled and manipulated (we call it "fudging") before being used in a model. Unfortunately, the validity of the results of a model is no better than the validity of the data that go into the model. You cannot blame a manager for resisting a model's "scientific" results when he or she knows that questionable data were used as input. This highlights the importance of the analyst understanding other business functions so that good data can be found and evaluated by the analyst. It also emphasizes the importance of sensitivity analysis, which is used to determine the impact of minor changes in input data. Some solutions are very robust and would not change at all for certain changes in the input data.

Developing a Solution

Hard-to-understand mathematics and one answer can be a problem in developing a solution.

HARD-TO-UNDERSTAND MATHEMATICS   The first concern in developing solutions is that although the mathematical models we use may be complex and powerful, they may not be completely understood. Fancy solutions to problems may have faulty logic or data. The aura of mathematics often causes managers to remain silent when they should be critical. The well-known operations researcher C. W. Churchman cautions that "because mathematics has been so revered a discipline in recent years, it tends to lull the unsuspecting into believing that he who thinks elaborately thinks well."[1]

ONLY ONE ANSWER IS LIMITING   The second problem is that quantitative models usually give just one answer to a problem. Most managers would like to have a *range* of options and not be

---

[1]C. W. Churchman. "Relativity Models in the Social Sciences," *Interfaces* 4, 1 (November 1973).

put in a take-it-or-leave-it position. A more appropriate strategy is for an analyst to present a range of options, indicating the effect that each solution has on the objective function. This gives managers a choice as well as information on how much it will cost to deviate from the optimal solution. It also allows problems to be viewed from a broader perspective, since nonquantitative factors can be considered.

Testing the Solution

The results of quantitative analysis often take the form of predictions of how things will work in the future if certain changes are made now. To get a preview of how well solutions will really work, managers are often asked how good the solution looks to them. The problem is that complex models tend to give solutions that are not intuitively obvious. Such solutions tend to be rejected by managers. The quantitative analyst now has the chance to work through the model and the assumptions with the manager in an effort to convince the manager of the validity of the results. In the process of convincing the manager, the analyst will have to review every assumption that went into the model. If there are errors, they may be revealed during this review. In addition, the manager will be casting a critical eye on everything that went into the model, and if he or she can be convinced that the model is valid, there is a good chance that the solution results are also valid.

Assumptions should be reviewed.

Analyzing the Results

Once a solution has been tested, the results must be analyzed in terms of how they will affect the total organization. You should be aware that even small changes in organizations are often difficult to bring about. If the results indicate large changes in organization policy, the quantitative analyst can expect resistance. In analyzing the results, the analyst should ascertain who must change and by how much, if the people who must change will be better or worse off, and who has the power to direct the change.

IN ACTION   PLATO Helps 2004 Olympic Games in Athens

The 2004 Olympic Games were held in Athens, Greece, over a period of 16 days. More than 2,000 athletes competed in 300 events in 28 sports. The events were held in 36 different venues (stadia, competition centers, etc.), and 3.6 million tickets were sold to people who would view these events. In addition, 2,500 members of international committees and 22,000 journalists and broadcasters attended these games. Home viewers spent more than 34 billion hours watching these sporting events. The 2004 Olympic Games was the biggest sporting event in the history of the world up to that point.

In addition to the sporting venues, other noncompetitive venues, such as the airport and Olympic village, had to be considered. A successful Olympics requires tremendous planning for the transportation system that will handle the millions of spectators. Three years of work and planning were needed for the 16 days of the Olympics.

The Athens Olympic Games Organizing Committee (ATHOC) had to plan, design, and coordinate systems that would be delivered by outside contractors. ATHOC personnel would later be responsible for managing the efforts of volunteers and paid staff during the operations of the games. To make the Athens Olympics run efficiently and effectively, the Process Logistics Advanced Technical Optimization (PLATO) project was begun. Innovative techniques from management science, systems engineering, and information technology were used to change the planning, design, and operations of venues.

The objectives of PLATO were to (1) facilitate effective organizational transformation, (2) help plan and manage resources in a cost-effective manner, and (3) document lessons learned so future Olympic committees could benefit. The PLATO project developed business-process models for the various venues, developed simulation models that enable the generation of what-if scenarios, developed software to aid in the creation and management of these models, and developed process steps for training ATHOC personnel in using these models. Generic solutions were developed so that this knowledge and approach could be made available to other users.

PLATO was credited with reducing the cost of the 2004 Olympics by over $69 million. Perhaps even more important is the fact that the Athens games were universally deemed an unqualified success. The resulting increase in tourism is expected to result in economic benefit to Greece for many years in the future.

Source: Based on D. A. Beis et al. PLATO Helps Athens Win Gold: Olympic Games Knowledge Modeling for Organizational Change and Resource Management," *Interfaces* 36, 1 (January–February 2006): 26–42.

8   Implementation—Not Just the Final Step

We have just presented some of the many problems that can affect the ultimate acceptance of the quantitative analysis approach and use of its models. It should be clear now that implementation isn't just another step that takes place after the modeling process is over. Each one of these steps greatly affects the chances of implementing the results of a quantitative study.

Lack of Commitment and Resistance to Change

Even though many business decisions can be made intuitively, based on hunches and experience, there are more and more situations in which quantitative models can assist. Some managers, however, fear that the use of a formal analysis process will reduce their decision-making power. Others fear that it may expose some previous intuitive decisions as inadequate. Still others just feel uncomfortable about having to reverse their thinking patterns with formal decision making. These managers often argue against the use of quantitative methods.

Many action-oriented managers do not like the lengthy formal decision-making process and prefer to get things done quickly. They prefer "quick and dirty" techniques that can yield immediate results. Once managers see some QA results that have a substantial payoff, the stage is set for convincing them that quantitative analysis is a beneficial tool.

Management support and user involvement are important.

We have known for some time that management support and user involvement are critical to the successful implementation of quantitative analysis projects. A Swedish study found that only 40% of projects suggested by quantitative analysts were ever implemented. But 70% of the quantitative projects initiated by users, and fully 98% of projects suggested by top managers, *were* implemented.

Lack of Commitment by Quantitative Analysts

Just as managers' attitudes are to blame for some implementation problems, analysts' attitudes are to blame for others. When the quantitative analyst is not an integral part of the department facing the problem, he or she sometimes tends to treat the modeling activity as an end in itself. That is, the analyst accepts the problem as stated by the manager and builds a model to solve only that problem. When the results are computed, he or she hands them back to the manager and considers the job done. The analyst who does not care whether these results help make the final decision is not concerned with implementation.

Successful implementation requires that the analyst not *tell* the users what to do, but work with them and take their feelings into account. An article in *Operations Research* describes an inventory control system that calculated reorder points and order quantities. But instead of insisting that computer-calculated quantities be ordered, a manual override feature was installed. This allowed users to disregard the calculated figures and substitute their own. The override was used quite often when the system was first installed. Gradually, however, as users came to realize that the calculated figures were right more often than not, they allowed the system's figures to stand. Eventually, the override feature was used only in special circumstances. This is a good example of how good relationships can aid in model implementation.

Summary

Quantitative analysis is a scientific approach to decision making. The quantitative analysis approach includes defining a problem, developing a model, acquiring input data, developing a solution, testing the solution, analyzing the results, and implementing the results. In using the quantitative approach, however, there can be potential problems, including conflicting viewpoints, the impact of quantitative analysis models on other departments, beginning assumptions, outdated solutions, fitting textbook models, understanding the model, acquiring good input data, hard-to-understand mathematics, obtaining only one answer, testing the solution, and analyzing the results. In using the quantitative analysis approach, implementation is not the final step. There can be a lack of commitment to the approach and resistance to change.

Glossary

Algorithm   A set of logical and mathematical operations performed in a specific sequence.

Break-Even Point   The quantity of sales that results in zero profit.

Business Analytics   A data-driven approach to decision making that allows companies to make better decisions.

Descriptive Analytics   The study and consolidation of historical data to describe how a company has performed in the past is performing now.

Deterministic Model   A model in which all values used in the model are known with complete certainty.

Input Data   Data that are used in a model in arriving at the final solution.

Mathematical Model   A model that uses mathematical equations and statements to represent the relationships within the model.

Model   A representation of reality or of a real-life situation.

Parameter   A measurable input quantity that is inherent in a problem.

Predictive Analytics   The use of techniques to forecast how things will be in the future based on patterns of past data.

Prescriptive Analytics   The use of optimization methods to provide new and better ways to operate based on specific business objectives.

Probabilistic Model   A model in which all values used in the model are not known with certainty but rather involve some chance or risk, often measured as a probability value.

Problem   A statement, which should come from a manager, that indicates a problem to be solved or an objective or a goal to be reached.

Quantitative Analysis or Management Science   A scientific approach that uses quantitative techniques as a tool in decision making.

Sensitivity Analysis   A process that involves determining how sensitive a solution is to changes in the formulation of a problem.

Variable   A measurable quantity that is subject to change.

Key Equations

(1)   Profit $= sX - f - vX$

where

$s =$ selling price per unit

$f =$ fixed cost

$v =$ variable cost per unit

$X =$ number of units sold

An equation to determine profit as a function of the selling price per unit, fixed costs, variable costs, and number of units sold.

(2) $\text{BEP} = \dfrac{f}{s - v}$

An equation to determine the break-even point (BEP) in units as a function of the selling price per unit (s), fixed costs (f), and variable costs (v).

Self-Test

- Before taking the self-test, refer to the learning objectives at the beginning of the chapter, the notes in the margins, and the glossary at the end of the chapter.
- Use the key at the end of the chapter to correct your answers.
- Restudy pages that correspond to any questions that you answered incorrectly or material you feel uncertain about.

1. In analyzing a problem, you should normally study
   a. the qualitative aspects.
   b. the quantitative aspects.
   c. both a and b.
   d. neither a nor b.

2. Quantitative analysis is
   a. a logical approach to decision making.
   b. a rational approach to decision making.
   c. a scientific approach to decision making.
   d. all of the above.

3. Frederick Winslow Taylor
   a. was a military researcher during World War II.
   b. pioneered the principles of scientific management.
   c. developed the use of the algorithm for QA.
   d. all of the above.

4. An input (such as variable cost per unit or fixed cost) for a model is an example of
   a. a decision variable.
   b. a parameter.
   c. an algorithm.
   d. a stochastic variable.

5. The point at which the total revenue equals total cost (meaning zero profit) is called the
   a. zero-profit solution.
   b. optimal-profit solution.
   c. break-even point.
   d. fixed-cost solution.
6. Quantitative analysis is typically associated with the use of
   a. schematic models.
   b. physical models.
   c. mathematical models.
   d. scale models.
7. Sensitivity analysis is most often associated with which step of the quantitative analysis approach?
   a. defining a problem
   b. acquiring input data
   c. implementing the results
   d. analyzing the results
8. A deterministic model is one in which
   a. there is some uncertainty about the parameters used in the model.
   b. there is a measurable outcome.
   c. all parameters used in the model are known with complete certainty.
   d. there is no available computer software.
9. The term *algorithm*
   a. is named after Algorismus.
   b. is named after a ninth-century Arabic mathematician.
   c. describes a series of steps or procedures to be repeated.
   d. all of the above.
10. An analysis to determine how much a solution would change if there were changes in the model or the input data is called
    a. sensitivity or postoptimality analysis.
    b. schematic or iconic analysis.
    c. futurama conditioning.
    d. both b and c.
11. Decision variables are
    a. controllable.
    b. uncontrollable.
    c. parameters.
    d. constant numerical values associated with any complex problem.
12. Which of the following categories of business analytics involves the use of optimization models?
    a. descriptive
    b. predictive
    c. prescriptive
    d. none of the above

Discussion Questions and Problems

Discussion Questions

1 What is the difference between quantitative and qualitative analysis? Give several examples.
2 Define *quantitative analysis*. What are some of the organizations that support the use of the scientific approach?
3 What are the three categories of business analytics?
4 What is the quantitative analysis process? Give several examples of this process.
5 Briefly trace the history of quantitative analysis. What happened to the development of quantitative analysis during World War II?
6 Give some examples of various types of models. What is a mathematical model? Develop two examples of mathematical models.
7 List some sources of input data.
8 What is implementation, and why is it important?
9 Describe the use of sensitivity analysis and postoptimality analysis in analyzing the results.
10 Managers are quick to claim that quantitative analysts talk to them in a jargon that does not sound like English. List four terms that might not be understood by a manager. Then explain in nontechnical terms what each term means.

11 Why do you think many quantitative analysts don't like to participate in the implementation process? What could be done to change this attitude?
12 Should people who will be using the results of a new quantitative model become involved in the technical aspects of the problem-solving procedure?
13 C. W. Churchman once said that "mathematics ... tends to lull the unsuspecting into believing that he who thinks elaborately thinks well." Do you think that the best QA models are the ones that are most elaborate and complex mathematically? Why?
14 What is the break-even point? What parameters are necessary to find it?

Problems

15 Gina Fox has started her own company, Foxy Shirts, which manufactures imprinted shirts for special occasions. Since she has just begun this operation, she rents the equipment from a local printing shop when necessary. The cost of using the equipment is $350. The materials used in one shirt cost $8, and Gina can sell these for $15 each.

(a) If Gina sells 20 shirts, what will her total revenue be? What will her total variable cost be?
(b) How many shirts must Gina sell to break even? What is the total revenue for this?

Note: means the problem may be solved with QM for Windows; means the problem may be solved with Excel QM; and means the problem may be solved with QM for Windows and/or Excel QM.

16 Ray Bond sells handcrafted yard decorations at county fairs. The variable cost to make these is $20 each, and he sells them for $50. The cost to rent a booth at the fair is $150. How many of these must Ray sell to break even?

17 Ray Bond, from Problem 1-16, is trying to find a new supplier that will reduce his variable cost of production to $15 per unit. If he was able to succeed in reducing this cost, what would the break-even point be?

18 Katherine D'Ann is planning to finance her college education by selling programs at the football games for State University. There is a fixed cost of $400 for printing these programs, and the variable cost is $3. There is also a $1,000 fee that is paid to the university for the right to sell these programs. If Katherine was able to sell programs for $5 each, how many would she have to sell in order to break even?

19 Katherine D'Ann, from Problem 1-18, has become concerned that sales may fall, as the team is on a terrible losing streak, and attendance has fallen off. In fact, Katherine believes that she will sell only 500 programs for the next game. If it was possible to raise the selling price of the program and still sell 500, what would the price have to be for Katherine to break even by selling 500?

20 Farris Billiard Supply sells all types of billiard equipment, and is considering manufacturing their own brand of pool cues. Mysti Farris, the production manager, is currently investigating the production of a standard house pool cue that should be very popular. Upon analyzing the costs, Mysti determines that the materials and labor cost for each cue is $25, and the fixed cost that must be covered is $2,400 per week. With a selling price of $40 each, how many pool cues must be sold to break even? What would the total revenue be at this break-even point?

21 Mysti Farris (see Problem 1-20) is considering raising the selling price of each cue to $50 instead of $40. If this is done while the costs remain the same, what would the new break-even point be? What would the total revenue be at this break-even point?

22 Mysti Farris (see Problem 1-20) believes that there is a high probability that 120 pool cues can be sold if the selling price is appropriately set. What selling price would cause the break-even point to be 120?

23 Golden Age Retirement Planners specializes in providing financial advice for people planning for a comfortable retirement. The company offers seminars on the important topic of retirement planning. For a typical seminar, the room rental at a hotel is $1,000, and the cost of advertising and other incidentals is about $10,000 per seminar. The cost of the materials and special gifts for each attendee is $60 per person attending the seminar. The company charges $250 per person to attend the seminar as this seems to be competitive with other companies in the same business. How many people must attend each seminar for Golden Age to break even?

24 A couple of entrepreneurial business students at State University decided to put their education into practice by developing a tutoring company for business students. While private tutoring was offered, it was determined that group tutoring before tests in the large statistics classes would be most beneficial. The students rented a room close to campus for $300 for 3 hours. They developed handouts based on past tests, and these handouts (including color graphs) cost $5 each. The tutor was paid $25 per hour, for a total of $75 for each tutoring session.

(a) If students are charged $20 to attend the session, how many students must enroll for the company to break even?

(b) A somewhat smaller room is available for $200 for 3 hours. The company is considering this possibility. How would this affect the break-even point?

25 Zoe Garcia is the manager of a small office support business that supplies copying, binding, and other services for local companies. Zoe must replace a worn-out copy machine that is used for black and white copying. Two machines are being considered, and each of these has a monthly lease cost plus a cost for each page that is copied. Machine 1 has a monthly lease cost of $600, and there is a cost of $0.010 per page copied. Machine 2 has a monthly lease cost of $400, and there is a cost of $0.015 per page copied. Customers are charged $0.05 per page for copies.

(a) What is the break-even point for each machine?

(b) If Zoe expects to make 10,000 copies per month, what would be the cost for each machine?

(c) If Zoe expects to make 30,000 copies per month, what would be the cost for each machine?

(d) At what volume (the number of copies) would the two machines have the same monthly cost? What would the total revenue for this number of copies?

Case Study

Food and Beverages at Southwestern University Football Games

Southwestern University (SWU), a large state college in Stephenville, Texas, 30 miles southwest of the Dallas/Fort Worth metroplex, enrolls close to 20,000 students. The school is the dominant force in the small city, with more students during fall and spring than permanent residents.

A longtime football powerhouse, SWU is a member of the Big Eleven conference and is usually in the top 20 in college football rankings. To bolster its chances of reaching the elusive and long-desired number-one ranking, in 2013 SWU hired the legendary Billy Bob Dillon as its head coach. Although the number-one ranking remained out of reach, attendance at the five Saturday home games each year increased. Prior to Dillon's arrival, attendance generally averaged 25,000–29,000. Season ticket sales bumped up by 10,000 just with the announcement of the new coach's arrival. Stephenville and SWU were ready to move to the big time!

With the growth in attendance came more fame, the need for a bigger stadium, and more complaints about seating, parking, long lines, and concession stand prices. Southwestern University's president, Dr. Marty Starr, was concerned not only about the cost of expanding the existing stadium versus building a new stadium but also about the ancillary activities. He wanted to be sure that these various support activities generated revenue adequate to pay for themselves. Consequently, he wanted the parking lots, game programs, and food service to all be handled as profit centers. At a recent meeting discussing the new stadium, Starr told the stadium manager, Hank Maddux, to develop a break-even chart and related data for each of the centers. He instructed Maddux to have the food service area break-even report ready for the next meeting. After discussion with other facility managers and his subordinates, Maddux developed the following table showing the suggested selling prices, and his estimate of variable costs, and the percent revenue by item. It also provides an estimate of the percentage of the total revenues that would be expected for each of the items based on historical sales data.

Maddux's fixed costs are interesting. He estimated that the prorated portion of the stadium cost would be as follows: salaries for food services at $100,000 ($20,000 for each of the five home games); 2,400 square feet of stadium space at $2 per

ITEM	SELLING PRICE/UNIT	VARIABLE COST/UNIT	PERCENT REVENUE
Soft drink	$1.50	$0.75	25%
Coffee	2.00	0.50	25
Hot dogs	2.00	0.80	20
Hamburgers	2.50	1.00	20
Misc. snacks	1.00	0.40	10

square foot per game; and six people per booth in each of the six booths for 5 hours at $7 an hour. These fixed costs will be proportionately allocated to each of the products based on the percentages provided in the table. For example, the revenue from soft drinks would be expected to cover 25% of the total fixed costs.

Maddux wants to be sure that he has a number of things for President Starr: (1) the total fixed cost that must be covered at each of the games; (2) the portion of the fixed cost allocated to each of the items; (3) what his unit sales would be at break-even for each item—that is, what sales of soft drinks, coffee, hot dogs, and hamburgers are necessary to cover the portion of the fixed cost allocated to each of these items; (4) what the dollar sales for each of these would be at these break-even points; and (5) realistic sales estimates per attendee for attendance of 60,000 and 35,000. (In other words, he wants to know how many dollars each attendee is spending on food at his projected break-even sales at present and if attendance grows to 60,000.) He felt this last piece of information would be helpful to understand how realistic the assumptions of his model are, and this information could be compared with similar figures from previous seasons.

Discussion Question

1. Prepare a brief report with the items noted so it is ready for Dr. Starr at the next meeting.

Adapted from J. Heizer and B. Render. *Operations Management*, 6th ed. Upper Saddle River, NJ: Prentice Hall, 2000, pp. 274–275.

Bibliography

Ackoff, R. L. *Scientific Method: Optimizing Applied Research Decisions*. New York: John Wiley & Sons, Inc., 1962.

Beam, Carrie. "ASP, the Art and Science of Practice: How I Started an OR/MS Consulting Practice with a Laptop, a Phone, and a PhD," *Interfaces* 34 (July–August 2004): 265–271.

Board, John, Charles Sutcliffe, and William T. Ziemba. "Applying Operations Research Techniques to Financial Markets," *Interfaces* 33 (March–April 2003): 12–24.

Churchman, C. W. "Relativity Models in the Social Sciences," *Interfaces* 4, 1 (November 1973).

Churchman, C. W. *The Systems Approach*. New York: Delacort Press, 1968.

Dekker, Rommert, Jacqueline Bloemhof, and Ioannis Mallidis . "Operations Research for Green Logistics—An Overview of Aspects, Issues, Contributions and Challenges," *European Journal of Operational Research* 219, 3 (June 2012): 671–679.

Dutta, Goutam. "Lessons for Success in OR/MS Practice Gained from Experiences in Indian and U.S. Steel Plants," *Interfaces* 30, 5 (September–October 2000): 23–30.

Eom, Sean B., and Eyong B. Kim. "A Survey of Decision Support System Applications (1995–2001)," *Journal of the Operational Research Society* 57, 11 (2006): 1264–1278.

Evans, James. R. "Business Analytics: The Next Frontier for Decision Sciences," *Decision Line* 43, 2 (March 2012).

Horowitz, Ira. "Aggregating Expert Ratings Using Preference-Neutral Weights: The Case of the College Football Polls," *Interfaces* 34 (July–August 2004): 314–320.

Keskinocak, Pinar, and Sridhar Tayur. "Quantitative Analysis for Internet-Enabled Supply Chains," *Interfaces* 31, 2 (March–April 2001): 70–89.

Laval, Claude, Marc Feyhl, and Steve Kakouros. "Hewlett-Packard Combined OR and Expert Knowledge to Design Its Supply Chains," *Interfaces* 35 (May–June 2005): 238–247.

Pidd, Michael. "Just Modeling Through: A Rough Guide to Modeling," *Interfaces* 29, 2 (March–April 1999): 118–132.

Saaty, T. L. "Reflections and Projections on Creativity in Operations Research and Management Science: A Pressing Need for a Shifting Paradigm," *Operations Research* 46, 1 (1998): 9–16.

Salveson, Melvin. "The Institute of Management Science: A Prehistory and Commentary," *Interfaces* 27, 3 (May–June 1997): 74–85.

Wright, P. Daniel, Matthew J. Liberatore, and Robert L. Nydick. "A Survey of Operations Research Models and Applications in Homeland Security," *Interfaces* 36 (November–December 2006): 514–529.

Solutions to Selected Problems

16	BEP = 5 units
18	BEP = 700 units
20	BEP = 160 per week; Total revenue = $6,400
22	$s = 45$
24	(a) BEP = 25 (b) BEP = 18.333

Solutions to Self-Tests

1.	c	**5.**	c	**9.**	d
2.	d	**6.**	c	**10.**	a
3.	b	**7.**	d	**11.**	a
4.	b	**8.**	c	**12.**	c

Probability Concepts and Applications

LEARNING OBJECTIVES

After completing this chapter, students will be able to:

1. Understand the basic foundations of probability analysis.
2. Describe statistically dependent and independent events.
3. Use Bayes' theorem to establish posterior probabilities.
4. Describe and provide examples of both discrete and continuous random variables.
5. Explain the difference between discrete and continuous probability distributions.
6. Calculate expected values and variances and use the normal table.

CHAPTER OUTLINE

1 Introduction

Life would be simpler if we knew without doubt what was going to happen in the future. The outcome of any decision would depend only on how logical and rational the decision was. If you lost money in the stock market, it would be because you failed to consider all the information or to make a logical decision. If you got caught in the rain, it would be because you simply forgot your umbrella. You could always avoid building a plant that was too large, investing in a company that would lose money, running out of supplies, or losing crops because of bad weather. There would be no such thing as a risky investment. Life would be simpler, but boring.

It wasn't until the sixteenth century that people started to quantify risks and to apply this concept to everyday situations. Today, the idea of risk or probability is a part of our lives. "There is a 40% chance of rain in Omaha today." "The Florida State University Seminoles are favored 2 to 1 over the Louisiana State University Tigers this Saturday." "There is a 50–50 chance that the stock market will reach an all-time high next month."

A probability is a numerical statement about the chance that an event will occur.

A **probability** *is a numerical statement about the likelihood that an event will occur.* In this chapter, we examine the basic concepts, terms, and relationships of probability and probability distributions that are useful in solving many quantitative analysis problems.

2 Fundamental Concepts

There are several rules, definitions, and concepts associated with probability that are very important in understanding the use of probability in decision making. These will be briefly presented with some examples to help clarify them.

Two Basic Rules of Probability

There are two basic rules regarding the mathematics of probability:

1. The probability, *P*, of any event or state of nature occurring is greater than or equal to 0 and less than or equal to 1. That is,

People often misuse the two basic rules of probabilities when they use statements such as, "I'm 110% sure we're going to win the big game."

$$0 \leq P(\text{event}) \leq 1 \tag{1}$$

A probability of 0 indicates that an event is never expected to occur. A probability of 1 means that an event is always expected to occur.

2. The sum of the simple probabilities for all possible outcomes of an activity must equal 1. Regardless of how probabilities are determined, they must adhere to these two rules.

This asset has been intentionally omitted from the text.

TABLE 2

Relative Frequency Approach to Probability for Paint Sales

QUANTITY DEMANDED (GALLONS)	NUMBER OF DAYS	PROBABILITY
0	40	0.20 (= 40/200)
1	80	0.40 (= 80/200)
2	50	0.25 (= 50/200)
3	20	0.10 (= 20/200)
4	10	0.05 (= 10/200)
	Total 200	1.00 (= 200/200)

Types of Probability

There are two different ways to determine probability: the **objective approach** and the **subjective approach**.

The **relative frequency approach** is an objective probability assessment. The probability assigned to an event is the relative frequency of that occurrence. In general,

$$P(\text{event}) = \frac{\text{Number of occurrences of the event}}{\text{Total number of trials or outcomes}}$$

Here is an example. Demand for white latex paint at Diversey Paint and Supply has always been 0, 1, 2, 3, or 4 gallons per day. (There are no other possible outcomes and when one occurs, no other can.) Over the past 200 working days, the owner notes the frequencies of demand as shown in Table 2. If this past distribution is a good indicator of future sales, we can find the probability of each possible outcome occurring in the future by converting the data into percentages.

Thus, the probability that sales are 2 gallons of paint on any given day is $P(2 \text{ gallons}) = 0.25 = 25\%$. The probability of any level of sales must be greater than or equal to 0 and less than or equal to 1. Since 0, 1, 2, 3, and 4 gallons exhaust all possible events or outcomes, the sum of their probability values must equal 1.

Objective probability can also be set using what is called the **classical** or **logical method**. Without performing a series of trials, we can often logically determine what the probabilities of various events should be. For example, the probability of tossing a fair coin once and getting a head is

$$P(\text{head}) = \frac{1}{2} \xleftarrow{\text{Number of ways of getting a head}}_{\text{Number of possible outcomes (head or tail)}}$$

Similarly, the probability of drawing a spade out of a deck of 52 playing cards can be logically set as

$$P(\text{spade}) = \frac{13}{52} \xleftarrow{\text{Number of chances of drawing a spade}}_{\text{Number of possible outcomes}}$$
$$= \frac{1}{4} = 0.25 = 25\%$$

When logic and past history are not available or appropriate, probability values can be assessed *subjectively*. The accuracy of subjective probabilities depends on the experience and judgment of the person making the estimates. A number of probability values cannot be determined unless the subjective approach is used. What is the probability that the price of gasoline will be more than $4 in the next few years? What is the probability that our economy will be in a severe depression in 2020? What is the probability that you will be president of a major corporation within 20 years?

There are several methods for making subjective probability assessments. Opinion polls can be used to help in determining subjective probabilities for possible election returns and potential political candidates. In some cases, experience and judgment must be used in making subjective assessments of probability values. A production manager, for example, might believe that the probability of manufacturing a new product without a single defect is 0.85. In the Delphi method, a panel of experts is assembled to make their predictions of the future.

Where do probabilities come from? Sometimes they are subjective and based on personal experiences. Other times they are objectively based on logical observations such as the roll of a die. Often, probabilities are derived from historical data.

Mutually Exclusive and Collectively Exhaustive Events

Events are said to be **mutually exclusive** if only one of the events can occur on any one trial. They are called **collectively exhaustive** if the list of outcomes includes every possible outcome. Many common experiences involve events that have both of these properties.

In tossing a coin, the possible outcomes are a head or a tail. Since both of them cannot occur on any one toss, the outcomes head and tail are mutually exclusive. Since obtaining a head and obtaining a tail represent every possible outcome, they are also collectively exhaustive.

Figure 1 provides a Venn diagram representation of mutually exclusive events. Let A be the event that a head is tossed, and let B be the event that a tail is tossed. The circles representing these events do not overlap, so the events are mutually exclusive.

The following situation provides an example of events that are not mutually exclusive. You are asked to draw one card from a standard deck of 52 playing cards. The following events are defined:

$$A = \text{event that a 7 is drawn}$$
$$B = \text{event that a heart is drawn}$$

FIGURE 1

Venn Diagram for Events That Are Mutually Exclusive

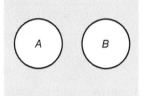

MODELING IN THE REAL WORLD — Liver Transplants in the United States

Defining the Problem

Defining the Problem

The scarcity of liver organs for transplants has reached critical levels in the United States; 1,131 individuals died in 1997 while waiting for a transplant. With only 4,000 liver donations per year, there are 10,000 patients on the waiting list, with 8,000 being added each year. There is a need to develop a model to evaluate policies for allocating livers to terminally ill patients who need them.

Developing a Model

Developing a Model

Doctors, engineers, researchers, and scientists worked together with Pritsker Corp. consultants in the process of creating the liver allocation model, called ULAM. One of the model's jobs would be to evaluate whether to list potential recipients on a national basis or regionally.

Acquiring Input Data

Acquiring Input Data

Historical information was available from the United Network for Organ Sharing (UNOS), from 1990 to 1995. The data were then stored in ULAM. "Poisson" probability processes described the arrivals of donors at 63 organ procurement centers and arrival of patients at 106 liver transplant centers.

Developing a Solution

Developing a Solution

ULAM provides probabilities of accepting an offered liver, where the probability is a function of the patient's medical status, the transplant center, and the quality of the offered liver. ULAM also models the daily probability of a patient changing from one status of criticality to another.

Testing the Solution

Testing the Solution

Testing involved a comparison of the model output to actual results over the 1992–1994 time period. Model results were close enough to actual results that ULAM was declared valid.

Analyzing the Results

Analyzing the Results

ULAM was used to compare more than 100 liver allocation policies and was then updated in 1998, with more recent data, for presentation to Congress.

Implementing the Results

Implementing the Results

Based on the projected results, the UNOS committee voted 18–0 to implement an allocation policy based on regional, not national, waiting lists. This decision is expected to save 2,414 lives over an 8-year period.

Source: Based on A. A. B. Pritsker. "Life and Death Decisions," *OR/MS Today* (August 1998): 22–28.

FIGURE 2

Venn Diagram for Events That Are Not Mutually Exclusive

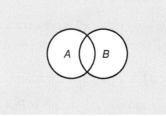

The probabilities can be assigned to these using the relative frequency approach. There are four 7s in the deck and thirteen hearts in the deck. Thus, we have

$$P(\text{a 7 is drawn}) = P(A) = {}^4\!/_{52}$$
$$P(\text{a heart is drawn}) = P(B) = {}^{13}\!/_{52}$$

These events are not mutually exclusive as the 7 of hearts is common to both event A and event B. Figure 2 provides a Venn diagram representing this situation. Notice that the two circles intersect, and this intersection is whatever is in common to both. In this example, the intersection would be the 7 of hearts.

Unions and Intersections of Events

The **intersection** of two events is the set of all outcomes that are common to both events. The word *and* is commonly associated with the intersection, as is the symbol $\cap$. There are several notations for the intersection of two events:

$$\text{Intersection of event } A \text{ and event } B = A \text{ and } B$$
$$= A \cap B$$
$$= AB$$

The notation for the probability would be

$$P(\text{Intersection of event } A \text{ and event } B) = P(A \text{ and } B)$$
$$= P(A \cap B)$$
$$= P(AB)$$

The probability of the intersection is sometimes called a **joint probability**, which implies that both events are occurring at the same time or jointly.

The **union** of two events is the set of all outcomes that are contained in either of these two events. Thus, any outcome that is in event A is in the union of the two events, and any outcome that is in event B is also in the union of the two events. The word *or* is commonly associated with the union, as is the symbol $\cup$. Typical notation for the union of two events would be

$$\text{Union of event } A \text{ and event } B = (A \text{ or } B)$$

The notation for the probability of the union of events would be

$$P(\text{Union of event } A \text{ and event } B) = P(A \text{ or } B)$$
$$= P(A \cup B)$$

In the previous example, the intersection of event A and event B would be

$$(A \text{ and } B) = \text{the 7 of hearts is drawn}$$

The notation for the probability would be

$$P(A \text{ and } B) = P(\text{7 of hearts is drawn}) = {}^1\!/_{52}$$

Also, the union of event A and event B would be

$$(A \text{ or } B) = (\text{either a 7 is drawn or a heart is drawn})$$

and the probability would be

$$P(A \text{ or } B) = P(\text{any 7 or any heart is drawn}) = {}^{16}/_{52}$$

To see why $P(A \text{ or } B) = {}^{16}/_{52}$ and not ${}^{17}/_{52}$ (which is $P(A) + P(B)$), count all of the cards that are in the union, and you will see there are 16. This will help you understand the general rule for the probability of the union of two events that is presented next.

Probability Rules for Unions, Intersections, and Conditional Probabilities

The general rule for the probability of the union of two events (sometimes called the additive rule) is the following:

$$P(A \text{ or } B) = P(A) + P(B) - P(A \text{ and } B) \tag{2}$$

To illustrate this with the example we have been using, to find the probability of the union of the two events (a 7 or a heart is drawn), we have

$$
\begin{aligned}
P(A \text{ or } B) &= P(A) + P(B) - P(A \text{ and } B) \\
&= {}^{4}/_{52} + {}^{13}/_{52} - {}^{1}/_{52} \\
&= {}^{16}/_{52}
\end{aligned}
$$

One of the most important probability concepts in decision making is the concept of a conditional probability. A **conditional probability** is the probability of an event occurring given that another event has already happened. The probability of event A given that event B has occurred is written as $P(A|B)$. When businesses make decisions, they often use market research of some type to help determine the likelihood of success. Given a good result from the market research, the probability of success would increase.

The probability that A will occur given that event B has occurred can be found by dividing the probability of the intersection of the two events (A and B) by the probability of the event that has occurred (B):

$$P(A|B) = \frac{P(AB)}{P(B)} \tag{3}$$

From this, the formula for the intersection of two events can be easily derived and written as

$$P(AB) = P(A|B)P(B) \tag{4}$$

In the card example, what is the probability that a 7 is drawn (event A) given that we know that the card drawn is a heart (event B)? With what we already know, and given the formula for conditional probability, we have

$$P(A|B) = \frac{P(AB)}{P(B)} = \frac{{}^{1}/_{52}}{{}^{13}/_{52}} = {}^{1}/_{13}$$

With this card example, it might be possible to determine this probability without using the formula. Given that a heart was drawn and there are 13 hearts with only one of these being a 7, we can determine that the probability is ${}^{1}/_{13}$. In business, however, we sometimes do not have this complete information and the formula is absolutely essential.

Two events are said to be **independent** if the occurrence of one has no impact on the occurrence of the other. Otherwise, the events are dependent.

For example, suppose a card is drawn from a deck of cards and it is then returned to the deck and a second drawing occurs. The probability of drawing a seven on the second draw is ${}^{4}/_{52}$ regardless of what was drawn on the first draw because the deck is exactly the same as it was on the first draw. Now contrast to a similar situation with two draws from a deck of cards, but the first card is not returned to the deck. Now there are only 51 cards left in the deck, and there are either three or four 7s in the deck depending on what the first card drawn happens to be.

A more precise definition of statistical independence would be the following: Event A and event B are independent if

$$P(A\,|\,B) = P(A)$$

Independence is a very important condition in probability as many calculations are simplified. One of these is the formula for the intersection of two events. If A and B are independent, then the probability of the intersection is

$$P(A \text{ and } B) = P(A)P(B)$$

Suppose a fair coin is tossed twice. The events are defined as:

A = event that a head is the result of the first toss

B = event that a head is the result of the second toss

These events are independent because the probability of a head on the second toss will be the same regardless of the result on the first toss. Because it is a fair coin, we know there are two equally likely outcomes on each toss (head or tail), so

$$P(A) = 0.5$$

and

$$P(B) = 0.5$$

Because A and B are independent,

$$P(AB) = P(A)P(B) = 0.5(0.5) = 0.25$$

Thus, there is a 0.25 probability that two tosses of a coin will result in two heads.

If events are not independent, then finding probabilities may be a bit more difficult. However, the results may be very valuable to a decision maker. A market research study about opening a new store in a particular location may have a positive outcome, and this would cause a revision of our probability assessment that the new store would be successful. The next section provides a means of revising probabilities based on new information.

3   Revising Probabilities with Bayes' Theorem

Bayes' theorem is used to incorporate additional information as it is made available and help create revised or *posterior probabilities* from the original or *prior probabilities*. This means that we can take new or recent data and then revise and improve upon our old probability estimates for an event (see Figure 3). Let us consider the following example.

A cup contains two dice identical in appearance. One, however, is fair (unbiased) and the other is loaded (biased). The probability of rolling a 3 on the fair die is $\frac{1}{6}$, or 0.166. The probability of tossing the same number on the loaded die is 0.60.

We have no idea which die is which, but select one by chance and toss it. The result is a 3. Given this additional piece of information, can we find the (revised) probability that the die rolled was fair? Can we determine the probability that it was the loaded die that was rolled?

FIGURE 3
Using Bayes' Process

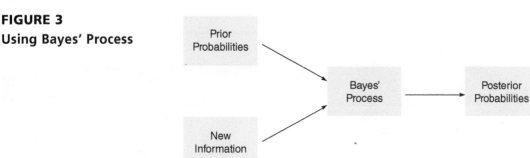

The answer to these questions is yes, and we do so by using the formula for joint probability under statistical dependence and Bayes' theorem. First, we take stock of the information and probabilities available. We know, for example, that since we randomly selected the die to roll, the probability of it being fair or loaded is 0.50:

$$P(\text{fair}) = 0.50 \quad P(\text{loaded}) = 0.50$$

We also know that

$$P(3\,|\,\text{fair}) = 0.166 \quad P(3\,|\,\text{loaded}) = 0.60$$

Next, we compute joint probabilities $P(3$ and fair$)$ and $P(3$ and loaded$)$ using the formula $P(AB) = P(A\,|\,B) \times P(B)$:

$$P(3 \text{ and fair}) = P(3\,|\,\text{fair}) \times P(\text{fair})$$
$$= (0.166)(0.50) = 0.083$$

$$P(3 \text{ and loaded}) = P(3\,|\,\text{loaded}) \times P(\text{loaded})$$
$$= (0.60)(0.50) = 0.300$$

A 3 can occur in combination with the state "fair die" or in combination with the state "loaded die." The sum of their probabilities gives the unconditional or marginal probability of a 3 on the toss, namely, $P(3) = 0.083 + 0.300 = 0.383$.

If a 3 does occur, and if we do not know which die it came from, the probability that the die rolled was the fair one is

$$P(\text{fair}\,|\,3) = \frac{P(\text{fair and }3)}{P(3)} = \frac{0.083}{0.383} = 0.22$$

The probability that the die rolled was loaded is

$$P(\text{loaded}\,|\,3) = \frac{P(\text{loaded and }3)}{P(3)} = \frac{0.300}{0.383} = 0.78$$

These two conditional probabilities are called the **revised** or **posterior probabilities** for the next roll of the die.

Before the die was rolled in the preceding example, the best we could say was that there was a 50–50 chance that it was fair (0.50 probability) and a 50–50 chance that it was loaded. After one roll of the die, however, we are able to revise our **prior probability** estimates. The new posterior estimate is that there is a 0.78 probability that the die rolled was loaded and only a 0.22 probability that it was not.

Using a table is often helpful in performing the calculations associated with Bayes' theorem. Table 3 provides the general layout for this, and Table 4 provides this specific example.

TABLE 3

Tabular Form of Bayes' Calculations Given That Event B Has Occurred

STATE OF NATURE	$P(B\,|\,$ STATE OF NATURE)	PRIOR PROBABILITY	JOINT PROBABILITY	POSTERIOR PROBABILITY
A	$P(B\,|\,A)$	$\times P(A)$	$= P(B \text{ and } A)$	$P(B \text{ and } A)/P(B) = P(A\,|\,B)$
A'	$P(B\,|\,A')$	$\times P(A')$	$= P(B \text{ and } A')$	$P(B \text{ and } A')/P(B) = P(A'\,|\,B)$
			$P(B)$	

TABLE 4

Bayes' Calculations Given That a 3 Is Rolled in Example 7

STATE OF NATURE	$P(3\,|\,$ STATE OF NATURE)	PRIOR PROBABILITY	JOINT PROBABILITY	POSTERIOR PROBABILITY
Fair die	0.166	$\times 0.5$	$= 0.083$	$0.083/0.383 = 0.22$
Loaded die	0.600	$\times 0.5$	$= 0.300$	$0.300/0.383 = 0.78$
			$P(3) = 0.383$	

General Form of Bayes' Theorem

Another way to compute revised probabilities is with Bayes' theorem.

Revised probabilities can also be computed in a more direct way using a general form for **Bayes' theorem**:

$$P(A|B) = \frac{P(B|A)P(A)}{P(B|A)P(A) + P(B|A')P(A')} \tag{5}$$

where

A' = the complement of the event A;
for example, if A is the event "fair die," then A' is "loaded die"

We originally saw in Equation 3 the conditional probability of event A, given event B, is

$$P(A|B) = \frac{P(AB)}{P(B)}$$

A Presbyterian minister, Thomas Bayes (1702–1761), did the work leading to this theorem.

Thomas Bayes derived his theorem from this. Appendix 1 shows the mathematical steps leading to Equation 5. Now let's return to the example.

Although it may not be obvious to you at first glance, we used this basic equation to compute the revised probabilities. For example, if we want the probability that the fair die was rolled given the first toss was a 3, namely, $P(\text{fair die} | 3 \text{ rolled})$, we can let

event "fair die" replace A in Equation 2-5

event "loaded die" replace A' in Equation 2-5

event "3 rolled" replace B in Equation 2-5

We can then rewrite Equation 5 and solve as follows:

$$P(\text{fair die} | 3 \text{ rolled})$$

$$= \frac{P(3 | \text{fair})P(\text{fair})}{P(3 | \text{fair})P(\text{fair}) + P(3 | \text{loaded})P(\text{loaded})}$$

$$= \frac{(0.166)(0.50)}{(0.166)(0.50) + (0.60)(0.50)}$$

$$= \frac{0.083}{0.383} = 0.22$$

This is the same answer that we computed earlier. Can you use this alternative approach to show that $P(\text{loaded die} | 3 \text{ rolled}) = 0.78$? Either method is perfectly acceptable.

4 Further Probability Revisions

Although one revision of prior probabilities can provide useful posterior probability estimates, additional information can be gained from performing the experiment a second time. If it is financially worthwhile, a decision maker may even decide to make several more revisions.

Returning to the previous example, we now attempt to obtain further information about the posterior probabilities as to whether the die just rolled is fair or loaded. To do so, let us toss the die a second time. Again, we roll a 3. What are the further revised probabilities?

To answer this question, we proceed as before, with only one exception. The probabilities $P(\text{fair}) = 0.50$ and $P(\text{loaded}) = 0.50$ remain the same, but now we must compute $P(3, 3 | \text{fair}) = (0.166)(0.166) = 0.027$ and $P(3, 3 | \text{loaded}) = (0.6)(0.6) = 0.36$. With these joint probabilities of two 3s on successive rolls, given the two types of dice, we may revise the probabilities:

$$P(3, 3 \text{ and fair}) = P(3, 3 | \text{fair}) \times P(\text{fair})$$
$$= (0.027)(0.5) = 0.013$$

$$P(3, 3 \text{ and loaded}) = P(3, 3 | \text{loaded}) \times P(\text{loaded})$$
$$= (0.36)(0.5) = 0.18$$

IN ACTION Flight Safety and Probability Analysis

With the horrific events of September 11, 2001, and the use of airplanes as weapons of mass destruction, airline safety has become an even more important international issue. How can we reduce the impact of terrorism on air safety? What can be done to make air travel safer overall? One answer is to evaluate various air safety programs and to use probability theory in the analysis of the costs of these programs.

Determining airline safety is a matter of applying the concepts of objective probability analysis. The chance of getting killed in a scheduled domestic flight is about 1 in 5 million. This is probability of about .0000002. Another measure is the number of deaths per passenger mile flown. The number is about 1 passenger per billion passenger miles flown, or a probability of about .000000001. Without question, flying is safer than many other forms of transportation, including driving. For a typical weekend, more people are killed in car accidents than a typical air disaster.

Analyzing new airline safety measures involves costs and the subjective probability that lives will be saved. One airline expert proposed a number of new airline safety measures. When the costs involved and probability of saving lives were taken into account, the result was about a $1 billion cost for every life saved on average. Using probability analysis will help determine which safety programs will result in the greatest benefit, and these programs can be expanded.

In addition, some proposed safety issues are not completely certain. For example, a Thermal Neutron Analysis device to detect explosives at airports had a probability of .15 of giving a false alarm, resulting in a high cost of inspection and long flight delays. This would indicate that money should be spent on developing more reliable equipment for detecting explosives. The result would be safer air travel with fewer unnecessary delays.

Without question, the use of probability analysis to determine and improve flight safety is indispensable. Many transportation experts hope that the same rigorous probability models used in the airline industry will some day be applied to the much more deadly system of highways and the drivers who use them.

Sources: Based on Robert Machol. "Flying Scared," *OR/MS Today* (October 1997): 32–37; and Arnold Barnett. "The Worst Day Ever," *OR/MS Today* (December 2001): 28–31.

Thus, the probability of rolling two 3s, a marginal probability, is $0.013 + 0.18 = 0.193$, the sum of the two joint probabilities:

$$P(\text{fair} \mid 3, 3) = \frac{P(3, 3 \text{ and fair})}{P(3, 3)}$$

$$= \frac{0.013}{0.193} = 0.067$$

$$P(\text{loaded} \mid 3, 3) = \frac{P(3, 3 \text{ and loaded})}{P(3, 3)}$$

$$= \frac{0.18}{0.193} = 0.933$$

What has this second roll accomplished? Before we rolled the die the first time, we knew only that there was a 0.50 probability that it was either fair or loaded. When the first die was rolled in the previous example, we were able to revise these probabilities:

probability the die is fair $= 0.22$

probability the die is loaded $= 0.78$

Now, after the second roll in this example, our refined revisions tell us that

probability the die is fair $= 0.067$

probability the die is loaded $= 0.933$

This type of information can be extremely valuable in business decision making.

5 Random Variables

We have just discussed various ways of assigning probability values to the outcomes of an experiment. Let us now use this probability information to compute the expected outcome, variance, and standard deviation of the experiment. This can help select the best decision among a number of alternatives.

TABLE 5   Examples of Random Variables

EXPERIMENT	OUTCOME	RANDOM VARIABLES	RANGE OF RANDOM VARIABLES
Stock 50 Christmas trees	Number of Christmas trees sold	X = number of Christmas trees sold	0, 1, 2, . . . , 50
Inspect 600 items	Number of acceptable items	Y = number of acceptable items	0, 1, 2, . . . , 600
Send out 5,000 sales letters	Number of people responding to the letters	Z = number of people responding to the letters	0, 1, 2, . . . , 5,000
Build an apartment building	Percent of building completed after 4 months	R = percent of building completed after 4 months	$0 \leq R \leq 100$
Test the lifetime of a lightbulb (minutes)	Length of time the bulb lasts up to 80,000 minutes	S = time the bulb burns	$0 \leq S \leq 80,000$

A **random variable** assigns a real number to every possible outcome or event in an experiment. It is normally represented by a letter such as X or Y. When the outcome itself is numerical or quantitative, the outcome numbers can be the random variable. For example, consider refrigerator sales at an appliance store. The number of refrigerators sold during a given day can be the random variable. Using X to represent this random variable, we can express this relationship as follows:

$$X = \text{number of refrigerators sold during the day}$$

In general, whenever the experiment has quantifiable outcomes, it is beneficial to define these quantitative outcomes as the random variable. Examples are given in Table 5.

When the outcome itself is not numerical or quantitative, it is necessary to define a random variable that associates each outcome with a unique real number. Several examples are given in Table 6.

There are two types of random variables: *discrete random variables* and *continuous random variables*. Developing probability distributions and making computations based on these distributions depends on the type of random variable.

Try to develop a few more examples of discrete random variables to be sure you understand this concept.

A random variable is a **discrete random variable** if it can assume only a finite or limited set of values. Which of the random variables in Table 5 are discrete random variables? Looking at Table 5, we can see that the variables associated with stocking 50 Christmas trees, inspecting 600 items, and sending out 5,000 letters are all examples of discrete random variables. Each of these random variables can assume only a finite or limited set of values. The number of Christmas trees sold, for example, can only be integer numbers from 0 to 50. There are 51 values that the random variable X can assume in this example.

A **continuous random variable** is a random variable that has an infinite or an unlimited set of values. Are there any examples of continuous random variables in Table 5 or 6? Looking

TABLE 6

Random Variables for Outcomes That Are Not Numbers

EXPERIMENT	OUTCOME	RANGE OF RANDOM VARIABLES	RANDOM VARIABLES
Students respond to a questionnaire	Strongly agree (SA) / Agree (A) / Neutral (N) / Disagree (D) / Strongly disagree (SD)	$X = \begin{cases} 5 \text{ if SA} \\ 4 \text{ if A} \\ 3 \text{ if N} \\ 2 \text{ if D} \\ 1 \text{ if SD} \end{cases}$	1, 2, 3, 4, 5
One machine is inspected	Defective / Not defective	$Y = \begin{cases} 0 \text{ if defective} \\ 1 \text{ if not defective} \end{cases}$	0, 1
Consumers respond to how they like a product	Good / Average / Poor	$Z = \begin{cases} 3 \text{ if good} \\ 2 \text{ if average} \\ 1 \text{ if poor} \end{cases}$	1, 2, 3

at Table 5, we can see that testing the lifetime of a lightbulb is an experiment whose results can be described with a continuous random variable. In this case, the random variable, S, is the time the bulb burns. It can last for 3,206 minutes, 6,500.7 minutes, 251.726 minutes, or any other value between 0 and 80,000 minutes. In most cases, the range of a continuous random variable is stated as: lower value $\leq S \leq$ upper value, such as $0 \leq S \leq 80,000$. The random variable R in Table 5 is also continuous. Can you explain why?

6   Probability Distributions

Earlier we discussed the probability values of an event. We now explore the properties of **probability distributions**. We see how popular distributions, such as the normal, Poisson, binomial, and exponential probability distributions, can save us time and effort. Since a random variable may be *discrete* or *continuous*, we consider **discrete probability distributions** and **continuous probability distributions** seperately.

Probability Distribution of a Discrete Random Variable

When we have a *discrete random variable*, there is a probability value assigned to each event. These values must be between 0 and 1, and they must sum to 1. Let's look at an example.

The 100 students in Pat Shannon's statistics class have just completed a math quiz that he gives on the first day of class. The quiz consists of five very difficult algebra problems. The grade on the quiz is the number of correct answers, so the grades theoretically could range from 0 to 5. However, no one in this class received a score of 0, so the grades ranged from 1 to 5. The random variable X is defined to be the grade on this quiz, and the grades are summarized in Table 7. This discrete probability distribution was developed using the relative frequency approach presented earlier.

The distribution follows the three rules required of all probability distributions: (1) the events are mutually exclusive and collectively exhaustive, (2) the individual probability values are between 0 and 1 inclusive, and (3) the total of the probability values sum to 1.

Although listing the probability distribution as we did in Table 7 is adequate, it can be difficult to get an idea about characteristics of the distribution. To overcome this problem, the probability values are often presented in graph form. The graph of the distribution in Table 7 is shown in Figure 4.

The graph of this probability distribution gives us a picture of its shape. It helps us identify the central tendency of the distribution, called the mean or **expected value**, and the amount of variability or spread of the distribution, called the **variance**.

Expected Value of a Discrete Probability Distribution

Once we have established a probability distribution, the first characteristic that is usually of interest is the *central tendency* of the distribution. The expected value, a measure of central tendency, is computed as the weighted average of the values of the random variable:

The expected value of a discrete distribution is a weighted average of the values of the random variable.

$$E(X) = \sum_{i=1}^{n} X_i\, P(X_i)$$

$$= X_1 P(X_1) + X_2 P(X_2) + \cdots + X_n P(X_n) \tag{6}$$

TABLE 7

Probability Distribution for Quiz Scores

RANDOM VARIABLE (X)-SCORE	NUMBER	PROBABILITY $P(X)$
5	10	$0.1 = 10/100$
4	20	$0.2 = 20/100$
3	30	$0.3 = 30/100$
2	30	$0.3 = 30/100$
1	10	$0.1 = 10/100$
	Total 100	$1.0 = 100/100$

FIGURE 4
Probability Distribution for Dr. Shannon's Class

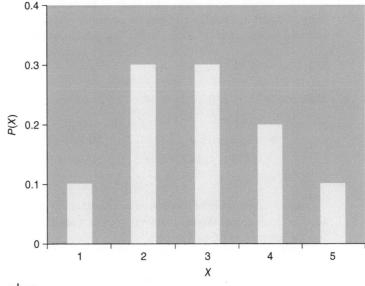

where

$$X_i = \text{random variable's possible values}$$

$$P(X_i) = \text{probability of each of the random variable's possible values}$$

$$\sum_{i=1}^{n} = \text{summation sign indicating we are adding all } n \text{ possible values}$$

$$E(X) = \text{expected value or mean of the random variable}$$

The expected value or mean of any discrete probability distribution can be computed by multiplying each possible value of the random variable, X_i, times the probability, $P(X_i)$, that outcome will occur and summing the results, $\sum$. Here is how the expected value can be computed for the quiz scores:

$$
\begin{aligned}
E(X) &= \sum_{i=1}^{5} X_i P(X_i) \\
&= X_1 P(X_1) + X_2 P(X_2) + X_3 P(X_3) + X_4 P(X_4) + X_5 P(X_5) \\
&= (5)(0.1) + (4)(0.2) + (3)(0.3) + (2)(0.3) + (1)(0.1) \\
&= 2.9
\end{aligned}
$$

The expected value of 2.9 is the mean score on the quiz.

Variance of a Discrete Probability Distribution

In addition to the central tendency of a probability distribution, most people are interested in the variability or the spread of the distribution. If the variability is low, it is much more likely that the outcome of an experiment will be close to the average or expected value. On the other hand, if the variability of the distribution is high, which means that the probability is spread out over the various random variable values, there is less chance that the outcome of an experiment will be close to the expected value.

A probability distribution is often described by its mean and variance. Even if most of the men in class (or the United States) have heights between 5 feet 6 inches and 6 feet 2 inches, there is still some small probability of outliers.

The *variance* of a probability distribution is a number that reveals the overall spread or dispersion of the distribution. For a discrete probability distribution, it can be computed using the following equation:

$$\sigma^2 = \text{Variance} = \sum_{i=1}^{n} [X_i - E(X)]^2 P(X_i) \tag{7}$$

where

$$X_i = \text{random variable's possible values}$$

$$E(X) = \text{expected value of the random variable}$$

$$[X_i - E(X)] = \text{difference between each value of the random variable and the expected value}$$

$$P(X_i) = \text{probability of each possible value of the random variable}$$

To compute the variance, each value of the random variable is subtracted from the expected value, squared, and multiplied times the probability of occurrence of that value. The results are then summed to obtain the variance. Here is how this procedure is done for Dr. Shannon's quiz scores:

$$\text{Variance} = \sum_{i=1}^{5} [X_i - E(X)]^2 P(X_i)$$

$$
\begin{aligned}
\text{Variance} &= (5 - 2.9)^2(0.1) + (4 - 2.9)^2(0.2) + (3 - 2.9)^2(0.3) + (2 - 2.9)^2(0.3) \\
&\quad + (1 - 2.9)^2(0.1) \\
&= (2.1)^2(0.1) + (1.1)^2(0.2) + (0.1)^2(0.3) + (-0.9)^2(0.3) + (-1.9)^2(0.1) \\
&= 0.441 + 0.242 + 0.003 + 0.243 + 0.361 \\
&= 1.29
\end{aligned}
$$

A related measure of dispersion or spread is the **standard deviation**. This quantity is also used in many computations involved with probability distributions. The standard deviation is just the square root of the variance:

$$\sigma = \sqrt{\text{Variance}} = \sqrt{\sigma^2} \tag{8}$$

where

$$\sqrt{} = \text{square root}$$
$$\sigma = \text{standard deviation}$$

The standard deviation for the random variable X in the example is

$$
\begin{aligned}
\sigma &= \sqrt{\text{Variance}} \\
&= \sqrt{1.29} = 1.14
\end{aligned}
$$

These calculations are easily performed in Excel. Program 1A provides the output for this example. Program 1B shows the inputs and formulas in Excel for calculating the mean, variance, and standard deviation in this example.

Probability Distribution of a Continuous Random Variable

There are many examples of *continuous random variables*. The time it takes to finish a project, the number of ounces in a barrel of butter, the high temperature during a given day, the exact length of a given type of lumber, and the weight of a railroad car of coal are all examples of continuous random variables. Since random variables can take on an infinite number of values, the fundamental probability rules for continuous random variables must be modified.

As with discrete probability distributions, the sum of the probability values must equal 1. Because there are an infinite number of values of the random variables, however, the probability of each value of the random variable must be 0. If the probability values for the random variable values were greater than 0, the sum would be infinitely large.

PROGRAM 1A

Excel 2013 Output for the Dr. Shannon Example

	A	B	C	D
1	X	P(X)	XP(X)	(X - E(X))²P(X)
2	5	0.1	0.5	0.441
3	4	0.2	0.8	0.242
4	3	0.3	0.9	0.003
5	2	0.3	0.6	0.243
6	1	0.1	0.1	0.361
7		E(X) = ΣXP(X) =	2.9	1.290
8				1.136

PROGRAM 1B

Formulas in an Excel Spreadsheet for the Dr. Shannon Example

	C	D
2	=A2*B2	=(A2-$C$7)^2*B2
3	=A3*B3	=(A3-$C$7)^2*B3
4	=A4*B4	=(A4-$C$7)^2*B4
5	=A5*B5	=(A5-$C$7)^2*B5
6	=A6*B6	=(A6-$C$7)^2*B6
7	=SUM(C2:C6)	=SUM(D2:D6)
8		=SQRT(D7)

FIGURE 5
Graph of Sample Density Function

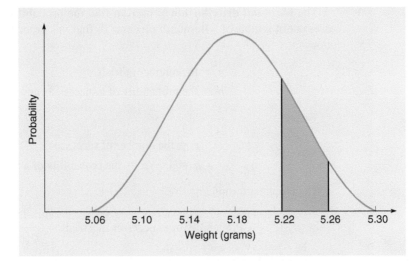

A probability density function, $f(X)$, is a mathematical way of describing the probability distribution.

With a continuous probability distribution, there is a continuous mathematical function that describes the probability distribution. This function is called the **probability density function** or simply the **probability function**. It is usually represented by $f(X)$. When working with continuous probability distributions, the probability function can be graphed, and the area underneath the curve represents probability. Thus, to find any probability, we simply find the area under the curve associated with the range of interest.

We now look at the sketch of a sample density function in Figure 5. This curve represents the probability density function for the weight of a particular machined part. The weight could vary from 5.06 to 5.30 grams, with weights around 5.18 grams being the most likely. The shaded area represents the probability the weight is between 5.22 and 5.26 grams.

If we wanted to know the probability of a part weighing exactly 5.1300000 grams, for example, we would have to compute the area of a line of width 0. Of course, this would be 0. This result may seem strange, but if we insist on enough decimal places of accuracy, we are bound to find that the weight differs from 5.1300000 grams *exactly*, be the difference ever so slight.

This is important because it means that, for any continuous distribution, the probability does not change if a single point is added to the range of values that is being considered. In Figure 5, this means the following probabilities are all exactly the same:

$$P(5.22 < X < 5.26) = P(5.22 < X \leq 5.26) = P(5.22 \leq X < 5.26)$$
$$= P(5.22 \leq X \leq 5.26)$$

The inclusion or exclusion of either endpoint (5.22 or 5.26) has no impact on the probability.

In this section, we have investigated the fundamental characteristics and properties of probability distributions in general. In the next three sections, we introduce three important continuous distributions—the normal distribution, the F distribution, and the exponential distribution—and two discrete distributions—the Poisson distribution and the binomial distribution.

7 The Binomial Distribution

Many business experiments can be characterized by the **Bernoulli process**. The probability of obtaining specific outcomes in a Bernoulli process is described by the binomial probability distribution. In order to be a Bernoulli process, an experiment must have the following characteristics:

1. Each trial in a Bernoulli process has only two possible outcomes. These are typically called a success and a failure, although examples might be yes or no, heads or tails, pass or fail, defective or good, and so on.
2. The probability stays the same from one trial to the next.
3. The trials are statistically independent.
4. The number of trials is a positive integer.

A common example of this process is tossing a coin.

The **binomial distribution** is used to find the probability of a specific number of successes out of n trials of a Bernoulli process. To find this probability, it is necessary to know the following:

$$n = \text{the number of trials}$$

$$p = \text{the probability of a success on any single trial}$$

We let

$$r = \text{the number of successes}$$

$$q = 1 - p = \text{the probability of a failure}$$

The binomial formula is

$$\text{Probability of } r \text{ successes in } n \text{ trials} = \frac{n!}{r!(n-r)!} p^r q^{n-r} \qquad (9)$$

The symbol ! means factorial, and $n! = n(n-1)(n-2) \ldots (1)$. For example,

$$4! = (4)(3)(2)(1) = 24$$

Also, $1! = 1$, and $0! = 1$ by definition.

Solving Problems with the Binomial Formula

A common example of a binomial distribution is the tossing of a coin and counting the number of heads. For example, if we wished to find the probability of 4 heads in 5 tosses of a coin, we would have

$$n = 5, r = 4, p = 0.5, \quad \text{and} \quad q = 1 - 0.5 = 0.5$$

Thus,

$$P(4 \text{ successes in } 5 \text{ trials}) = \frac{5!}{4!(5-4)!} 0.5^4 0.5^{5-4}$$

$$= \frac{5(4)(3)(2)(1)}{4(3)(2)(1)(1!)} (0.0625)(0.5) = 0.15625$$

Thus, the probability of 4 heads in 5 tosses of a coin is 0.15625 or about 16%.

Using Equation 9, it is also possible to find the entire probability distribution (all the possible values for r and the corresponding probabilities) for a binomial experiment. The probability distribution for the number of heads in 5 tosses of a fair coin is shown in Table 8 and then graphed in Figure 6.

TABLE 8

Binomial Probability Distribution for $n = 5$ and $p = 0.50$

NUMBER OF HEADS (r)	PROBABILITY $= \dfrac{5!}{r!(5-r)!}(0.5)^r(0.5)^{5-r}$
0	$0.03125 = \dfrac{5!}{0!(5-0)!}(0.5)^0(0.5)^{5-0}$
1	$0.15625 = \dfrac{5!}{1!(5-1)!}(0.5)^1(0.5)^{5-1}$
2	$0.31250 = \dfrac{5!}{2!(5-2)!}(0.5)^2(0.5)^{5-2}$
3	$0.31250 = \dfrac{5!}{3!(5-3)!}(0.5)^3(0.5)^{5-3}$
4	$0.15625 = \dfrac{5!}{4!(5-4)!}(0.5)^4(0.5)^{5-4}$
5	$0.03125 = \dfrac{5!}{5!(5-5)!}(0.5)^5(0.5)^{5-5}$

FIGURE 6

Binomial Probability Distribution for $n = 5$ and $p = 0.50$

Solving Problems with Binomial Tables

MSA Electronics is experimenting with the manufacture of a new type of transistor that is very difficult to mass produce at an acceptable quality level. Every hour a supervisor takes a random sample of 5 transistors produced on the assembly line. The probability that any one transistor is defective is considered to be 0.15. MSA wants to know the probability of finding 3, 4, or 5 defectives if the true percentage defective is 15%.

For this problem, $n = 5$, $p = 0.15$, and $r = 3$, 4, or 5. Although we could use the formula for each of these values, it is easier to use binomial tables for this. Appendix: Binomial Probabilities gives a binomial table for a broad range of values for n, r, and p. A portion of this appendix is shown in Table 9. To find these probabilities, we look through the $n = 5$ section and find the

TABLE 9 A Sample Table for the Binomial Distribution

		P									
n	*r*	0.05	0.10	0.15	0.20	0.25	0.30	0.35	0.40	0.45	0.50
1	0	0.9500	0.9000	0.8500	0.8000	0.7500	0.7000	0.6500	0.6000	0.5500	0.5000
	1	0.0500	0.1000	0.1500	0.2000	0.2500	0.3000	0.3500	0.4000	0.4500	0.5000
2	0	0.9025	0.8100	0.7225	0.6400	0.5625	0.4900	0.4225	0.3600	0.3025	0.2500
	1	0.0950	0.1800	0.2500	0.3200	0.3750	0.4200	0.4550	0.4800	0.4950	0.5000
	2	0.0025	0.0100	0.0225	0.0400	0.0625	0.0900	0.1225	0.1600	0.2025	0.2500
3	0	0.8574	0.7290	0.6141	0.5120	0.4219	0.3430	0.2746	0.2160	0.1664	0.1250
	1	0.1354	0.2430	0.3251	0.3840	0.4219	0.4410	0.4436	0.4320	0.4084	0.3750
	2	0.0071	0.0270	0.0574	0.0960	0.1406	0.1890	0.2389	0.2880	0.3341	0.3750
	3	0.0001	0.0010	0.0034	0.0080	0.0156	0.0270	0.0429	0.0640	0.0911	0.1250
4	0	0.8145	0.6561	0.5220	0.4096	0.3164	0.2401	0.1785	0.1296	0.0915	0.0625
	1	0.1715	0.2916	0.3685	0.4096	0.4219	0.4116	0.3845	0.3456	0.2995	0.2500
	2	0.0135	0.0486	0.0975	0.1536	0.2109	0.2646	0.3105	0.3456	0.3675	0.3750
	3	0.0005	0.0036	0.0115	0.0256	0.0469	0.0756	0.1115	0.1536	0.2005	0.2500
	4	0.0000	0.0001	0.0005	0.0016	0.0039	0.0081	0.0150	0.0256	0.0410	0.0625
5	0	0.7738	0.5905	0.4437	0.3277	0.2373	0.1681	0.1160	0.0778	0.0503	0.0313
	1	0.2036	0.3281	0.3915	0.4096	0.3955	0.3602	0.3124	0.2592	0.2059	0.1563
	2	0.0214	0.0729	0.1382	0.2048	0.2637	0.3087	0.3364	0.3456	0.3369	0.3125
	3	0.0011	0.0081	0.0244	0.0512	0.0879	0.1323	0.1811	0.2304	0.2757	0.3125
	4	0.0000	0.0005	0.0022	0.0064	0.0146	0.0284	0.0488	0.0768	0.1128	0.1563
	5	0.0000	0.0000	0.0001	0.0003	0.0010	0.0024	0.0053	0.0102	0.0185	0.0313
6	0	0.7351	0.5314	0.3771	0.2621	0.1780	0.1176	0.0754	0.0467	0.0277	0.0156
	1	0.2321	0.3543	0.3993	0.3932	0.3560	0.3025	0.2437	0.1866	0.1359	0.0938
	2	0.0305	0.0984	0.1762	0.2458	0.2966	0.3241	0.3280	0.3110	0.2780	0.2344
	3	0.0021	0.0146	0.0415	0.0819	0.1318	0.1852	0.2355	0.2765	0.3032	0.3125
	4	0.0001	0.0012	0.0055	0.0154	0.0330	0.0595	0.0951	0.1382	0.1861	0.2344
	5	0.0000	0.0001	0.0004	0.0015	0.0044	0.0102	0.0205	0.0369	0.0609	0.0938
	6	0.0000	0.0000	0.0000	0.0001	0.0002	0.0007	0.0018	0.0041	0.0083	0.0156

PROGRAM 2A

Excel Output for the Binomial Example

Using the cell references eliminates the need to retype the formula if you change a parameter such as p or r.

1	The Binomial Distribution	
2	X = random variable for number of successes	
3	n =	5	number of trials
4	p =	0.5	probability of a success
5	r =	4	specific number of successes
6		
7	Cumulative probability	P(X ≤ r) = 0.9688
8	Probability of exactly r successes	P(X = r) = 0.1563

PROGRAM 2B

Function in an Excel 2013 Spreadsheet for Binomial Probabilities

The function BINOM.DIST (r,n,p,TRUE) returns the cumulative probability.

	C
7	=BINOMDIST(B5,B3,B4,TRUE)
8	=BINOMDIST(B5,B3,B4,FALSE)

$p = 0.15$ column. In the row where $r = 3$, we see 0.0244. Thus, $P(r = 3) = 0.0244$. Similarly, $P(r = 4) = 0.0022$, and $P(r = 5) = 0.0001$. By adding these three probabilities, we have the probability that the number of defects is 3 or more:

$$P(3 \text{ or more defects}) = P(3) + P(4) + P(5)$$
$$= 0.0244 + 0.0022 + 0.0001 = 0.0267$$

The expected value (or mean) and the variance of a binomial random variable may be easily found. These are

$$\text{Expected value (mean)} = np \qquad (10)$$

$$\text{Variance} = np(1 - p) \qquad (11)$$

The expected value and variance for the MSA Electronics example are computed as follows:

$$\text{Expected value} = np = 5(0.15) = 0.75$$
$$\text{Variance} = np(1 - p) = 5(0.15)(0.85) = 0.6375$$

Programs 2A and 2B illustrate how Excel is used for binomial probabilities.

8 The Normal Distribution

The normal distribution affects a large number of processes in our lives (e.g., filling boxes of cereal with 32 ounces of corn flakes). Each normal distribution depends on the mean and standard deviation.

One of the most popular and useful continuous probability distributions is the **normal distribution**. The probability density function of this distribution is given by the rather complex formula

$$f(X) = \frac{1}{\sigma\sqrt{2\pi}}e^{\frac{-(x-\mu)^2}{2\sigma^2}} \qquad (12)$$

The normal distribution is specified completely when values for the mean, μ, and the standard deviation, σ, are known. Figure 7 shows several different normal distributions with the same standard deviation and different means. As shown, differing values of μ will shift the average or center of the normal distribution. The overall shape of the distribution remains the same. On the other hand, when the standard deviation is varied, the normal curve either flattens out or becomes steeper. This is shown in Figure 8.

As the standard deviation, σ, becomes smaller, the normal distribution becomes steeper. When the standard deviation becomes larger, the normal distribution has a tendency to flatten out or become broader.

FIGURE 7

Normal Distribution with Different Values for μ

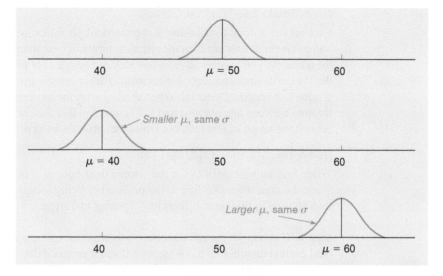

FIGURE 8

Normal Distribution with Different Values for σ

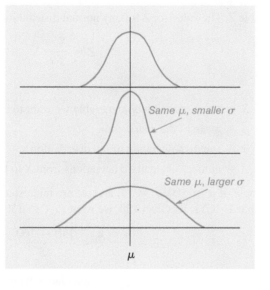

IN ACTION — Probability Assessments of Curling Champions

Probabilities are used every day in sporting activities. In many sporting events, there are questions involving strategies that must be answered to provide the best chance of winning the game. In baseball, should a particular batter be intentionally walked in key situations at the end of the game? In football, should a team elect to try for a two-point conversion after a touchdown? In soccer, should a penalty kick ever be aimed directly at the goal keeper? In curling, in the last round, or "end" of a game, is it better to be behind by one point and have the hammer or is it better to be ahead by one point and not have the hammer? An attempt was made to answer this last question.

In curling, a granite stone, or "rock," is slid across a sheet of ice 14 feet wide and 146 feet long. Four players on each of two teams take alternating turns sliding the rock, trying to get it as close as possible to the center of a circle called the "house." The team with the rock closest to this scores points. The team that is behind at the completion of a round or end has the advantage in

the next end by being the last team to slide the rock. This team is said to "have the hammer." A survey was taken of a group of experts in curling, including a number of former world champions. In this survey, about 58% of the respondents favored having the hammer and being down by one going into the last end. Only about 42% preferred being ahead and not having the hammer.

Data were also collected from 1985 to 1997 at the Canadian Men's Curling Championships (also called the Brier). Based on the results over this time period, it is better to be ahead by one point and not have the hammer at the end of the ninth end rather than be behind by one and have the hammer, as many people prefer. This differed from the survey results. Apparently, world champions and other experts preferred to have more control of their destiny by having the hammer even though it put them in a worse situation.

Source: Based on Keith A. Willoughby and Kent J. Kostuk. "Preferred Scenarios in the Sport of Curling," *Interfaces* 34, 2 (March–April 2004): 117–122.

Area Under the Normal Curve

Because the normal distribution is symmetrical, its midpoint (and highest point) is at the mean. Values on the X axis are then measured in terms of how many standard deviations they lie from the mean. As you may recall from our earlier discussion of probability distributions, the area under the curve (in a continuous distribution) describes the probability that a random variable has a value in a specified interval. When dealing with the uniform distribution, it is easy to compute the area between any points a and b. The normal distribution requires mathematical calculations beyond the scope of this text, but tables that provide areas or probabilities are readily available.

Using the Standard Normal Table

When finding probabilities for the normal distribution, it is best to draw the normal curve and shade the area corresponding to the probability being sought. The normal distribution table can then be used to find probabilities by following two steps.

Step 1. Convert the normal distribution to what we call a *standard normal distribution*. A standard normal distribution has a mean of 0 and a standard deviation of 1. All normal tables are set up to handle random variables with $\mu = 0$ and $\sigma = 1$. Without a standard normal distribution, a different table would be needed for each pair of μ and σ values. We call the new standard random variable Z. The value for Z for any normal distribution is computed from this equation:

$$Z = \frac{X - \mu}{\sigma} \tag{13}$$

where

X = value of the random variable we want to measure

μ = mean of the distribution

σ = standard deviation of the distribution

Z = number of standard deviations from X to the mean, μ

For example, if $\mu = 100$, $\sigma = 15$, and we are interested in finding the probability that the random variable X (IQ) is less than 130, we want $P(X < 130)$:

$$Z = \frac{X - \mu}{\sigma} = \frac{130 - 100}{15}$$

$$= \frac{30}{15} = 2 \text{ standard deviations}$$

This means that the point X is 2.0 standard deviations to the right of the mean. This is shown in Figure 9.

FIGURE 9

Normal Distribution Showing the Relationship Between *Z* Values and *X* Values

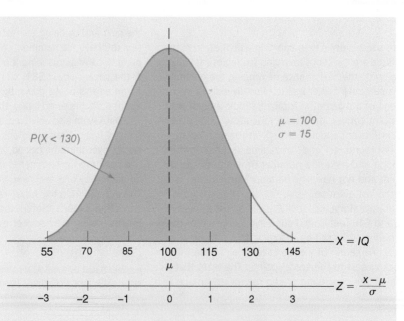

Step 2. Look up the probability from a table of normal curve areas. Table 10, which also appears as as Appendix: Areas Under the Standard Normal Curve, is such a table of areas for the standard normal distribution. It is set up to provide the area under the curve to the left of any specified value of Z.

Let's see how Table 10 can be used. The column on the left lists values of Z, with the second decimal place of Z appearing in the top row. For example, for a value of $Z = 2.00$ as just computed, find 2.0 in the left-hand column and 0.00 in the top row. In the body of the table, we find that the area sought is 0.97725, or 97.7%. Thus,

$$P(X < 130) = P(Z < 2.00) = 97.7\%$$

This suggests that if the mean IQ score is 100, with a standard deviation of 15 points, the probability that a randomly selected person's IQ is less than 130 is 97.7%. This is also the probability that the IQ is less than or equal to 130. To find the probability that the IQ is greater than 130, we simply note that this is the complement of the previous event and the total area under the curve (the total probability) is 1. Thus,

$$P(X > 130) = 1 - P(X \le 130) = 1 - P(Z \le 2) = 1 - 0.97725 = 0.02275$$

While Table 10 does not give negative Z values, the symmetry of the normal distribution can be used to find probabilities associated with negative Z values. For example, $P(Z < -2) = P(Z > 2)$.

To feel comfortable with the use of the standard normal probability table, we need to work a few more examples. We now use the Haynes Construction Company as a case in point.

To be sure you understand the concept of symmetry in Table 10, try to find the probability such as $P(X < 85)$. Note that the standard normal table shows only positive Z values.

Haynes Construction Company Example

Haynes Construction Company builds primarily three- and four-unit apartment buildings (called triplexes and quadraplexes) for investors, and it is believed that the total construction time in days follows a normal distribution. The mean time to construct a triplex is 100 days, and the standard deviation is 20 days. Recently, the president of Haynes Construction signed a contract to complete a triplex in 125 days. Failure to complete the triplex in 125 days would result in severe penalty fees. What is the probability that Haynes Construction will not be in violation of their construction contract? The normal distribution for the construction of triplexes is shown in Figure 10.

To compute this probability, we need to find the shaded area under the curve. We begin by computing Z for this problem:

$$Z = \frac{X - \mu}{\sigma}$$

$$= \frac{125 - 100}{20}$$

$$= \frac{25}{20} = 1.25$$

Looking in Table 10 for a Z value of 1.25, we find an area under the curve of 0.89435. (We do this by looking up 1.2 in the left-hand column of the table and then moving to the 0.05 column to find the value for $Z = 1.25$.) Therefore, the probability of not violating the contract is 0.89435, or about an 89% chance.

FIGURE 10

Normal Distribution for Haynes Construction

$P(X \le 125)$

0.89435

$\mu = 100$ days

$X = 125$ days

$\sigma = 20$ days

$Z = 1.25$

TABLE 10 Standardized Normal Distribution Function

Z	AREA UNDER THE NORMAL CURVE									
	0.00	0.01	0.02	0.03	0.04	0.05	0.06	0.07	0.08	0.09
0.0	.50000	.50399	.50798	.51197	.51595	.51994	.52392	.52790	.53188	.53586
0.1	.53983	.54380	.54776	.55172	.55567	.55962	.56356	.56749	.57142	.57535
0.2	.57926	.58317	.58706	.59095	.59483	.59871	.60257	.60642	.61026	.61409
0.3	.61791	.62172	.62552	.62930	.63307	.63683	.64058	.64431	.64803	.65173
0.4	.65542	.65910	.66276	.66640	.67003	.67364	.67724	.68082	.68439	.68793
0.5	.69146	.69497	.69847	.70194	.70540	.70884	.71226	.71566	.71904	.72240
0.6	.72575	.72907	.73237	.73565	.73891	.74215	.74537	.74857	.75175	.75490
0.7	.75804	.76115	.76424	.76730	.77035	.77337	.77637	.77935	.78230	.78524
0.8	.78814	.79103	.79389	.79673	.79955	.80234	.80511	.80785	.81057	.81327
0.9	.81594	.81859	.82121	.82381	.82639	.82894	.83147	.83398	.83646	.83891
1.0	.84134	.84375	.84614	.84849	.85083	.85314	.85543	.85769	.85993	.86214
1.1	.86433	.86650	.86864	.87076	.87286	.87493	.87698	.87900	.88100	.88298
1.2	.88493	.88686	.88877	.89065	.89251	.89435	.89617	.89796	.89973	.90147
1.3	.90320	.90490	.90658	.90824	.90988	.91149	.91309	.91466	.91621	.91774
1.4	.91924	.92073	.92220	.92364	.92507	.92647	.92785	.92922	.93056	.93189
1.5	.93319	.93448	.93574	.93699	.93822	.93943	.94062	.94179	.94295	.94408
1.6	.94520	.94630	.94738	.94845	.94950	.95053	.95154	.95254	.95352	.95449
1.7	.95543	.95637	.95728	.95818	.95907	.95994	.96080	.96164	.96246	.96327
1.8	.96407	.96485	.96562	.96638	.96712	.96784	.96856	.96926	.96995	.97062
1.9	.97128	.97193	.97257	.97320	.97381	.97441	.97500	.97558	.97615	.97670
2.0	.97725	.97778	.97831	.97882	.97932	.97982	.98030	.98077	.98124	.98169
2.1	.98214	.98257	.98300	.98341	.98382	.98422	.98461	.98500	.98537	.98574
2.2	.98610	.98645	.98679	.98713	.98745	.98778	.98809	.98840	.98870	.98899
2.3	.98928	.98956	.98983	.99010	.99036	.99061	.99086	.99111	.99134	.99158
2.4	.99180	.99202	.99224	.99245	.99266	.99286	.99305	.99324	.99343	.99361
2.5	.99379	.99396	.99413	.99430	.99446	.99461	.99477	.99492	.99506	.99520
2.6	.99534	.99547	.99560	.99573	.99585	.99598	.99609	.99621	.99632	.99643
2.7	.99653	.99664	.99674	.99683	.99693	.99702	.99711	.99720	.99728	.99736
2.8	.99744	.99752	.99760	.99767	.99774	.99781	.99788	.99795	.99801	.99807
2.9	.99813	.99819	.99825	.99831	.99836	.99841	.99846	.99851	.99856	.99861
3.0	.99865	.99869	.99874	.99878	.99882	.99886	.99889	.99893	.99896	.99900
3.1	.99903	.99906	.99910	.99913	.99916	.99918	.99921	.99924	.99926	.99929
3.2	.99931	.99934	.99936	.99938	.99940	.99942	.99944	.99946	.99948	.99950
3.3	.99952	.99953	.99955	.99957	.99958	.99960	.99961	.99962	.99964	.99965
3.4	.99966	.99968	.99969	.99970	.99971	.99972	.99973	.99974	.99975	.99976
3.5	.99977	.99978	.99978	.99979	.99980	.99981	.99981	.99982	.99983	.99983
3.6	.99984	.99985	.99985	.99986	.99986	.99987	.99987	.99988	.99988	.99989
3.7	.99989	.99990	.99990	.99990	.99991	.99991	.99992	.99992	.99992	.99992
3.8	.99993	.99993	.99993	.99994	.99994	.99994	.99994	.99995	.99995	.99995
3.9	.99995	.99995	.99996	.99996	.99996	.99996	.99996	.99996	.99997	.99997

FIGURE 11

Probability That Haynes Will Receive the Bonus by Finishing in 75 Days or Less

$P(X \le 75 \text{ days})$
Area of Interest

0.89435

$X = 75$ days

$\mu = 100$ days

$Z = -1.25$

Now let us look at the Haynes problem from another perspective. If the firm finishes this triplex in 75 days or less, it will be awarded a bonus payment of $5,000. What is the probability that Haynes will receive the bonus?

Figure 11 illustrates the probability we are looking for in the shaded area. The first step is again to compute the Z value:

$$Z = \frac{X - \mu}{\sigma}$$

$$= \frac{75 - 100}{20}$$

$$= \frac{-25}{20} = -1.25$$

This Z value indicates that 75 days is -1.25 standard deviations to the left of the mean. But the standard normal table is structured to handle only positive Z values. To solve this problem, we observe that the curve is symmetric. The probability that Haynes will finish in *75 days or less is equivalent* to the probability that it will finish in *more than 125 days*. A moment ago (in Figure 10) we found the probability that Haynes will finish in less than 125 days. That value is 0.89435. So the probability it takes more than 125 days is

$$P(X > 125) = 1.0 - P(X \le 125)$$
$$= 1.0 - 0.89435 = 0.10565$$

Thus, the probability of completing the triplex in 75 days or less is 0.10565, or about 11%.

One final example: What is the probability that the triplex will take between 110 and 125 days? We see in Figure 12 that

$$P(110 < X < 125) = P(X \le 125) - P(X < 110)$$

That is, the shaded area in the graph can be computed by finding the probability of completing the building in 125 days or less *minus* the probability of completing it in 110 days or less.

FIGURE 12

Probability That Haynes Will Complete in 110 to 125 Days

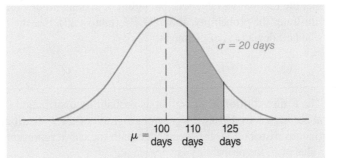

$\sigma = 20$ days

$\mu = $ 100 days   110 days   125 days

PROGRAM 3A

Excel 2013 Output for the Normal Distribution Example

	A	B
1	X is a normal random variable	
2	with mean, μ, and standard deviation, σ.	
3	μ =	100
4	σ =	20
5	x =	75
6	P(X ≤ x) =	0.10565
7	P(X > x) =	0.89435

PROGRAM 3B

Function in an Excel 2013 Spreadsheet for the Normal Distribution Example

	B
6	=NORMDIST(B5,B3,B4,TRUE)
7	=1-B6

Note that $P(X \leq 125 \text{ days})$ is equal to 0.89435. To find $P(X < 110 \text{ days})$, we follow the two steps developed earlier:

1.
$$Z = \frac{X - \mu}{\sigma} = \frac{110 - 100}{20} = \frac{10}{20}$$
$$= 0.5 \text{ standard deviations}$$

2. From Table 10, the area for $Z = 0.50$ is 0.69146. So the probability the triplex can be completed in less than 110 days is 0.69146. Finally,

$$P(110 \leq X \leq 125) = 0.89435 - 0.69146 = 0.20289$$

The probability that it will take between 110 and 125 days is about 20%. Programs 3A and 3B show how Excel can be used for this.

The Empirical Rule

While the probability tables for the normal distribution can provide precise probabilities, many situations require less precision. The empirical rule was derived from the normal distribution and is an easy way to remember some basic information about normal distributions. The empirical rule states that for a normal distribution

approximately 68% of the values will be within ± 1 standard deviation of the mean

approximately 95% of the values will be within ± 2 standard deviations of the mean

almost all (about 99.7%) of the values will be within ± 3 standard deviations of the mean

Figure 13 illustrates the empirical rule. The area from point a to point b in the first drawing represents the probability, approximately 68%, that the random variable will be within ± 1 standard deviation of the mean. The middle drawing illustrates the probability, approximately 95%, that the random variable will be within ± 2 standard deviations of the mean. The last drawing illustrates the probability, about 99.7% (almost all), that the random variable will be within ± 3 standard deviations of the mean.

9 The F Distribution

The **F distribution** is a continuous probability distribution that is helpful in testing hypotheses about variances. Figure 14 provides a graph of the F distribution. As with a graph for any continuous distribution, the area underneath the curve represents probability. Note that for a large value of F, the probability is very small.

The F statistic is the ratio of two sample variances from independent normal distributions. Every F distribution has two sets of degrees of freedom associated with it. One of the degrees of freedom is associated with the numerator of the ratio, and the other is associated with the denominator of the ratio. The degrees of freedom are based on the sample sizes used in calculating the numerator and denominator.

FIGURE 13
Approximate Probabilities from the Empirical Rule

Figure 13 is very important, and you should comprehend the meanings of ±1, 2, and 3 standard deviation symmetrical areas.

Managers often speak of 95% and 99% confidence intervals, which roughly refer to ±2 and 3 standard deviation graphs.

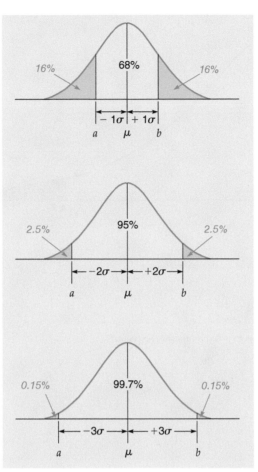

Appendix: *F* Distribution Values provides values of *F* associated with the upper tail of the distribution for certain probabilities (denoted by α) and degrees of freedom for the numerator (df_1) and degrees of freedom for the denominator (df_2).

To find the *F* value that is associated with a particular probability and degrees of freedom, refer to Appendix: *F* Distribution Values. The following notation will be used:

$$df_1 = \text{degrees of freedom for the numerator}$$

$$df_2 = \text{degrees of freedom for the denominator}$$

Consider the following example:

$$df_1 = 5$$
$$df_2 = 6$$
$$\alpha = 0.05$$

FIGURE 14
The *F* Distribution

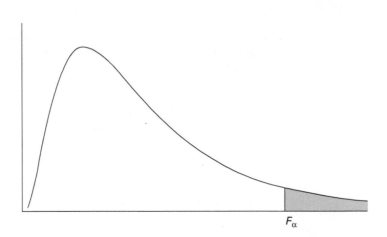

FIGURE 15

F Value for 0.05
Probability with 5 and
6 Degrees of Freedom

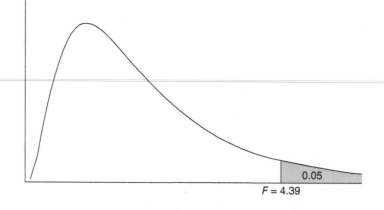

$F = 4.39$

PROGRAM 4A

**Excel 2013 Output for
the *F* Distribution**

	A	B	C	D
1	F Distribution with df1 and df2 degrees of freedom			
2	To find F given α			
3	df1 =	5		
4	df2 =	6		
5	α =	0.05		
6	F-value =	4.39		
7				
8	To find the probability to the right of a calculated value, f			
9	df1 =	5		
10	df2 =	6		
11	f =	4.2		
12	P(F > f) =	0.0548		

PROGRAM 4B

**Functions in an Excel
2013 Spreadsheet for
the *F* Distribution**

	B
6	=FINV(B5,B3,B4)
12	=FDIST(B11,B9,B10)

From Appendix: *F* Distribution Values, we get

$$F_{\alpha, \, df1, \, df2} = F_{0.05, \, 5, \, 6} = 4.39$$

This means

$$P(F > 4.39) = 0.05$$

The probability is very low (only 5%) that the *F* value will exceed 4.39. There is a 95% probability that it will not exceed 4.39. This is illustrated in Figure 15. Appendix: *F* Distribution Values also provides *F* values associated with $\alpha = 0.01$. Programs 4A and 4B illustrate Excel functions for the *F* distribution.

10   The Exponential Distribution

The *exponential distribution*, also called the **negative exponential distribution**, is used in dealing with queuing problems. The exponential distribution often describes the time required to service a customer. The exponential distribution is a continuous distribution. Its probability function is given by

$$f(X) = \mu e^{-\mu x} \qquad (14)$$

where

X = random variable (service times)

μ = average number of units the service facility can handle in a specific period of time

e = 2.718 (the base of the natural logarithm)

FIGURE 16
Exponential Distribution

The general shape of the exponential distribution is shown in Figure 16. Its expected value and variance can be shown to be

$$\text{Expected value} = \frac{1}{\mu} = \text{Average service time} \qquad (15)$$

$$\text{Variance} = \frac{1}{\mu^2} \qquad (16)$$

As with any other continuous distribution, probabilities are found by determining the area under the curve. For the normal distribution, we found the area by using a table of probabilities. For the exponential distribution, the probabilities can be found using the exponent key on a calculator with the formula below. The probability that an exponentially distributed time (X) required to serve a customer is less than or equal to time t is given by the formula

$$P(X \leq t) = 1 - e^{-\mu t} \qquad (17)$$

The time period used in describing μ determines the units for the time t. For example, if μ is the average number served per hour, the time t must be given in hours. If μ is the average number served per minute, the time t must be given in minutes.

Arnold's Muffler Example

Arnold's Muffler Shop installs new mufflers on automobiles and small trucks. The mechanic can install new mufflers at a rate of about three per hour, and this service time is exponentially distributed. What is the probability that the time to install a new muffler would be $^1/_2$ hour or less? Using Equation 17, we have

$$X = \text{exponentially distributed service time}$$
$$\mu = \text{average number that can be served per time period} = 3 \text{ per hour}$$
$$t = {}^1/_2 \text{ hour} = 0.5 \text{ hour}$$

$$P(X \leq 0.5) = 1 - e^{-3(0.5)} = 1 - e^{-1.5} = 1 - 0.2231 = 0.7769$$

Figure 17 shows the area under the curve from 0 to 0.5 to be 0.7769. Thus, there is about a 78% chance the time will be no more than 0.5 hour and about a 22% chance that the time will be longer than this. Similarly, we could find the probability that the service time is no more $^1/_3$ hour or $^2/_3$ hour, as follows:

$$P\left(X \leq \frac{1}{3}\right) = 1 - e^{-3\left(\frac{1}{3}\right)} = 1 - e^{-1} = 1 - 0.3679 = 0.6321$$

$$P\left(X \leq \frac{2}{3}\right) = 1 - e^{-3\left(\frac{2}{3}\right)} = 1 - e^{-2} = 1 - 0.1353 = 0.8647$$

FIGURE 17

Probability That the Mechanic Will Install a Muffler in 0.5 Hour

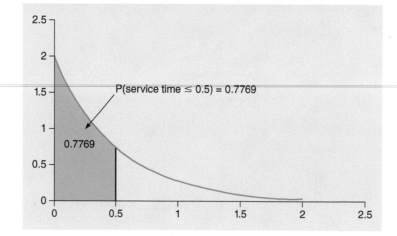

PROGRAM 5A

Excel 2013 Output for the Exponential Distribution

	A	B	C
1	Exponential distribution - the random variable (X) is time		
2	Average number per time period = μ =	3	per hour
3	t =	0.5000	hours
4	P(X ≤ t) =	0.7769	
5	P(X > t) =	0.2231	

Program 5B

Function in an Excel 2013 Spreadsheet for the Exponential Distribution

	B
4	=EXPONDIST(B3,B2,TRUE)
5	=1-B4

While Equation 17 provides the probability that the time (X) is less than or equal to a particular value t, the probability that the time is greater than a particular value t is found by observing that these two events are complementary. For example, to find the probability that the mechanic at Arnold's Muffler Shop would take longer than 0.5 hour, we have

$$P(X > 0.5) = 1 - P(X \le 0.5) = 1 - 0.7769 = 0.2231$$

Programs 5A and 5B illustrate how a function in Excel can find exponential probabilities.

11   The Poisson Distribution

An important **discrete probability distribution** is the **Poisson distribution**.[1] The distribution describes situations in which customers arrive independently during a certain time interval, and the number of arrivals depends on the length of the time interval. Examples are patients arriving at a health clinic, customers arriving at a bank window, passengers arriving at an airport, and telephone calls going through a central exchange.

The Poisson probability distribution is used in many queuing models to represent arrival patterns.

The formula for the Poisson distribution is

$$P(X) = \frac{\lambda^x e^{-\lambda}}{X!} \tag{18}$$

---

[1] This distribution, derived by Siméon Denis Poisson in 1837, is pronounced "pwah-sahn."

where

$P(X)$ = probability of exactly X arrivals or occurrences

λ = average number of arrivals per unit of time (the mean arrival rate), pronounced "lambda"

e = 2.718, the base of the natural logarithm

X = number of occurrences $(0, 1, 2, \ldots)$

The mean and variance of the Poisson distribution are equal and are computed simply as

$$\text{Expected value} = \lambda \tag{19}$$

$$\text{Variance} = \lambda \tag{20}$$

With the help of the table in Appendix: Values of $e^{-\lambda}$ for Use in the Poisson Distribution, the values of $e^{-\lambda}$ are easy to find. We can use these in the formula to find probabilities. For example, if $\lambda = 2$, from Appendix: Values of $e^{-\lambda}$ for Use in the Poisson Distribution we find $e^{-2} = 0.1353$. The Poisson probabilities that X is 0, 1, and 2 when $\lambda = 2$ are as follows:

$$P(X) = \frac{e^{-\lambda}\lambda^x}{X!}$$

$$P(0) = \frac{e^{-2}2^0}{0!} = \frac{(0.1353)1}{1} = 0.1353 \approx 14\%$$

$$P(1) = \frac{e^{-2}2^1}{1!} = \frac{e^{-2}2}{1} = \frac{0.1353(2)}{1} = 0.2706 \approx 27\%$$

$$P(2) = \frac{e^{-2}2^2}{2!} = \frac{e^{-2}4}{2(1)} = \frac{0.1353(4)}{2} = 0.2706 \approx 27\%$$

These probabilities, as well as others for $\lambda = 2$ and $\lambda = 4$, are shown in Figure 18. Notice that the chances that 9 or more customers will arrive in a particular time period are virtually nil. Programs 6A and 6B illustrate how Excel can be used to find Poisson probabilities.

It should be noted that the exponential and Poisson distributions are related. If the number of occurrences per time period follows a Poisson distribution, then the time between occurrences follows an exponential distribution. For example, if the number of phone calls arriving at a customer service center followed a Poisson distribution with a mean of 10 calls per hour, the time between each phone call would be exponentially distributed with a mean time between calls of $\frac{1}{10}$ hour (6 minutes).

FIGURE 18
Sample Poisson Distributions with $\lambda = 2$ and $\lambda = 4$

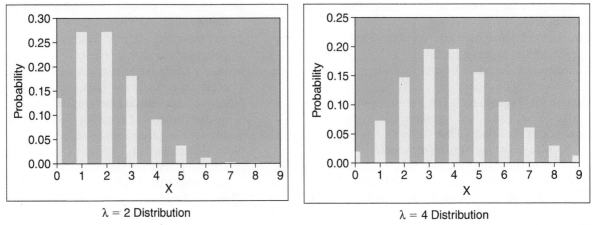

λ = 2 Distribution   λ = 4 Distribution

PROGRAM 6A

Excel 2013 Output for the Poisson Distribution

	A	B	C	D	E	F	G	H
1	Poisson distribution - the random variable is the number of occurrences per time period							
2		λ =	2					
3	x		P(X)	P(X ≤ x)				
4	0		0.1353	0.1353				
5	1		0.2707	0.4060				
6	2		0.7293	0.6767				

PROGRAM 6B

Functions in an Excel 2013 Spreadsheet for the Poisson Distribution

	B	C
4	=POISSON(A4,$B$2,FALSE)	=POISSON(A4,$B$2,TRUE)
5	=POISSON(A5,$B$2,FALSE)	=POISSON(A5,$B$2,TRUE)
6	=1-B5	=POISSON(A6,$B$2,TRUE)

Summary

This chapter presents the fundamental concepts of probability and probability distributions. Probability values can be obtained objectively or subjectively. A single probability value must be between 0 and 1, and the sum of all probability values for all possible outcomes must be equal to 1. In addition, probability values and events can have a number of properties. These properties include mutually exclusive, collectively exhaustive, statistically independent, and statistically dependent events. Rules for computing probability values depend on these fundamental properties. It is also possible to revise probability values when new information becomes available. This can be done using Bayes' theorem.

We also covered the topics of random variables, discrete probability distributions (such as Poisson and binomial), and continuous probability distributions (such as normal, F, and exponential). A probability distribution is any statement of a probability function having a set of collectively exhaustive and mutually exclusive events. All probability distributions follow the basic probability rules mentioned previously.

Basic probability concepts and distributions are used for decision theory, inventory control, Markov analysis, project management, simulation, and statistical quality control.

Glossary

Bayes' Theorem   A formula that is used to revise probabilities based on new information.

Bernoulli Process   A process with two outcomes in each of a series of independent trials in which the probabilities of the outcomes do not change.

Binomial Distribution   A discrete distribution that describes the number of successes in independent trials of a Bernoulli process.

Classical or **Logical Method**   An objective way of assessing probabilities based on logic.

Collectively Exhaustive Events   A collection of all possible outcomes of an experiment.

Conditional Probability   The probability of one event occurring given that another has taken place.

Continuous Probability Distribution   A probability distribution with a continuous random variable.

Continuous Random Variable   A random variable that can assume an infinite or unlimited set of values.

Discrete Probability Distribution   A probability distribution with a discrete random variable.

Discrete Random Variable   A random variable that can only assume a finite or limited set of values.

Expected Value   The (weighted) average of a probability distribution.

F Distribution   A continuous probability distribution that is the ratio of the variances of samples from two independent normal distributions.

Independent Events   The situation in which the occurrence of one event has no effect on the probability of occurrence of a second event.

Intersection   The set of all outcomes that are common to both events.

Joint Probability   The probability of events occurring together (or one after the other).

Mutually Exclusive Events   A situation in which only one event can occur on any given trial or experiment.

Negative Exponential Distribution   A continuous probability distribution that describes the time between customer arrivals in a queuing situation.

Normal Distribution   A continuous bell-shaped distribution that is a function of two parameters, the mean and standard deviation of the distribution.

Objective Approach   A method of determining probability values based on historical data or logic.

Poisson Distribution   A discrete probability distribution used in queuing theory.

Prior Probability   A probability value determined before new or additional information is obtained. It is sometimes called an a priori probability estimate.

Probability   A statement about the likelihood of an event occurring. It is expressed as a numerical value between 0 and 1, inclusive.

Probability Density Function   The mathematical function that describes a continuous probability distribution. It is represented by $f(X)$.

Probability Distribution   The set of all possible values of a random variable and their associated probabilities.

Random Variable   A variable that assigns a number to every possible outcome of an experiment.

Relative Frequency Approach   An objective way of determining probabilities based on observing frequencies over a number of trials.

Revised or **Posterior Probability**   A probability value that results from new or revised information and prior probabilities.

Standard Deviation   The square root of the variance.

Subjective Approach   A method of determining probability values based on experience or judgment.

Union   The set of all outcomes that are contained in either of these two events.

Variance   A measure of dispersion or spread of the probability distribution.

Key Equations

(1) $0 \le P(\text{event}) \le 1$

A basic statement of probability.

(2) $P(A \text{ or } B) = P(A) + P(B) - P(A \text{ and } B)$

Probability of the union of two events.

(3) $P(A|B) = \dfrac{P(AB)}{P(B)}$

Conditional probability.

(4) $P(AB) = P(A|B)P(B)$

Probability of the intersection of two events.

(5) $P(A|B) = \dfrac{P(B|A)P(A)}{P(B|A)P(A) + P(B|A')P(A')}$

Bayes' theorem in general form.

(6) $E(X) = \sum\limits_{i=1}^{n} X_i P(X_i)$

An equation that computes the expected value (mean) of a discrete probability distribution.

(7) $\sigma^2 = \text{Variance} = \sum\limits_{i=1}^{n} [X_i - E(X)]^2 P(X_i)$

An equation that computes the variance of a discrete probability distribution.

(8) $\sigma = \sqrt{\text{Variance}} = \sqrt{\sigma^2}$

An equation that computes the standard deviation from the variance.

(9)   Probability of r successes in n trials $= \dfrac{n!}{r!(n-r)!} p^r q^{n-r}$

A formula that computes probabilities for the binomial probability distribution.

(10)   Expected value (mean) $= np$

The expected value of the binomial distribution.

(11) $\text{Variance} = np(1-p)$

The variance of the binomial distribution.

(12) $f(X) = \dfrac{1}{\sigma\sqrt{2\pi}} e^{\frac{-(x-\mu)^2}{2\sigma^2}}$

The density function for the normal probability distribution.

(13) $Z = \dfrac{X - \mu}{\sigma}$

An equation that computes the number of standard deviations, Z, the point X is from the mean μ.

(14) $f(X) = \mu e^{-\mu x}$

The exponential distribution.

(15)   Expected value $= \dfrac{1}{\mu}$

The expected value of an exponential distribution.

(16)   Variance $= \dfrac{1}{\mu^2}$

The variance of an exponential distribution.

(17) $P(X \le t) = 1 - e^{-\mu t}$

Formula to find the probability that an exponential random variable (X) is less than or equal to time t.

(18) $P(X) = \dfrac{\lambda^x e^{-\lambda}}{X!}$

The Poisson distribution.

(19)   Expected value $= \lambda$

The mean of a Poisson distribution.

(20)   Variance $= \lambda$

The variance of a Poisson distribution.

Solved Problems

Solved Problem 1

In the past 30 days, Roger's Rural Roundup has sold 8, 9, 10, or 11 lottery tickets. It never sold fewer than 8 or more than 11. Assuming that the past is similar to the future, find the probabilities for the number of tickets sold if sales were 8 tickets on 10 days, 9 tickets on 12 days, 10 tickets on 6 days, and 11 tickets on 2 days:

Solution

SALES	NO. DAYS	PROBABILITY
8	10	0.333
9	12	0.400
10	6	0.200
11	2	0.067
Total	30	1.000

Solved Problem 2

A class contains 30 students. Ten are female (F) and U.S. citizens (U); 12 are male (M) and U.S. citizens; 6 are female and non-U.S. citizens (N); 2 are male and non-U.S. citizens.

A name is randomly selected from the class roster and it is female. What is the probability that the student is a U.S. citizen?

Solution

$$P(FU) = {}^{10}/_{30} = 0.333$$
$$P(FN) = {}^{6}/_{30} = 0.200$$
$$P(MU) = {}^{12}/_{30} = 0.400$$
$$P(MN) = {}^{2}/_{30} = 0.067$$
$$P(F) = P(FU) + P(FN) = 0.333 + 0.200 = 0.533$$
$$P(M) = P(MU) + P(MN) = 0.400 + 0.067 = 0.467$$
$$P(U) = P(FU) + P(MU) = 0.333 + 0.400 = 0.733$$
$$P(N) = P(FN) + P(MN) = 0.200 + 0.067 = 0.267$$
$$P(U|F) = \frac{P(FU)}{P(F)} = \frac{0.333}{0.533} = 0.625$$

Solved Problem 3

Your professor tells you that if you score an 85 or better on your midterm exam, then you have a 90% chance of getting an A for the course. You think you have only a 50% chance of scoring 85 or better. Find the probability that *both* your score is 85 or better *and* you receive an A in the course.

Solution

$$P(A \text{ and } 85) = P(A|85) \times P(85) = (0.90)(0.50)$$
$$= 45\%$$

Solved Problem 4

A statistics class was asked if it believed that all tests on the Monday following the football game win over their archrival should be postponed automatically. The results were as follows:

Strongly agree	40
Agree	30
Neutral	20
Disagree	10
Strongly disagree	0
	100

Transform this into a numeric score, using the following random variable scale, and find a probability distribution for the results:

Strongly agree	5
Agree	4
Neutral	3
Disagree	2
Strongly disagree	1

Solution

OUTCOME	PROBABILITY, $P(X)$
Strongly agree (5)	$0.4 = 40/100$
Agree (4)	$0.3 = 30/100$
Neutral (3)	$0.2 = 20/100$
Disagree (2)	$0.1 = 10/100$
Strongly disagree (1)	$0.0 = 0/100$
Total	$1.0 = 100/100$

Solved Problem 5

For Solved Problem 4, let X be the numeric score. Compute the expected value of X.

Solution

$$E(X) = \sum_{i=1}^{5} X_i P(X_i) = X_1 P(X_1) + X_2 P(X_2)$$
$$+ X_3 P(X_3) + X_4 P(X_4) + X_5 P(X_5)$$
$$= 5(0.4) + 4(0.3) + 3(0.2) + 2(0.1) + 1(0)$$
$$= 4.0$$

Solved Problem 6

Compute the variance and standard deviation for the random variable X in Solved Problems 4 and 5.

Solution

$$\text{Variance} = \sum_{i=1}^{5} (X_i - E(X))^2 P(X_i)$$
$$= (5 - 4)^2(0.4) + (4 - 4)^2(0.3) + (3 - 4)^2(0.2) + (2 - 4)^2(0.1) + (1 - 4)^2(0.0)$$
$$= (1)^2(0.4) + (0)^2(0.3) + (-1)^2(0.2) + (-2)^2(0.1) + (-3)^2(0.0)$$
$$= 0.4 + 0.0 + 0.2 + 0.4 + 0.0 = 1.0$$

The standard deviation is
$$\sigma = \sqrt{\text{Variance}} = \sqrt{1} = 1$$

Solved Problem 7

A candidate for public office has claimed that 60% of voters will vote for her. If 5 registered voters were sampled, what is the probability that exactly 3 would say they favor this candidate?

Solution

We use the binomial distribution with $n = 5, p = 0.6$, and $r = 3$:

$$P(\text{exactly 3 successes in 5 trials}) = \frac{n!}{r!(n-r)!} p^r q^{n-r} = \frac{5!}{3!(5-3)!}(0.6)^3(0.4)^{5-3} = 0.3456$$

Solved Problem 8

The length of the rods coming out of our new cutting machine can be said to approximate a normal distribution with a mean of 10 inches and a standard deviation of 0.2 inch. Find the probability that a rod selected randomly will have a length

(a) of less than 10.0 inches
(b) between 10.0 and 10.4 inches
(c) between 10.0 and 10.1 inches
(d) between 10.1 and 10.4 inches
(e) between 9.6 and 9.9 inches
(f) between 9.9 and 10.4 inches
(g) between 9.886 and 10.406 inches

Solution

First, compute the standard normal distribution, the Z value:

$$Z = \frac{X - \mu}{\sigma}$$

Next, find the area under the curve for the given Z value by using a standard normal distribution table.

(a) $P(X < 10.0) = 0.50000$
(b) $P(10.0 < X < 10.4) = 0.97725 - 0.50000 = 0.47725$
(c) $P(10.0 < X < 10.1) = 0.69146 - 0.50000 = 0.19146$
(d) $P(10.1 < X < 10.4) = 0.97725 - 0.69146 = 0.28579$
(e) $P(9.6 < X < 9.9) = 0.97725 - 0.69146 = 0.28579$
(f) $P(9.9 < X < 10.4) = 0.19146 + 0.47725 = 0.66871$
(g) $P(9.886 < X < 10.406) = 0.47882 + 0.21566 = 0.69448$

Self-Test

- Before taking the self-test, refer to the learning objectives at the beginning of the chapter, the notes in the margins, and the glossary at the end of the chapter.
- Use the key at the end of the chapter to correct your answers.
- Restudy pages that correspond to any questions that you answered incorrectly or material you feel uncertain about.

1. If only one event may occur on any one trial, then the events are said to be
   a. independent.
   b. exhaustive.
   c. mutually exclusive.
   d. continuous.
2. New probabilities that have been found using Bayes' theorem are called
   a. prior probabilities.
   b. posterior probabilities.
   c. Bayesian probabilities.
   d. joint probabilities.
3. A measure of central tendency is
   a. expected value.
   b. variance.
   c. standard deviation.
   d. all of the above.
4. To compute the variance, of a discrete random variable you need to know the
   a. variable's possible values.
   b. expected value of the variable.
   c. probability of each possible value of the variable.
   d. all of the above.
5. The square root of the variance is the
   a. expected value.
   b. standard deviation.
   c. area under the normal curve.
   d. all of the above.
6. Which of the following is an example of a discrete distribution?
   a. the normal distribution
   b. the exponential distribution
   c. the Poisson distribution
   d. the Z distribution

7. The total area under the curve for any continuous distribution must equal
   a. 1.
   b. 0.
   c. 0.5.
   d. none of the above.
8. Probabilities for all the possible values of a discrete random variable
   a. may be greater than 1.
   b. may be negative on some occasions.
   c. must sum to 1.
   d. are represented by area underneath the curve.
9. In a standard normal distribution, the mean is equal to
   a. 1.
   b. 0.
   c. the variance.
   d. the standard deviation.
10. The probability of two or more independent events occurring is the
    a. marginal probability.
    b. simple probability.
    c. conditional probability.
    d. joint probability.
    e. all of the above.
11. In the normal distribution, 95.45% of the population lies within
    a. 1 standard deviation of the mean.
    b. 2 standard deviations of the mean.
    c. 3 standard deviations of the mean.
    d. 4 standard deviations of the mean.

12. If a normal distribution has a mean of 200 and a standard deviation of 10, 99.7% of the population falls within what range of values?
    a. 170–230
    b. 180–220
    c. 190–210
    d. 175–225
    e. 170–220
13. If two events are mutually exclusive, then the probability of the intersection of these two events will equal
    a. 0.
    b. 0.5.
    c. 1.0.
    d. cannot be determined without more information.
14. If $P(A) = 0.4$ and $P(B) = 0.5$ and $P(A \text{ and } B) = 0.2$, then $P(B|A) =$
    a. 0.80.
    b. 0.50.
    c. 0.10.
    d. 0.40.
    e. none of the above.
15. If $P(A) = 0.4$ and $P(B) = 0.5$ and $P(A \text{ and } B) = 0.2$, then $P(A \text{ or } B) =$
    a. 0.7.
    b. 0.9.
    c. 1.1.
    d. 0.2.
    e. none of the above.

Discussion Questions and Problems

Discussion Questions

1 What are the two basic laws of probability?
2 What is the meaning of mutually exclusive events? What is meant by collectively exhaustive? Give an example of each.
3 Describe the various approaches used in determining probability values.
4 Why is the probability of the intersection of two events subtracted in the sum of the probability of two events?
5 Describe what it means for two events to be independent.
6 What is Bayes' theorem, and when can it be used?
7 Describe the characteristics of a Bernoulli process. How is a Bernoulli process associated with the binomial distribution?
8 What is a random variable? What are the various types of random variables?

9 What is the difference between a discrete probability distribution and a continuous probability distribution? Give your own example of each.
10 What is the expected value, and what does it measure? How is it computed for a discrete probability distribution?
11 What is the variance, and what does it measure? How is it computed for a discrete probability distribution?
12 Name three business processes that can be described by the normal distribution.
13 A card is drawn from a standard deck of playing cards. For each of the following pairs of events, indicate if the events are mutually exclusive and indicate if the events are exhaustive.

   (a) Draw a spade and draw a club.
   (b) Draw a face card and draw a number card.
   (c) Draw an ace and draw a three.

(d) Draw a red card and draw a black card.

(e) Draw a five and draw a diamond.

(f) Draw a red card and draw a diamond.

Problems

- 14 A student taking Management Science 301 at East Haven University will receive one of the five possible grades for the course: A, B, C, D, or F. The distribution of grades over the past 2 years is as follows:

GRADE	NUMBER OF STUDENTS
A	80
B	75
C	90
D	30
F	25
	Total 300

If this past distribution is a good indicator of future grades, what is the probability of a student receiving a C in the course?

- 15 A silver dollar is flipped twice. Calculate the probability of each of the following occurring:

  (a) a head on the first flip
  (b) a tail on the second flip given that the first toss was a head
  (c) two tails
  (d) a tail on the first and a head on the second
  (e) a tail on the first and a head on the second or a head on the first and a tail on the second
  (f) at least one head on the two flips

- 16 An urn contains 8 red chips, 10 green chips, and 2 white chips. A chip is drawn and replaced, and then a second chip drawn. What is the probability of

  (a) a white chip on the first draw?
  (b) a white chip on the first draw and a red on the second?
  (c) two green chips being drawn?
  (d) a red chip on the second, given that a white chip was drawn on the first?

- 17 Evertight, a leading manufacturer of quality nails, produces 1-, 2-, 3-, 4-, and 5-inch nails for various uses. In the production process, if there is an overrun or the nails are slightly defective, they are placed in a common bin. Yesterday, 651 of the 1-inch nails, 243 of the 2-inch nails, 41 of the 3-inch nails, 451 of the 4-inch nails, and 333 of the 5-inch nails were placed in the bin.

  (a) What is the probability of reaching into the bin and getting a 4-inch nail?
  (b) What is the probability of getting a 5-inch nail?

(c) If a particular application requires a nail that is 3 inches or shorter, what is the probability of getting a nail that will satisfy the requirements of the application?

- 18 Last year, at Northern Manufacturing Company, 200 people had colds during the year. One hundred fifty-five people who did no exercising had colds, and the remainder of the people with colds were involved in a weekly exercise program. Half of the 1,000 employees were involved in some type of exercise.

  (a) What is the probability that an employee will have a cold next year?
  (b) Given that an employee is involved in an exercise program, what is the probability that he or she will get a cold next year?
  (c) What is the probability that an employee who is not involved in an exercise program will get a cold next year?
  (d) Are exercising and getting a cold independent events? Explain your answer.

- 19 The Springfield Kings, a professional basketball team, has won 12 of its last 20 games and is expected to continue winning at the same percentage rate. The team's ticket manager is anxious to attract a large crowd to tomorrow's game but believes that depends on how well the Kings perform tonight against the Galveston Comets. He assesses the probability of drawing a large crowd to be 0.90 should the team win tonight. What is the probability that the team wins tonight and that there will be a large crowd at tomorrow's game?

- 20 David Mashley teaches two undergraduate statistics courses at Kansas College. The class for Statistics 201 consists of 7 sophomores and 3 juniors. The more advanced course, Statistics 301, has 2 sophomores and 8 juniors enrolled. As an example of a business sampling technique, Professor Mashley randomly selects, from the stack of Statistics 201 registration cards, the class card of one student and then places that card back in the stack. If that student was a sophomore, Mashley draws another card from the Statistics 201 stack; if not, he randomly draws a card from the Statistics 301 group. Are these two draws independent events? What is the probability of

  (a) a junior's name on the first draw?
  (b) a junior's name on the second draw, given that a sophomore's name was drawn first?
  (c) a junior's name on the second draw, given that a junior's name was drawn first?
  (d) a sophomore's name on both draws?
  (e) a junior's name on both draws?
  (f) one sophomore's name and one junior's name on the two draws, regardless of order drawn?

Note: ⚲ means the problem may be solved with QM for Windows; ✕ means the problem may be solved with Excel QM; and ⚲ means the problem may be solved with QM for Windows and/or Excel QM.

21 The oasis outpost of Abu Ilan, in the heart of the Negev desert, has a population of 20 Bedouin tribesmen and 20 Farima tribesmen. El Kamin, a nearby oasis, has a population of 32 Bedouins and 8 Farima. A lost Israeli soldier, accidentally separated from his army unit, is wandering through the desert and arrives at the edge of one of the oases. The soldier has no idea which oasis he has found, but the first person he spots at a distance is a Bedouin. What is the probability that he wandered into Abu Ilan? What is the probability that he is in El Kamin?

22 The lost Israeli soldier mentioned in Problem 21 decides to rest for a few minutes before entering the desert oasis he has just found. Closing his eyes, he dozes off for 15 minutes, wakes, and walks toward the center of the oasis. The first person he spots this time he again recognizes as a Bedouin. What is the posterior probability that he is in El Kamin?

23 Ace Machine Works estimates that the probability its lathe tool is properly adjusted is 0.8. When the lathe is properly adjusted, there is a 0.9 probability that the parts produced pass inspection. If the lathe is out of adjustment, however, the probability of a good part being produced is only 0.2. A part randomly chosen is inspected and found to be acceptable. At this point, what is the posterior probability that the lathe tool is properly adjusted?

24 The Boston South Fifth Street Softball League consists of three teams: Mama's Boys, team 1; the Killers, team 2; and the Machos, team 3. Each team plays the other teams just once during the season. The win–loss record for the past 5 years is as follows:

WINNER	(1)	(2)	(3)
Mama's Boys (1)	X	3	4
The Killers (2)	2	X	1
The Machos (3)	1	4	X

Each row represents the number of wins over the past 5 years. Mama's Boys beat the Killers 3 times, beat the Machos 4 times, and so on.

(a) What is the probability that the Killers will win every game next year?

(b) What is the probability that the Machos will win at least one game next year?

(c) What is the probability that Mama's Boys will win exactly one game next year?

(d) What is the probability that the Killers will win fewer than two games next year?

25 The schedule for the Killers next year is as follows (refer to Problem 24):

Game 1: The Machos

Game 2: Mama's Boys

(a) What is the probability that the Killers will win their first game?

(b) What is the probability that the Killers will win their last game?

(c) What is the probability that the Killers will break even—win exactly one game?

(d) What is the probability that the Killers will win every game?

(e) What is the probability that the Killers will lose every game?

(f) Would you want to be the coach of the Killers?

26 The Northside Rifle team has two markspersons, Dick and Sally. Dick hits a bull's-eye 90% of the time, and Sally hits a bull's-eye 95% of the time.

(a) What is the probability that either Dick or Sally or both will hit the bull's-eye if each takes one shot?

(b) What is the probability that Dick and Sally will both hit the bull's-eye?

(c) Did you make any assumptions in answering the preceding questions? If you answered yes, do you think that you are justified in making the assumption(s)?

27 In a sample of 1,000 representing a survey from the entire population, 650 people were from Laketown, and the rest of the people were from River City. Out of the sample, 19 people had some form of cancer. Thirteen of these people were from Laketown.

(a) Are the events of living in Laketown and having some sort of cancer independent?

(b) Which city would you prefer to live in, assuming that your main objective was to avoid having cancer?

28 Compute the probability of "loaded die, given that a 3 was rolled," as shown in the example in Section 3, this time using the general form of Bayes' theorem from Equation 5.

29 Which of the following are probability distributions? Why?

(a)

RANDOM VARIABLE X	PROBABILITY
2	0.1
−1	0.2
0	0.3
1	0.25
2	0.15

(b)

RANDOM VARIABLE Y	PROBABILITY
1	1.1
1.5	0.2
2	0.3
2.5	0.25
3	−1.25

(c)

RANDOM VARIABLE Z	PROBABILITY
1	0.1
2	0.2
3	0.3
4	0.4
5	0.0

• 30 Harrington Health Food stocks 5 loaves of Neutro-Bread. The probability distribution for the sales of Neutro-Bread is listed in the following table. How many loaves will Harrington sell on average?

NUMBER OF LOAVES SOLD	PROBABILITY
0	0.05
1	0.15
2	0.20
3	0.25
4	0.20
5	0.15

• 31 What are the expected value and variance of the following probability distribution?

RANDOM VARIABLE X	PROBABILITY
1	0.05
2	0.05
3	0.10
4	0.10
5	0.15
6	0.15
7	0.25
8	0.15

✖: 32 There are 10 questions on a true–false test. A student feels unprepared for this test and randomly guesses the answer for each of these.

(a) What is the probability that the student gets exactly 7 correct?

(b) What is the probability that the student gets exactly 8 correct?

(c) What is the probability that the student gets exactly 9 correct?

(d) What is the probability that the student gets exactly 10 correct?

(e) What is the probability that the student gets more than 6 correct?

✖: 33 Gary Schwartz is the top salesman for his company. Records indicate that he makes a sale on 70% of his sales calls. If he calls on four potential clients, what is the probability that he makes exactly 3 sales? What is the probability that he makes exactly 4 sales?

✖: 34 If 10% of all disk drives produced on an assembly line are defective, what is the probability that there will be exactly one defect in a random sample of 5 of these? What is the probability that there will be no defects in a random sample of 5?

✖: 35 Trowbridge Manufacturing produces cases for personal computers and other electronic equipment. The quality control inspector for this company believes that a particular process is out of control. Normally, only 5% of all cases are deemed defective due to discolorations. If 6 such cases are sampled, what is the probability that there will be 0 defective cases if the process is operating correctly? What is the probability that there will be exactly 1 defective case?

✖: 36 Refer to the Trowbridge Manufacturing example in Problem 35. The quality control inspection procedure is to select 6 items, and if there are 0 or 1 defective cases in the group of 6, the process is said to be in control. If the number of defects is more than 1, the process is out of control. Suppose that the true proportion of defective items is 0.15. What is the probability that there will be 0 or 1 defects in a sample of 6 if the true proportion of defects is 0.15?

✖: 37 An industrial oven used to cure sand cores for a factory manufacturing engine blocks for small cars is able to maintain fairly constant temperatures. The temperature range of the oven follows a normal distribution with a mean of 450°F and a standard deviation of 25°F. Leslie Larsen, president of the factory, is concerned about the large number of defective cores that have been produced in the past several months. If the oven gets hotter than 475°F, the core is defective. What is the probability that the oven will cause a core to be defective? What is the probability that the temperature of the oven will range from 460° to 470°F?

✖: 38 Steve Goodman, production foreman for the Florida Gold Fruit Company, estimates that the average sale of oranges is 4,700 and the standard deviation is 500 oranges. Sales follow a normal distribution.

(a) What is the probability that sales will be greater than 5,500 oranges?

(b) What is the probability that sales will be greater than 4,500 oranges?

(c) What is the probability that sales will be less than 4,900 oranges?

(d) What is the probability that sales will be less than 4,300 oranges?

✖: 39 Susan Williams has been the production manager of Medical Suppliers, Inc., for the past 17 years. Medical Suppliers, Inc., is a producer of bandages and arm slings. During the past 5 years, the demand for No-Stick bandages has been fairly constant. On the average, sales have been about 87,000 packages of No-Stick. Susan has reason to believe that the distribution of No-Stick follows a normal curve, with a standard deviation of 4,000 packages. What is the probability that sales will be less than 81,000 packages?

40 Armstrong Faber produces a standard number-two pencil called Ultra-Lite. Since Chuck Armstrong started Armstrong Faber, sales have grown steadily. With the increase in the price of wood products, however, Chuck has been forced to increase the price of the Ultra-Lite pencils. As a result, the demand for Ultra-Lite has been fairly stable over the past 6 years. On the average, Armstrong Faber has sold 457,000 pencils each year. Furthermore, 90% of the time sales have been between 454,000 and 460,000 pencils. It is expected that the sales follow a normal distribution with a mean of 457,000 pencils. Estimate the standard deviation of this distribution. (*Hint:* Work backward from the normal table to find Z. Then apply Equation 13.)

41 The time to complete a construction project is normally distributed with a mean of 60 weeks and a standard deviation of 4 weeks.

(a) What is the probability the project will be finished in 62 weeks or less?

(b) What is the probability the project will be finished in 66 weeks or less?

(c) What is the probability the project will take longer than 65 weeks?

42 A new integrated computer system is to be installed worldwide for a major corporation. Bids on this project are being solicited, and the contract will be awarded to one of the bidders. As a part of the proposal for this project, bidders must specify how long the project will take. There will be a significant penalty for finishing late. One potential contractor determines that the average time to complete a project of this type is 40 weeks with a standard deviation of 5 weeks. The time required to complete this project is assumed to be normally distributed.

(a) If the due date of this project is set at 40 weeks, what is the probability that the contractor will have to pay a penalty (i.e., the project will not be finished on schedule)?

(b) If the due date of this project is set at 43 weeks, what is the probability that the contractor will have to pay a penalty (i.e., the project will not be finished on schedule)?

(c) If the bidder wishes to set the due date in the proposal so that there is only a 5% chance of being late (and consequently only a 5% chance of having to pay a penalty), what due date should be set?

43 Patients arrive at the emergency room of Costa Valley Hospital at an average of 5 per day. The demand for emergency room treatment at Costa Valley follows a Poisson distribution.

(a) Using Appendix: Values of $e^{-\lambda}$ for Use in the Poisson Distribution, compute the probability of exactly 0, 1, 2, 3, 4, and 5 arrivals per day.

(b) What is the sum of these probabilities, and why is the number less than 1?

44 Using the data in Problem 43, determine the probability of more than 3 visits for emergency room service on any given day.

45 Cars arrive at Carla's Muffler shop for repair work at an average of 3 per hour, following an exponential distribution.

(a) What is the expected time between arrivals?

(b) What is the variance of the time between arrivals?

46 A particular test for the presence of steroids is to be used after a professional track meet. If steroids are present, the test will accurately indicate this 95% of the time. However, if steroids are not present, the test will indicate this 90% of the time (so it is wrong 10% of the time and predicts the presence of steroids). Based on past data, it is believed that 2% of the athletes do use steroids. This test is administered to one athlete, and the test is positive for steroids. What is the probability that this person actually used steroids?

47 Market Researchers, Inc., has been hired to perform a study to determine if the market for a new product will be good or poor. In similar studies performed in the past, whenever the market actually was good, the market research study indicated that it would be good 85% of the time. On the other hand, whenever the market actually was poor, the market study incorrectly predicted it would be good 20% of the time. Before the study is performed, it is believed there is a 70% chance the market will be good. When Market Researchers, Inc., performs the study for this product, the results predict the market will be good. Given the results of this study, what is the probability that the market actually will be good?

48 Policy Pollsters is a market research firm specializing in political polls. Records indicate in past elections, when a candidate was elected, Policy Pollsters had accurately predicted this 80% of the time and they were wrong 20% of the time. Records also show, for losing candidates, Policy Pollsters accurately predicted they would lose 90% of the time and they were only wrong 10% of the time. Before the poll is taken, there is a 50% chance of winning the election. If Policy Pollsters predicts a candidate will win the election, what is the probability that the candidate will actually win? If Policy Pollsters predicts that a candidate will lose the election, what is the probability that the candidate will actually lose?

49 Burger City is a large chain of fast-food restaurants specializing in gourmet hamburgers. A mathematical model is now used to predict the success of new restaurants based on location and demographic information for that area. In the past, 70% of all restaurants that were opened were successful. The mathematical model has been tested in the existing restaurants to determine how effective it is. For the restaurants that were successful, 90% of the time the model predicted they would be, while 10% of the

time the model predicted a failure. For the restaurants that were not successful, when the mathematical model was applied, 20% of the time it incorrectly predicted a successful restaurant while 80% of the time it was accurate and predicted an unsuccessful restaurant. If the model is used on a new location and predicts the restaurant will be successful, what is the probability that it actually is successful?

50 A mortgage lender attempted to increase its business by marketing its subprime mortgage. This mortgage is designed for people with a less-than-perfect credit rating, and the interest rate is higher to offset the extra risk. In the past year, 20% of these mortgages resulted in foreclosure as customers defaulted on their loans. A new screening system has been developed to determine whether to approve customers for the subprime loans. When the system is applied to a credit application, the system will classify the application as "Approve for loan" or "Reject for loan." When this new system was applied to recent customers who had defaulted on their loans, 90% of these customers were classified as "Reject." When this same system was applied to recent loan customers who had not defaulted on their loan payments, 70% of these customers were classified as "Approve for loan."

(a) If a customer did not default on a loan, what is the probability that the rating system would have classified the applicant in the reject category?

(b) If the rating system had classified the applicant in the reject category, what is the probability that the customer would not default on a loan?

51 Use the F table in Appendix: F Distribution Values to find the value of F for the upper 5% of the F distribution with

(a) $df_1 = 5, df_2 = 10$
(b) $df_1 = 8, df_2 = 7$
(c) $df_1 = 3, df_2 = 5$
(d) $df_1 = 10, df_2 = 4$

52 Use the F table in Appendix: F Distribution Values to find the value of F for the upper 1% of the F distribution with

(a) $df_1 = 15, df_2 = 6$
(b) $df_1 = 12, df_2 = 8$
(c) $df_1 = 3, df_2 = 5$
(d) $df_1 = 9, df_2 = 7$

53 For each of the following F values, determine whether the probability indicated is greater than or less than 5%:

(a) $P(F_{3,4} > 6.8)$
(b) $P(F_{7,3} > 3.6)$
(c) $P(F_{20,20} > 2.6)$
(d) $P(F_{7,5} > 5.1)$
(e) $P(F_{7,5} < 5.1)$

54 For each of the following F values, determine whether the probability indicated is greater than or less than 1%:

(a) $P(F_{5,4} > 14)$
(b) $P(F_{6,3} > 30)$
(c) $P(F_{10,12} > 4.2)$
(d) $P(F_{2,3} > 35)$
(e) $P(F_{2,3} < 35)$

55 Nite Time Inn has a toll-free telephone number so that customers can call at any time to make a reservation. A typical call takes about 4 minutes to complete, and the time required follows an exponential distribution. Find the probability that a call takes

(a) 3 minutes or less
(b) 4 minutes or less
(c) 5 minutes or less
(d) longer than 5 minutes

56 During normal business hours on the east coast, calls to the toll-free reservation number of the Nite Time Inn arrive at a rate of 5 per minute. It has been determined that the number of calls per minute can be described by the Poisson distribution. Find the probability that in the next minute, the number of calls arriving will be

(a) exactly 5
(b) exactly 4
(c) exactly 3
(d) exactly 6
(e) less than 2

57 In the Arnold's Muffler example for the exponential distribution in this chapter, the average rate of service was given as 3 per hour, and the times were expressed in hours. Convert the average service rate to the number per minute and convert the times to minutes. Find the probabilities that the service times will be less than $1/2$ hour, $1/3$ hour, and $2/3$ hour. Compare these probabilities to the probabilities found in the example.

Internet Homework Problems

See our Internet home page, at www.pearsonhighered.com/render, for additional homework problems, Problems 58 to 65.

Case Study

WTVX

WTVX, Channel 6, is located in Eugene, Oregon, home of the University of Oregon's football team. The station was owned and operated by George Wilcox, a former Duck (University of Oregon football player). Although there were other television stations in Eugene, WTVX was the only station that had a weatherperson who was a member of the American Meteorological Society (AMS). Every night, Joe Hummel would be introduced as the only weatherperson in Eugene who was a member of the AMS. This was George's idea, and he believed that this gave his station the mark of quality and helped with market share.

In addition to being a member of AMS, Joe was also the most popular person on any of the local news programs. Joe was always trying to find innovative ways to make the weather interesting, and this was especially difficult during the winter months when the weather seemed to remain the same over long periods of time. Joe's forecast for next month, for example, was that there would be a 70% chance of rain *every* day, and that what happens on one day (rain or shine) was not in any way dependent on what happened the day before.

One of Joe's most popular features of the weather report was to invite questions during the actual broadcast. Questions would be phoned in, and they were answered on the spot by Joe. Once a 10-year-old boy asked what caused fog, and Joe did an excellent job of describing some of the various causes.

Occasionally, Joe would make a mistake. For example, a high school senior asked Joe what the chances were of getting 15 days of rain in the next month (30 days). Joe made a quick calculation: $(70\%) \times (15 \text{ days}/30 \text{ days}) = (70\%)(1/2) = 35\%$. Joe quickly found out what it was like being wrong in a university town. He had over 50 phone calls from scientists, mathematicians, and other university professors, telling him that he had made a big mistake in computing the chances of getting 15 days of rain during the next 30 days. Although Joe didn't understand all of the formulas the professors mentioned, he was determined to find the correct answer and make a correction during a future broadcast.

Discussion Questions

1. What are the chances of getting 15 days of rain during the next 30 days?
2. What do you think about Joe's assumptions concerning the weather for the next 30 days?

Bibliography

Berenson, Mark, David Levine, and Timothy Krehbiel. *Basic Business Statistics*, 10th ed. Upper Saddle River, NJ: Prentice Hall, 2006.

Campbell, S. *Flaws and Fallacies in Statistical Thinking*. Upper Saddle River, NJ: Prentice Hall, 1974.

Feller, W. *An Introduction to Probability Theory and Its Applications*, Vols. 1 and 2. New York: John Wiley & Sons, Inc., 1957 and 1968.

Groebner, David, Patrick Shannon, Phillip Fry, and Kent Smith. *Business Statistics*, 8th ed. Upper Saddle River, NJ: Prentice Hall, 2011.

Hanke, J. E., A. G. Reitsch, and D. W. Wichern. *Business Forecasting*, 9th ed. Upper Saddle River, NJ: Prentice Hall, 2008.

Huff, D. *How to Lie with Statistics*. New York: W. W. Norton & Company, Inc., 1954.

Newbold, Paul, William Carlson, and Betty Thorne. *Statistics for Business and Economics*, 6th ed. Upper Saddle River, NJ: Prentice Hall, 2007.

Appendix 1: Derivation of Bayes' Theorem

We know that the following formulas are correct:

$$P(A \mid B) = \frac{P(AB)}{P(B)} \tag{1}$$

$$P(B \mid A) = \frac{P(AB)}{P(A)}$$

[which can be rewritten as $P(AB) = P(B|A)P(A)$] and (2)

$$P(B|A') = \frac{P(A'B)}{P(A')}$$

[which can be rewritten as $P(A'B) = P(B|A')P(A')$]. (3)

Furthermore, by definition, we know that

$$P(B) = P(AB) + P(A'B)$$
$$= P(B|A)P(A) + P(B|A')P(A') \qquad (4)$$

from (2)   from (3)

Substituting Equations 2 and 4 into Equation 1, we have

$$P(A|B) = \frac{P(AB)}{P(B)} \qquad \text{from (2)}$$

$$= \frac{P(B|A)P(A)}{P(B|A)P(A) + P(B|A')P(A')} \qquad (5)$$

from (4)

This is the general form of Bayes' theorem, shown as Equation 5 in this chapter.

Solutions to Selected Problems

14	0.30
16	(a) 0.10 (b) 0.04 (c) 0.25 (d) 0.40
18	(a) 0.20 (b) 0.09 (c) 0.31 (d) dependent
20	(a) 0.3 (b) 0.3 (c) 0.8 (d) 0.49 (e) 0.24 (f) 0.27
22	0.719
24	(a) 0.08 (b) 0.84 (c) 0.44 (d) 0.92
26	(a) 0.995 (b) 0.885 (c) Assumed events are independent
28	0.78
30	2.85
32	(a) 0.1172 (b) 0.0439 (c) 0.0098 (d) 0.0010 (e) 0.1719
34	0.328, 0.590
36	0.776
38	(a) 0.0548 (b) 0.6554 (c) 0.6554 (d) 0.2119
40	1829.27
42	(a) 0.5 (b) 0.27425 (c) 48.2
44	0.7365
46	0.162

Solutions to Self-Tests

1.	c	**6.**	c	**11.**	b
2.	b	**7.**	a	**12.**	a
3.	a	**8.**	c	**13.**	a
4.	d	**9.**	b	**14.**	b
5.	b	**10.**	d	**15.**	a

Chi-Square Goodness-of-Fit Test Background

When an analyst tries to fit a statistical model to observed data, he or she may wonder how well the model actually reflects, or is dependent upon the statistical distribution of the observed data. This is important since many statistical models are quite sensitive to the distribution of the observed data upon which they are based. For example, the F-test, used in regression is sensitive to departures from Normality of the error terms. One test that allows a researcher to examine the distribution of the observed data is the Chi-Square Goodness of Fit test. The Chi-Square Goodness of Fit test statistic is defined by

$$\chi^2 = \sum_{i=1}^{k} \frac{\left(f_{o_i} - f_{e_i}\right)^2}{f_{e_i}},$$

where f_{o_i} is the observed frequency in category i; f_{e_i} is the expected frequency in the corresponding category i; the number of categories used for constructing the test statistic is k; the degrees of freedom (df) are (k-q-1); with q being the number of population parameters from the hypothesized population that are estimated from sample data if needed. For example, for a Binomial distribution with a known n, the probability of success, p, may be estimated from the sample data; for the Poisson distribution, the mean rate, λ, may be required; for the Exponential distribution, the parameter λ may be needed; and for the Normal distribution, μ and σ, the mean and standard deviation, respectively, may be required. Therefore, $q \geq 0$. Furthermore, it should be remembered that the test

statistic is the sum of the individual terms $\dfrac{\left(f_{o_i} - f_{e_i}\right)^2}{f_{e_i}}$, $i = 1, 2, ..., k$.

When doing a χ^2 goodness-of-fit test, we are testing whether or not the data comes from the hypothesized distribution. It is typical to use a cut-off value of alpha (α) = 0.05.

Hypothesis testing has a null hypothesis, denoted H_0 and an alternative hypothesis, denoted H_1 or H_a. We are in a court of "statistics" sufficient evidence leads to the "guilty/reject" verdict; whereas insufficient evidence leads to a "not guilty/fail to reject" verdict. Note that in a court of law, the court never says that someone on trial is "innocent", only guilty or not guilty.

Method 1.

Let χ^2_{Cal} denote the value we determine from the data, the test statistic, χ^2. Then we want to see what the $Pr(\chi^2 \geq \chi^2_{Cal})$ is. If the probability is greater than 0.05, we say that "we fail to reject that the data comes from …. distribution." On the other hand, a value less than 0.05 would indicate that the alternative hypothesis is true; hence we would say "we reject the null hypothesis: the data does not come from this distribution.

For this approach we can use Excel$^©$ in either of the following ways:

Use CHISQ.DIST.RT(χ^2_{Cal},df) or use 1- CHISQ.DIST(χ^2_{Cal},df, true) to determine the probability in the right hand tail. Note that the RT means to find the area in the tail to the right of χ^2_{Cal}, whereas the second formula says to take 1- the cumulative probability.

Rule: if this probability $\geq \alpha$ fail to reject H_0;

        if this probability $< \alpha$ reject H_0 in favour of H_1.

Method 2.

Another approach is to find the "benchmark or critical" χ^2 value from Chi-Square tables or by using Excel such that $Pr(\chi^2 \geq \chi^2_{crit}) = \alpha$, where χ^2_{crit} [or $(\chi^2)^*$] is called the benchmark or critical value such that the area to the left of χ^2_{crit} is $(1-\alpha)$ and the area to the right of χ^2_{crit} is α. For this approach we can use Excel$^©$ in either of the following ways to find χ^2_{crit}

CHISQ.INV.RT(α, df) or CHISQ.INV($1-\alpha$, df).

Rule: if $\chi^2_{Cal} \leq \chi^2_{crit}$ fail to reject H_0

if $\chi^2_{Cal} > \chi^2_{crit}$ reject H_0 in favour of H_1.

Realize that another choice for α is 0.01 rather than 0.05, which has a larger χ^2_{crit}. Why? Note that an important assumption of the Chi-Square test is that for each category i, we must have $f_{e_i} \geq 5$, see for example Rosner, B. (2011). *Fundamentals of Biostatistics* (7th Edition). Boston, MA: Brooks/Cole. If each of the k categories does not meet this assumption, a number of the k categories will have to be combined, and the degrees of freedom will have to be adjusted. Furthermore, it is important to note that large differences in the observed and expected frequencies can lead to large χ^2 test values. Some of the χ^2_{crit} [or $(\chi^2)^*$] are given below for $\alpha = 0.05$ and 0.01 and for different degrees of freedom (df). Note that α in the table and figure is labelled "p."

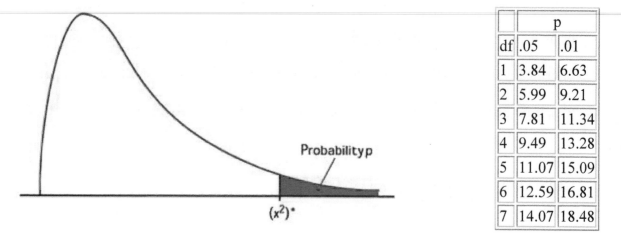

df	p	
	.05	.01
1	3.84	6.63
2	5.99	9.21
3	7.81	11.34
4	9.49	13.28
5	11.07	15.09
6	12.59	16.81
7	14.07	18.48

From http://www.statisticshowto.com/wp-content/uploads/2013/09/chi-square.jpg, Accessed on June 17, 2015.

Chi-Square Goodness-of-Fit Test: Bernoulli Trials

An experiment consists of tossing a coin many times. After tossing the coin 100 times, you obtained 42 heads and 58 tails.

i.) Perform a chi-square goodness of fit test using $\alpha=0.05$ to investigate whether the coin used is fair.

ii.) What is the smallest number of heads you should obtain which will provide you with enough evidence to conclude that the coin used is not fair? (This is a bit hard)

Chi-Square Goodness-of-Fit Test: Binomial

i)   A gambler has repeated an experiment 100 times. Each experiment consists of rolling a die three times. A success on each toss of the die is getting a six, and a failure is getting anything less than a six. Hence, in each experiment, the gambler can get 0, 1, 2, or 3 successes.

Based on the data below, determine whether we can decide if the die is fair, using using $\alpha = 0.05$.

Outcome	Frequency	Cumulative Frequency
0	25	25
1	25	50
2	30	80
3	20	100

ii)   The Hanner Gambling Casino, Kentucky, USA, is under investigation by several federal agencies for using "loaded" dice at its casino. An investigator for one of the agencies contacted you and told you that a die that was seized from the casino was rolled 1000 times. Of the 1000 tosses, 175 tosses turned up as a "Snake Eye" or a single dot, the remaining tosses were not a Snake Eye. Determine using a 1% level of significance if the die is fair or not.

Chi-Square Goodness-of-Fit Test: Poisson

Various Social Networking Web sites provide free access for posting pictures or sharing documents. Of course, to run the Web sites, various advertisers pay the Web site every time a user clicks on one of their ads. Managers of one Web site plan to use the Poisson distribution to summarize concisely the volume of traffic headed to advertisers from their website. During a recent weekday evening (from 8:00 pm to 11:00 pm) the number of ads clicked by 685 users was recorded. This data is considered to be representative of typical browsing patterns of users. The data is provided in the table below:

	Number of Ads Clicked					
	0	1	2	3	4	5
Number of Users	368	233	69	13	1	1

Determine if this data can be considered to be Poisson distributed using a 5% level of significance. Does your answer change if you use a 1% level of significance? Why?

Chi-Square Goodness-of-Fit Test: Multinomial

A multinomial distribution is an extension of the Binomial in which there are more than two possible outcomes per trial. The properties of the multinomial experiment are as follows: the experiment consists of a fixed number n trials; the outcome of each trial can be classified into one of k categories called cells; the probability p_i that the outcome will fall into cell i remains constant for each trial and $\sum_{i=1}^{k} p_i = 1$; and each trial of the experiment is independent of the other trials. From experimental data, we obtain a set of observed frequencies f_{o_i}, i=1,2,..,k with $\sum_{i=1}^{k} f_{o_i} = n$. Of course, the expected frequencies, f_{e_i} would be calculated by np_i, i=1, 2,..,k. Note that when all the p_i are equal to 1/k, the distribution is called the Discrete Uniform Distribution.

Company Comfy has recently conducted an aggressive advertising campaign to maintain and possibly increase its market share of fabric softener. Currently its market share is 45%. Its main competitor, Softa, has 40% of the market, and a number of other companies account for the remaining 15% of the market. To determine if the market share of the companies has changed, Comfy contacted 400 customers, through an on-line survey and asked them about their fabric softener preferences. Of the 400 customers, 204 indicated a preference for Comfy's products, 164 indicated a preference for Softa's products, and the remaining 32 preferred the products of one of the other companies. Using a 5% level of significance determine if the market shares have changed for the companies.

Chi-Square Test: Normal Distribution

There are a number of different approaches for testing whether a data set is derived from a Normal population. One approach is given here, and the Standard Normal Curve is provided below for your review. Another approach is by looking at the Q-Q plot of the ordered data versus the Normal Order Statistics for that sample size, see Tiku, M. L., Tan, W. Y. & Balakrishnan, N. (1986). *Robust Inference*. New York, NY: Marcel Dekker

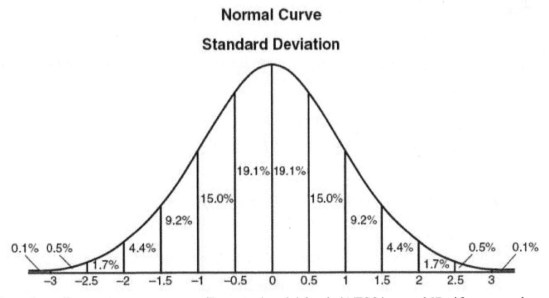

From http://www.regentsprep.org/Regents/math/algtrig/ATS2/normal67.gif, accessed June 16, 2015.

Let $(X_1, X_2, X_3, \ldots, X_n)$ represent our original data set. Calculate $\bar{X}$ and S using the Data Analysis Toolpak - Descriptive Statistics from Excel$^{©}$ if they are needed. That is you have not specified what μ and/or σ are in your null hypothesis. Then we can calculate the standardized values, $Z_i = \dfrac{(X_i - \bar{X})}{S}$, $i = 1, 2, \ldots, n$. Realize that under the hypothesis that the data are from a Normal Distribution, the Z_i's are the standardized normal scores. Under this assumption, we can determine the Bin Numbers needed for doing observed frequencies from the Standard Normal Distribution. Examining the standard Normal Distribution plot from above, which we know is symmetric about zero, we can use the following 10 intervals: $(Z \le -2.0)$; $(-2.0 < Z \le -1.5)$; $(-1.5 < Z \le -1.0)$; $(-1.0 < Z \le -0.5)$; $(-0.5 < Z \le 0)$; $(0 < Z \le 0.5)$; $(0.5 < Z \le 1.0)$; $(1.0 < Z \le 1.5)$; $(1.5 < Z \le 2.0)$; and $(Z > 2.0)$. Note that each of these intervals is 0.5 standard Normal standard deviations in width. Thus, for Excel$^{©}$, the required Bin Numbers are: -2, -1.5, -1.0, -0.5, 0, 0.5, 1.0, 1.5, and 2.

The frequency function in Excel$^{©}$ can then be used for calculating the observed frequency in each category of the standardized values. Recall that we need to select 10 cells for the frequencies and use the combination of <Crtl>+<Shift> +<Enter> since more than once cell is being used to paste a formula into. For each of the categories, we need to calculate the expected frequency. First, calculate the cumulative probability of each interval using the Excel$^{©}$ function NORM.S.DIST(Z, cumulative) where Z is a standard normal Z-score and cumulative is "True." Then we can calculate the probabilities for the individual categories:

$Pr(Z \le -2.0) = $ NORM.S.DIST(-2.0,True);

$Pr(-2.0 < Z \le -1.5) = $ NORM.S.DIST(-1.5, True) - NORM.S.DIST(-2.0,True)

….

$Pr(1.0 < Z \le 1.5) = $ NORM.S.DIST(1.5, True) - NORM.S.DIST(1.0, True), etc.

Finally, each of these probabilities is multiplied by n, the number of the observations. The χ^2_{Cal} is then determined, observing the rule of $f_{e_i} \ge 5$ and the degrees of freedom would be (k-q-1) where k is the number of categories meeting the $f_{e_i} \ge 5$ rule and q=2 since we calculated $\bar{X}$ and S. Note that if we were hypothesizing that the population mean, μ, and population standard deviation, σ, were specific values, then q=0. Then method 1 or method 2, described above would be used for checking our null hypothesis. See the layout below:

Chi-Square Goodness-of-Fit Test: Normal

Using Yahoo! Canada's Financial data for your favourite stock, https://ca.finance.yahoo.com/, accessed June 17, 2015, determine if the closing price, opening price, high, or low for the day are Normally Distributed. Use 5 years of data. Note that Apple Inc.'s symbol is APPL and Microsoft Corporation's is MFST.

Decision Analysis

After completing this chapter, students will be able to:

1. List the steps of the decision-making process.
2. Describe the types of decision-making environments.
3. Make decisions under uncertainty.
4. Use probability values to make decisions under risk.
5. Develop accurate and useful decision trees.
6. Revise probability estimates using Bayesian analysis.
7. Use computers to solve basic decision-making problems.
8. Understand the importance and use of utility theory in decision making.

CHAPTER OUTLINE

Summary • Glossary • Key Equations • Solved Problems • Self-Test • Discussion Questions and Problems • Internet Homework Problems • Case Study: Starting Right Corporation • Case Study: Blake Electronics • Internet Case Studies • Bibliography

From Chapter 3 of *Quantitative Analysis for Management*, Twelfth Edition. Barry Render, Ralph M. Stair, Jr., Michael E. Hanna, and Trevor S. Hale. Copyright © 2015 by Pearson Education, Inc. All rights reserved.

1 Introduction

Decision theory is an analytic and systematic way to tackle problems.

A good decision is based on logic.

To a great extent, the successes or failures that a person experiences in life depend on the decisions that he or she makes. The person who managed the ill-fated space shuttle *Challenger* is no longer working for NASA. The person who designed the top-selling Mustang became president of Ford. Why and how did these people make their respective decisions? In general, what is involved in making good decisions? One decision may make the difference between a successful career and an unsuccessful one. **Decision theory** is an analytic and systematic approach to the study of decision making. In this chapter, we present the mathematical models useful in helping managers make the best possible decisions.

What makes the difference between good and bad decisions? A good decision is one that is based on logic, considers all available data and possible alternatives, and applies the quantitative approach we are about to describe. Occasionally, a good decision results in an unexpected or unfavorable outcome. But if it is made properly, it is *still* a good decision. A bad decision is one that is not based on logic, does not use all available information, does not consider all alternatives, and does not employ appropriate quantitative techniques. If you make a bad decision but are lucky and a favorable outcome occurs, you have *still* made a bad decision. Although occasionally good decisions yield bad results, in the long run, using decision theory will result in successful outcomes.

2 The Six Steps in Decision Making

Whether you are deciding about getting a haircut today, building a multimillion-dollar plant, or buying a new camera, the steps in making a good decision are basically the same:

Six Steps in Decision Making

1. Clearly define the problem at hand.
2. List the possible alternatives.
3. Identify the possible outcomes or states of nature.
4. List the payoff (typically profit) of each combination of alternatives and outcomes.
5. Select one of the mathematical decision theory models.
6. Apply the model and make your decision.

We use the Thompson Lumber Company case as an example to illustrate these decision theory steps. John Thompson is the founder and president of Thompson Lumber Company, a profitable firm located in Portland, Oregon.

The first step is to define the problem.

Step 1. The problem that John Thompson identifies is whether to expand his product line by manufacturing and marketing a new product, backyard storage sheds.

Thompson's second step is to generate the alternatives that are available to him. In decision theory, an **alternative** is defined as a course of action or a strategy that the decision maker can choose.

The second step is to list alternatives.

Step 2. John decides that his alternatives are to construct (1) a large new plant to manufacture the storage sheds, (2) a small plant, or (3) no plant at all (i.e., he has the option of not developing the new product line).

One of the biggest mistakes that decision makers make is to leave out some important alternatives. Although a particular alternative may seem to be inappropriate or of little value, it might turn out to be the best choice.

The next step involves identifying the possible outcomes of the various alternatives. A common mistake is to forget about some of the possible outcomes. Optimistic decision makers tend to ignore bad outcomes, whereas pessimistic managers may discount a favorable outcome. If you don't consider all possibilities, you will not be making a logical decision, and the results may be undesirable. If you do not think the worst can happen, you may design another Edsel automobile. In decision theory, those outcomes over which the decision maker has little or no control are called **states of nature**.

TABLE 1
Decision Table with Conditional Values for Thompson Lumber

| | STATE OF NATURE | |
ALTERNATIVE	FAVORABLE MARKET ($)	UNFAVORABLE MARKET ($)
Construct a large plant	200,000	−180,000
Construct a small plant	100,000	−20,000
Do nothing	0	0

Note: It is important to include all alternatives, including "do nothing."

The third step is to identify possible outcomes.

Step 3. Thompson determines that there are only two possible outcomes: the market for the storage sheds could be favorable, meaning that there is a high demand for the product, or it could be unfavorable, meaning that there is a low demand for the sheds.

Once the alternatives and states of nature have been identified, the next step is to express the payoff resulting from each possible combination of alternatives and outcomes. In decision theory, we call such payoffs or profits **conditional values**. Not every decision, of course, can be based on money alone—any appropriate means of measuring benefit is acceptable.

The fourth step is to list payoffs.

During the fourth step, the decision maker can construct decision or payoff tables.

Step 4. Because Thompson wants to maximize his profits, he can use *profit* to evaluate each consequence.

John Thompson has already evaluated the potential profits associated with the various outcomes. With a favorable market, he thinks a large facility would result in a net profit of $200,000 to his firm. This $200,000 is a *conditional value* because Thompson's receiving the money is conditional upon both his building a large factory and having a good market. The conditional value if the market is unfavorable would be a $180,000 net loss. A small plant would result in a net profit of $100,000 in a favorable market, but a net loss of $20,000 would occur if the market was unfavorable. Finally, doing nothing would result in $0 profit in either market. The easiest way to present these values is by constructing a **decision table**, sometimes called a **payoff table**. A decision table for Thompson's conditional values is shown in Table 1. All of the alternatives are listed down the left side of the table, and all of the possible outcomes or states of nature are listed across the top. The body of the table contains the actual payoffs.

The last two steps are to select and apply the decision theory model.

Steps 5 and 6. The last two steps are to select a decision theory model and apply it to the data to help make the decision. Selecting the model depends on the environment in which you're operating and the amount of risk and uncertainty involved.

3 Types of Decision-Making Environments

The types of decisions people make depend on how much knowledge or information they have about the situation. There are three decision-making environments:

- Decision making under certainty
- Decision making under uncertainty
- Decision making under risk

In the environment of **decision making under certainty**, decision makers know with certainty the consequence of every alternative or decision choice. Naturally, they will choose the alternative that will maximize their well-being or will result in the best outcome. For example, let's say that you have $1,000 to invest for a 1-year period. One alternative is to open a savings account paying 4% interest and another is to invest in a government Treasury bond paying 6% interest. If both investments are secure and guaranteed, there is a certainty that the Treasury bond will pay a higher return. The return after 1 year will be $60 in interest.

Probabilities are not known.

In **decision making under uncertainty**, there are several possible outcomes for each alternative, and the decision maker does not know the probabilities of the various outcomes. As an example, the probability that a Democrat will be president of the United States 25 years from now is not known. Sometimes it is impossible to assess the probability of success of a new undertaking or product. The criteria for decision making under uncertainty are explained in Section 4.

Probabilities are known.

In **decision making under risk**, there are several possible outcomes for each alternative, and the decision maker knows the probability of occurrence of each outcome. We know, for example, that when playing cards using a standard deck, the probability of being dealt a club is 0.25. The probability of rolling a 5 on a die is 1/6. In decision making under risk, the decision maker usually attempts to maximize his or her expected well-being. Decision theory models for business problems in this environment typically employ two equivalent criteria: maximization of expected monetary value and minimization of expected opportunity loss.

In the Thompson Lumber example, John Thompson is faced with decision making under uncertainty. If either a large plant or a small plant is constructed, the actual payoff depends on the state of nature, and probabilities are not known. If probabilities for a favorable market and for an unfavorable market were known, the environment would change from uncertainty to risk. For the third alternative, do nothing, the payoff does not depend on the state of nature and is known with certainty.

4   Decision Making Under Uncertainty

The presentation in this section of the criteria for decision making under uncertainty (and also for decision making under risk) is based on the assumption that the payoff is something in which larger values are better and high values are desirable. For payoffs such as profit, total sales, total return on investment, and interest earned, the best decision would be one that resulted in some type of maximum payoff. However, there are situations in which lower payoff values (e.g., cost) are better, and these payoffs would be minimized rather than maximized. The statement of the decision criteria would be modified slightly for such minimization problems. These differences will be mentioned in this section, and an example will be provided in a later section.

Several criteria exist for making decisions under conditions of uncertainty. The ones that we cover in this section are as follows:

1. Optimistic
2. Pessimistic
3. Criterion of realism (Hurwicz)
4. Equally likely (Laplace)
5. Minimax regret

The first four criteria can be computed directly from the decision (payoff) table, whereas the minimax regret criterion requires use of the opportunity loss table. Let's take a look at each of the five models and apply them to the Thompson Lumber example.

Optimistic

Maximax is an optimistic approach.

In using the **optimistic** criterion, the best (maximum) payoff for each alternative is considered and the alternative with the best (maximum) of these is selected. Hence, the optimistic criterion is sometimes called the **maximax** criterion. In Table 2, we see that Thompson's optimistic choice is the first alternative, "construct a large plant." By using this criterion, the highest of all possible payoffs ($200,000 in this example) may be achieved, while if any other alternative were selected, it would be impossible to achieve a payoff this high.

In using the optimistic criterion for minimization problems in which lower payoffs (e.g., cost) are better, you would look at the best (minimum) payoff for each alternative and choose the alternative with the best (minimum) of these.

TABLE 2
Thompson's Maximax Decision

ALTERNATIVE	STATE OF NATURE		MAXIMUM IN A ROW ($)
	FAVORABLE MARKET ($)	UNFAVORABLE MARKET ($)	
Construct a large plant	200,000	−180,000	(200,000) ◄ Maximax
Construct a small plant	100,000	−20,000	100,000
Do nothing	0	0	0

TABLE 3

Thompson's Maximin Decision

	STATE OF NATURE		
ALTERNATIVE	FAVORABLE MARKET ($)	UNFAVORABLE MARKET ($)	MINIMUM IN A ROW ($)
Construct a large plant	200,000	−180,000	−180,000
Construct a small plant	100,000	−20,000	−20,000
Do nothing	0	0	⓪ ← Maximin

Pessimistic

Maximin is a pessimistic approach.

In using the *pessimistic* criterion, the worst (minimum) payoff for each alternative is considered and the alternative with the best (maximum) of these is selected. Hence, the pessimistic criterion is sometimes called the **maximin** criterion. This criterion guarantees the payoff will be at least the maximin value (the best of the worst values). Choosing any other alternative may allow a worse (lower) payoff to occur.

Thompson's maximin choice, "do nothing," is shown in Table 3. This decision is associated with the maximum of the minimum number within each row or alternative.

In using the pessimistic criterion for minimization problems in which lower payoffs (e.g., cost) are better, you would look at the worst (maximum) payoff for each alternative and choose the alternative with the best (minimum) of these.

Both the maximax and maximin criteria consider only one extreme payoff for each alternative, while all other payoffs are ignored. The next criterion considers both of these extremes.

Criterion of Realism (Hurwicz Criterion)

Criterion of realism uses the weighted average approach.

Often called the **weighted average**, the **criterion of realism** (the **Hurwicz criterion**) is a compromise between an optimistic and a pessimistic decision. To begin, a **coefficient of realism**, α, is selected. This measures the degree of optimism of the decision maker and is between 0 and 1. When α is 1, the decision maker is 100% optimistic about the future. When α is 0, the decision maker is 100% pessimistic about the future. The advantage of this approach is that it allows the decision maker to build in personal feelings about relative optimism and pessimism. The weighted average is computed as follows:

$$\text{Weighted average} = \alpha(\text{best in row}) + (1 - \alpha)(\text{worst in row})$$

For a maximization problem, the best payoff for an alternative is the highest value, and the worst payoff is the lowest value. Note that when $\alpha = 1$, this is the same as the optimistic criterion, and when $\alpha = 0$ this is the same as the pessimistic criterion. This value is computed for each alternative, and the alternative with the highest weighted average is then chosen.

If we assume that John Thompson sets his coefficient of realism, α, to be 0.80, the best decision would be to construct a large plant. As seen in Table 4, this alternative has the highest weighted average: $124,000 = (0.80)(\$200,000) = (0.20)(-\$180,000)$.

In using the criterion of realism for minimization problems, the best payoff for an alternative would be the lowest payoff in the row and the worst would be the highest payoff in the row. The alternative with the lowest weighted average is then chosen.

TABLE 4

Thompson's Criterion of Realism Decision

	STATE OF NATURE		
ALTERNATIVE	FAVORABLE MARKET ($)	UNFAVORABLE MARKET ($)	CRITERION OF REALISM OR WEIGHTED AVERAGE ($\alpha = 0.8$) $
Construct a large plant	200,000	−180,000	124,000 ← Realism
Construct a small plant	100,000	−20,000	76,000
Do nothing	0	0	0

TABLE 5
Thompson's Equally Likely Decision

| | STATE OF NATURE | | |
ALTERNATIVE	FAVORABLE MARKET ($)	UNFAVORABLE MARKET ($)	ROW AVERAGE ($)
Construct a large plant	200,000	−180,000	10,000
Construct a small plant	100,000	−20,000	40,000 ← Equally likely
Do nothing	0	0	0

Because there are only two states of nature in the Thompson Lumber example, only two payoffs for each alternative are present and both are considered. However, if there are more than two states of nature, this criterion will ignore all payoffs except the best and the worst. The next criterion will consider all possible payoffs for each decision.

Equally Likely (Laplace)

Equally likely criterion uses the average outcome.

One criterion that uses all the payoffs for each alternative is the **equally likely**, also called **Laplace**, decision criterion. This involves finding the average payoff for each alternative, and selecting the alternative with the best or highest average. The equally likely approach assumes that all probabilities of occurrence for the states of nature are equal, and thus each state of nature is equally likely.

The equally likely choice for Thompson Lumber is the second alternative, "construct a small plant." This strategy, shown in Table 5, is the one with the maximum average payoff.

In using the equally likely criterion for minimization problems, the calculations are exactly the same, but the best alternative is the one with the lowest average payoff.

Minimax Regret

Minimax regret criterion is based on opportunity loss.

The next decision criterion that we discuss is based on **opportunity loss** or **regret**. Opportunity loss refers to the difference between the optimal profit or payoff for a given state of nature and the actual payoff received for a particular decision for that state of nature. In other words, it's the amount lost by not picking the best alternative in a given state of nature.

The first step is to create the opportunity loss table by determining the opportunity loss for not choosing the best alternative for each state of nature. Opportunity loss for any state of nature, or any column, is calculated by subtracting each payoff in the column from the *best* payoff in the same column. For a favorable market, the best payoff is $200,000 as a result of the first alternative, "construct a large plant." The opportunity loss is 0, meaning that it is impossible to achieve a higher payoff in this state of nature. If the second alternative is selected, a profit of $100,000 would be realized in a favorable market, and this is compared to the best payoff of $200,000. Thus, the opportunity loss is 200,000 − 100,000 = 100,000. Similarly, if "do nothing" is selected, the opportunity loss would be 200,000 − 0 = 200,000.

For an unfavorable market, the best payoff is $0 as a result of the third alternative, "do nothing," so this has 0 opportunity loss. The opportunity losses for the other alternatives are found by subtracting the payoffs from this best payoff ($0) in this state of nature as shown in Table 6. Thompson's opportunity loss table is shown as Table 7.

TABLE 6
Determining Opportunity Losses for Thompson Lumber

| STATE OF NATURE | |
FAVORABLE MARKET ($)	UNFAVORABLE MARKET ($)
200,000 − 200,000	0 − (−180,000)
200,000 − 100,000	0 − (−20,000)
200,000 − 0	0 − 0

TABLE 7
Opportunity Loss Table for Thompson Lumber

| | STATE OF NATURE | |
ALTERNATIVE	FAVORABLE MARKET ($)	UNFAVORABLE MARKET ($)
Construct a large plant	0	180,000
Construct a small plant	100,000	20,000
Do nothing	200,000	0

TABLE 8

Thompson's Minimax Decision Using Opportunity Loss

	STATE OF NATURE		
ALTERNATIVE	FAVORABLE MARKET ($)	UNFAVORABLE MARKET ($)	MAXIMUM IN A ROW ($)
Construct a large plant	0	180,000	180,000
Construct a small plant	100,000	20,000	100,000 ← Minimax
Do nothing	200,000	0	200,000

Using the opportunity loss (regret) table, the **minimax regret** criterion first consider the maximum (worst) opportunity loss for each alternative. Next, looking at these maximum values, pick that alternative with the minimum (or best) number. By doing this, the opportunity loss actually realized is guaranteed to be no more than this minimax value. In Table 8, we can see that the minimax regret choice is the second alternative, "construct a small plant." When this alternative is selected, we know the maximum opportunity loss cannot be more than 100,000 (the *mini*mum of the *max*imum regrets).

In calculating the opportunity loss for minimization problems such as those involving costs, the best (lowest) payoff or cost in a column is subtracted from each payoff in that column. Once the opportunity loss table has been constructed, the minimax regret criterion is applied in exactly the same way as just described. The maximum opportunity loss for each alternative is found, and the alternative with the minimum of these maximums is selected. As with maximization problems, the opportunity loss can never be negative.

We have considered several decision-making criteria to be used when probabilities of the states of nature are not known and cannot be estimated. Now we will see what to do if the probabilities are available.

5 Decision Making Under Risk

Decision making under risk is a decision situation in which several possible states of nature may occur, and the probabilities of these states of nature are known. In this section, we consider one of the most popular methods of making decisions under risk: selecting the alternative with the highest expected monetary value (or simply expected value). We also use the probabilities with the opportunity loss table to minimize the expected opportunity loss.

Expected Monetary Value

Given a decision table with conditional values (payoffs) that are monetary values, and probability assessments for all states of nature, it is possible to determine the **expected monetary value (EMV)** for each alternative. The *expected value*, or the *mean value*, is the long-run average value of that decision. The EMV for an alternative is just the sum of possible payoffs of the alternative, each weighted by the probability of that payoff occurring.

EMV is the weighted sum of possible payoffs for each alternative.

This could also be expressed simply as the expected value of *X*, or *E(X)*.

$$\text{EMV(alternative)} = \sum X_i P(X_i) \tag{1}$$

TABLE 9
Decision Table with Probabilities and EMVs for Thompson Lumber

| ALTERNATIVE | STATE OF NATURE | | EMV ($) |
	FAVORABLE MARKET ($)	UNFAVORABLE MARKET ($)	
Construct a large plant	200,000	−180,000	10,000
Construct a small plant	100,000	−20,000	40,000 Best EMV
Do nothing	0	0	0
Probabilities	0.50	0.50	

where

X_i = payoff for the alternative in state of nature i

$P(X_i)$ = probability of achieving payoff X_i (i.e., probability of state of nature i)

Σ = summation symbol

If this were expanded, it would become

EMV (alternative)

= (payoff in first state of nature) × (probability of first state of nature)

  + (payoff in second state of nature) × (probability of second state of nature)

  + ⋯ + (payoff in last state of nature) × (probability of last state of nature)

The alternative with the maximum EMV is then chosen.

Suppose that John Thompson now believes that the probability of a favorable market is exactly the same as the probability of an unfavorable market; that is, each state of nature has a 0.50 probability. Which alternative would give the greatest EMV? To determine this, John has expanded the decision table, as shown in Table 9. His calculations follow:

EMV (large plant) = ($200,000)(0.50) + (−$180,000)(0.50) = $10,000

EMV (small plant) = ($100,000)(0.50) + (−$20,000)(0.50) = $40,000

EMV (do nothing) = ($0)(0.50) + ($0)(0.50) = $0

The largest expected value ($40,000) results from the second alternative, "construct a small plant." Thus, Thompson should proceed with the project and put up a small plant to manufacture storage sheds. The EMVs for the large plant and for doing nothing are $10,000 and $0, respectively.

When using the EMV criterion with minimization problems, the calculations are the same, but the alternative with the smallest EMV is selected.

Expected Value of Perfect Information

John Thompson has been approached by Scientific Marketing, Inc., a firm that proposes to help John make the decision about whether to build the plant to produce storage sheds. Scientific Marketing claims that its technical analysis will tell John with certainty whether the market is favorable for his proposed product. In other words, it will change his environment from one of decision making under risk to one of decision making under certainty. This information could prevent John from making a very expensive mistake. Scientific Marketing would charge Thompson $65,000 for the information. What would you recommend to John? Should he hire the firm to make the marketing study? Even if the information from the study is perfectly accurate, is it worth $65,000? What would it be worth? Although some of these questions are difficult to answer, determining the value of such *perfect information* can be very useful. It places an upper bound on what you should be willing to spend on information such as that being sold by Scientific Marketing. In this section, two related terms are investigated: the **expected value of perfect information** (EVPI) and the **expected value with perfect information** (EVwPI). These techniques can help John make his decision about hiring the marketing firm.

EVPI places an upper bound on what to pay for information.

The expected value *with* perfect information is the expected or average return, in the long run, if we have perfect information before a decision has to be made. To calculate this value, we choose the best alternative for each state of nature and multiply its payoff times the probability of occurrence of that state of nature.

$$\text{EVwPI} = \sum(\text{best payoff in state of nature } i)(\text{probability of state of nature } i) \qquad (2)$$

If this were expanded, it would become

EVwPI

$= (\text{best payoff in first state of nature}) \times (\text{probability of first state of nature})$

$+ (\text{best payoff in second state of nature}) \times (\text{probability of second state of nature})$

$+ \cdots + (\text{best payoff in last state of nature}) \times (\text{probability of last state of nature})$

The EVPI is the expected value *with* perfect information minus the expected value *without* perfect information (i.e., the best or maximum EMV). Thus, the EVPI is the improvement in EMV that results from having perfect information.

$$\text{EVPI} = \text{EVwPI} - \text{Best EMV} \qquad (3)$$

EVPI is the expected value with perfect information minus the maximum EMV.

By referring to Table 9, Thompson can calculate the maximum that he would pay for information, that is, the EVPI. He follows a three-stage process. First, the best payoff in each state of nature is found. If the perfect information says the market will be favorable, the large plant will be constructed, and the profit will be $200,000. If the perfect information says the market will be unfavorable, the "do nothing" alternative is selected, and the profit will be 0. These values are shown in the "with perfect information" row in Table 10. Second, the expected value *with* perfect information is computed. Then, using this result, EVPI is calculated.

The expected value with perfect information is

$$\text{EVwPI} = (\$200,000)(0.50) + (\$0)(0.50) = \$100,000$$

Thus, if we had perfect information, the payoff would average $100,000.

The maximum EMV without additional information is $40,000 (from Table 9). Therefore, the increase in EMV is

$$\text{EVPI} = \text{EVwPI} - \text{maximum EMV}$$
$$= \$100,000 - \$40,000$$
$$= \$60,000$$

Thus, the *most* Thompson would be willing to pay for perfect information is $60,000. This, of course, is again based on the assumption that the probability of each state of nature is 0.50.

This EVPI also tells us that the most we would pay for any information (perfect or imperfect) is $60,000. In a later section, we'll see how to place a value on imperfect or sample information.

In finding the EVPI for minimization problems, the approach is similar. The best payoff in each state of nature is found, but this is the lowest payoff for that state of nature rather than the highest. The EVwPI is calculated from these lowest payoffs, and this is compared to the best (lowest) EMV without perfect information. The EVPI is the improvement that results, and this is the best EMV − EVwPI.

TABLE 10
Decision Table with Perfect Information

ALTERNATIVE	STATE OF NATURE		EMV ($)
	FAVORABLE MARKET ($)	UNFAVORABLE MARKET ($)	
Construct a large plant	200,000	−180,000	10,000
Construct a small plant	100,000	−20,000	40,000
Do nothing	0	0	0
With perfect information	200,000	0	(100,000) ← EVwPI
Probabilities	0.50	0.50	

TABLE 11
EOL Table for Thompson Lumber

| | STATE OF NATURE | | |
| | FAVORABLE MARKET ($) | UNFAVORABLE MARKET ($) | |
ALTERNATIVE			EOL
Construct a large plant	0	180,000	90,000
Construct a small plant	100,000	20,000	60,000 ← Best EOL
Do nothing	200,000	0	100,000
Probabilities	0.50	0.50	

Expected Opportunity Loss

EOL is the cost of not picking the best solution.

An alternative approach to maximizing EMV is to minimize *expected opportunity loss* (EOL). First, an opportunity loss table is constructed. Then the EOL is computed for each alternative by multiplying the opportunity loss by the probability and adding these together. In Table 7, we presented the opportunity loss table for the Thompson Lumber example. Using these opportunity losses, we compute the EOL for each alternative by multiplying the probability of each state of nature times the appropriate opportunity loss value and adding these together:

$$\text{EOL(construct large plant)} = (0.5)(\$0) + (0.5)(\$180,000)$$
$$= \$90,000$$

$$\text{EOL(construct small plant)} = (0.5)(\$100,000) + (0.5)(\$20,000)$$
$$= \$60,000$$

$$\text{EOL(do nothing)} = (0.5)(\$200,000) + (0.5)(\$0)$$
$$= \$100,000$$

EOL will always result in the same decision as the maximum EMV.

Table 11 gives these results. Using minimum EOL as the decision criterion, the best decision would be the second alternative, "construct a small plant."

It is important to note that minimum EOL will always result in the same decision as maximum EMV, and that the EVPI will always equal the minimum EOL. Referring to the Thompson case, we used the payoff table to compute the EVPI to be $60,000. Note that this is the minimum EOL we just computed.

Sensitivity Analysis

Sensitivity analysis investigates how our decision might change with different input data.

In previous sections, we determined that the best decision (with the probabilities known) for Thompson Lumber was to construct the small plant, with an expected value of $40,000. This conclusion depends on the values of the economic consequences and the two probability values of a favorable and an unfavorable market. *Sensitivity analysis* investigates how our decision might change given a change in the problem data. In this section, we investigate the impact that a change in the probability values would have on the decision facing Thompson Lumber. We first define the following variable:

$$P = \text{probability of a favorable market}$$

Because there are only two states of nature, the probability of an unfavorable market must be $1 - P$.

We can now express the EMVs in terms of P, as shown in the following equations. A graph of these EMV values is shown in Figure 1.

$$\text{EMV(large plant)} = \$200,000P - \$180,000(1 - P)$$
$$= \$200,000P - \$180,000 + 180,000P$$
$$= \$380,000P - \$180,000$$

$$\text{EMV(small plant)} = \$100,000P - \$20,000(1 - P)$$
$$= \$100,000P - \$20,000 + 20,000P$$
$$= \$120,000P - \$20,000$$

$$\text{EMV(do nothing)} = \$0P + \$0(1 - P) = \$0$$

FIGURE 1
Sensitivity Analysis

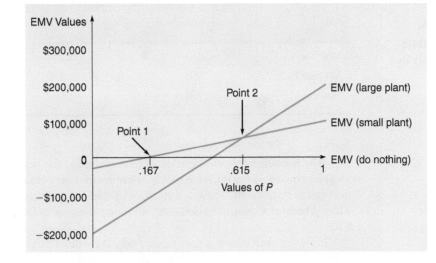

As you can see in Figure 1, the best decision is to do nothing as long as P is between 0 and the probability associated with point 1, where the EMV for doing nothing is equal to the EMV for the small plant. When P is between the probabilities for points 1 and 2, the best decision is to build the small plant. Point 2 is where the EMV for the small plant is equal to the EMV for the large plant. When P is greater than the probability for point 2, the best decision is to construct the large plant. Of course, this is what you would expect as P increases. The value of P at points 1 and 2 can be computed as follows:

$$\text{Point 1: EMV (do nothing)} = \text{EMV (small plant)}$$

$$0 = \$120,000P - \$20,000 \quad P = \frac{20,000}{120,000} = 0.167$$

$$\text{Point 2: EMV (small plant)} = \text{EMV (large plant)}$$

$$\$120,000P - \$20,000 = \$380,000P - \$180,000$$

$$260,000P = 160,000 \quad P = \frac{160,000}{260,000} = 0.615$$

The results of this sensitivity analysis are displayed in the following table:

BEST ALTERNATIVE	RANGE OF P VALUES
Do nothing	Less than 0.167
Construct a small plant	0.167 − 0.615
Construct a large plant	Greater than 0.615

6 A Minimization Example

The previous examples have illustrated how to apply the decision-making criterion when the payoffs are to be maximized. The following example illustrates how the criteria are applied to problems in which the payoffs are costs that should be minimized.

The Decision Sciences department at State University will be signing a 3-year lease for a new copy machine, and three different machines are being considered. For each of these, there is a monthly fee, which includes service on the machine, plus a charge for each copy. The number of copies that would be made each month is uncertain, but the department has estimated that the number of copies per month could be 10,000 or 20,000 or 30,000 per month. The monthly cost for each machine based on each of the three levels of activity is shown in Table 12.

TABLE 12

Payoff Table with Monthly Copy Costs for Business Analytics Department

	10,000 COPIES PER MONTH	20,000 COPIES PER MONTH	30,000 COPIES PER MONTH
Machine A	950	1,050	1,150
Machine B	850	1,100	1,350
Machine C	700	1,000	1,300

Which machine should be selected? To determine the best alternative, a specific criterion must be chosen. If the decision maker is optimistic, only the best (minimum) payoff for each decision is considered. These are shown in Table 13, and the best (minimum) of these is 700. Thus, Machine C would be selected, allowing the possibility of achieving this best cost of $700.

If the decision maker is pessimistic, only the worst (maximum) payoff for each decision is considered. These are also shown in Table 13, and the best (minimum) of these is 1,150. Thus, Machine A would be selected based on the pessimistic criterion. This would guarantee that the cost would be no more than 1,150, regardless of which state of nature occurred.

Using Hurwicz criterion, if we assume that the decision maker is 70% optimistic (the coefficient of realism is 0.7), the weighted average of the best and the worst payoff for each alternative would be calculated using the formula:

$$\text{Weighted average} = 0.7(\text{best payoff}) + (1 - 0.7)(\text{worst payoff})$$

For each of the three copy machines, we would get the following values.

$$\text{Machine A: } 0.7(950) + 0.3(1,150) = 1,010$$
$$\text{Machine B: } 0.7(850) + 0.3(1,350) = 1,000$$
$$\text{Machine C: } 0.7(700) + 0.3(1,300) = 880$$

The decision would be to select Machine C based on this criterion because it has the lowest weighted average cost.

For the equally likely criterion, the average payoff for each machine would be calculated.

$$\text{Machine A: } (950 + 1,050 + 1,150)/3 = 1,050$$
$$\text{Machine B: } (850 + 1,100 + 1,350)/3 = 1,100$$
$$\text{Machine C: } (700 + 1,000 + 1,300)/3 = 1,000$$

Based on the equally likely criterion, Machine C would be selected because it has the lowest average cost.

To apply EMV criterion, probabilities must be known for each state of nature. Past records indicate that 40% of the time the number of copies made in a month was 10,000, while 30% of the time it was 20,000 and 30% of the time it was 30,000. The probabilities for the three states of nature would be 0.4, 0.3, and 0.3. We can use these to calculate the EMVs, and the results are shown in Table 14. Machine C would be selected because it has the lowest EMV. The monthly cost would average $970 with this machine, while the other machines would average a higher cost.

TABLE 13

Best and Worst Payoffs (Costs) for Business Analytics Department

	10,000 COPIES PER MONTH	20,000 COPIES PER MONTH	30,000 COPIES PER MONTH	BEST PAYOFF (MINIMUM)	WORST PAYOFF (MAXIMUM)
Machine A	950	1,050	1,150	950	1,150
Machine B	850	1,100	1,350	850	1,350
Machine C	700	1,000	1,300	700	1,300

TABLE 14

Expected Monetary Values and Expected Value with Perfect Information for Business Analytics Department

	10,000 COPIES PER MONTH	20,000 COPIES PER MONTH	30,000 COPIES PER MONTH	EMV
Machine A	950	1,050	1,150	1,040
Machine B	850	1,100	1,350	1,075
Machine C	700	1,000	1,300	970
With perfect information	700	1,000	1,150	925
Probability	0.4	0.3	0.3	

TABLE 15

Opportunity Loss Table for Business Analytics Department

	10,000 COPIES PER MONTH	20,000 COPIES PER MONTH	30,000 COPIES PER MONTH	MAXIMUM	EOL
Machine A	250	50	0	250	115
Machine B	150	100	200	200	150
Machine C	0	0	150	150	45
Probability	0.4	0.3	0.3		

To find EVPI, we first find the payoffs (costs) that would be experienced with perfect information. The best payoff in each state of nature is the lowest value (cost) in that state of nature, as shown in the bottom row of Table 14. These values are used to calculate EVwPI. With these costs, we find

$$EVwPI = \$925$$
$$\text{Best EMV without perfect information} = \$970$$
$$EVPI = 970 - 925 = \$45$$

Perfect information would lower the expected value by $45.

To apply criteria based on opportunity loss, we must first develop the opportunity loss table. In each state of nature, the opportunity loss indicates how much worse each payoff is than the best possible payoff in that state of nature. The best payoff (cost) would be the lowest cost. Thus, to get the opportunity loss in this case, we subtract the lowest value in each column from all the values in that column and we obtain the opportunity loss table.

Once the opportunity loss table has been developed, the minimax regret criterion is applied exactly as it was for the Thompson Lumber example. The maximum regret for each alternative is found and the alternative with the minimum of these maximums is selected. As seen in Table 15, the minimum of these maximums is 150 so Machine C would be selected based on this criterion.

The probabilities are used to compute the expected opportunity losses as shown in Table 15. Machine C has the lowest EOL of $45, so it would be selected based on the minimum EOL criterion. As previously noted, the minimum EOL is equal to the expected value of perfect information.

7 Using Software for Payoff Table Problems

It is easy to use QM for Windows or Excel QM or even Excel 2013 without any add-ins to perform the calculations associated with payoff tables. The Thompson Lumber example is used in the following examples for illustration.

QM for Windows

To use QM for Windows for the Thompson Lumber example, select Modules – Decision Theory. Then enter New-Payoff Tables, and a window appears allowing you to set up the problem. Enter a title, the number of options (alternatives), the number of scenarios (states of nature),

PROGRAM 1A

QM for Windows Input for Thompson Lumber Example

PROGRAM 1B

QM for Windows Output Screen for Thompson Lumber Example

and specify if it is to be maximized or minimized. In this example, there are three alternatives or options, and two states of nature or scenarios. When these are entered, click OK and a window appears (Program 1A) allowing you to enter the probabilities and payoffs. You can also change the names of the alternatives and states of nature by simply typing over the default names. When you click *Solve*, the output in Program 1B appears. Additional output such as EVPI and opportunity loss results are available by clicking Window on the screen where the output is displayed.

Excel QM

To use Excel QM for the Thompson Lumber example, from the Excel QM ribbon in Excel 2013, click *Alphabetical* Menu and select *Decision Analysis – Decision Tables*. When the window opens to enter the parameters of the problem, you should enter a title, the number of alternatives, the number of states of nature, and specify if it is to be maximized or minimized. Click OK and an empty payoff table is created. You simply enter the probabilities, payoffs, and names for the rows and columns. The calculations are performed automatically and the results are shown in Program 2A. While the formulas are automatically developed in Excel QM, Program 2B shows the important formulas in this example. To see the formulas in Excel, simply hold down the control key and press the grave accent (`) key (usually found above the Tab key). To return Excel 2013 spreadsheet display to the numbers instead of the formulas, simply press the keys again.

PROGRAM 2A

Excel QM Results for Thompson Lumber Example

	A	B	C	D	E	F	G	H	I
1	Thompson Lumber			To see the formulas, hold down the control key (Ctrl) and press the ` (grave accent) key, which is usually found above the Tab key.					
2									
3	Decision Tables								
4		Enter the profits in the main body of the data table. Enter probabilities in the first row if you want to compute the expected value.							
5									
6	Data				Results				
7	Profit	Favorable Market	Unfavorable Market		EMV	Minimum	Maximum		
8	Probability	0.5	0.5						
9	Large plant	200000	-180000		10000	-180000	200000		
10	Small plant	100000	-20000		40000	-20000	100000		
11	Do nothing	0	0		0	0	0		
12				Maximum	40000	0	200000		
13									
14	Expected Value of Perfect Information								
15	Column best	200000	0		100000	<-Expected value WITH perfect information			
16					40000	<-Best expected value			
17					60000	<-Expected value OF perfect information			
18									
19	Regret								
20		Favorable Market	Unfavorable Market		Expected	Maximum			
21	Probability	0.5	0.5						
22	Large plant	0	180000		90000	180000			
23	Small plant	100000	20000		60000	100000			
24	Do nothing	200000	0		100000	200000			
25				Minimum	60000	100000			

PROGRAM 2B

Key Formulas in Excel QM for Thompson Lumber Example

	E	F	G
9	=SUMPRODUCT($B$8:$C$8,B9:C9)	=MIN(B9:C9)	=MAX(B9:C9)
10	=SUMPRODUCT($B$8:$C$8,B10:C10)	=MIN(B10:C10)	=MAX(B10:C10)
11	=SUMPRODUCT($B$8:$C$8,B11:C11)	=MIN(B11:C11)	=MAX(B11:C11)
12	=MAX(E9:E11)	=MAX(F9:F11)	=MAX(G9:G11)
13			
14			
15	=SUMPRODUCT($B$8:$C$8,B15:C15)	<-Expected value W	
16	=E12	<-Best expected val	
17	=E15-E12	<-Expected value O	
18			
19			
20	Expected	Maximum	
21			
22	=SUMPRODUCT($B$8:$C$8,B22:C22)	=MAX(B22:C22)	
23	=SUMPRODUCT($B$8:$C$8,B23:C23)	=MAX(B23:C23)	
24	=SUMPRODUCT($B$8:$C$8,B24:C24)	=MAX(B24:C24)	
25	=MIN(E22:E24)	=MIN(F22:F24)	

8 Decision Trees

Any problem that can be presented in a decision table can also be graphically illustrated in a **decision tree**. All decision trees are similar in that they contain *decision points* or **decision nodes** and *state-of-nature points* or **state-of-nature nodes**:

- A decision node from which one of several alternatives may be chosen
- A state-of-nature node out of which one state of nature will occur

In drawing the tree, we begin at the left and move to the right. Thus, the tree presents the decisions and outcomes in sequential order. Lines or branches from the squares (decision nodes) represent alternatives, and branches from the circles represent the states of nature. Figure 2 gives the basic decision tree for the Thompson Lumber example. First, John decides whether to construct a large plant, a small plant, or no plant. Then, once that decision is made, the possible states of nature or outcomes (favorable or unfavorable market) will occur. The next step is to put the payoffs and probabilities on the tree and begin the analysis.

FIGURE 2

Thompson's Decision Tree

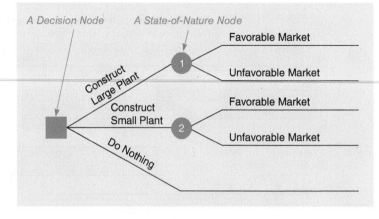

Analyzing problems with decision trees involves five steps:

Five Steps of Decision Tree Analysis

1. Define the problem.
2. Structure or draw the decision tree.
3. Assign probabilities to the states of nature.
4. Estimate payoffs for each possible combination of alternatives and states of nature.
5. Solve the problem by computing EMVs for each state-of-nature node. This is done by working backward, that is, starting at the right of the tree and working back to decision nodes on the left. Also, at each decision node, the alternative with the best EMV is selected.

The final decision tree with the payoffs and probabilities for John Thompson's decision situation is shown in Figure 3. Note that the payoffs are placed at the right side of each of the tree's branches. The probabilities are shown in parentheses next to each state of nature. Beginning with the payoffs on the right of the figure, the EMVs for each state-of-nature node are then calculated and placed by their respective nodes. The EMV of the first node is $10,000. This represents the branch from the decision node to construct a large plant. The

FIGURE 3

Completed and Solved Decision Tree for Thompson Lumber

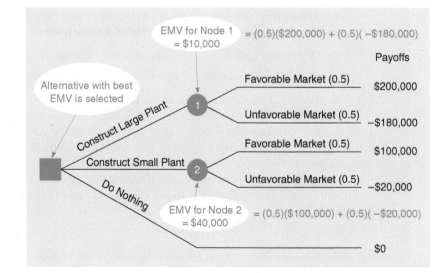

EMV for node 2, to construct a small plant, is $40,000. Building no plant or doing nothing has, of course, a payoff of $0. The branch leaving the decision node leading to the state-of-nature node with the highest EMV should be chosen. In Thompson's case, a small plant should be built.

A MORE COMPLEX DECISION FOR THOMPSON LUMBER—SAMPLE INFORMATION When **sequential decisions** need to be made, decision trees are much more powerful tools than decision tables. Let's say that John Thompson has two decisions to make, with the second decision dependent on the outcome of the first. Before deciding about building a new plant, John has the option of conducting his own marketing research survey, at a cost of $10,000. The information from his survey could help him decide whether to construct a large plant, a small plant, or not to build at all. John recognizes that such a market survey will not provide him with *perfect* information, but it may help quite a bit nevertheless.

All outcomes and alternatives must be considered.

John's new decision tree is represented in Figure 4. Let's take a careful look at this more complex tree. Note that *all possible outcomes and alternatives* are included in their logical sequence. This is one of the strengths of using decision trees in making decisions. The user is forced to examine all possible outcomes, including unfavorable ones. He or she is also forced to make decisions in a logical, sequential manner.

FIGURE 4

Larger Decision Tree with Payoffs and Probabilities for Thompson Lumber

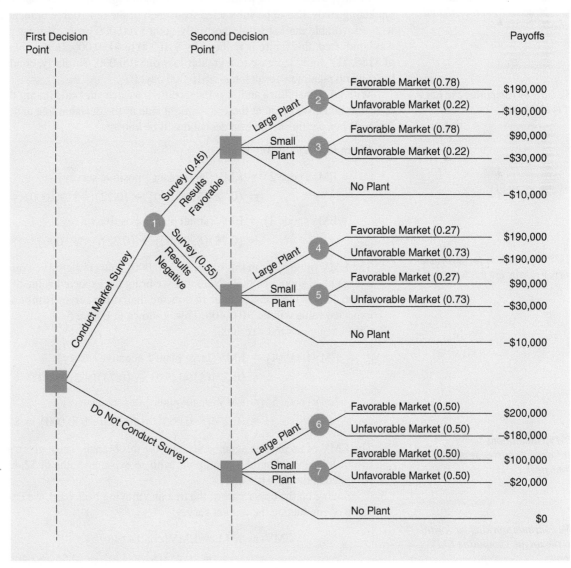

Examining the tree, we see that Thompson's first decision point is whether to conduct the $10,000 market survey. If he chooses not to do the study (the lower part of the tree), he can either construct a large plant, a small plant, or no plant. This is John's second decision point. The market will be either favorable (0.50 probability) or unfavorable (also 0.50 probability) if he builds. The payoffs for each of the possible consequences are listed along the right side. As a matter of fact, the lower portion of John's tree is *identical* to the simpler decision tree shown in Figure 3. Why is this so?

The upper part of Figure 4 reflects the decision to conduct the market survey. State-of-nature node 1 has two branches. There is a 45% chance that the survey results will indicate a favorable market for storage sheds. We also note that the probability is 0.55 that the survey results will be negative. The derivation of this probability will be discussed in the next section.

Most of the probabilities are conditional probabilities.

The rest of the probabilities shown in parentheses in Figure 4 are all **conditional probabilities** or **posterior probabilities** (these probabilities will also be discussed in the next section). For example, 0.78 is the probability of a favorable market for the sheds given a favorable result from the market survey. Of course, you would expect to find a high probability of a favorable market given that the research indicated that the market was good. Don't forget, though, there is a chance that John's $10,000 market survey didn't result in perfect or even reliable information. Any market research study is subject to error. In this case, there is a 22% chance that the market for sheds will be unfavorable given that the survey results are positive.

We note that there is a 27% chance that the market for sheds will be favorable given that John's survey results are negative. The probability is much higher, 0.73, that the market will actually be unfavorable given that the survey was negative.

The cost of the survey had to be subtracted from the original payoffs.

Finally, when we look to the payoff column in Figure 4, we see that $10,000, the cost of the marketing study, had to be subtracted from each of the top 10 tree branches. Thus, a large plant with a favorable market would normally net a $200,000 profit. But because the market study was conducted, this figure is reduced by $10,000 to $190,000. In the unfavorable case, the loss of $180,000 would increase to a greater loss of $190,000. Similarly, conducting the survey and building no plant now results in a −$10,000 payoff.

We start by computing the EMV of each branch.

With all probabilities and payoffs specified, we can start calculating the EMV at each state-of-nature node. We begin at the end, or right side of the decision tree and work back toward the origin. When we finish, the best decision will be known.

1. Given favorable survey results,

$$\text{EMV(node 2)} = \text{EMV(large plant | positive survey)}$$
$$= (0.78)(\$190,000) + (0.22)(-\$190,000) = \$106,400$$

$$\text{EMV(node 3)} = \text{EMV(small plant | positive survey)}$$
$$= (0.78)(\$90,000) + (0.22)(-\$30,000) = \$63,600$$

EMV calculations for favorable survey results are made first.

The EMV of no plant in this case is −$10,000. Thus, if the survey results are favorable, a large plant should be built. Note that we bring the expected value of this decision ($106,400) to the decision node to indicate that, if the survey results are positive, our expected value will be $106,400. This is shown in Figure 5.

2. Given negative survey results,

$$\text{EMV(node 4)} = \text{EMV(large plant | negative survey)}$$
$$= (0.27)(\$190,000) + (0.73)(-\$190,000) = -\$87,400$$

$$\text{EMV(node 5)} = \text{EMV(small plant | negative survey)}$$
$$= (0.27)(\$90,000) + (0.73)(-\$30,000) = \$2,400$$

EMV calculations for unfavorable survey results are done next.

The EMV of no plant is again −$10,000 for this branch. Thus, given a negative survey result, John should build a small plant with an expected value of $2,400, and this figure is indicated at the decision node.

3. Continuing on the upper part of the tree and moving backward, we compute the expected value of conducting the market survey:

We continue working backward to the origin, computing EMV values.

$$\text{EMV(node 1)} = \text{EMV(conduct survey)}$$
$$= (0.45)(\$106,400) + (0.55)(\$2,400)$$
$$= \$47,880 + \$1,320 = \$49,200$$

FIGURE 5
Thompson's Decision Tree with EMVs Shown

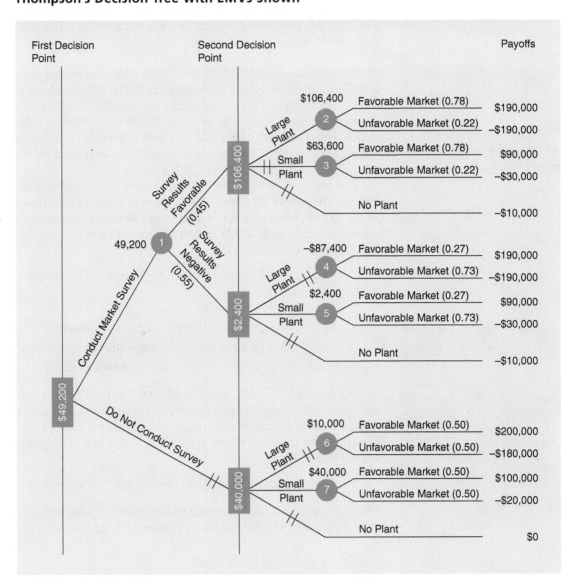

4. If the market survey is *not* conducted,

$$EMV(node\ 6) = EMV(large\ plant)$$
$$= (0.50)(\$200,000) + (0.50)(-\$180,000)$$
$$= \$10,000$$

$$EMV(node\ 7) = EMV(small\ plant)$$
$$= (0.50)(\$100,000) + (0.50)(-\$20,000)$$
$$= \$40,000$$

The EMV of no plant is $0.

Thus, building a small plant is the best choice, given that the marketing research is not performed.

5. We move back to the first decision node and choose the best alternative. The EMV of conducting the survey is $49,200, versus an EMV of $40,000 for not conducting the study, so the best choice is to *seek* marketing information. If the survey results are favorable, John should construct a large plant, but if the research is negative, John should construct a small plant.

93

In Figure 5, these expected values are placed on the decision tree. Notice on the tree that a pair of slash lines / / through a decision branch indicates that a particular alternative is dropped from further consideration. This is because its EMV is lower than the EMV for the best alternative. After you have solved several decision tree problems, you may find it easier to do all of your computations on the tree diagram.

EVSI measures the value of sample information.

EXPECTED VALUE OF SAMPLE INFORMATION   With the market survey he intends to conduct, John Thompson knows that his best decision will be to build a large plant if the survey is favorable or a small plant if the survey results are negative. But John also realizes that conducting the market research is not free. He would like to know what the actual value of doing a survey is. One way of measuring the value of market information is to compute the **expected value of sample information** (EVSI) which is the increase in expected value resulting from the sample information.

The expected value *with* sample information (EV with SI) is found from the decision tree, and the cost of the sample information is added to this since this was subtracted from all the payoffs before the EV with SI was calculated. The expected value *without* sample information (EV without SI) is then subtracted from this to find the value of the sample information.

$$\text{EVSI} = (\text{EV with SI} + \text{cost}) - (\text{EV without SI}) \tag{4}$$

where

$$\text{EVSI} = \text{expected value of sample information}$$
$$\text{EV with SI} = \text{expected value with sample information}$$
$$\text{EV without SI} = \text{expected value without sample information}$$

In John's case, his EMV would be $59,200 *if* he hadn't already subtracted the $10,000 study cost from each payoff. (Do you see why this is so? If not, add $10,000 back into each payoff, as in the original Thompson problem, and recompute the EMV of conducting the market study.) From the lower branch of Figure 5, we see that the EMV of *not* gathering the sample information is $40,000. Thus,

$$\text{EVSI} = (\$49,200 + \$10,000) - \$40,000 = \$59,200 - \$40,000 = \$19,200$$

This means that John could have paid up to $19,200 for a market study and still come out ahead. Since it costs only $10,000, the survey is indeed worthwhile.

Efficiency of Sample Information

There may be many types of sample information available to a decision maker. In developing a new product, information could be obtained from a survey, from a focus group, from other market research techniques, or from actually using a test market to see how sales will be. While none of these sources of information are perfect, they can be evaluated by comparing the EVSI with the EVPI. If the sample information was perfect, then the efficiency would be 100%. The **efficiency of sample information** is

$$\text{Efficiency of sample information} = \frac{\text{EVSI}}{\text{EVPI}}100\% \tag{5}$$

In the Thompson Lumber example,

$$\text{Efficiency of sample information} = \frac{19,200}{60,000}100\% = 32\%$$

Thus, the market survey is only 32% as efficient as perfect information.

Sensitivity Analysis

As with payoff tables, sensitivity analysis can be applied to decision trees as well. The overall approach is the same. Consider the decision tree for the expanded Thompson Lumber problem shown in Figure 5. How sensitive is our decision (to conduct the marketing survey) to the probability of favorable survey results?

Let p be the probability of favorable survey results. Then $(1 - p)$ is the probability of negative survey results. Given this information, we can develop an expression for the EMV of conducting the survey, which is node 1:

$$\text{EMV}(\text{node } 1) = (\$106{,}400)p + (\$2{,}400)(1 - p)$$
$$= \$104{,}000p + \$2{,}400$$

We are indifferent when the EMV of conducting the marketing survey, node 1, is the same as the EMV of not conducting the survey, which is \$40,000. We can find the indifference point by equating EMV(node 1) to \$40,000:

$$\$104{,}000p + \$2{,}400 = \$40{,}000$$
$$\$104{,}000p = \$37{,}600$$
$$p = \frac{\$37{,}600}{\$104{,}000} = 0.36$$

As long as the probability of favorable survey results, p, is greater than 0.36, our decision will stay the same. When p is less than 0.36, our decision will be not to conduct the survey.

We could also perform sensitivity analysis for other problem parameters. For example, we could find how sensitive our decision is to the probability of a favorable market given favorable survey results. At this time, this probability is 0.78. If this value goes up, the large plant becomes more attractive. In this case, our decision would not change. What happens when this probability goes down? The analysis becomes more complex. As the probability of a favorable market given favorable survey results goes down, the small plant becomes more attractive. At some point, the small plant will result in a higher EMV (given favorable survey results) than the large plant. This, however, does not conclude our analysis. As the probability of a favorable market given favorable survey results continues to fall, there will be a point where not conducting the survey, with an EMV of \$40,000, will be more attractive than conducting the marketing survey. We leave the actual calculations to you. It is important to note that sensitivity analysis should consider *all* possible consequences.

9   How Probability Values Are Estimated by Bayesian Analysis

Bayes' theorem allows decision makers to revise probability values.

There are many ways of getting probability data for a problem such as Thompson's. The numbers (such as 0.78, 0.22, 0.27, 0.73 in Figure 4) can be assessed by a manager based on experience and intuition. They can be derived from historical data, or they can be computed from other available data using Bayes' theorem. The advantage of Bayes' theorem is that it incorporates both our initial estimates of the probabilities and information about the accuracy of the information source (e.g., market research survey).

The Bayes' theorem approach recognizes that a decision maker does not know with certainty what state of nature will occur. It allows the manager to revise his or her initial or prior probability assessments based on new information. The revised probabilities are called posterior probabilities.

Calculating Revised Probabilities

In the Thompson Lumber case solved in Section 8, we made the assumption that the following four conditional probabilities were known:

$$P(\text{favorable market(FM)} \mid \text{survey results positive}) = 0.78$$
$$P(\text{unfavorable market(UM)} \mid \text{survey results positive}) = 0.22$$
$$P(\text{favorable market(FM)} \mid \text{survey results negative}) = 0.27$$
$$P(\text{unfavorable market(UM)} \mid \text{survey results negative}) = 0.73$$

TABLE 16

Market Survey Reliability in Predicting States of Nature

| | STATE OF NATURE | |
| | FAVORABLE MARKET (FM) | UNFAVORABLE MARKET (UM) |
RESULT OF SURVEY		
Positive (predicts favorable market for product)	$P(\text{survey positive} \mid \text{FM}) = 0.70$	$P(\text{survey positive} \mid \text{UM}) = 0.20$
Negative (predicts unfavorable market for product)	$P(\text{survey negative} \mid \text{FM}) = 0.30$	$P(\text{survey negative} \mid \text{UM}) = 0.80$

We now show how John Thompson was able to derive these values with Bayes' theorem. From discussions with market research specialists at the local university, John knows that special surveys such as his can either be positive (i.e., predict a favorable market) or be negative (i.e., predict an unfavorable market). The experts have told John that, statistically, of all new products with a *favorable market* (FM), market surveys were positive and predicted success correctly 70% of the time. Thirty percent of the time the surveys falsely predicted negative results or an *unfavorable market* (UM). On the other hand, when there was actually an unfavorable market for a new product, 80% of the surveys correctly predicted negative results. The surveys incorrectly predicted positive results the remaining 20% of the time. These conditional probabilities are summarized in Table 16. They are an indication of the accuracy of the survey that John is thinking of undertaking.

Note that without any market survey information, John's best estimates of a favorable and unfavorable market are

$$P(\text{FM}) = 0.50$$
$$P(\text{UM}) = 0.50$$

These are referred to as the *prior probabilities*.

We are now ready to compute Thompson's revised or posterior probabilities. These desired probabilities are the reverse of the probabilities in Table 16. We need the probability of a favorable or unfavorable market given a positive or negative result from the market study. The general form of Bayes' theorem is

$$P(A \mid B) = \frac{P(B \mid A)P(A)}{P(B \mid A)P(A) + P(B \mid A')P(A')} \tag{6}$$

where

$$A, B = \text{any two events}$$
$$A' = \text{complement of } A$$

We can let A represent a favorable market and B represent a positive survey. Then, substituting the appropriate numbers into this equation, we obtain the conditional probabilities, given that the market survey is positive:

$$P(\text{FM} \mid \text{survey positive}) = \frac{P(\text{survey positive} \mid \text{FM})P(\text{FM})}{P(\text{survey positive} \mid \text{FM})P(\text{FM}) + P(\text{survey positive} \mid \text{UM})P(\text{UM})}$$

$$= \frac{(0.70)(0.50)}{(0.70)(0.50) + (0.20)(0.50)} = \frac{0.35}{0.45} = 0.78$$

$$P(\text{UM} \mid \text{survey positive}) = \frac{P(\text{survey positive} \mid \text{UM})P(\text{UM})}{P(\text{survey positive} \mid \text{UM})P(\text{UM}) + P(\text{survey positive} \mid \text{FM})P(\text{FM})}$$

$$= \frac{(0.20)(0.50)}{(0.20)(0.50) + (0.70)(0.50)} = \frac{0.10}{0.45} = 0.22$$

Note that the denominator (0.45) in these calculations is the probability of a positive survey. An alternative method for these calculations is to use a probability table as shown in Table 17.

TABLE 17
Probability Revisions Given a Positive Survey

STATE OF NATURE	CONDITIONAL PROBABILITY P(SURVEY POSITIVE $\vert$ STATE OF NATURE)	PRIOR PROBABILITY	POSTERIOR PROBABILITY	
			JOINT PROBABILITY	P(STATE OF NATURE $\vert$ SURVEY POSITIVE)
FM	0.70	× 0.50	= 0.35	0.35/0.45 = 0.78
UM	0.20	× 0.50	= 0.10	0.10/0.45 = 0.22
		P(survey results positive)	= 0.45	1.00

The conditional probabilities, given that the market survey is negative, are

$$P(\text{FM} \mid \text{survey negative}) = \frac{P(\text{survey negative} \mid \text{FM})P(\text{FM})}{P(\text{survey negative} \mid \text{FM})P(\text{FM}) + P(\text{survey negative} \mid \text{UM})P(\text{UM})}$$

$$= \frac{(0.30)(0.50)}{(0.30)(0.50) + (0.80)(0.50)} = \frac{0.15}{0.55} = 0.27$$

$$P(\text{UM} \mid \text{survey negative}) = \frac{P(\text{survey negative} \mid \text{UM})P(\text{UM})}{P(\text{survey negative} \mid \text{UM})P(\text{UM}) + P(\text{survey negative} \mid \text{FM})P(\text{FM})}$$

$$= \frac{(0.80)(0.50)}{(0.80)(0.50) + (0.30)(0.50)} = \frac{0.40}{0.55} = 0.73$$

Note that the denominator (0.55) in these calculations is the probability of a negative survey. These computations given a negative survey could also have been performed in a table instead, as in Table 18.

The calculations shown in Tables 17 and 18 can easily be performed in Excel spreadsheets. Programs 3A and 3B show the final output for this example and the formulas.

New probabilities provide valuable information.

The posterior probabilities now provide John Thompson with estimates for each state of nature if the survey results are positive or negative. As you know, John's **prior probability** of success without a market survey was only 0.50. Now he is aware that the probability of successfully marketing storage sheds will be 0.78 if his survey shows positive results. His chances of success drop to 27% if the survey report is negative. This is valuable management information, as we saw in the earlier decision tree analysis.

Potential Problem in Using Survey Results

In many decision-making problems, survey results or pilot studies are done before an actual decision (such as building a new plant or taking a particular course of action) is made. As discussed earlier in this section, Bayes' analysis is used to help determine the correct

TABLE 18
Probability Revisions Given a Negative Survey

STATE OF NATURE	CONDITIONAL PROBABILITY P(SURVEY NEGATIVE $\vert$ STATE OF NATURE)	PRIOR PROBABILITY	POSTERIOR PROBABILITY	
			JOINT PROBABILITY	P(STATE OF NATURE $\vert$ SURVEY NEGATIVE)
FM	0.30	× 0.50	= 0.15	0.15/0.55 = 0.27
UM	0.80	× 0.50	= 0.40	0.40/0.55 = 0.73
		P(survey results negative)	= 0.55	1.00

PROGRAM 3A

**Results of Bayes'
Calculations in Excel 2013**

	A	B	C	D	E
1	Bayes Theorem for Thompson Lumber Example				
2					
3	Fill in cells B7, B8, and C7				
4					
5	Probability Revisions Given a Positive Survey				
6	State of Nature	P(Sur.Pos.|state of nature)	Prior Prob.	Joint Prob.	Posterior Probability
7	FM	0.7	0.5	0.35	0.78
8	UM	0.2	0.5	0.1	0.22
9			P(Sur.pos.)=	0.45	
10					
11	Probability Revisions Given a Negative Survey				
12	State of Nature	P(Sur.Pos.|state of nature)	Prior Prob.	Joint Prob.	Posterior Probability
13	FM	0.3	0.5	0.15	0.27
14	UM	0.8	0.5	0.4	0.73
15			P(Sur.neg.)=	0.55	

PROGRAM 3B

**Formulas Used for Bayes'
Calculations in Excel 2013**

	B	C	D	E
7	0.7	0.5	=B7*C7	=D7/$D$9
8	0.2	=1-C7	=B8*C8	=D8/$D$9
9		P(Sur.pos.)=	=SUM(D7:D8)	
11				
13	=1-B7	=C7	=B13*C13	=D13/$D$15
14	=1-B8	=C8	=B14*C14	=D14/$D$15
15		P(Sur.neg.)=	=SUM(D13:D14)	

conditional probabilities that are needed to solve these types of decision theory problems. In computing these conditional probabilities, we need to have data about the surveys and their accuracies. If a decision to build a plant or to take another course of action is actually made, we can determine the accuracy of our surveys. Unfortunately, we cannot always get data about those situations in which the decision was not to build a plant or not to take some course of action. Thus, sometimes when we use survey results, we are basing our probabilities only on those cases in which a decision to build a plant or take some course of action is actually made. This means that, in some situations, conditional probability information may not be not quite as accurate as we would like. Even so, calculating conditional probabilities helps to refine the decision-making process and, in general, to make better decisions.

10   Utility Theory

We have focused on the EMV criterion for making decisions under risk. However, there are many occasions in which people make decisions that would appear to be inconsistent with the EMV criterion. When people buy insurance, the amount of the premium is greater than the expected payout to them from the insurance company because the premium includes the expected payout, the overhead cost, and the profit for the insurance company. A person involved in a lawsuit may choose to settle out of court rather than go to trial even if the expected value of going to trial is greater than the proposed settlement. A person buys a lottery ticket even though the expected return is negative. Casino games of all types have negative expected returns for the player, and yet millions of people play these games. A businessperson may rule out one potential decision because it could bankrupt the firm if things go bad, even though the expected return for this decision is better than that of all other alternatives.

Why do people make decisions that don't maximize their EMV? They do this because the monetary value is not always a true indicator of the overall value of the result of the

FIGURE 6
Your Decision Tree for the Lottery Ticket

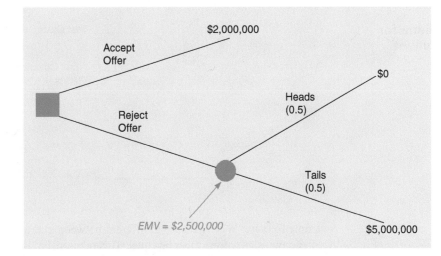

The overall value of the result of a decision is called utility.

decision. The overall worth of a particular outcome is called **utility**, and rational people make decisions that maximize the expected utility. Although at times the monetary value is a good indicator of utility, there are other times when it is not. This is particularly true when some of the values involve an extremely large payoff or an extremely large loss. Suppose that you are the lucky holder of a lottery ticket. Five minutes from now a fair coin could be flipped, and if it comes up tails, you would win $5 million. If it comes up heads, you would win nothing. Just a moment ago a wealthy person offered you $2 million for your ticket. Let's assume that you have no doubts about the validity of the offer. The person will give you a certified check for the full amount, and you are absolutely sure the check would be good.

A decision tree for this situation is shown in Figure 6. The EMV for rejecting the offer indicates that you should hold on to your ticket, but what would you do? Just think, $2 million for *sure* instead of a 50% chance at nothing. Suppose you were greedy enough to hold on to the ticket, and then lost. How would you explain that to your friends? Wouldn't $2 million be enough to be comfortable for a while?

Most people would choose to sell the ticket for $2 million. Most of us, in fact, would probably be willing to settle for a lot less. Just how low we would go is, of course, a matter of personal preference. People have different feelings about seeking or avoiding risk. Using the EMV alone is not always a good way to make these types of decisions.

EMV is not always the best approach.

One way to incorporate your own attitudes toward risk is through **utility theory**. In the next section, we explore first how to measure utility and then how to use utility measures in decision making.

Measuring Utility and Constructing a Utility Curve

The first step in using utility theory is to assign utility values to each monetary value in a given situation. It is convenient to begin **utility assessment** by assigning the worst outcome a utility of 0 and the best outcome a utility of 1. Although any values may be used as long as the utility for the best outcome is greater than the utility for the worst outcome, using 0 and 1 has some benefits. Because we have chosen to use 0 and 1, all other outcomes will have a utility value between 0 and 1. In determining the utilities of all outcomes, other than the best or worst outcome, a **standard gamble** is considered. This gamble is shown in Figure 7.

Utility assessment assigns the worst outcome a utility of 0 and the best outcome a utility of 1.

In Figure 7, p is the probability of obtaining the best outcome, and $(1 - p)$ is the probability of obtaining the worst outcome. Assessing the utility of any other outcome involves determining the probability (p), which makes you indifferent between alternative 1, which is the gamble between the best and worst outcomes, and alternative 2, which is obtaining the other

When you are indifferent, the expected utilities are equal.

FIGURE 7
Standard Gamble for Utility Assessment

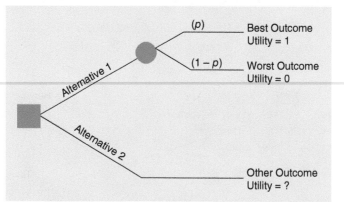

outcome for sure. When you are indifferent between alternatives 1 and 2, the expected utilities for these two alternatives must be equal. This relationship is shown as

Expected utility of alternative 2 = Expected utility of alternative 1

Utility of other outcome = (p)(utility of *best* outcome, which is 1)

$+ (1 - p)$(utility of the *worst* outcome, which is 0)

Utility of other outcome = $(p)(1) + (1 - p)(0) = p$ (7)

Now all you have to do is to determine the value of the probability (p) that makes you indifferent between alternatives 1 and 2. In setting the probability, you should be aware that utility assessment is completely subjective. It's a value set by the decision maker that can't be measured on an objective scale. Let's take a look at an example.

Once utility values have been determined, a utility curve can be constructed.

Jane Dickson would like to construct a utility curve revealing her preference for money between $0 and $10,000. A **utility curve** is a graph that plots utility value versus monetary value. She can invest her money either in a bank savings account or in a real estate deal.

If the money is invested in the bank, in 3 years Jane would have $5,000. If she invested in the real estate, after 3 years she could either have nothing or $10,000. Jane, however, is very conservative. Unless there is an 80% chance of getting $10,000 from the real estate deal, Jane would prefer to have her money in the bank, where it is safe. What Jane has done here is to assess her utility for $5,000. When there is an 80% chance (this means that p is 0.8) of getting $10,000, Jane is indifferent between putting her money in real estate and putting it in the bank. Jane's utility for $5,000 is thus equal to 0.8, which is the same as the value for p. This utility assessment is shown in Figure 8.

Other utility values can be assessed in the same way. For example, what is Jane's utility for $7,000? What value of p would make Jane indifferent between $7,000 and the gamble that would result in either $10,000 or $0? For Jane, there must be a 90% chance of getting the $10,000. Otherwise, she would prefer the $7,000 for sure. Thus, her utility for $7,000 is 0.90. Jane's utility for $3,000 can be determined in the same way. If there were a 50% chance of obtaining the $10,000, Jane would be indifferent between having $3,000 for sure and taking the gamble of either winning

FIGURE 8
Utility of $5,000

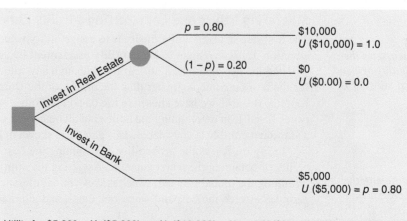

Utility for $5,000 = U ($5,000) = pU ($10,000) + $(1 - p)$ U ($0) = $(0.8)(1) + (0.2)(0) = 0.8$

FIGURE 9
Utility Curve for Jane Dickson

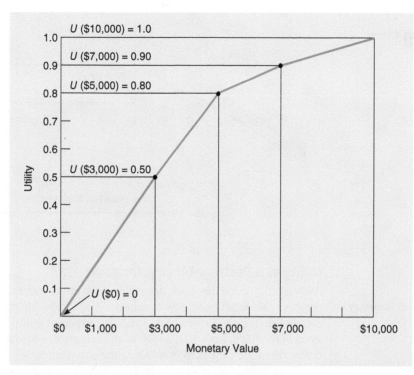

the $10,000 or getting nothing. Thus, the utility of $3,000 for Jane is 0.5. Of course, this process can be continued until Jane has assessed her utility for as many monetary values as she wants. These assessments, however, are enough to get an idea of Jane's feelings toward risk. In fact, we can plot these points in a utility curve, as is done in Figure 9. In the figure, the assessed utility points of $3,000, $5,000, and $7,000 are shown by dots, and the rest of the curve is inferred from these.

Jane's utility curve is typical of a **risk avoider**. A risk avoider is a decision maker who gets less utility or pleasure from a greater risk and tends to avoid situations in which high losses might occur. As monetary value increases on her utility curve, the utility increases at a slower rate.

Figure 10 illustrates that a person who is a **risk seeker** has an opposite-shaped utility curve. This decision maker gets more utility from a greater risk and higher potential payoff. As monetary value increases on his or her utility curve, the utility increases at an increasing rate. A person who is *indifferent* to risk has a utility curve that is a straight line. The shape of a person's utility curve depends on the specific decision being considered, the monetary values involved in the situation, the person's psychological frame of mind, and how the person feels about the future. It may well be that you have one utility curve for some situations you face and completely different curves for others.

The shape of a person's utility curve depends on many factors.

FIGURE 10
Preferences for Risk

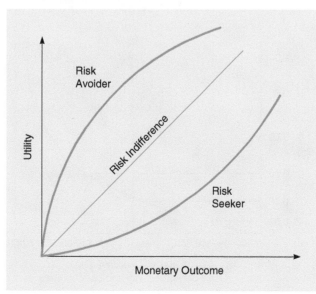

FIGURE 11
Decision Facing Mark Simkin

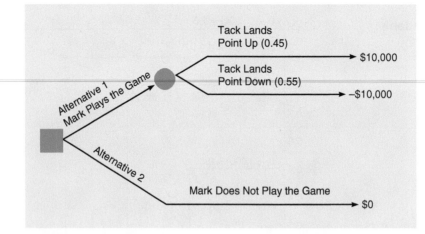

Utility as a Decision-Making Criterion

Utility values replace monetary values.

After a utility curve has been determined, the utility values from the curve are used in making decisions. Monetary outcomes or values are replaced with the appropriate utility values and then decision analysis is performed as usual. The expected utility for each alternative is computed instead of the EMV. Let's take a look at an example in which a decision tree is used and expected utility values are computed in selecting the best alternative.

Mark Simkin loves to gamble. He decides to play a game that involves tossing thumbtacks in the air. If the point on the thumbtack is facing up after it lands, Mark wins $10,000. If the point on the thumbtack is down, Mark loses $10,000. Should Mark play the game (alternative 1) or should he not play the game (alternative 2)?

Alternatives 1 and 2 are displayed in the tree shown in Figure 11. As can be seen, alternative 1 is to play the game. Mark believes that there is a 45% chance of winning $10,000 and a 55% chance of suffering the $10,000 loss. Alternative 2 is not to gamble. What should Mark do? Of course, this depends on Mark's utility for money. As stated previously, he likes to gamble. Using the procedure just outlined, Mark was able to construct a utility curve showing his preference for money. Mark has a total of $20,000 to gamble, so he has constructed the utility curve based on a best payoff of $20,000 and a worst payoff of a $20,000 loss. This curve appears in Figure 12.

Mark's objective is to maximize expected utility.

We see that Mark's utility for −$10,000 is 0.05, his utility for not playing ($0) is 0.15, and his utility for $10,000 is 0.30. These values can now be used in the decision tree. Mark's objective is to maximize his expected utility, which can be done as follows:

Step 1.
$$U(-\$10,000) = 0.05$$
$$U(\$0) = 0.15$$
$$U(\$10,000) = 0.30$$

FIGURE 12
Utility Curve for Mark Simkin

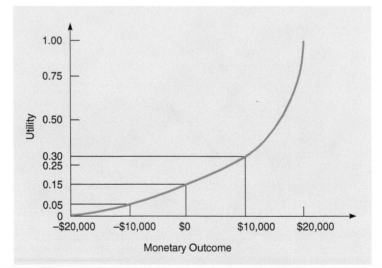

IN ACTION   Multiattribute Utility Model Aids in Disposal of Nuclear Weapons

When the Cold War between the United States and the USSR ended, the two countries agreed to dismantle a large number of nuclear weapons. The exact number of weapons is not known, but the total number has been estimated to be over 40,000. The plutonium recovered from the dismantled weapons presented several concerns. The National Academy of Sciences characterized the possibility that the plutonium could fall into the hands of terrorists as a very real danger. Also, plutonium is very toxic to the environment, so a safe and secure disposal process was critical. Deciding what disposal process would be used was no easy task.

Due to the long relationship between the United States and the USSR during the Cold War, it was necessary that the plutonium disposal process for each country occur at approximately the same time. Whichever method was selected by one country would have to be approved by the other country. The U.S. Department of Energy (DOE) formed the Office of Fissile Materials Disposition (OFMD) to oversee the process of selecting the approach to use for disposal of the plutonium. Recognizing that the decision could be controversial, the OFMD used a team of operations research analysts associated with the Amarillo National Research Center. This OR group used a multiattribute utility (MAU) model to combine several performance measures into one single measure.

A total of 37 performance measures were used in evaluating 13 different possible alternatives. The MAU model combined these measures and helped to rank the alternatives as well as identify the deficiencies of some alternatives. The OFMD recommended two of the alternatives with the highest rankings, and development was begun on both of them. This parallel development permitted the United States to react quickly when the USSR's plan was developed. The USSR used an analysis based on this same MAU approach. The United States and the USSR chose to convert the plutonium from nuclear weapons into mixed oxide fuel, which is used in nuclear reactors to make electricity. Once the plutonium is converted to this form, it cannot be used in nuclear weapons.

The MAU model helped the United States and the USSR deal with a very sensitive and potentially hazardous issue in a way that considered economic, nonproliferation, and ecology issues. The framework is now being used by Russia to evaluate other policies related to nuclear energy.

Source: Based on John C. Butler et al. "The United States and Russia Evaluate Plutonium Disposition Options with Multiattribute Utility Theory," *Interfaces* 35, 1 (January–February 2005): 88–101.

Step 2. Replace monetary values with utility values. Refer to Figure 13. Here are the expected utilities for alternatives 1 and 2:

$$E(\text{alternative 1: play the game}) = (0.45)(0.30) + (0.55)(0.05)$$
$$= 0.135 + 0.027 = 0.162$$

$$E(\text{alternative 2: don't play the game}) = 0.15$$

Therefore, alternative 1 is the best strategy using utility as the decision criterion. If EMV had been used, alternative 2 would have been the best strategy. The utility curve is a risk-seeker utility curve, and the choice of playing the game certainly reflects this preference for risk.

FIGURE 13

Using Expected Utilities in Decision Making

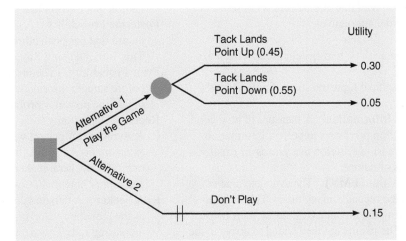

Summary

Decision theory is an analytic and systematic approach to studying decision making. Six steps are usually involved in making decisions in three environments: decision making under certainty, uncertainty, and risk. In decision making under uncertainty, decision tables are constructed to compute criteria such as maximax, maximin, criterion of realism, equally likely, and minimax regret. Methods such as determining expected monetary value (EMV), expected value of perfect information (EVPI), expected opportunity loss (EOL), and sensitivity analysis are used in decision making under risk.

Decision trees are another option, particularly for larger decision problems, when one decision must be made before other decisions can be made. For example, a decision to take a sample or to perform market research is made before we decide to construct a large plant, a small one, or no plant. In this case, we can also compute the expected value of sample information (EVSI) to determine the value of the market research. The efficiency of sample information compares the EVSI to the EVPI. Bayesian analysis can be used to revise or update probability values using both the prior probabilities and other probabilities related to the accuracy of the information source.

Glossary

Alternative A course of action or a strategy that may be chosen by a decision maker.

Coefficient of Realism (α) A number from 0 to 1. When the coefficient is close to 1, the decision criterion is optimistic. When the coefficient is close to 0, the decision criterion is pessimistic.

Conditional Probability A posterior probability.

Conditional Value or Payoff A consequence, normally expressed in a monetary value, that occurs as a result of a particular alternative and state of nature.

Criterion of Realism A decision-making criterion that uses a weighted average of the best and worst possible payoffs for each alternative.

Decision Making under Certainty A decision-making environment in which the future outcomes or states of nature are known.

Decision Making under Risk A decision-making environment in which several outcomes or states of nature may occur as a result of a decision or alternative. The probabilities of the outcomes or states of nature are known.

Decision Making under Uncertainty A decision-making environment in which several outcomes or states of nature may occur. The probabilities of these outcomes, however, are not known.

Decision Node (Point) In a decision tree, this is a point where the best of the available alternatives is chosen. The branches represent the alternatives.

Decision Table A payoff table.

Decision Theory An analytic and systematic approach to decision making.

Decision Tree A graphical representation of a decision-making situation.

Efficiency of Sample Information A measure of how good the sample information is relative to perfect information.

Equally Likely A decision criterion that places an equal weight on all states of nature.

Expected Monetary Value (EMV) The average value of a decision if it can be repeated many times. This is determined by multiplying the monetary values by their respective probabilities. The results are then added to arrive at the EMV.

Expected Value of Perfect Information (EVPI) The average or expected value of information if it were completely accurate. The increase in EMV that results from having perfect information.

Expected Value of Sample Information (EVSI) The increase in EMV that results from having sample or imperfect information.

Expected Value with Perfect Information (EVwPI) The average or expected value of a decision if perfect knowledge of the future is available.

Hurwicz Criterion The criterion of realism.

Laplace Criterion The equally likely criterion.

Maximax An optimistic decision-making criterion. This selects the alternative with the highest possible return.

Maximin A pessimistic decision-making criterion. This alternative maximizes the minimum payoff. It selects the alternative with the best of the worst possible payoffs.

Minimax Regret A criterion that minimizes the maximum opportunity loss.

Opportunity Loss The amount you would lose by not picking the best alternative. For any state of nature, this is the difference between the consequences of any alternative and the best possible alternative.

Optimistic Criterion The maximax criterion.

Payoff Table A table that lists the alternatives, states of nature, and payoffs in a decision-making situation.

Posterior Probability A conditional probability of a state of nature that has been adjusted based on sample information. This is found using Bayes' theorem.

Prior Probability The initial probability of a state of nature before sample information is used with Bayes' theorem to obtain the posterior probability.

Regret Opportunity loss.

Risk Avoider A person who avoids risk. On the utility curve, as the monetary value, the utility increases at a decreasing rate. This decision maker gets less utility for a greater risk and higher potential returns.

Risk Seeker A person who seeks risk. On the utility curve, as the monetary value increases, the utility increases at an increasing rate. This decision maker gets more pleasure for a greater risk and higher potential returns.

Sequential Decisions   Decisions in which the outcome of one decision influences other decisions.

Standard Gamble   The process used to determine utility values.

State of Nature   An outcome or occurrence over which the decision maker has little or no control.

State-of-Nature Node   In a decision tree, a point where the EMV is computed. The branches coming from this node represent states of nature.

Utility   The overall value or worth of a particular outcome.

Utility Assessment   The process of determining the utility of various outcomes. This is normally done using a standard gamble between any outcome for sure and a gamble between the worst and best outcomes.

Utility Curve   A graph or curve that reveals the relationship between utility and monetary values. When this curve has been constructed, utility values from the curve can be used in the decision-making process.

Utility Theory   A theory that allows decision makers to incorporate their risk preference and other factors into the decision-making process.

Weighted Average Criterion   Another name for the criterion of realism.

Key Equations

(1) $\text{EMV}(\text{alternative } i) = \sum X_i P(X_i)$

An equation that computes expected monetary value.

(2) $\text{EVwPI} = \sum (\text{best payoff in state of nature } i) \\ \times (\text{probability of state of nature } i)$

An equation that computes the expected value with perfect information.

(3) $\text{EVPI} = \text{EVwPI} - \text{Best EMV}$

An equation that computes the expected value of perfect information.

(4) $\text{EVSI} = (\text{EV with SI} + \text{cost}) - (\text{EV without SI})$

An equation that computes the expected value (EV) of sample information (SI).

(5) Efficiency of sample information $= \dfrac{\text{EVSI}}{\text{EVPI}} 100\%$

An equation that compares sample information to perfect information.

(6) $P(A|B) = \dfrac{P(B|A)P(A)}{P(B|A)P(A) + P(B|A')P(A')}$

Bayes' theorem—the conditional probability of event A given that event B has occurred.

(7) Utility of other outcome $= (p)(1) + (1 - p)(0) = p$

An equation that determines the utility of an intermediate outcome.

Solved Problems

Solved Problem 1

Maria Rojas is considering the possibility of opening a small dress shop on Fairbanks Avenue, a few blocks from the university. She has located a good mall that attracts students. Her options are to open a small shop, a medium-sized shop, or no shop at all. The market for a dress shop can be good, average, or bad. The probabilities for these three possibilities are 0.2 for a good market, 0.5 for an average market, and 0.3 for a bad market. The net profit or loss for the medium-sized and small shops for the various market conditions are given in the following table. Building no shop at all yields no loss and no gain.

a. What do you recommend?
b. Calculate the EVPI.
c. Develop the opportunity loss table for this situation. What decisions would be made using the minimax regret criterion and the minimum EOL criterion?

ALTERNATIVE	GOOD MARKET ($)	AVERAGE MARKET ($)	BAD MARKET ($)
Small shop	75,000	25,000	−40,000
Medium-sized shop	100,000	35,000	−60,000
No shop	0	0	0

Solution

a. Since the decision-making environment is risk (probabilities are known), it is appropriate to use the EMV criterion. The problem can be solved by developing a payoff table that contains all alternatives, states of nature, and probability values. The EMV for each alternative is also computed, as in the following table:

| | STATE OF NATURE | | | |
ALTERNATIVE	GOOD MARKET ($)	AVERAGE MARKET ($)	BAD MARKET ($)	EMV ($)
Small shop	75,000	25,000	−40,000	15,500
Medium-sized shop	100,000	35,000	−60,000	19,500
No shop	0	0	0	0
Probabilities	0.20	0.50	0.30	

$$\text{EMV(small shop)} = (0.2)(\$75{,}000) + (0.5)(\$25{,}000) + (0.3)(-\$40{,}000) = \$15{,}500$$
$$\text{EMV(medium shop)} = (0.2)(\$100{,}000) + (0.5)(\$35{,}000) + (0.3)(-\$60{,}000) = \$19{,}500$$
$$\text{EMV(no shop)} = (0.2)(\$0) + (0.5)(\$0) + (0.3)(\$0) = \$0$$

As can be seen, the best decision is to build the medium-sized shop. The EMV for this alternative is $19,500.

b. $\text{EVwPI} = (0.2)\$100{,}000 + (0.5)\$35{,}000 + (0.3)\$0 = \$37{,}500$

$\text{EVPI} = \$37{,}500 - \$19{,}500 = \$18{,}000$

c. The opportunity loss table is shown here.

| | STATE OF NATURE | | | | |
ALTERNATIVE	GOOD MARKET ($)	AVERAGE MARKET ($)	BAD MARKET ($)	MAXIMUM ($)	EOL ($)
Small shop	25,000	10,000	40,000	40,000	22,000
Medium-sized shop	0	0	60,000	60,000	18,000
No shop	100,000	35,000	0	100,000	37,500
Probabilities	0.20	0.50	0.30		

The best payoff in a good market is 100,000, so the opportunity losses in the first column indicate how much worse each payoff is than 100,000. The best payoff in an average market is 35,000, so the opportunity losses in the second column indicate how much worse each payoff is than 35,000. The best payoff in a bad market is 0, so the opportunity losses in the third column indicate how much worse each payoff is than 0.

The minimax regret criterion considers the maximum regret for each decision, and the decision corresponding to the minimum of these is selected. The decision would be to build a small shop since the maximum regret for this is 40,000, while the maximum regret for each of the other two alternatives is higher as shown in the opportunity loss table.

The decision based on the EOL criterion would be to build the medium shop. Note that the minimum EOL ($18,000) is the same as the EVPI computed in part b. The calculations are

$$\text{EOL(small)} = (0.2)25{,}000 + (0.5)10{,}000 + (0.3)40{,}000 = 22{,}000$$
$$\text{EOL(medium)} = (0.2)0 + (0.5)0 + (0.3)60{,}000 = 18{,}000$$
$$\text{EOL(no shop)} = (0.2)100{,}000 + (0.5)35{,}000 + (0.3)0 = 37{,}500$$

Cal Bender and Becky Addison have known each other since high school. Two years ago they entered the same university and today they are taking undergraduate courses in the business school. Both hope to graduate with degrees in finance. In an attempt to make extra money and to use some of the knowledge gained from their business courses, Cal and Becky have decided to look into the possibility of starting a small company that would provide word processing services to students who needed term papers or other reports prepared in a professional manner. Using a systems approach, Cal and Becky have identified three strategies. Strategy 1 is to invest in a fairly expensive microcomputer system with a high-quality laser printer. In a favorable market, they should be able to obtain a net profit of $10,000 over the next 2 years. If the market is unfavorable, they can lose $8,000. Strategy 2 is to purchase a less expensive system. With a favorable market, they could get a return during the next 2 years of $8,000. With an unfavorable market, they would incur a loss of $4,000. Their final strategy, strategy 3, is to do nothing. Cal is basically a risk taker, whereas Becky tries to avoid risk.

a. What type of decision procedure should Cal use? What would Cal's decision be?
b. What type of decision maker is Becky? What decision would Becky make?
c. If Cal and Becky were indifferent to risk, what type of decision approach should they use? What would you recommend if this were the case?

Solution

The problem is one of decision making under uncertainty. Before answering the specific questions, a decision table should be developed showing the alternatives, states of nature, and related consequences.

ALTERNATIVE	FAVORABLE MARKET ($)	UNFAVORABLE MARKET ($)
Strategy 1	10,000	−8,000
Strategy 2	8,000	−4,000
Strategy 3	0	0

a. Since Cal is a risk taker, he should use the maximax decision criteria. This approach selects the row that has the highest or maximum value. The $10,000 value, which is the maximum value from the table, is in row 1. Thus, Cal's decision is to select strategy 1, which is an optimistic decision approach.
b. Becky should use the maximin decision criteria because she wants to avoid risk. The minimum or worst outcome for each row, or strategy, is identified. These outcomes are −$8,000 for strategy 1, −$4,000 for strategy 2, and $0 for strategy 3. The maximum of these values is selected. Thus, Becky would select strategy 3, which reflects a pessimistic decision approach.
c. If Cal and Becky are indifferent to risk, they could use the equally likely approach. This approach selects the alternative that maximizes the row averages. The row average for strategy 1 is $1,000 [i.e., $1,000 = ($10,000 − $8,000)/2]. The row average for strategy 2 is $2,000, and the row average for strategy 3 is $0. Thus, using the equally likely approach, the decision is to select strategy 2, which maximizes the row averages.

Monica Britt has enjoyed sailing small boats since she was 7 years old, when her mother started sailing with her. Today, Monica is considering the possibility of starting a company to produce small sailboats for the recreational market. Unlike other mass-produced sailboats, however, these boats will be made specifically for children between the ages of 10 and 15. The boats will be of the highest quality and extremely stable, and the sail size will be reduced to prevent problems of capsizing.

Her basic decision is whether to build a large manufacturing facility, a small manufacturing facility, or no facility at all. With a favorable market, Monica can expect to make $90,000 from the large facility or $60,000 from the smaller facility. If the market is unfavorable, however, Monica estimates that she would lose $30,000 with a large facility, and she would lose only $20,000 with the small facility. Because of the expense involved in developing the initial molds and acquiring the necessary equipment

FIGURE 14

Monica's Decision Tree, Listing Alternatives, States of Nature, Probability Values, and Financial Outcomes for Solved Problem 3

to produce fiberglass sailboats for young children, Monica has decided to conduct a pilot study to make sure that the market for the sailboats will be adequate. She estimates that the pilot study will cost her $10,000. Furthermore, the pilot study can be either favorable or unfavorable. Monica estimates that the probability of a favorable market given a favorable pilot study is 0.8. The probability of an unfavorable market given an unfavorable pilot study result is estimated to be 0.9. Monica feels that there is a 0.65 chance that the pilot study will be favorable. Of course, Monica could bypass the pilot study and simply make the decision as to whether to build a large plant, small plant, or no facility at all. Without doing any testing in a pilot study, she estimates that the probability of a favorable market is 0.6. What do you recommend? Compute the EVSI.

Solution

Before Monica starts to solve this problem, she should develop a decision tree that shows all alternatives, states of nature, probability values, and economic consequences. This decision tree is shown in Figure 14.

The EMV at each of the numbered nodes is calculated as follows:

$$\text{EMV(node 2)} = 60,000(0.6) + (-20,000)0.4 = 28,000$$
$$\text{EMV(node 3)} = 90,000(0.6) + (-30,000)0.4 = 42,000$$
$$\text{EMV(node 4)} = 50,000(0.8) + (-30,000)0.2 = 34,000$$
$$\text{EMV(node 5)} = 80,000(0.8) + (-40,000)0.2 = 56,000$$
$$\text{EMV(node 6)} = 50,000(0.1) + (-30,000)0.9 = -22,000$$
$$\text{EMV(node 7)} = 80,000(0.1) + (-40,000)0.9 = -28,000$$
$$\text{EMV(node 1)} = 56,000(0.65) + (-10,000)0.35 = 32,900$$

At each of the square nodes with letters, the decisions would be:

Node B: Choose Large Facility since the EMV = $42,000.

Node C: Choose Large Facility since the EMV = $56,000.

Node D: Choose No Facility since the EMV = −$10,000.

Node A: Choose Do Not Conduct Study since the EMV ($42,000) for this is higher than EMV(node 1), which is $32,900.

Based on the EMV criterion, Monica would select Do Not Conduct Study and then select Large Facility. The EMV of this decision is $42,000. Choosing to conduct the study would result in an EMV of only $32,900. Thus, the expected value of sample information is

$$\text{EVSI} = \$32,900 + \$10,000 - \$42,000$$
$$= \$900$$

Solved Problem 4

Developing a small driving range for golfers of all abilities has long been a desire of John Jenkins. John, however, believes that the chance of a successful driving range is only about 40%. A friend of John's has suggested that he conduct a survey in the community to get a better feeling of the demand for such a facility. There is a 0.9 probability that the research will be favorable if the driving range facility will be successful. Furthermore, it is estimated that there is a 0.8 probability that the marketing research will be unfavorable if indeed the facility will be unsuccessful. John would like to determine the chances of a successful driving range given a favorable result from the marketing survey.

Solution

This problem requires the use of Bayes' theorem. Before we start to solve the problem, we will define the following terms:

$P(\text{SF})$ = probability of successful driving range facility

$P(\text{UF})$ = probability of unsuccessful driving range facility

$P(\text{RF}|\text{SF})$ = probability that the research will be favorable given a successful driving range facility

$P(\text{RU}|\text{SF})$ = probability that the research will be unfavorable given a successful driving range facility

$P(\text{RU}|\text{UF})$ = probability that the research will be unfavorable given an unsuccessful driving range facility

$P(\text{RF}|\text{UF})$ = probability that the research will be favorable given an unsuccessful driving range facility

Now, we can summarize what we know:

$$P(\text{SF}) = 0.4$$
$$P(\text{RF}|\text{SF}) = 0.9$$
$$P(\text{RU}|\text{UF}) = 0.8$$

From this information we can compute three additional probabilities that we need to solve the problem:

$$P(\text{UF}) = 1 - P(\text{SF}) = 1 - 0.4 = 0.6$$
$$P(\text{RU}|\text{SF}) = 1 - P(\text{RF}|\text{SF}) = 1 - 0.9 = 0.1$$
$$P(\text{RF}|\text{UF}) = 1 - P(\text{RU}|\text{UF}) = 1 - 0.8 = 0.2$$

Now we can put these values into Bayes' theorem to compute the desired probability:

$$P(\text{SF}|\text{RF}) = \frac{P(\text{RF}|\text{SF}) \times P(\text{SF})}{P(\text{RF}|\text{SF}) \times P(\text{SF}) + P(\text{RF}|\text{UF}) \times P(\text{UF})}$$

$$= \frac{(0.9)(0.4)}{(0.9)(0.4) + (0.2)(0.6)}$$

$$= \frac{0.36}{(0.36 + 0.12)} = \frac{0.36}{0.48} = 0.75$$

In addition to using formulas to solve John's problem, it is possible to perform all calculations in a table:

Revised Probabilities Given a Favorable Research Result

STATE OF NATURE	CONDITIONAL PROBABILITY		PRIOR PROBABILITY		JOINT PROBABILITY	POSTERIOR PROBABILITY
Favorable market	0.9	×	0.4	=	0.36	0.36/0.48 = 0.75
Unfavorable market	0.2	×	0.6	=	0.12	0.12/0.48 = 0.25
					0.48	

As you can see from the table, the results are the same. The probability of a successful driving range given a favorable research result is 0.36/0.48, or 0.75.

Self-Test

- Before taking the self-test, refer to the learning objectives at the beginning of the chapter, the notes in the margins, and the glossary at the end of the chapter.
- Use the key at the end of the chapter to correct your answers.
- Restudy pages that correspond to any questions that you answered incorrectly or material you feel uncertain about.

1. In decision theory terminology, a course of action or a strategy that may be chosen by a decision maker is called
   a. a payoff.
   b. an alternative.
   c. a state of nature.
   d. none of the above.

2. In decision theory, probabilities are associated with
   a. payoffs.
   b. alternatives.
   c. states of nature.
   d. none of the above.

3. If probabilities are available to the decision maker, then the decision-making environment is called
   a. certainty.
   b. uncertainty.
   c. risk.
   d. none of the above.

4. Which of the following is a decision-making criterion that is used for decision making under risk?
   a. expected monetary value criterion
   b. Hurwicz criterion (criterion of realism)
   c. optimistic (maximax) criterion
   d. equally likely criterion

5. The minimum expected opportunity loss is
   a. equal to the highest expected payoff.
   b. greater than the expected value with perfect information.
   c. equal to the expected value of perfect information.
   d. computed when finding the minimax regret decision.

6. In using the criterion of realism (Hurwicz criterion), the coefficient of realism (α)
   a. is the probability of a good state of nature.

   b. describes the degree of optimism of the decision maker.
   c. describes the degree of pessimism of the decision maker.
   d. is usually less than zero.

7. The most that a person should pay for perfect information is
   a. the EVPI.
   b. the maximum EMV minus the minimum EMV.
   c. the maximum EOL.
   d. the maximum EMV.

8. The minimum EOL criterion will always result in the same decision as
   a. the maximax criterion.
   b. the minimax regret criterion.
   c. the maximum EMV criterion.
   d. the equally likely criterion.

9. A decision tree is preferable to a decision table when
   a. a number of sequential decisions are to be made.
   b. probabilities are available.
   c. the maximax criterion is used.
   d. the objective is to maximize regret.

10. Bayes' theorem is used to revise probabilities. The new (revised) probabilities are called
    a. prior probabilities.
    b. sample probabilities.
    c. survey probabilities.
    d. posterior probabilities.

11. On a decision tree, at each state-of-nature node,
    a. the alternative with the greatest EMV is selected.
    b. an EMV is calculated.
    c. all probabilities are added together.
    d. the branch with the highest probability is selected.

12. The EVSI
    a. is found by subtracting the EMV without sample information from the EMV with sample information.
    b. is always equal to the expected value of perfect information.
    c. equals the EMV with sample information assuming no cost for the information minus the EMV without sample information.
    d. is usually negative.
13. The efficiency of sample information
    a. is the EVSI/(maximum EMV without SI) expressed as a percentage.
    b. is the EVPI/EVSI expressed as a percentage.
    c. would be 100% if the sample information were perfect.
    d. is computed using only the EVPI and the maximum EMV.
14. On a decision tree, once the tree has been drawn and the payoffs and probabilities have been placed on the tree,

the analysis (computing EMVs and selecting the best alternative)
    a. working backward (starting on the right and moving to the left).
    b. working forward (starting on the left and moving to the right).
    c. starting at the top of the tree and moving down.
    d. starting at the bottom of the tree and moving up.
15. In assessing utility values,
    a. the worst outcome is given a utility of -1.
    b. the best outcome is given a utility of 0.
    c. the worst outcome is given a utility of 0.
    d. the best outcome is given a value of -1.
16. If a rational person selects an alternative that does not maximize the EMV, we would expect that this alternative
    a. minimizes the EMV.
    b. maximizes the expected utility.
    c. minimizes the expected utility.
    d. has zero utility associated with each possible payoff.

Discussion Questions and Problems

Discussion Questions

1 Give an example of a good decision that you made that resulted in a bad outcome. Also give an example of a bad decision that you made that had a good outcome. Why was each decision good or bad?

2 Describe what is involved in the decision process.

3 What is an alternative? What is a state of nature?

4 Discuss the differences among decision making under certainty, decision making under risk, and decision making under uncertainty.

5 What techniques are used to solve decision-making problems under uncertainty? Which technique results in an optimistic decision? Which technique results in a pessimistic decision?

6 Define *opportunity loss*. What decision-making criteria are used with an opportunity loss table?

7 What information should be placed on a decision tree?

8 Describe how you would determine the best decision using the EMV criterion with a decision tree.

9 What is the difference between prior and posterior probabilities?

10 What is the purpose of Bayesian analysis? Describe how you would use Bayesian analysis in the decision-making process.

11 What is the EVSI? How is this computed?

12 How is the efficiency of sample information computed?

13 What is the overall purpose of utility theory?

14 Briefly discuss how a utility function can be assessed. What is a standard gamble, and how is it used in determining utility values?

15 How is a utility curve used in selecting the best decision for a particular problem?

16 What is a risk seeker? What is a risk avoider? How does the utility curve for these types of decision makers differ?

Problems

Q• 17 Kenneth Brown is the principal owner of Brown Oil, Inc. After quitting his university teaching job, Ken has been able to increase his annual salary by a factor of over 100. At the present time, Ken is forced to consider purchasing some more equipment for Brown Oil because of competition. His alternatives are shown in the following table:

EQUIPMENT	FAVORABLE MARKET ($)	UNFAVORABLE MARKET ($)
Sub 100	300,000	−200,000
Oiler J	250,000	−100,000
Texan	75,000	−18,000

For example, if Ken purchases a Sub 100 and if there is a favorable market, he will realize a profit of $300,000. On the other hand, if the market is

Note: Q means the problem may be solved with QM for Windows; ✗ means the problem may be solved with Excel QM; and Q means the problem may be solved with QM for Windows and/or Excel QM.

111

unfavorable, Ken will suffer a loss of $200,000. But Ken has always been a very optimistic decision maker.

(a) What type of decision is Ken facing?
(b) What decision criterion should he use?
(c) What alternative is best?

18 Although Ken Brown (discussed in Problem 17) is the principal owner of Brown Oil, his brother Bob is credited with making the company a financial success. Bob is vice president of finance. Bob attributes his success to his pessimistic attitude about business and the oil industry. Given the information from Problem 17, it is likely that Bob will arrive at a different decision. What decision criterion should Bob use, and what alternative will he select?

19 The *Lubricant* is an expensive oil newsletter to which many oil giants subscribe, including Ken Brown (see Problem 17 for details). In the last issue, the letter described how the demand for oil products would be extremely high. Apparently, the American consumer will continue to use oil products even if the price of these products doubles. Indeed, one of the articles in the *Lubricant* states that the chances of a favorable market for oil products was 70%, while the chance of an unfavorable market was only 30%. Ken would like to use these probabilities in determining the best decision.

(a) What decision model should be used?
(b) What is the optimal decision?
(c) Ken believes that the $300,000 figure for the Sub 100 with a favorable market is too high. How much lower would this figure have to be for Ken to change his decision made in part *b*?

20 Mickey Lawson is considering investing some money that he inherited. The following payoff table gives the profits that would be realized during the next year for each of three investment alternatives Mickey is considering:

DECISION ALTERNATIVE	STATE OF NATURE	
	GOOD ECONOMY	POOR ECONOMY
Stock market	80,000	−20,000
Bonds	30,000	20,000
CDs	23,000	23,000
Probability	0.5	0.5

(a) What decision would maximize expected profits?
(b) What is the maximum amount that should be paid for a perfect forecast of the economy?

21 Develop an opportunity loss table for the investment problem that Mickey Lawson faces in Problem 20. What decision would minimize the expected opportunity loss? What is the minimum EOL?

22 Allen Young has always been proud of his personal investment strategies and has done very well over the past several years. He invests primarily in the stock market. Over the past several months, however, Allen has become very concerned about the stock market as a good investment. In some cases, it would have been better for Allen to have his money in a bank than in the market. During the next year, Allen must decide whether to invest $10,000 in the stock market or in a certificate of deposit (CD) at an interest rate of 9%. If the market is good, Allen believes that he could get a 14% return on his money. With a fair market, he expects to get an 8% return. If the market is bad, he will most likely get no return at all—in other words, the return would be 0%. Allen estimates that the probability of a good market is 0.4, the probability of a fair market is 0.4, and the probability of a bad market is 0.2, and he wishes to maximize his long-run average return.

(a) Develop a decision table for this problem.
(b) What is the best decision?

23 In Problem 22, you helped Allen Young determine the best investment strategy. Now, Young is thinking about paying for a stock market newsletter. A friend of Young said that these types of letters could predict very accurately whether the market would be good, fair, or poor. Then, based on these predictions, Allen could make better investment decisions.

(a) What is the most that Allen would be willing to pay for a newsletter?
(b) Young now believes that a good market will give a return of only 11% instead of 14%. Will this information change the amount that Allen would be willing to pay for the newsletter? If your answer is yes, determine the most that Allen would be willing to pay, given this new information.

24 Today's Electronics specializes in manufacturing modern electronic components. It also builds the equipment that produces the components. Phyllis Weinberger, who is responsible for advising the president of Today's Electronics on electronic manufacturing equipment, has developed the following table concerning a proposed facility:

	PROFIT ($)		
	STRONG MARKET	FAIR MARKET	POOR MARKET
Large facility	550,000	110,000	−310,000
Medium-sized facility	300,000	129,000	−100,000
Small facility	200,000	100,000	−32,000
No facility	0	0	0

(a) Develop an opportunity loss table.
(b) What is the minimax regret decision?

25 Brilliant Color is a small supplier of chemicals and equipment that are used by some photographic stores to process 35mm film. One product that Brilliant Color supplies is BC-6. John Kubick, president of Brilliant Color, normally stocks 11, 12, or 13 cases of BC-6 each week. For each case that John sells, he receives a profit of $35. Like many photographic chemicals, BC-6 has a very short shelf life, so if a case is not sold by the end of the week, John must discard it. Since each case costs John $56, he loses $56 for every case that is not sold by the end of the week. There is a probability of 0.45 of selling 11 cases, a probability of 0.35 of selling 12 cases, and a probability of 0.2 of selling 13 cases.

(a) Construct a decision table for this problem. Include all conditional values and probabilities in the table.

(b) What is your recommended course of action?

(c) If John is able to develop BC-6 with an ingredient that stabilizes it so that it no longer has to be discarded, how would this change your recommended course of action?

26 Megley Cheese Company is a small manufacturer of several different cheese products. One of the products is a cheese spread that is sold to retail outlets. Jason Megley must decide how many cases of cheese spread to manufacture each month. The probability that the demand will be six cases is 0.1, seven cases is 0.3, eight cases is 0.5, and nine cases is 0.1. The cost of every case is $45, and the price that Jason gets for each case is $95. Unfortunately, any cases not sold by the end of the month are of no value, due to spoilage. How many cases of cheese should Jason manufacture each month?

27 Farm Grown, Inc., produces cases of perishable food products. Each case contains an assortment of vegetables and other farm products. Each case costs $5 and sells for $15. If there are any cases not sold by the end of the day, they are sold to a large food processing company for $3 a case. The probability that daily demand will be 100 cases is 0.3, the probability that daily demand will be 200 cases is 0.4, and the probability that daily demand will be 300 cases is 0.3. Farm Grown has a policy of always satisfying customer demands. If its own supply of cases is less than the demand, it buys the necessary vegetables from a competitor. The estimated cost of doing this is $16 per case.

(a) Draw a decision table for this problem.

(b) What do you recommend?

28 In Problem 27, Farm Grown, Inc. has reason to believe the probabilities may not be reliable due to changing conditions. If these probabilities are ignored, what decision would be made using the optimistic criterion? What decision would be made using the pessimistic criterion?

29 Mick Karra is the manager of MCZ Drilling Products, which produces a variety of specialty valves for oil field equipment. Recent activity in the oil fields has caused demand to increase drastically, and a decision has been made to open a new manufacturing facility. Three locations are being considered, and the size of the facility would not be the same in each location. Thus, overtime might be necessary at times. The following table gives the total monthly cost (in $1,000s) for each possible location under each demand possibility. The probabilities for the demand levels have been determined to be 20% for low demand, 30% for medium demand, and 50% for high demand.

	DEMAND IS LOW	DEMAND IS MEDIUM	DEMAND IS HIGH
Ardmore, OK	85	110	150
Sweetwater, TX	90	100	120
Lake Charles, LA	110	120	130

(a) Which location would be selected based on the optimistic criterion?

(b) Which location would be selected based on the pessimistic criterion?

(c) Which location would be selected based on the minimax regret criterion?

(d) Which location should be selected to minimize the expected cost of operation?

(e) How much is a perfect forecast of the demand worth?

(f) Which location would minimize the expected opportunity loss?

(g) What is the expected value of perfect information in this situation?

30 Even though independent gasoline stations have been having a difficult time, Susan Solomon has been thinking about starting her own independent gasoline station. Susan's problem is to decide how large her station should be. The annual returns will depend on both the size of her station and a number of marketing factors related to the oil industry and demand for gasoline. After a careful analysis, Susan developed the following table:

SIZE OF FIRST STATION	GOOD MARKET ($)	FAIR MARKET ($)	POOR MARKET ($)
Small	50,000	20,000	−10,000
Medium	80,000	30,000	−20,000
Large	100,000	30,000	−40,000
Very large	300,000	25,000	−160,000

For example, if Susan constructs a small station and the market is good, she will realize a profit of $50,000.

(a) Develop a decision table for this decision.
(b) What is the maximax decision?
(c) What is the maximin decision?
(d) What is the equally likely decision?
(e) What is the criterion of realism decision? Use an α value of 0.8.
(f) Develop an opportunity loss table.
(g) What is the minimax regret decision?

31 Beverly Mills has decided to lease a hybrid car to save on gasoline expenses and to do her part to help keep the environment clean. The car she selected is available from only one dealer in the local area, but that dealer has several leasing options to accommodate a variety of driving patterns. All the leases are for 3 years and require no money at the time of signing the lease. The first option has a monthly cost of $330, a total mileage allowance of 36,000 miles (an average of 12,000 miles per year), and a cost of $0.35 per mile for any miles over 36,000. The following table summarizes each of the three lease options:

3-YEAR LEASE	MONTHLY COST	MILEAGE ALLOWANCE	COST PER EXCESS MILE
Option 1	$330	36,000	$0.35
Option 2	$380	45,000	$0.25
Option 3	$430	54,000	$0.15

Beverly has estimated that, during the 3 years of the lease, there is a 40% chance she will drive an average of 12,000 miles per year, a 30% chance she will drive an average of 15,000 miles per year, and a 30% chance that she will drive 18,000 miles per year. In evaluating these lease options, Beverly would like to keep her costs as low as possible.

(a) Develop a payoff (cost) table for this situation.
(b) What decision would Beverly make if she were optimistic?
(c) What decision would Beverly make if she were pessimistic?
(d) What decision would Beverly make if she wanted to minimize her expected cost (monetary value)?
(e) Calculate the expected value of perfect information for this problem.

32 Refer to the leasing decision facing Beverly Mills in Problem 31. Develop the opportunity loss table for this situation. Which option would be chosen based on the minimax regret criterion? Which alternative would result in the lowest expected opportunity loss?

33 The game of roulette is popular in many casinos around the world. In Las Vegas, a typical roulette wheel has the numbers 1–36 in slots on the wheel. Half of these slots are red, and the other half are black. In the United States, the roulette wheel typically also has the numbers 0 (zero) and 00 (double zero), and both of these are on the wheel in green slots. Thus, there are 38 slots on the wheel. The dealer spins the wheel and sends a small ball in the opposite direction of the spinning wheel. As the wheel slows, the ball falls into one of the slots, and that is the winning number and color. One of the bets available is simply red or black, for which the odds are 1 to 1. If the player bets on either red or black, and that happens to be the winning color, the player wins the amount of her bet. For example, if the player bets $5 on red and wins, she is paid $5 and she still has her original bet. On the other hand, if the winning color is black or green when the player bets red, the player loses the entire bet.

(a) What is the probability that a player who bets red will win the bet?
(b) If a player bets $10 on red every time the game is played, what is the expected monetary value (expected win)?
(c) In Europe, there is usually no 00 on the wheel, just the 0. With this type of game, what is the probability that a player who bets red will win the bet? If a player bets $10 on red every time in this game (with no 00), what is the expected monetary value?
(d) Since the expected profit (win) in a roulette game is negative, why would a rational person play the game?

34 Refer to the Problem 33 for details about the game of roulette. Another bet in a roulette game is called a "straight up" bet, which means that the player is betting that the winning number will be the number that she chose. In a game with 0 and 00, there are a total of 38 possible outcomes (the numbers 1 to 36 plus 0 and 00), and each of these has the same chance of occurring. The payout on this type of bet is 35 to 1, which means the player is paid 35 and gets to keep the original bet. If a player bets $10 on the number 7 (or any single number), what is the expected monetary value (expected win)?

35 The Technically Techno company has several patents for a variety of different Flash memory devices that are used in computers, cell phones, and a variety of other things. A competitor has recently introduced a product based on technology very similar to something patented by Technically Techno last year. Consequently, Technically Techno has sued the other company for copyright infringement. Based on the facts in the case as well as the record of the lawyers involved, Technically Techno believes there is a 40%

chance that it will be awarded $300,000 if the lawsuit goes to court. There is a 30% chance that they would be awarded only $50,000 if they go to court and win, and there is a 30% chance they would lose the case and be awarded nothing. The estimated cost of legal fees if they go to court is $50,000. However, the other company has offered to pay Technically Techno $75,000 to settle the dispute without going to court. The estimated legal cost of this would only be $10,000. If Technically Techno wished to maximize the expected gain, should they accept the settlement offer?

36 A group of medical professionals is considering the construction of a private clinic. If the medical demand is high (i.e., there is a favorable market for the clinic), the physicians could realize a net profit of $100,000. If the market is not favorable, they could lose $40,000. Of course, they don't have to proceed at all, in which case there is no cost. In the absence of any market data, the best the physicians can guess is that there is a 50–50 chance the clinic will be successful. Construct a decision tree to help analyze this problem. What should the medical professionals do?

37 The physicians in Problem 36 have been approached by a market research firm that offers to perform a study of the market at a fee of $5,000. The market researchers claim their experience enables them to use Bayes' theorem to make the following statements of probability:

probability of a favorable market given
a favorable study = 0.82

probability of an unfavorable market given
a favorable study = 0.18

probability of a favorable market given
an unfavorable study = 0.11

probability of an unfavorable market given
an unfavorable study = 0.89

probability of a favorable research study = 0.55

probability of an unfavorable research study = 0.45

(a) Develop a new decision tree for the medical professionals to reflect the options now open with the market study.
(b) Use the EMV approach to recommend a strateg
(c) What is the expected value of sample informa... tion? How much might the physicians be willing to pay for a market study?
(d) Calculate the efficiency of this sample information.

38 Jerry Smith is thinking about opening a bicycle shop in his hometown. Jerry loves to take his own bike on 50-mile trips with his friends, but he believes that any small business should be started only if there is

a good chance of making a profit. Jerry can open a small shop, a large shop, or no shop at all. The profits will depend on the size of the shop and whether the market is favorable or unfavorable for his products. Because there will be a 5-year lease on the building that Jerry is thinking about using, he wants to make sure that he makes the correct decision. Jerry is also thinking about hiring his old marketing professor to conduct a marketing research study. If the study is conducted, the study could be favorable (i.e., predicting a favorable market) or unfavorable (i.e., predicting an unfavorable market). Develop a decision tree for Jerry.

39 Jerry Smith (see Problem 38) has done some analysis about the profitability of the bicycle shop. If Jerry builds the large bicycle shop, he will earn $60,000 if the market is favorable, but he will lose $40,000 if the market is unfavorable. The small shop will return a $30,000 profit in a favorable market and a $10,000 loss in an unfavorable market. At the present time, he believes that there is a 50–50 chance that the market will be favorable. His old marketing professor will charge him $5,000 for the marketing research. It is estimated that there is a 0.6 probability that the survey will be favorable. Furthermore, there is a 0.9 probability that the market will be favorable given a favorable outcome from the study. However, the marketing professor has warned Jerry that there is only a probability of 0.12 of a favorable market if the marketing research results are not favorable. Jerry is confused.

(a) Should Jerry use the marketing research?
(b) Jerry, however, is unsure the 0.6 probability of a favorable marketing research study is correct. How sensitive is Jerry's decision to this probability value? How far can this probability value deviate from 0.6 without causing Jerry to change his decision?

40 Bill Holliday is not sure what she should do. He can build a quadplex (i.e., a building with four apartments), build a duplex, gather additional information, or simply do nothing. If he gathers additional information, the results could be either favorable or unfavorable, but it would cost him $3,000 to gather the information. Bill believes that there is a 50–50 chance that the information will be favorable. If the rental market is favorable, Bill will earn $15,000 with the quadplex or $5,000 with the duplex. Bill doesn't have the financial resources to do both. With an unfavorable rental market, however, Bill could lose $20,000 with the quadplex or $10,000 with the duplex. Without gathering additional information, Bill estimates that the probability of a favorable rental market is 0.7. A favorable report from the study would increase the probability of a favorable

rental market to 0.9. Furthermore, an unfavorable report from the additional information would decrease the probability of a favorable rental market to 0.4. Of course, Bill could forget all of these numbers and do nothing. What is your advice to Bill?

41 Peter Martin is going to help his brother who wants to open a food store. Peter initially believes that there is a 50–50 chance that his brother's food store would be a success. Peter is considering doing a market research study. Based on historical data, there is a 0.8 probability that the marketing research will be favorable given a successful food store. Moreover, there is a 0.7 probability that the marketing research will be unfavorable given an unsuccessful food store.

(a) If the marketing research is favorable, what is Peter's revised probability of a successful food store for his brother?

(b) If the marketing research is unfavorable, what is Peter's revised probability of a successful food store for his brother?

(c) If the initial probability of a successful food store is 0.60 (instead of 0.50), find the probabilities in parts a and b.

42 Mark Martinko has been a class A racquetball player for the past 5 years, and one of his biggest goals is to own and operate a racquetball facility. Unfortunately, Mark's thinks that the chance of a successful racquetball facility is only 30%. Mark's lawyer has recommended that he employ one of the local marketing research groups to conduct a survey concerning the success or failure of a racquetball facility. There is a 0.8 probability that the research will be favorable given a successful racquetball facility. In addition, there is a 0.7 probability that the research will be unfavorable given an unsuccessful facility. Compute revised probabilities of a successful racquetball facility given a favorable and given an unfavorable survey.

43 A financial advisor has recommended two possible mutual funds for investment: Fund A and Fund B. The return that will be achieved by each of these depends on whether the economy is good, fair, or poor. A payoff table has been constructed to illustrate this situation:

| | STATE OF NATURE | | |
INVESTMENT	GOOD ECONOMY	FAIR ECONOMY	POOR ECONOMY
Fund A	$10,000	$2,000	−$5,000
Fund B	$6,000	$4,000	0
Probability	0.2	0.3	0.5

(a) Draw the decision tree to represent this situation.

(b) Perform the necessary calculations to determine which of the two mutual funds is better. Which one should you choose to maximize the expected value?

(c) Suppose there is question about the return of Fund A in a good economy. It could be higher or

lower than $10,000. What value for this would cause a person to be indifferent between Fund A and Fund B (i.e., the EMVs would be the same)?

44 Jim Sellers is thinking about producing a new type of electric razor for men. If the market were favorable, he would get a return of $100,000, but if the market for this new type of razor were unfavorable, he would lose $60,000. Since Ron Bush is a good friend of Jim Sellers, Jim is considering the possibility of using Bush Marketing Research to gather additional information about the market for the razor. Ron has suggested that Jim use either a survey or a pilot study to test the market. The survey would be a sophisticated questionnaire administered to a test market. It will cost $5,000. Another alternative is to run a pilot study. This would involve producing a limited number of the new razors and trying to sell them in two cities that are typical of American cities. The pilot study is more accurate but is also more expensive. It will cost $20,000. Ron Bush has suggested that it would be a good idea for Jim to conduct either the survey or the pilot before Jim makes the decision concerning whether to produce the new razor. But Jim is not sure if the value of the survey or the pilot is worth the cost.

Jim estimates that the probability of a successful market without performing a survey or pilot study is 0.5. Furthermore, the probability of a favorable survey result given a favorable market for razors is 0.7, and the probability of a favorable survey result given an unsuccessful market for razors is 0.2. In addition, the probability of an unfavorable pilot study given an unfavorable market is 0.9, and the probability of an unsuccessful pilot study result given a favorable market for razors is 0.2.

(a) Draw the decision tree for this problem without the probability values.

(b) Compute the revised probabilities needed to complete the decision, and place these values in the decision tree.

(c) What is the best decision for Jim? Use EMV as the decision criterion.

45 Jim Sellers has been able to estimate his utility for a number of different values. He would like to use these utility values in making the decision in Problem 44: $U(-\$80,000) = 0$, $U(-\$65,000) = 0.5$, $U(-\$60,000) = 0.55$, $U(-\$20,000) = 0.7$, $U(-\$5,000) = 0.8$, $U(\$0) = 0.81$, $U(\$80,000) = 0.9$, $U(\$95,000) = 0.95$, and $U(\$100,000) = 1$. Resolve Problem 44 using utility values. Is Jim a risk avoider?

46. Two states of nature exist for a particular situation: a good economy and a poor economy. An economic study may be performed to obtain more information about which of these will actually occur in the coming year. The study may forecast either a good

economy or a poor economy. Currently there is a 60% chance that the economy will be good and a 40% chance that it will be poor. In the past, whenever the economy was good, the economic study predicted it would be good 80% of the time. (The other 20% of the time the prediction was wrong.) In the past, whenever the economy was poor, the economic study predicted it would be poor 90% of the time. (The other 10% of the time the prediction was wrong.)

(a) Use Bayes' theorem and find the following:

P(good economy | prediction of good economy)

P(poor economy | prediction of good economy)

P(good economy | prediction of poor economy)

P(poor economy | prediction of poor economy)

(b) Suppose the initial (prior) probability of a good economy is 70% (instead of 60%), and the probability of a poor economy is 30% (instead of 40%). Find the posterior probabilities in part a based on these new values.

47 The Long Island Life Insurance Company sells a term life insurance policy. If the policy holder dies during the term of the policy, the company pays $100,000. If the person does not die, the company pays out nothing and there is no further value to the policy. The company uses actuarial tables to determine the probability that a person with certain characteristics will die during the coming year. For a particular individual, it is determined that there is a 0.001 chance that the person will die in the next year and a 0.999 chance that the person will live and the company will pay out nothing. The cost of this policy is $200 per year. Based on the EMV criterion, should the individual buy this insurance policy? How would utility theory help explain why a person would buy this insurance policy?

48 In Problem 37, you helped the medical professionals analyze their decision using expected monetary value as the decision criterion. This group has also assessed their utility for money: $U(-\$45,000) = 0$, $U(-\$40,000) = 0.1$, $U(-\$5,000) = 0.7$, $U(\$0) = 0.9$, $U(\$95,000) = 0.99$, and $U(\$100,000) = 1$. Use expected utility as the decision criterion, and determine the best decision for the medical professionals. Are the medical professionals risk seekers or risk avoiders?

49 In this chapter, a decision tree was developed for John Thompson (see Figure 5 for the complete decision tree analysis). After completing the analysis, John was not completely sure that he is indifferent to risk. After going through a number of standard gambles, John was able to assess his utility for money. Here are some of the utility assessments:

$U(-\$190,000) = 0$, $U(-\$180,000) = 0.05$,
$U(-\$30,000) = 0.10$, $U(-\$20,000) = 0.15$,
$U(-\$10,000) = 0.2$, $U(\$0) = 0.3$, $U(\$90,000) =$

0.15, $U(\$100,000) = 0.6$, $U(\$190,000) = 0.95$, and $U(\$200,000) = 1.0$. If John maximizes his expected utility, does his decision change?

50 In the past few years, the traffic problems in Lynn McKell's hometown have gotten worse. Now, Broad Street is congested about half the time. The normal travel time to work for Lynn is only 15 minutes when Broad Street is used and there is no congestion. With congestion, however, it takes Lynn 40 minutes to get to work. If Lynn decides to take the expressway, it will take 30 minutes regardless of the traffic conditions. Lynn's utility for travel time is: $U(15 \text{ minutes}) = 0.9$, $U(30 \text{ minutes}) = 0.7$, and $U(40 \text{ minutes}) = 0.2$.

(a) Which route will minimize Lynn's expected travel time?
(b) Which route will maximize Lynn's utility?
(c) When it comes to travel time, is Lynn a risk seeker or a risk avoider?

51 Coren Chemical, Inc., develops industrial chemicals that are used by other manufacturers to produce photographic chemicals, preservatives, and lubricants. One of their products, K-1000, is used by several photographic companies to make a chemical that is used in the film-developing process. To produce K-1000 efficiently, Coren Chemical uses the batch approach, in which a certain number of gallons is produced at one time. This reduces setup costs and allows Coren Chemical to produce K-1000 at a competitive price. Unfortunately, K-1000 has a very short shelf life of about 1 month.

Coren Chemical produces K-1000 in batches of 500 gallons, 1,000 gallons, 1,500 gallons, and 2,000 gallons. Using historical data, David Coren was able to determine that the probability of selling 500 gallons of K-1000 is 0.2. The probabilities of selling 1,000, 1,500, and 2,000 gallons are 0.3, 0.4, and 0.1, respectively. The question facing David is how many gallons to produce of K-1000 in the next batch run. K-1000 sells for $20 per gallon. Manufacturing cost is $12 per gallon, and handling costs and warehousing costs are estimated to be $1 per gallon. In the past, David has allocated advertising costs to K-1000 at $3 per gallon. If K-1000 is not sold after the batch run, the chemical loses much of its important properties as a developer. It can, however, be sold at a salvage value of $13 per gallon. Furthermore, David has guaranteed to his suppliers that there will always be an adequate supply of K-1000. If David does run out, he has agreed to purchase a comparable chemical from a competitor at $25 per gallon. David sells all of the chemical at $20 per gallon, so his shortage means that David loses the $5 to buy the more expensive chemical.

(a) Develop a decision tree of this problem.
(b) What is the best solution?
(c) Determine the expected value of perfect information.

52 The Jamis Corporation is involved with waste management. During the past 10 years it has become one of the largest waste disposal companies in the Midwest, serving primarily Wisconsin, Illinois, and Michigan. Bob Jamis, president of the company, is considering the possibility of establishing a waste treatment plant in Mississippi. From past experience, Bob believes that a small plant in northern Mississippi would yield a $500,000 profit regardless of the market for the facility. The success of a medium-sized waste treatment plant would depend on the market. With a low demand for waste treatment, Bob expects a $200,000 return. A medium demand would yield a $700,000 return in Bob's estimation, and a high demand would return $800,000. Although a large facility is much riskier, the potential return is much greater. With a high demand for waste treatment in Mississippi, the large facility should return a million dollars. With a medium demand, the large facility will return only $400,000. Bob estimates that the large facility would be a big loser if there were a low demand for waste treatment. He estimates that he would lose approximately $200,000 with a large treatment facility if demand were indeed low. Looking at the economic conditions for the upper part of the state of Mississippi and using his experience in the field, Bob estimates that the probability of a low demand for treatment plants is 0.15. The probability for a medium-demand facility is approximately 0.40, and the probability of a high demand for a waste treatment facility is 0.45.

Because of the large potential investment and the possibility of a loss, Bob has decided to hire a market research team that is based in Jackson, Mississippi. This team will perform a survey to get a better feeling for the probability of a low, medium, or high demand for a waste treatment facility. The cost of the survey is $50,000. To help Bob determine whether to go ahead with the survey, the marketing research firm has provided Bob with the following information:

P(survey results | possible outcomes)

	SURVEY RESULTS		
POSSIBLE OUTCOME	LOW SURVEY RESULTS	MEDIUM SURVEY RESULTS	HIGH SURVEY RESULTS
Low demand	0.7	0.2	0.1
Medium demand	0.4	0.5	0.1
High demand	0.1	0.3	0.6

As you see, the survey could result in three possible outcomes. Low survey results mean that a low demand is likely. In a similar fashion, medium survey results or high survey results would mean a medium or a high demand, respectively. What should Bob do?

53 Mary is considering opening a new grocery store in town. She is evaluating three sites: downtown, the mall, and out at the busy traffic circle. Mary calculated the value of successful stores at these locations as follows: downtown, $250,000; the mall, $300,000; the circle, $400,000. Mary calculated the losses if unsuccessful to be $100,000 at either downtown or the mall and $200,000 at the circle. Mary figures her chance of success to be 50% downtown, 60% at the mall, and 75% at the traffic circle.

(a) Draw a decision tree for Mary and select her best alternative.

(b) Mary has been approached by a marketing research firm that offers to study the area to determine if another grocery store is needed. The cost of this study is $30,000. Mary believes there is a 60% chance that the survey results will be positive (show a need for another grocery store). SRP = survey results positive, SRN = survey results negative, SD = success downtown, SM = success at mall, SC = success at circle, SD' = don't succeed downtown, and so on. For studies of this nature:
$P(\text{SRP} \mid \text{success}) = 0.7$,
$P(\text{SRN} \mid \text{success}) = 0.3$,
$P(\text{SRP} \mid \text{not success}) = 0.2$; and
$P(\text{SRN} \mid \text{not success}) = 0.8$.
Calculate the revised probabilities for success (and not success) for each location, depending on survey results.

(c) How much is the marketing research worth to Mary? Calculate the EVSI.

54. Sue Reynolds has to decide if she should get information (at a cost of $20,000) to invest in a retail store. If she gets the information, there is a 0.6 probability that the information will be favorable and a 0.4 probability that the information will not be favorable. If the information is favorable, there is a 0.9 probability that the store will be a success. If the information is not favorable, the probability of a successful store is only 0.2. Without any information, Sue estimates that the probability of a successful store will be 0.6. A successful store will give a return of $100,000. If the store is built but is not successful, Sue will see a loss of $80,000. Of course, she could always decide not to build the retail store.

(a) What do you recommend?

(b) What impact would a 0.7 probability of obtaining favorable information have on Sue's decision? The probability of obtaining unfavorable information would be 0.3.

(c) Sue believes that the probabilities of a successful and an unsuccessful retail store given favorable information might be 0.8 and 0.2, respectively, instead of 0.9 and 0.1, respectively. What impact, if any, would this have on Sue's decision and the best EMV?

(d) Sue had to pay $20,000 to get information. Would her decision change if the cost of the information increased to $30,000?

(e) Using the data in this problem and the following utility table, compute the expected utility. Is this the curve of a risk seeker or a risk avoider?

MONETARY VALUE	UTILITY
$100,000	1
$80,000	0.4
$0	0.2
−$20,000	0.1
−$80,000	0.05
−$100,000	0

(f) Compute the expected utility given the following utility table. Does this utility table represent a risk seeker or a risk avoider?

MONETARY VALUE	UTILITY
$100,000	1
$80,000	0.9
$0	0.8
−$20,000	0.6
−$80,000	0.4
−$100,000	0

Internet Homework Problems

See our Internet home page, at www.pearsonhighered.com/render, for additional homework problems, Problems 55 to 60.

Case Study

Starting Right Corporation

After watching a movie about a young woman who quit a successful corporate career to start her own baby food company, Julia Day decided that she wanted to do the same. In the movie, the baby food company was very successful. Julia knew, however, that it is much easier to make a movie about a successful woman starting her own company than to actually do it. The product had to be of the highest quality, and Julia had to get the best people involved to launch the new company. Julia resigned from her job and launched her new company—Starting Right.

Julia decided to target the upper end of the baby food market by producing baby food that contained no preservatives but had a great taste. Although the price would be slightly higher than for existing baby food, Julia believed that parents would be willing to pay more for a high-quality baby food. Instead of putting baby food in jars, which would require preservatives to stabilize the food, Julia decided to try a new approach. The baby food would be frozen. This would allow for natural ingredients, no preservatives, and outstanding nutrition.

Getting good people to work for the new company was also important. Julia decided to find people with experience in finance, marketing, and production to get involved with Starting Right. With her enthusiasm and charisma, Julia was able to find such a group. Their first step was to develop prototypes of the new frozen baby food and to perform a small pilot test of the new product. The pilot test received rave reviews.

The final key to getting the young company off to a good start was to raise funds. Three options were considered:

corporate bonds, preferred stock, and common stock. Julia decided that each investment should be in blocks of $30,000. Furthermore, each investor should have an annual income of at least $40,000 and a net worth of $100,000 to be eligible to invest in Starting Right. Corporate bonds would return 13% per year for the next 5 years. Julia furthermore guaranteed that investors in the corporate bonds would get at least $20,000 back at the end of 5 years. Investors in preferred stock should see their initial investment increase by a factor of 4 with a good market or see the investment worth only half of the initial investment with an unfavorable market. The common stock had the greatest potential. The initial investment was expected to increase by a factor of 8 with a good market, but investors would lose everything if the market was unfavorable. During the next 5 years, it was expected that inflation would increase by a factor of 4.5% each year.

Discussion Questions

1. Sue Pansky, a retired elementary school teacher, is considering investing in Starting Right. She is very conservative and is a risk avoider. What do you recommend?
2. Ray Cahn, who is currently a commodities broker, is also considering an investment, although he believes that there is only an 11% chance of success. What do you recommend?
3. Lila Battle has decided to invest in Starting Right. While she believes that Julia has a good chance of being

119

successful, Lila is a risk avoider and very conservative. What is your advice to Lila?

4. George Yates believes that there is an equally likely chance for success. What is your recommendation?

5. Peter Metarko is extremely optimistic about the market for the new baby food. What is your advice for Pete?

6. Julia Day has been told that developing the legal documents for each fundraising alternative is expensive. Julia would like to offer alternatives for both risk-averse and risk-seeking investors. Can Julia delete one of the financial alternatives and still offer investment choices for risk seekers and risk avoiders?

Case Study

Blake Electronics

In 1979, Steve Blake founded Blake Electronics in Long Beach, California, to manufacture resistors, capacitors, inductors, and other electronic components. During the Vietnam War, Steve was a radio operator, and it was during this time that he became proficient at repairing radios and other communications equipment. Steve viewed his 4-year experience with the army with mixed feelings. He hated army life, but this experience gave him the confidence and the initiative to start his own electronics firm.

Over the years, Steve kept the business relatively unchanged. By 1992, total annual sales were in excess of $2 million. In 1996, Steve's son, Jim, joined the company after finishing high school and 2 years of courses in electronics at Long Beach Community College. Jim was always aggressive in high school athletics, and he became even more aggressive as general sales manager of Blake Electronics. This aggressiveness bothered Steve, who was more conservative. Jim would make deals to supply companies with electronic components before he bothered to find out if Blake Electronics had the ability or capacity to produce the components. On several occasions this behavior caused the company some embarrassing moments when Blake Electronics was unable to produce the electronic components for companies with which Jim had made deals.

In 2000, Jim started to go after government contracts for electronic components. By 2002, total annual sales had increased to more than $10 million, and the number of employees exceeded 200. Many of these employees were electronic specialists and graduates of electrical engineering programs from top colleges and universities. But Jim's tendency to stretch Blake Electronics to contracts continued as well, and by 2007, Blake Electronics had a reputation with government agencies as a company that could not deliver what it promised. Almost overnight, government contracts stopped, and Blake Electronics was left with an idle workforce and unused manufacturing equipment. This high overhead started to melt away profits, and in 2009, Blake Electronics was faced with the possibility of sustaining a loss for the first time in its history.

In 2010, Steve decided to look at the possibility of manufacturing electronic components for home use. Although this was a totally new market for Blake Electronics, Steve was convinced that this was the only way to keep Blake

Figure 15 Master Control Center

Master Control Box

Outlet Adapter

Light Switch Adapter

Lightbulb Disk

Electronics from dipping into the red. The research team at Blake Electronics was given the task of developing new electronic devices for home use. The first idea from the research team was the Master Control Center. The basic components for this system are shown in Figure 15.

The heart of the system is the master control box. This unit, which would have a retail price of $250, has two rows of five buttons. Each button controls one light or appliance and can be set as either a switch or a rheostat. When set as a switch, a light finger touch on the button turns a light or appliance on or off. When set as a rheostat, a finger touching the button controls the intensity of the light. Leaving your finger on the button makes the light go through a complete cycle ranging from off to bright and back to off again.

To allow for maximum flexibility, each master control box is powered by two D-sized batteries that can last up to a year, depending on usage. In addition, the research team has developed three versions of the master control box—versions A, B, and C. If a family wants to control more than 10 lights or appliances, another master control box can be purchased.

The lightbulb disk, which would have a retail price of $2.50, is controlled by the master control box and is used to control the intensity of any light. A different disk is available for each button position for all three master control boxes. By inserting the lightbulb disk between the lightbulb and the socket, the appropriate button on the master control box can completely control the intensity of the light. If a standard light switch is used, it must be on at all times for the master control box to work.

One disadvantage of using a standard light switch is that only the master control box can be used to control the particular light. To avoid this problem, the research team developed a special light switch adapter that would sell for $15. When this device is installed, either the master control box or the light switch adapter can be used to control the light.

When used to control appliances other than lights, the master control box must be used in conjunction with one or more outlet adapters. The adapters are plugged into a standard wall outlet, and the appliance is then plugged into the adapter. Each outlet adapter has a switch on top that allows the appliance to be controlled from the master control box or the outlet adapter. The price of each outlet adapter would be $25.

The research team estimated that it would cost $500,000 to develop the equipment and procedures needed to manufacture the master control box and accessories. If successful, this venture could increase sales by approximately $2 million. But will the master control boxes be a successful venture? With a 60% chance of success estimated by the research team, Steve had serious doubts about trying to market the master control boxes even though he liked the basic idea. Because of his reservations, Steve decided to send requests for proposals (RFPs) for additional marketing research to 30 marketing research companies in southern California.

The first RFP to come back was from a small company called Marketing Associates, Inc. (MAI), which would charge $100,000 for the survey. According to its proposal, MAI has been in business for about 3 years and has conducted about 100 marketing research projects. MAI's major strengths appeared to be individual attention to each account, experienced staff, and

TABLE 19   Success Figures for MAI

| | SURVEY RESULTS | | |
OUTCOME	FAVORABLE	UNFAVORABLE	TOTAL
Successful venture	35	20	55
Unsuccessful venture	15	30	45

fast work. Steve was particularly interested in one part of the proposal, which revealed MAI's success record with previous accounts. This is shown in Table 19.

The only other proposal to be returned was by a branch office of Iverstine and Walker, one of the largest marketing research firms in the country. The cost for a complete survey would be $300,000. While the proposal did not contain the same success record as MAI, the proposal from Iverstine and Walker did contain some interesting information. The chance of getting a favorable survey result, given a successful venture, was 90%. On the other hand, the chance of getting an unfavorable survey result, given an unsuccessful venture, was 80%. Thus, it appeared to Steve that Iverstine and Walker would be able to predict the success or failure of the master control boxes with a great amount of certainty.

Steve pondered the situation. Unfortunately, both marketing research teams gave different types of information in their proposals. Steve concluded that there would be no way that the two proposals could be compared unless he got additional information from Iverstine and Walker. Furthermore, Steve wasn't sure what he would do with the information, and if it would be worth the expense of hiring one of the marketing research firms.

Discussion Questions

1. Does Steve need additional information from Iverstine and Walker?
2. What would you recommend?

![www] **Internet Case Studies**

See our Internet home page, at www.pearsonhighered.com/render, for these additional case studies:

(1) **Drink-At-Home, Inc.:** This case involves the development and marketing of a new beverage.
(2) **Ruth Jones' Heart Bypass Operation:** This case deals with a medical decision regarding surgery.
(3) **Ski Right:** This case involves the development and marketing of a new ski helmet.
(4) **Study Time:** This case is about a student who must budget time while studying for a final exam.

Bibliography

Abbas, Ali E. "Invariant Utility Functions and Certain Equivalent Transformations," *Decision Analysis* 4, 1(March 2007): 17–31.

Carassus, Laurence, and Miklós Rásonyi. "Optimal Strategies and Utility-Based Prices Converge When Agents' Preferences Do," *Mathematics of Operations Research* 32, 1 (February 2007): 102–117.

Congdon, Peter. *Bayesian Statistical Modeling*. New York: John Wiley & Sons, Inc., 2001.

Ewing, Paul L., Jr. "Use of Decision Analysis in the Army Base Realignment and Closure (BRAC) 2005 Military Value Analysis," *Decision Analysis* 3 (March 2006): 33–49.

Hammond, J. S., R. L. Kenney, and H. Raiffa. "The Hidden Traps in Decision Making," *Harvard Business Review* (September–October 1998): 47–60.

Hurley, William J. "The 2002 Ryder Cup: Was Strange's Decision to Put Tiger Woods in the Anchor Match a Good One?" *Decision Analysis* 4, 1 (March 2007): 41–45.

Kirkwood, C. W. "An Overview of Methods for Applied Decision Analysis," *Interfaces* 22, 6 (November–December 1992): 28–39.

Kirkwood, C. W. "Approximating Risk Aversion in Decision Analysis Applications," *Decision Analysis* 1 (March 2004): 51–67.

Luce, R., and H. Raiffa. *Games and Decisions*. New York: John Wiley & Sons, Inc., 1957.

Maxwell, Daniel T. "Improving Hard Decisions," *OR/MS Today* 33, 6 (December 2006): 51–61.

Patchak, William M. "Software Survey: Decision Analysis." *OR/MS Today* 39, 5 (October 2012).

Paté-Cornell, M. Elisabeth, and Robin L. Dillon. "The Respective Roles of Risk and Decision Analyses in Decision Support," *Decision Analysis* 3 (December 2006): 220–232.

Pennings, Joost M. E., and Ale Smidts. "The Shape of Utility Functions and Organizational Behavior," *Management Science* 49, 9 (September 2003): 1251–1263.

Raiffa, Howard, John W. Pratt, and Robert Schlaifer. *Introduction to Statistical Decision Theory*. Boston: MIT Press, 1995.

Raiffa, Howard, and Robert Schlaifer. *Applied Statistical Decision Theory*. New York: John Wiley & Sons, Inc., 2000.

Render, B., and R. M. Stair. *Cases and Readings in Management Science*, 2nd ed. Boston: Allyn & Bacon, Inc., 1988.

Schlaifer, R. *Analysis of Decisions Under Uncertainty*. New York: McGraw-Hill Book Company, 1969.

Smith, James E., and Robert L. Winkler. "The Optimizer's Curse: Skepticism and Postdecision Surprise in Decision Analysis," *Management Science* 52 (March 2006): 311–322.

van Binsbergen, Jules H., and Leslie M. Marx. "Exploring Relations Between Decision Analysis and Game Theory," *Decision Analysis* 4, 1 (March 2007): 32–40.

Wallace, Stein W. "Decision Making Under Uncertainty: Is Sensitivity Analysis of Any Use?" *Operations Research* 48, 1 (2000): 20–25.

Solutions to Selected Problems

18	Maximin criterion; Texan
20	(a) Stock market (b) $21,500
22	(b) CD
24	(b) Medium
26	8 cases
30	(b) Very large (c) Small (c) Very large (d) Very large (f) Very large
32	Minimax regret decision: Option 2; Minimum EOL decision: Option 2
34	$-$0.526
36	Construct the clinic (EMV $= 30{,}000$)
40	Do not gather information; build quadplex
42	0.533; 0.109
44	(c) Conduct the survey. If the survey is favorable, produce razor; if not favorable, don't produce razor.
46	(a) 0.923, 0.077, 0.25, 0.75 (b) 0.949, 0.051, 0.341, 0.659
48	Do not use study. Risk avoiders.
50	(a) Broad (b) Expressway (c) Risk avoider

Solutions to Self-Tests

1.	b	**7.**	a	**12.**	c
2.	c	**8.**	c	**13.**	c
3.	c	**9.**	a	**14.**	a
4.	a	**10.**	d	**15.**	c
5.	c	**11.**	b	**16.**	b
6.	b				

Regression Models

CHAPTER OUTLINE

From Chapter 4 of *Quantitative Analysis for Management*, Twelfth Edition. Barry Render, Ralph M. Stair, Jr., Michael E. Hanna, and Trevor S. Hale. Copyright © 2015 by Pearson Education, Inc. All rights reserved.

1 Introduction

Two purposes of regression analysis are to understand the relationship between variables and to predict the value of one based on the other.

Regression analysis is a very valuable tool for today's manager. Regression has been used to model things such as the relationship between level of education and income, the price of a house and the square footage, and the sales volume for a company relative to the dollars spent on advertising. When businesses are trying to decide which location is best for a new store or branch office, regression models are often used. Cost estimation models are often regression models. The applicability of regression analysis is virtually limitless.

There are generally two purposes for regression analysis. The first is to understand the relationship between variables such as advertising expenditures and sales. The second purpose is to predict the value of one variable based on the value of the other. Because of this, regression is a very important forecasting technique.

In this chapter, the simple linear regression model will first be developed, and then a more complex multiple regression model will be used to incorporate even more variables into our model. In any regression model, the variable to be predicted is called the **dependent variable** or **response variable**. The value of this is said to be dependent upon the value of an **independent variable**, which is sometimes called an **explanatory variable** or a **predictor variable**.

2 Scatter Diagrams

A scatter diagram is a graph of the data.

To investigate the relationship between variables, it is helpful to look at a graph of the data. Such a graph is often called a **scatter diagram** or a **scatter plot**. Normally the independent variable is plotted on the horizontal axis and the dependent variable is plotted on the vertical axis. The following example will illustrate this.

Triple A Construction Company renovates old homes in Albany. Over time, the company has found that its dollar volume of renovation work is dependent on the Albany area payroll. The figures for Triple A's revenues and the amount of money earned by wage earners in Albany for the past 6 years are presented in Table 1. Economists have predicted the local area payroll to be $600 million next year, and Triple A wants to plan accordingly.

Figure 1 provides a scatter diagram for the Triple A Construction data given in Table 1. This graph indicates that higher values for the local payroll seem to result in higher sales for the company. There is not a perfect relationship because not all the points lie in a straight line, but there is a relationship. A line has been drawn through the data to help show the relationship that exists between the payroll and sales. The points do not all lie on the line, so there would be some error involved if we tried to predict sales based on payroll using this or any other line. Many lines could be drawn through these points, but which one best represents the true relationship? Regression analysis provides the answer to this question.

TABLE 1

Triple A Construction Company Sales and Local Payroll

TRIPLE A'S SALES ($100,000s)	LOCAL PAYROLL ($100,000,000s)
6	3
8	4
9	6
5	4
4.5	2
9.5	5

FIGURE 1

Scatter Diagram of Triple A Construction Company Data

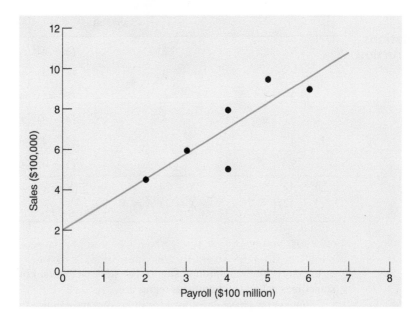

3   Simple Linear Regression

In any regression model, there is an implicit assumption (which can be tested) that a relationship exists between the variables. There is also some random error that cannot be predicted. The underlying simple linear regression model is

$$Y = \beta_0 + \beta_1 X + \epsilon \tag{1}$$

where

*The dependent variable is **Y** and the independent variable is **X**.*

Y = dependent variable (response variable)

X = independent variable (predictor variable or explanatory variable)

β_0 = intercept (value of Y when $X = 0$)

β_1 = slope of regression line

ϵ = random error

Estimates of the slope and intercept are found from sample data.

The true values for the intercept and slope are not known, and therefore they are estimated using sample data. The regression equation based on sample data is given as

$$\hat{Y} = b_0 + b_1 X \tag{2}$$

where

$\hat{Y}$ = predicted value of Y

b_0 = estimate of β_0, based on sample results

b_1 = estimate of β_1, based on sample results

In the Triple A Construction example, we are trying to predict the sales, so the dependent variable (Y) would be sales. The variable we use to help predict sales is the Albany area payroll, so this is the independent variable (X). Although any number of lines can be drawn through these points to show a relationship between X and Y in Figure 1, the line that will be chosen is the one that in some way minimizes the errors. **Error** is defined as

$$\text{Error} = (\text{Actual value}) - (\text{Predicted value})$$

$$e = Y - \hat{Y} \tag{3}$$

The regression line minimizes the sum of the squared errors.

Since errors may be positive or negative, the average error could be zero even though there are extremely large errors—both positive and negative. To eliminate the difficulty of negative errors canceling positive errors, the errors can be squared. The best regression line will be defined

TABLE 2

Regression Calculations for Triple A Construction

Y	X	$(X - \bar{X})^2$	$(X - \bar{X})(Y - \bar{Y})$
6	3	$(3 - 4)^2 = 1$	$(3 - 4)(6 - 7) = 1$
8	4	$(4 - 4)^2 = 0$	$(4 - 4)(8 - 7) = 0$
9	6	$(6 - 4)^2 = 4$	$(6 - 4)(9 - 7) = 4$
5	4	$(4 - 4)^2 = 0$	$(4 - 4)(5 - 7) = 0$
4.5	2	$(2 - 4)^2 = 4$	$(2 - 4)(4.5 - 7) = 5$
9.5	5	$(5 - 4)^2 = 1$	$(5 - 4)(9.5 - 7) = 2.5$
$\Sigma Y = 42$	$\Sigma X = 24$	$\Sigma(X - \bar{X})^2 = 10$	$\Sigma(X - \bar{X})(Y - \bar{Y}) = 12.5$
$\bar{Y} = 42/6 = 7$	$\bar{X} = 24/6 = 4$		

as the one with the minimum sum of the squared errors. For this reason, regression analysis is sometimes called **least-squares** regression.

Statisticians have developed formulas that we can use to find the equation of a straight line that would minimize the sum of the squared errors. The simple linear regression equation is

$$\hat{Y} = b_0 + b_1 X$$

The following formulas can be used to compute the intercept and the slope:

$$\bar{X} = \frac{\Sigma X}{n} = \text{average (mean) of } X \text{ values}$$

$$\bar{Y} = \frac{\Sigma Y}{n} = \text{average (mean) of } Y \text{ values}$$

$$b_1 = \frac{\Sigma(X - \bar{X})(Y - \bar{Y})}{\Sigma(X - \bar{X})^2} \tag{4}$$

$$b_0 = \bar{Y} - b_1\bar{X} \tag{5}$$

The preliminary calculations are shown in Table 2. There are other "shortcut" formulas that are helpful when doing the computations on a calculator, and these are presented in Appendix 1. They will not be shown here, as computer software will be used for most of the other examples in this chapter.

Computing the slope and intercept of the regression equation for the Triple A Construction Company example, we have

$$\bar{X} = \frac{\Sigma X}{6} = \frac{24}{6} = 4$$

$$\bar{Y} = \frac{\Sigma X}{6} = \frac{42}{6} = 7$$

$$b_1 = \frac{\Sigma(X - \bar{X})(Y - \bar{Y})}{\Sigma(X - \bar{X})^2} = \frac{12.5}{10} = 1.25$$

$$b_0 = \bar{Y} - b_1\bar{X} = 7 - (1.25)(4) = 2$$

The estimated regression equation therefore is

$$\hat{Y} = 2 + 1.25X$$

or

$$\text{sales} = 2 + 1.25(\text{payroll})$$

If the payroll next year is $600 million ($X = 6$), then the predicted value would be

$$\hat{Y} = 2 + 1.25(6) = 9.5$$

or $950,000.

One of the purposes of regression is to understand the relationship among variables. This model tells us that for each \$100 million (represented by X) increase in the payroll, we would expect the sales to increase by \$125,000 since $b_1 = 1.25$ (\$100,000s). This model helps Triple A Construction see how the local economy and company sales are related.

4 Measuring the Fit of the Regression Model

Deviations (errors) may be positive or negative.

A regression equation can be developed for any variables X and Y, even random numbers. We certainly would not have any confidence in the ability of one random number to predict the value of another random number. How do we know that the model is actually helpful in predicting Y based on X? Should we have confidence in this model? Does the model provide better predictions (smaller errors) than simply using the average of the Y values?

In the Triple A Construction example, sales figures (Y) varied from a low of 4.5 to a high of 9.5, and the mean was 7. If each sales value is compared with the mean, we see how far they deviate from the mean and we could compute a measure of the total variability in sales. Because Y is sometimes higher and sometimes lower than the mean, there may be both positive and negative deviations. Simply summing these values would be misleading because the negatives would cancel out the positives, making it appear that the numbers are closer to the mean than they actually are. To prevent this problem, we will use the **sum of squares total (SST)** to measure the total variability in Y:

The SST measures the total variability in Y about the mean.

$$\text{SST} = \Sigma(Y - \bar{Y})^2 \tag{6}$$

If we did not use X to predict Y, we would simply use the mean of Y as the prediction, and the SST would measure the accuracy of our predictions. However, a regression line may be used to predict the value of Y, and while there are still errors involved, the sum of these squared errors will be less than the total sum of squares just computed. The **sum of squares error (SSE)** is

The SSE measures the variability in Y about the regression line.

$$\text{SSE} = \Sigma e^2 = \Sigma(Y - \hat{Y})^2 \tag{7}$$

Table 3 provides the calculations for the Triple A Construction example. The mean ($\bar{Y} = 7$) is compared to each value and we get

$$\text{SST} = 22.5$$

The prediction ($\hat{Y}$) for each observation is computed and compared to the actual value. This results in

$$\text{SSE} = 6.875$$

The SSE is much lower than the SST. Using the regression line has reduced the variability in the sum of squares by $22.5 - 6.875 = 15.625$. This is called the **sum of squares regression (SSR)** and indicates how much of the total variability in Y is explained by the regression model. Mathematically, this can be calculated as

$$\text{SSR} = \Sigma(\hat{Y} - \bar{Y})^2 \tag{8}$$

TABLE 3 Sum of Squares for Triple A Construction

Y	X	$(Y - \bar{Y})^2$	$\hat{Y}$	$(Y - \hat{Y})^2$	$(\hat{Y} - \bar{Y})^2$
6	3	$(6 - 7)^2 = 1$	$2 + 1.25(3) = 5.75$	0.0625	1.563
8	4	$(8 - 7)^2 = 1$	$2 + 1.25(4) = 7.00$	1	0
9	6	$(9 - 7)^2 = 4$	$2 + 1.25(6) = 9.50$	0.25	6.25
5	4	$(5 - 7)^2 = 4$	$2 + 1.25(4) = 7.00$	4	0
4.5	2	$(4.5 - 7)^2 = 6.25$	$2 + 1.25(2) = 4.50$	0	6.25
9.5	5	$(9.5 - 7)^2 = 6.25$	$2 + 1.25(5) = 8.25$	1.5625	1.563
		$\Sigma(Y - \bar{Y})^2 = 22.5$		$\Sigma(Y - \hat{Y})^2 = 6.875$	$\Sigma(\hat{Y} - \bar{Y})^2 = 15.625$
$\bar{Y} = 7$		$\text{SST} = 22.5$		$\text{SSE} = 6.875$	$\text{SSR} = 15.625$

FIGURE 2

Deviations from the Regression Line and from the Mean

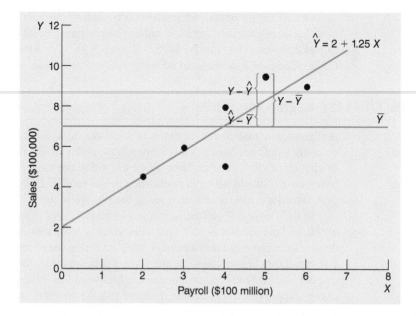

Table 3 indicates

$$SSR = 15.625$$

There is a very important relationship between the sums of squares that we have computed:

$$(\text{Sum of squares total}) = (\text{Sum of squares due to regression}) + (\text{Sum of squares error})$$
$$SST = SSR + SSE \tag{9}$$

Figure 2 displays the data for Triple A Construction. The regression line is shown, as is a line representing the mean of the Y values. The errors used in computing the sums of squares are shown on this graph. Notice how the sample points are closer to the regression line than they are to the mean.

Coefficient of Determination

r^2 is the proportion of variability in Y that is explained by the regression equation.

The SSR is sometimes called the explained variability in Y while the SSE is the unexplained variability in Y. The proportion of the variability in Y that is explained by the regression equation is called the **coefficient of determination** and is denoted by r^2. Thus,

$$r^2 = \frac{SSR}{SST} = 1 - \frac{SSE}{SST} \tag{10}$$

Thus, r^2 can be found using either the SSR or the SSE. For Triple A Construction, we have

$$r^2 = \frac{15.625}{22.5} = 0.6944$$

This means that about 69% of the variability in sales (Y) is explained by the regression equation based on payroll (X).

If every point lies on the regression line, $r^2 = 1$ and SSE = 0.

If every point in the sample were on the regression line (meaning all errors are 0), then 100% of the variability in Y could be explained by the regression equation, so $r^2 = 1$ and SSE $= 0$. The lowest possible value of r^2 is 0, indicating that X explains 0% of the variability in Y. Thus, r^2 can range from a low of 0 to a high of 1. In developing regression equations, a good model will have an r^2 value close to 1.

Correlation Coefficient

The correlation coefficient ranges from −1 to +1.

Another measure related to the coefficient of determination is the **coefficient of correlation**. This measure also expresses the degree or strength of the linear relationship. It is usually expressed as r and can be any number between and including $+1$ and -1. Figure 3 illustrates

FIGURE 3

Four Values of the Correlation Coefficient

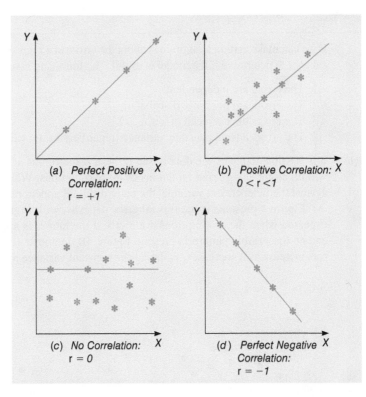

possible scatter diagrams for different values of r. The value of r is the square root of r^2. It is negative if the slope is negative, and it is positive if the slope is positive. Thus,

$$r = \pm\sqrt{r^2} \qquad (11)$$

For the Triple A Construction example with $r^2 = 0.6944$,

$$r = \sqrt{0.6944} = 0.8333$$

We know it is positive because the slope is $+1.25$.

IN ACTION **Using Regression as Part of Improvement Initiative at Trane/Ingersoll Rand**

Trane U.S. Inc. is a brand of Ingersoll Rand and is a leader in both home and commercial air conditioning. In an effort to improve quality and efficiency, the company consolidated its manufacturing of evaporator and condenser coils into one location in South Carolina. A key part of the coil unit is a header, which controls the flow of water or refrigerant through the coil. With about 120 unique headers produced on each shift, with increased demand for their air conditioners due to federal refrigerant standards, and with growing pressure to reduce costs, Trane began an improvement initiative in 2010.

Value stream mapping, a lean manufacturing technique, was used to visualize the entire process and identify waste in the system. A new layout was suggested to improve processing and reduce the overall time of production. To predict how well the new layout would perform in the manufacture of the headers, data was collected about the time to move materials into position, time to set up a job, time to set up a machine, and time to process a job. Several regression models were developed to

determine which job characteristics were most significant in the various times involved in processing, and to measure the variability in times. These were used in simulation models that were developed to determine the overall impact of the new layout and to determine where bottlenecks might occur. One of the bottlenecks, at a robotic machine for welding, was eliminated by retooling the robot to allow the machine operator to operate both sides of the robot. This enables the robot to process two headers simultaneously.

The improvement initiatives from this project are estimated to save over $700,000 per year. This project highlighted the importance of data-based analytics and lean manufacturing tools in identifying the improvement tactics for complex value streams. The company plans similar improvement initiatives for other value streams in the future.

Source: Based on John B. Jensen, Sanjay L. Ahire, and Manoj K. Malhotra. "Trane/Ingersoll Rand Combines Lean and Operations Research Tools to Redesign Feeder Manufacturing Operations," *Interfaces* 43, 4 (July–August 2013): 325–340.

5 Assumptions of the Regression Model

If we can make certain assumptions about the errors in a regression model, we can perform statistical tests to determine if the model is useful. The following assumptions are made about the errors:

1. The errors are independent.
2. The errors are normally distributed.
3. The errors have a mean of zero.
4. The errors have a constant variance (regardless of the value of X).

A plot of the errors may highlight problems with the model.

It is possible to check the data to see if these assumptions are met. Often a plot of the residuals will highlight any glaring violations of the assumptions. When the errors (residuals) are plotted against the independent variable, the pattern should appear random.

Figure 4 presents some typical error patterns, with Figure 4A displaying a pattern that is expected when the assumptions are met and the model is appropriate. The errors are random and no discernible pattern is present. Figure 4B demonstrates an error pattern in which the errors increase as X increases, violating the constant variance assumption. Figure 4C shows errors

FIGURE 4A

Pattern of Errors Indicating Randomness

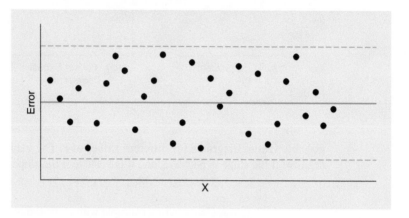

FIGURE 4B

Nonconstant Error Variance

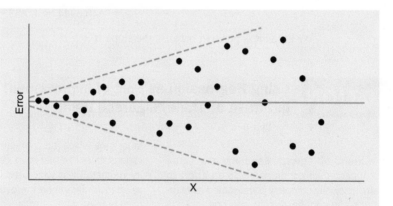

FIGURE 4C

Errors Indicate Relationship Is Not Linear

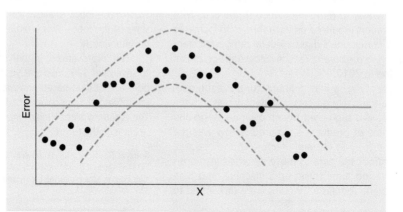

consistently increasing at first, and then consistently decreasing. A pattern such as this would indicate that the model is not linear and some other form (perhaps quadratic) should be used. In general, patterns in the plot of the errors indicate problems with the assumptions or the model specification.

Estimating the Variance

The error variance is estimated by the MSE.

While the errors are assumed to have constant variance (σ^2), this is usually not known. It can be estimated from the sample results. The estimate of σ^2 is the **mean squared error** (MSE) and is denoted by s^2. The MSE is the sum of squares due to error divided by the degrees of freedom:[1]

$$s^2 = \text{MSE} = \frac{\text{SSE}}{n - k - 1} \tag{12}$$

where

$$n = \text{number of observations in the sample}$$
$$k = \text{number of independent variables}$$

In the Triple A Construction example, $n = 6$ and $k = 1$. So

$$s^2 = \text{MSE} = \frac{\text{SSE}}{n - k - 1} = \frac{6.8750}{6 - 1 - 1} = \frac{6.8750}{4} = 1.7188$$

From this we can estimate the standard deviation as

$$s = \sqrt{\text{MSE}} \tag{13}$$

This is called the **standard error of the estimate** or the *standard deviation of the regression*. In this example,

$$s = \sqrt{\text{MSE}} = \sqrt{1.7188} = 1.31$$

This is used in many of the statistical tests about the model. It is also used to find interval estimates for both Y and regression coefficients.[2]

6 Testing the Model for Significance

Both the MSE and r^2 provide a measure of accuracy in a regression model. However, when the sample size is too small, it is possible to get good values for both of these even if there is no relationship between the variables in the regression model. To determine whether these values are meaningful, it is necessary to test the model for significance.

To see if there is a linear relationship between X and Y, a statistical hypothesis test is performed. The underlying linear model was given in Equation 1 as

$$Y = \beta_0 + \beta_1 X + \epsilon$$

An F *test is used to determine if there is a relationship between* X *and* Y.

If $\beta_1 = 0$, then Y does not depend on X in any way. The null hypothesis says there is no linear relationship between the two variables (i.e., $\beta_1 = 0$). The alternate hypothesis is that there is a linear relationship (i.e., $\beta_1 \neq 0$). If the null hypothesis can be rejected, then we have proven that a linear relationship does exist, so X is helpful in predicting Y. The F distribution is used for testing this hypothesis. Appendix: F Distribution Values contains values for the F distribution that can be used when calculations are performed by hand. The results of the test can also be obtained from both Excel and QM for Windows.

The F statistic used in the hypothesis test is based on the MSE (seen in the previous section) and the mean squared regression (MSR). The MSR is calculated as

$$\text{MSR} = \frac{\text{SSR}}{k} \tag{14}$$

---

[1]See bibliography at end of this chapter for books with further details.
[2]The MSE is a common measure of accuracy in forecasting. When used with techniques besides regression, it is common to divide the SSE by n rather than $n - k - 1$.

where

$$k = \text{number of independent variables in the model}$$

The F statistic is

$$F = \frac{\text{MSR}}{\text{MSE}} \tag{15}$$

Based on the assumptions regarding the errors in a regression model, this calculated F statistic is described by the F distribution with

$$\text{degrees of freedom for the numerator} = \text{df}_1 = k$$
$$\text{degrees of freedom for the denominator} = \text{df}_2 = n - k - 1$$

where

$$k = \text{the number of independent } (X) \text{ variables}$$

If there is very little error, the denominator (MSE) of the F statistic is very small relative to the numerator (MSR), and the resulting F statistic would be large. This would be an indication that the model is useful. A significance level related to the value of the F statistic is then found. Whenever the F value is large, the observed significance level (p-value) will be low, indicating that it is extremely unlikely that this could have occurred by chance. When the F value is large (with a resulting small significance level), we can reject the null hypothesis that there is no linear relationship. This means that there is a linear relationship and the values of MSE and r^2 are meaningful.

The hypothesis test just described is summarized here:

If the significance level for the **F** *test is low, there is a relationship between* **X** *and* **Y**.

Steps in Hypothesis Test for a Significant Regression Model

1. Specify null and alternative hypotheses:

$$H_0 : \beta_1 = 0$$
$$H_1 : \beta_1 \neq 0$$

2. Select the level of significance (α). Common values are 0.01 and 0.05.

3. Calculate the value of the test statistic using the formula

$$F = \frac{\text{MSR}}{\text{MSE}}$$

4. Make a decision using one of the following methods:
   (a) Reject the null hypothesis if the test statistic is greater than the F value from the table in Appendix: F Distribution Values. Otherwise, do not reject the null hypothesis:

$$\text{Reject if } F_{\text{calculated}} > F_{\alpha, \text{df}_1, \text{df}_2}$$
$$\text{df}_1 = k$$
$$\text{df}_2 = n - k - 1$$

   (b) Reject the null hypothesis if the **observed significance level**, or **p-value**, is less than the level of significance (α). Otherwise, do not reject the null hypothesis:

$$p\text{-value} = P(F > \text{calculated test statistic})$$
$$\text{Reject if } p\text{-value} < \alpha$$

Triple A Construction Example

To illustrate the process of testing the hypothesis about a significant relationship, consider the Triple A Construction example. Appendix: *F* Distribution Values will be used to provide values for the *F* distribution.

Step 1.

$$H_0 : \beta_1 = 0 \quad \text{(no linear relationship between } X \text{ and } Y\text{)}$$
$$H_1 : \beta_1 \neq 0 \quad \text{(linear relationship exists between } X \text{ and } Y\text{)}$$

Step 2.

$$\text{Select } \alpha = 0.05$$

Step 3. Calculate the value of the test statistic. The MSE was already calculated to be 1.7188. The MSR is then calculated so that *F* can be found:

$$\text{MSR} = \frac{\text{SSR}}{k} = \frac{15.6250}{1} = 15.6250$$

$$F = \frac{\text{MSR}}{\text{MSE}} = \frac{15.6250}{1.7188} = 9.09$$

Step 4. (a) Reject the null hypothesis if the test statistic is greater than the *F* value from the table in Appendix: *F* Distribution Values:

$$df_1 = k = 1$$
$$df_2 = n - k - 1 = 6 - 1 - 1 = 4$$

The value of *F* associated with a 5% level of significance and with degrees of freedom 1 and 4 is found in Appendix: *F* Distribution Values. Figure 5 illustrates this:

$$F_{0.05,1,4} = 7.71$$
$$F_{\text{calculated}} = 9.09$$
$$\text{Reject } H_0 \text{ because } 9.09 > 7.71$$

Thus, there is sufficient data to conclude that there is a statistically significant relationship between *X* and *Y*, so the model is helpful. The strength of this relationship is measured by $r^2 = 0.69$. Thus, we can conclude that about 69% of the variability in sales (*Y*) is explained by the regression model based on local payroll (*X*).

The Analysis of Variance (ANOVA) Table

When software such as Excel or QM for Windows is used to develop regression models, the output provides the observed significance level, or *p*-value, for the calculated *F* value. This is then compared to the level of significance (α) to make the decision.

FIGURE 5

F **Distribution for Triple A Construction Test for Significance**

F = 7.71   9.09

TABLE 4

Analysis of Variance Table for Regression

	DF	SS	MS	F	SIGNIFICANCE F
Regression	k	SSR	MSR $= $ SSR$/k$	MSR/MSE	$P(F > $ MSR/MSE$)$
Residual	$n - k - 1$	SSE	MSE $= $ SSE$/(n - k - 1)$		
Total	$n - 1$	SST			

Table 4 provides summary information about the ANOVA table. This shows how the numbers in the last three columns of the table are computed. The last column of this table, labeled Significance F, is the p-value, or observed significance level, which can be used in the hypothesis test about the regression model.

Triple A Construction ANOVA Example

The Excel output that includes the ANOVA table for the Triple A Construction data is shown in the next section. The observed significance level for $F = 9.0909$ is given to be 0.0394. This means

$$P(F > 9.0909) = 0.0394$$

Because this probability is less than 0.05 (α), we would reject the hypothesis of no linear relationship and conclude that there is a linear relationship between X and Y. Note in Figure 5 that the area under the curve to the right of 9.09 is clearly less than 0.05, which is the area to the right of the F value associated with a 0.05, level of significance.

7 Using Computer Software for Regression

Software such as Excel 2013, Excel QM, and QM for Windows is usually used for the regression calculations. All of these will be illustrated using the Triple A Construction example.

Excel 2013

To use Excel 2013 for regression, enter the data in columns. Click the *Data* tab to access the data ribbon. Then select *Data Analysis*, as shown in Program 1A. If *Data Analysis* does not appear on the Data ribbon, the Excel add-in for this has not yet been activated. See Appendix: Using Excel QM and Excel Add-Ins at the end of the text for instructions on how to activate this. Once this add-in is activated, it will remain on the *Data* ribbon for future use.

When the *Data Analysis* window opens, scroll down to and highlight *Regression* and click *OK*, as illustrated in Program 1A. The Regression window will open, as shown in Program 1B, and you can input the X and Y ranges. Check the *Labels* box because the cells with the variable name were included in the first row of the X and Y ranges. To have the output presented on this page rather than on a new worksheet, select *Output Range* and give a cell address for the start of the output. Click the *OK* button, and the output appears in the output range specified. Program 1C shows the intercept (2), slope (1.25), and other information that was previously calculated for the Triple A Construction example.

The sums of squares are shown in the column headed by SS. Another name for *error* is **residual**. In Excel, the **sum of squares error** is shown as the sum of squares residual. The values in this output are the same values shown in Table 3:

$$\text{Sum of squares regression} = \text{SSR} = 15.625$$
$$\text{Sum of squares error (residual)} = 6.8750$$
$$\text{Sum of squares total} = \text{SST} = 22.5$$

The coefficient of determination (r^2) is shown to be 0.6944. The coefficient of correlation (r) is called *Multiple R* in the Excel output, and this is 0.8333.

PROGRAM 1A

Accessing the Regression Option in Excel 2013

Click *OK*.

Go to the *Data* tab.

Select *Data Analysis*.

When Data Analysis window opens, scroll down to *Regression*.

PROGRAM 1B

Data Input for Regression in Excel 2013

Specify the *X* and *Y* ranges.

Check the *Labels* box if the first row in the *X* and *Y* ranges includes the variable names.

Specify location for the output. To put this on the current worksheet, click *Output Range* and give a cell location for this to begin.

Click *OK* to have Excel develop the regression model.

PROGRAM 1C

Excel 2013 Output for Triple A Construction Example

A high r^2 (close to 1) is desirable.

A low (*e.g.*, less than 0.05) *Significance F* (*p*-value for overall model) indicates a significant relationship between *X* and *Y*.

The SSR (regression), SSE (residual or error), and SST (total) are shown in the SS column of the ANOVA table.

The regression coefficients are given here.

Excel QM

To use Excel QM for regression, from the Excel QM ribbon select the module by clicking *Alphabetical - Forecasting - Multiple Regression* as shown in Program 2A. A window will open to allow you to specify the size of the problem, as shown in Program 2B. Enter a name or title for the problem, the number of past observations, and the number of independent (*X*) variables. For the Triple A Construction example, there are 6 past periods of data and 1 independent variable. When you click *OK*, a spreadsheet will appear for you to enter the *X* and *Y* data in the shaded area. The calculations are automatically performed, so there is nothing to do after entering the data. The results are seen in Program 2C.

PROGRAM 2A Using Excel QM for Regression

PROGRAM 2B

Initializing the Spreadsheet in Excel QM

PROGRAM 2C

Input and Results for Regression in Excel QM

QM for Windows

To develop a regression equation using QM for Windows for the Triple A Construction Company data, select the *Forecasting* module and select *New*. Then choose *Least Squares—Simple and Multiple Regression*, as illustrated in Program 3A. This opens the window shown in Program 3B. Enter the number of observations (6 in this example) and specify the number of independent variables (1 in this example). Left-click *OK* and a window opens allowing you to input the data as shown in Program 3C. After entering the data, click *Solve*, and the forecasting results shown in Program 3D are displayed. The equation as well as other information is provided on this screen. Note the regression equation is displayed across two lines. Additional output, including the ANOVA table, is available by clicking the *Window* option on the toolbar.

PROGRAM 3A

QM for Windows Regression Option in Forecasting Module

PROGRAM 3B

QM for Windows Screen to Initialize the Problem

PROGRAM 3C

Data Input for Triple A Construction Example

	Triple A Construction	
	Dpndnt var, Y	X1
Observation 1	6	3
Observation 2	8	4
Observation 3	9	6
Observation 4	5	4
Observation 5	4.5	2
Observation 6	9.5	5

PROGRAM 3D

QM for Windows Output for Triple A Construction Example

Measure	
Error Measures	
Bias (Mean Error)	0
MAD (Mean Absolute Deviation)	.833
MSE (Mean Squared Error)	1.146
Standard Error (denom=n-2=4)	1.311
MAPE (Mean Absolute Percent Error)	.126
Regression line	
Dpndnt var, Y = 2	
+ 1.25 * X1	
Statistics	
Correlation coefficient	.833
Coefficient of determination (r^2)	.694

Additional information is available by clicking *Window*.

Regression equation is across two lines.

Window Help
Cascade
Tile
Edit Data
1 Forecasting Results
2 Details and Error Analysis
3 ANOVA Summary
4 Sum of Squares Computations
5 Graph

8 Multiple Regression Analysis

A multiple regression model has more than one independent variable.

The **multiple regression model** is a practical extension of the model we just observed. It allows us to build a model with several independent variables. The underlying model is

$$Y = \beta_0 + \beta_1 X_1 + \beta_2 X_2 + \cdots + \beta_k X_k + \epsilon \tag{16}$$

where

Y = dependent variable (response variable)

X_i = ith independent variable (predictor variable or explanatory variable)

β_0 = intercept (value of Y when all $X_i = 0$)

β_i = coefficient of the ith independent variable

k = number of independent variables

ϵ = random error

To estimate the values of these coefficients, a sample is taken and the following equation is developed:

$$\hat{Y} = b_0 + b_1 X_1 + b_2 X_2 + \cdots + b_k X_k \tag{17}$$

where

$\hat{Y}$ = predicted value of Y

b_0 = sample intercept (and is an estimate of β_0)

b_i = sample coefficient of ith variable (and is an estimate of β_i)

Consider the case of Jenny Wilson Realty, a real estate company in Montgomery, Alabama. Jenny Wilson, owner and broker for this company, wants to develop a model to determine a suggested listing price for houses based on the size of the house and the age of the house. She selects a sample of houses that have sold recently in a particular area, and she records the selling price, the square footage of the house, the age of the house, and also the

TABLE 5

Jenny Wilson Real Estate Data

SELLING PRICE ($)	SQUARE FOOTAGE	AGE	CONDITION
95,000	1,926	30	Good
119,000	2,069	40	Excellent
124,800	1,720	30	Excellent
135,000	1,396	15	Good
142,800	1,706	32	Mint
145,000	1,847	38	Mint
159,000	1,950	27	Mint
165,000	2,323	30	Excellent
182,000	2,285	26	Mint
183,000	3,752	35	Good
200,000	2,300	18	Good
211,000	2,525	17	Good
215,000	3,800	40	Excellent
219,000	1,740	12	Mint

condition (good, excellent, or mint) of each house as shown in Table 5. Initially Jenny plans to use only the square footage and age to develop a model, although she wants to save the information on condition of the house to use later. She wants to find the coefficients for the following multiple regression model:

$$\hat{Y} = b_0 + b_1 X_1 + b_2 X_2$$

where

$\hat{Y}$ = predicted value of dependent variable (selling price)

b_0 = Y intercept

X_1 and X_2 = value of the two independent variables (square footage and age), respectively

b_1 and b_2 = slopes for X_1 and X_2, respectively

Excel can be used to develop multiple regression models.

The mathematics of multiple regression becomes quite complex, so we leave formulas for b_0, b_1, and b_2 to regression textbooks.[3] Excel can be used to develop a multiple regression model just as it was used for a simple linear regression model. When entering the data in Excel, it is important that all of the independent variables are in adjoining columns to facilitate the input. From the *Data* tab in Excel, select *Data Analysis* and then *Regression*, as shown earlier, in Program 1A. This opens the regression window to allow the input, as shown in Program 4A. Note that the *X Range* includes the data in two columns (B and C) because there are two independent variables. The Excel output that Jenny Wilson obtains is shown in Program 4B, and it provides the following equation:

$$\hat{Y} = b_0 + b_1 X_1 + b_2 X_2$$
$$= 146{,}630.89 + 43.82\, X_1 - 2898.69\, X_2$$

Evaluating the Multiple Regression Model

A multiple regression model can be evaluated in a manner similar to the way a simple linear regression model is evaluated. Both the *p*-value for the *F* test and r^2 can be interpreted the same with multiple regression models as they are with simple linear regression

---

[3]See, for example, Norman R. Draper and Harry Smith. *Applied Regression Analysis*, 3rd ed. New York: John Wiley & Sons, Inc., 1998.

PROGRAM 4A

Input Screen for Jenny Wilson Realty Multiple Regression in Excel 2013

PROGRAM 4B

Excel 2013 Output Screen for Jenny Wilson Realty Multiple Regression Example

models. However, as there is more than one independent variable, the hypothesis that is being tested with the F test is that all the coefficients are equal to 0. If all these are 0, then none of the independent variables in the model is helpful in predicting the dependent variable.

To determine which of the independent variables in a multiple regression model is significant, a significance test on the coefficient for each variable is performed. While statistics textbooks can provide the details of these tests, the results of these tests are automatically displayed in the Excel output. The null hypothesis is that the coefficient is 0 (H_0:$\beta_i = 0$) and the alternate hypothesis is that it is not 0 (H_1:$\beta_i \neq 0$). The test statistic is calculated in Excel, and the p-value is given. If the p-value is lower than the level of significance (α), then the null hypothesis is rejected and it can be concluded that the variable is significant.

Jenny Wilson Realty Example

In the Jenny Wilson Realty example in Program 4B, the overall model is statistically significant and useful in predicting the selling price of the house because the p-value for the F test is 0.002. The r^2 value is 0.6719, so 67% of the variability in selling price for these houses can be explained by the regression model. However, there were two independent variables in the model—square footage and age. It is possible that one of these is significant and the other is not. The F test simply indicates that the model as a whole is significant.

Two significance tests can be performed to determine if square footage or age (or both) are significant. In Program 4B, the results of two hypothesis tests are provided. The first test for variable X_1 (square footage) is

$$H_0 : \beta_1 = 0$$
$$H_1 : \beta_1 \neq 0$$

Using a 5% level of significance ($\alpha = 0.05$), the null hypothesis is rejected because the p-value for this is 0.0013. Thus, square footage is helpful in predicting the price of a house.

Similarly, the variable X_2 (age) is tested using the Excel output, and the p-value is 0.0039. The null hypothesis is rejected because this is less than 0.05. Thus, age is also helpful in predicting the price of a house.

9 Binary or Dummy Variables

A dummy variable is also called an indicator variable or a binary variable.

All of the variables we have used in regression examples have been quantitative variables such as sales figures, payroll numbers, square footage, and age. These have all been easily measurable and have had numbers associated with them. There are many times when we believe a qualitative variable rather than a quantitative variable would be helpful in predicting the dependent variable Y. For example, regression may be used to find a relationship between annual income and certain characteristics of the employees. Years of experience at a particular job would be a quantitative variable. However, information regarding whether or not a person has a college degree might also be important. This would not be a measurable value or quantity, so a special variable called a **dummy variable** (or a **binary variable** or an **indicator variable**) would be used. A dummy variable is assigned a value of 1 if a particular condition is met (e.g., a person has a college degree), and a value of 0 otherwise.

Return to the Jenny Wilson Realty example. Jenny believes that a better model can be developed if the condition of the property is included. To incorporate the condition of the house into the model, Jenny looks at the information available (see Table 5), and sees that the three categories are good condition, excellent condition, and mint condition. Since these are not quantitative variables, she must use dummy variables. These are defined as

$$X_3 = 1 \text{ if house is in excellent condition}$$
$$= 0 \text{ otherwise}$$
$$X_4 = 1 \text{ if house is in mint condition}$$
$$= 0 \text{ otherwise}$$

The number of dummy variables must equal 1 less than the number of categories of a qualitative variable.

Notice there is no separate variable for "good" condition. If X_3 and X_4 are both 0, then the house cannot be in excellent or mint condition, so it must be in good condition. When using dummy variables, the number of variables must be 1 less than the number of categories. In this problem, there were three categories (good, excellent, and mint condition) so we must have two dummy variables. If we had mistakenly used too many variables and the number of dummy variables equaled the number of categories, then the mathematical computations could not be performed or would not give reliable values.

These dummy variables will be used with the two previous variables (X_1 - square footage, and X_2 - age) to try to predict the selling prices of houses for Jenny Wilson. Programs 5A and 5B provide the Excel input and output for this new data, and this shows how the dummy variables were coded. The significance level for the F test is 0.00017, so this model is statistically significant. The coefficient of determination (r^2) is 0.898, so this is a much better model than the previous one. The regression equation is

$$\hat{Y} = 121{,}658 + 56.43X_1 - 3{,}962X_2 + 33{,}162X_3 + 47{,}369X_4$$

PROGRAM 5A

Input Screen for Jenny Wilson Realty Example with Dummy Variables in Excel 2013

	A	B	C	D	E	F
1	Jenny Wilson Realty					
2						
3	SELL PRICE	SF	AGE	X3 (Exc.)	X4 (Mint)	Condition
4	95000	1926	30	0	0	Good
5	119000	2069	40	1	0	Excellent
6	124800	1720	30	1	0	Excellent
7	135000	1396	15	0	0	Good
8	142800	1706	32	0	1	Mint
9	145000	1847	38	0	1	Mint
10	159000	1950	27	0	1	Mint
11	165000	2323	30	1	0	Excellent
12	182000	2285	26	0	1	Mint
13	183000	3752	35	0	0	Good
14	200000	2300	18	0	0	Good
15	211000	2525	17	0	0	Good
16	215000	3800	40	1	0	Excellent
17	219000	1740	12	0	1	Mint

Regression dialog box:
Input
Input Y Range: $A$3:$A$17
Input X Range: $B$3:$E$17
☑ Labels   ☐ Constant is Zero
☐ Confidence Level: 95 %
OK   Cancel   Help

The X range includes columns B, C, D, and E but not F.

Output options
◉ Output Range:
◯ New Worksheet
◯ New Workbook
Residuals
☐ Residuals   ☐ Residual Plots
☐ Standardized Residuals   ☐ Line Fit Plots
Normal Probability
☐ Normal Probability Plots

PROGRAM 5B

Output Screen for Jenny Wilson Realty Example with Dummy Variables in Excel 2013

19	SUMMARY OUTPUT					
20						
21	*Regression Statistics*					
22	Multiple R	0.9476				

The coefficient of age is negative indicating that the price decreases as the house gets older.

Each of the variables individually is helpful since the p-values for each of these is low (much less than 5%).

28	ANOVA					
29		df	SS	MS	F	Significance F
30	Regression	4	17794427451.3	4448606862.8	19.80444	0.00017
31	Residual	9	2021641120.1	224626791.1		
32	Total	13	19816068571.4			
33						
34		Coefficients	Standard Error	t Stat	P-value	Lower 95%	Upper 95%	Lower 95.0%	Upper 95.0%
35	Intercept	121658.45	17426.614	6.981	0.000				
36	SF	56.43	6.948	8.122	0.000				
37	AGE	-3962.82	596.028	-6.649	0.000				
38	X3 (Exc.)	33162.65	12179.621	2.723	0.023				
39	X4 (Mint)	47369.25	10649.269	4.448	0.002				

The overall model is helpful since the *Significance F* probability is low (much less than 5%).

This indicates that a house in excellent condition ($X_3 = 1, X_4 = 0$) would sell for about $33,162 more than a house in good condition ($X_3 = 0, X_4 = 0$). A house in mint condition ($X_3 = 0, X_4 = 1$) would sell for about $47,369 more than a house in good condition.

10 Model Building

The value of r^2 can never decrease when more variables are added to the model.

The adjusted r^2 may decrease when more variables are added to the model.

In developing a good regression model, possible independent variables are identified and the best ones are selected to be used in the model. The best model is a statistically significant model with a high r^2 and few variables.

As more variables are added to a regression model, r^2 will usually increase, and it cannot decrease. It is tempting to keep adding variables to a model to try to increase r^2. However, if too many independent variables are included in the model, problems can arise. For this reason, the **adjusted r^2** value is often used (rather than r^2) to determine if an additional independent variable is beneficial. The adjusted r^2 takes into account the number of independent variables in the model, and it is possible for the adjusted r^2 to decrease. The formula for r^2 is

$$r^2 = \frac{\text{SSR}}{\text{SST}} = 1 - \frac{\text{SSE}}{\text{SST}}$$

The adjusted r^2 is

$$\text{Adjusted } r^2 = 1 - \frac{\text{SSE}/(n - k - 1)}{\text{SST}/(n - 1)} \tag{18}$$

Notice that as the number of variables (k) increases, $n - k - 1$ will decrease. This causes SSE$/(n - k - 1)$ to increase, and consequently the adjusted r^2 will decrease unless the extra variable in the model causes a significant decrease in the SSE. Thus, the reduction in error (and SSE) must be sufficient to offset the change in k.

As a general rule of thumb, if the adjusted r^2 increases when a new variable is added to the model, the variable should probably remain in the model. If the adjusted r^2 decreases when a new variable is added, the variable should not remain in the model. Other factors should also be considered when trying to build the model, but they are beyond the introductory level of this chapter.

A variable should not be added to the model if it causes the adjusted r² *to decrease.*

Stepwise Regression

While the process of model building may be tedious, there are many statistical software packages that include stepwise regression procedures to do this. **Stepwise regression** is an automated process to systematically add or delete independent variables from a regression model. A *forward stepwise procedure* puts the most significant variable in the model first and then adds the next variable that will improve the model the most, given that the first variable is already in the model. Variables continue to be added in this fashion until all the variables are in the model or until any remaining variables do not significantly improve the model. A *backward stepwise procedure* begins with all independent variables in the model, and one by one the least helpful variables are deleted. This continues until only significant variables remain. Many variations of these stepwise models exist.

Multicollinearity

In the Jenny Wilson Realty example illustrated in Program 5B, we saw an r^2 of about 0.90 and an adjusted r^2 of 0.85. While other variables such as the size of the lot, the number of bedrooms, and the number of bathrooms might be related to the selling price of a house, we may not want to include these in the model. It is likely that these variables would be correlated with the square footage of the house (e.g., more bedrooms usually means a larger house), which is already included in the model. Thus, the information provided by these additional variables might be duplication of information already in the model.

Multicollinearity exists when a variable is correlated to other variables.

When an independent variable is correlated with one other independent variable, the variables are said to be **collinear**. If an independent variable is correlated with a combination of other independent variables, the condition of **multicollinearity** exists. This can create problems in interpreting the coefficients of the variables as several variables are providing duplicate information. For example, if two independent variables were monthly salary expenses for a company and annual salary expenses for a company, the information provided in one is also provided in the other. Several sets of regression coefficients for these two variables would yield exactly the same results. Thus, individual interpretation of these variables would be questionable, although the model itself is still good for prediction purposes. When multicollinearity exists, the overall F test is still valid, but the hypothesis tests related to the individual coefficients are not. A variable may appear to be significant when it is insignificant, or a variable may appear to be insignificant when it is significant.

11 Nonlinear Regression

The regression models we have seen are linear models. However, at times there exist nonlinear relationships between variables. Some simple variable transformations can be used to create an apparently linear model from a nonlinear relationship. This allows us to use Excel and other linear regression programs to perform the calculations. We will demonstrate this in the following example.

Transformations may be used to turn a nonlinear model into a linear model.

On every new automobile sold in the United States, the fuel efficiency (as measured by miles per gallon [MPG] of gasoline) of the automobile is prominently displayed on the

TABLE 6

Automobile Weight Versus MPG

MPG	WEIGHT (1,000 LB.)	MPG	WEIGHT (1,000 LB.)
12	4.58	20	3.18
13	4.66	23	2.68
15	4.02	24	2.65
18	2.53	33	1.70
19	3.09	36	1.95
19	3.11	42	1.92

window sticker. The MPG is related to several factors, one of which is the weight of the automobile. Engineers at Colonel Motors, in an attempt to improve fuel efficiency, have been asked to study the impact of weight on MPG. They have decided that a regression model should be used to do this.

A sample of 12 new automobiles was selected, and the weight and MPG rating were recorded. Table 6 provides this data. A scatter diagram of this data in Figure 6A shows the weight and MPG. A linear regression line is drawn through the points. Excel was used to develop a simple linear regression equation to relate the MPG (Y) to the weight in 1,000 lb. (X_1) in the form

$$\hat{Y} = b_0 + b_1 X_1$$

The Excel output is shown in Program 6. From this we get the equation

$$\hat{Y} = 47.6 - 8.2 X_1$$

or

$$MPG = 47.6 - 8.2(\text{weight in 1,000 lb.})$$

The model is useful since the significance level for the F test is small and $r^2 = 0.7446$. However, further examination of the graph in Figure 6A brings into question the use of a linear model. Perhaps a nonlinear relationship exists, and maybe the model should be modified

FIGURE 6A

Linear Model for MPG Data

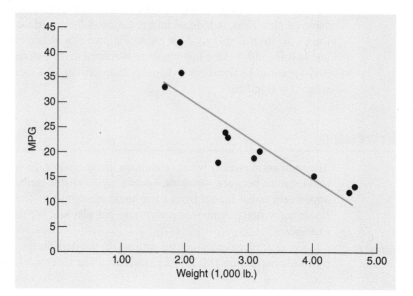

FIGURE 6B
Nonlinear Model for MPG Data

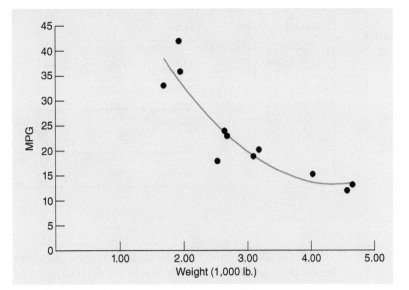

to account for this. A quadratic model is illustrated in Figure 6B. This model would be of the form

$$\text{MPG} = b_0 + b_1(\text{weight}) + b_2(\text{weight})^2$$

The easiest way to develop this model is to define a new variable

$$X_2 = (\text{weight})^2$$

This gives us the model

$$\hat{Y} = b_0 + b_1 X_1 + b_2 X_2$$

We can create another column in Excel, and again run the regression tool. The output is shown in Program 7. The new equation is

$$\hat{Y} = 79.8 - 30.2 X_1 + 3.4 X_2$$

A low significance value for F and a high r² are indications of a good model.

The significance level for F is low (0.0002) so the model is useful, and $r^2 = 0.8478$. The adjusted r^2 increased from 0.719 to 0.814, so this new variable definitely improved the model.

PROGRAM 6

Excel 2013 Output with Linear Regression Model for MPG Data

	A	B	C	D	E	F	G	H	I	J	K	L
1	Automobile Weight vs. MPG			SUMMARY OUTPUT								
2												
3	MPG (Y)	Weight (X1)		Regression Statistics								
4	12	4.58		Multiple R	0.8629							
5	13	4.66		R Square	0.7446							
6	15	4.02		Adjusted R Squ	0.7190							
7	18	2.53		Standard Error	5.0076							
8	19	3.09		Observations	12							
9	19	3.11										
10	20	3.18		ANOVA								
11	23	2.68			df	SS	MS	F	Significance F			
12	24	2.65		Regression	1	730.9090	730.9090	29.1480	0.0003			
13	33	1.70		Residual	10	250.7577	25.0758					
14	36	1.95		Total	11	981.6667						
15	42	1.92										
16					Coefficients	Standard Error	t Stat	P-value	Lower 95%	Upper 95%	Lower 95.0%	Upper 95.0%
17				Intercept	47.619	4.813	9.894	0.000	36.895	58.344	36.895	58.344
18				Weight (X1)	-8.246	1.527	-5.399	0.000	-11.649	-4.843	-11.649	-4.843

PROGRAM 7

Excel 2013 Output with Nonlinear Regression Model for MPG Data

	A	B	C	D	E	F	G	H	I	J	K	L
1	Automobile Weight vs. MPG			SUMMARY OUTPUT								
2												
3	MPG (Y)	Weight (X1)	WeightSq.(X2)	*Regression Statistics*								
4	12	4.58	20.98	Multiple R	0.9208							
5	13	4.66	21.72	R Square	0.8478							
6	15	4.02	16.16	Adjusted R Square	0.8140							
7	18	2.53	6.40	Standard Error	4.0745							
8	19	3.09	9.55	Observations	12.0000							
9	19	3.11	9.67									
10	20	3.18	10.11	ANOVA								
11	23	2.68	7.18			df	SS	MS	F	Significance F		
12	24	2.65	7.02	Regression		2	832.2557	416.1278	25.0661	0.0002		
13	33	1.70	2.89	Residual		9	149.4110	16.6012				
14	36	1.95	3.80	Total		11	981.6667					
15	42	1.92	3.69									
16					Coefficients	Standard Erro	t Stat	P-value	Lower 95%	Upper 95%	ower 95.0%	Jpper 95.0%
17				Intercept	79.7888	13.5962	5.8685	0.0002	49.0321	110.5454	49.0321	110.5454
18				Weight (X1)	-30.2224	8.9809	-3.3652	0.0083	-50.5386	-9.9062	-50.5386	-9.9062
19				WeightSq.(X2)	3.4124	1.3811	2.4708	0.0355	0.2881	6.5367	0.2881	6.5367

This model is good for prediction purposes. However, we should not try to interpret the coefficients of the variables due to the correlation between X_1 (weight) and X_2 (weight squared). Normally we would interpret the coefficient for X_1 as the change in Y that results from a 1-unit change in X_1, while holding all other variables constant. Obviously holding one variable constant while changing the other is impossible in this example since $X_2 = X_1^2$. If X_1 changes, then X_2 must change also. This is an example of a problem that exists when multicollinearity is present.

Other types of nonlinearities can be handled using a similar approach. A number of transformations exist that may help to develop a linear model from variables with nonlinear relationships.

12 Cautions and Pitfalls in Regression Analysis

This chapter has provided a brief introduction into regression analysis, one of the most widely used quantitative techniques in business. However, some common errors are made with regression models, so caution should be observed when using this.

If the assumptions are not met, the statistical tests may not be valid. Any interval estimates are also invalid, although the model can still be used for prediction purposes.

A high correlation does not mean one variable is causing a change in the other.

Correlation does not necessarily mean causation. Two variables (such as the price of automobiles and your annual salary) may be highly correlated to one another, but one is not causing the other to change. They may both be changing due to other factors such as the economy in general or the inflation rate.

If multicollinearity is present in a multiple regression model, the model is still good for prediction, but interpretation of individual coefficients is questionable. The individual tests on the regression coefficients are not valid.

The regression equation should not be used with values of X that are below the lowest value of X or above the highest value of X found in the sample.

Using a regression equation beyond the range of X is very questionable. A linear relationship may exist within the range of values of X in the sample. What happens beyond this range is unknown; the linear relationship may become nonlinear at some point. For example, there is usually a linear relationship between advertising and sales within a limited range. As more money is spent on advertising, sales tend to increase even if everything else is held constant. However, at some point, increasing advertising expenditures will have less impact on sales unless the company does other things to help, such as opening new markets or expanding the product offerings. If advertising is increased and nothing else changes, the sales will probably level off at some point.

Related to the limitation regarding the range of X is the interpretation of the intercept (b_0). Since the lowest value for X in a sample is often much greater than 0, the intercept is a point on the regression line beyond the range of X. Therefore, we should not be concerned if the t-test for this coefficient is not significant as we should not be using the regression equation to predict a value of Y when $X = 0$. This intercept is merely used in defining the line that fits the sample points the best.

Using the F test and concluding a linear regression model is helpful in predicting Y does not mean that this is the best relationship. While this model may explain much of the variability in Y, it is possible that a nonlinear relationship might explain even more. Similarly, if it is concluded that no linear relationship exists, another type of relationship could exist.

A significant F *value may occur even when the relationship is not strong.*

A statistically significant relationship does not mean it has any practical value. With large enough samples, it is possible to have a statistically significant relationship, but r^2 might be 0.01. This would normally be of little use to a manager. Similarly, a high r^2 could be found due to random chance if the sample is small. The F test must also show significance to place any value in r^2.

Summary

Regression analysis is an extremely valuable quantitative tool. Using scatter diagrams helps to see relationships between variables. The F test is used to determine if the results can be considered useful. The coefficient of determination (r^2) is used to measure the proportion of variability in Y that is explained by the regression model. The correlation coefficient measures the relationship between two variables.

Multiple regression involves the use of more than one independent variable. Dummy variables (binary or indicator variables) are used with qualitative or categorical data. Nonlinear models can be transformed into linear models.

We saw how to use Excel to develop regression models. Interpretation of computer output was presented, and several examples were provided.

Glossary

Adjusted r^2   A measure of the explanatory power of a regression model that takes into consideration the number of independent variables in the model.

Binary Variable   See Dummy Variable.

Coefficient of Correlation (r)   A measure of the strength of the relationship between two variables.

Coefficient of Determination (r^2)   The percent of the variability in the dependent variable (Y) that is explained by the regression equation.

Collinearity   A condition that exists when one independent variable is correlated with another independent variable.

Dependent Variable   The Y variable in a regression model. This is what is being predicted.

Dummy Variable   A variable used to represent a qualitative factor or condition. Dummy variables have values of 0 or 1. This is also called a binary variable or an indicator variable.

Error   The difference between the actual value (Y) and the predicted value ($\hat{Y}$).

Explanatory Variable   The independent variable in a regression equation.

Independent Variable   The X variable in a regression equation. This is used to help predict the dependent variable.

Least Squares   A reference to the criterion used to select the regression line, to minimize the squared distances between the estimated straight line and the observed values.

Mean Squared Error (MSE)   An estimate of the error variance.

Multicollinearity   A condition that exists when one independent variable is correlated with other independent variables.

Multiple Regression Model   A regression model that has more than one independent variable.

Observed Significance Level   Another name for p-value.

p-Value   A probability value that is used when testing a hypothesis. The hypothesis is rejected when this is low.

Predictor Variable   Another name for explanatory variable.

Regression Analysis   A forecasting procedure that uses the least-squares approach on one or more independent variables to develop a forecasting model.

Residual   Another term for error.

Response Variable   The dependent variable in a regression equation.

Scatter Diagrams or **Scatter Plot**   Diagrams of the variable to be forecasted, plotted against another variable, such as time. Also called scatter plots.

Standard Error of the Estimate   An estimate of the standard deviation of the errors and is sometimes called the standard deviation of the regression.

Stepwise Regression   An automated process to systematically add or delete independent variables from a regression model.

Sum of Squares Error (SSE)   The total sum of the squared differences between each observation (Y) and the predicted value ($\hat{Y}$).

Sum of Squares Regression (SSR)   The total sum of the squared differences between each predicted value ($\hat{Y}$) and the mean ($\overline{Y}$).

Sum of Squares Total (SST)   The total sum of the squared differences between each observation (Y) and the mean ($\overline{Y}$).

Key Equations

(1) $Y = \beta_0 + \beta_1 X + \epsilon$

Underlying linear model for simple linear regression.

(2) $\hat{Y} = b_0 + b_1 X$

Simple linear regression model computed from a sample.

(3) $e = Y - \hat{Y}$

Error in regression model.

(4) $b_1 = \dfrac{\Sigma (X - \overline{X})(Y - \overline{Y})}{\Sigma (X - \overline{X})^2}$

Slope in the regression line.

(5) $b_0 = \overline{Y} - b_1 \overline{X}$

The intercept in the regression line.

(6) $\text{SST} = \Sigma (Y - \overline{Y})^2$

Total sums of squares.

(7) $\text{SSE} = \Sigma e^2 = \Sigma (Y - \hat{Y})^2$

Sum of squares due to error.

(8) $\text{SSR} = \Sigma (\hat{Y} - \overline{Y})^2$

Sum of squares due to regression.

(9) $\text{SST} = \text{SSR} + \text{SSE}$

Relationship among sums of squares in regression.

(10) $r^2 = \dfrac{\text{SSR}}{\text{SST}} = 1 - \dfrac{\text{SSE}}{\text{SST}}$

Coefficient of determination.

(11) $r = \pm \sqrt{r^2}$

Coefficient of correlation. This has the same sign as the slope.

(12) $s^2 = \text{MSE} = \dfrac{\text{SSE}}{n - k - 1}$

An estimate of the variance of the errors in regression; n is the sample size and k is the number of independent variables.

(13) $s = \sqrt{\text{MSE}}$

An estimate of the standard deviation of the errors. Also called the standard error of the estimate.

(14) $\text{MSR} = \dfrac{\text{SSR}}{k}$

Mean square regression. k is the number of independent variables.

(15) $F = \dfrac{\text{MSR}}{\text{MSE}}$

F statistic used to test significance of overall regression model.

(16) $Y = \beta_0 + \beta_1 X_1 + \beta_2 X_2 + \cdots + \beta_k X_k + \epsilon$

Underlying model for multiple regression model.

(17) $\hat{Y} = b_0 + b_1 X_1 + b_2 X_2 + \cdots + b_k X_k$

Multiple regression model computed from a sample.

(18) Adjusted $r^2 = 1 - \dfrac{\text{SSE}/(n - k - 1)}{\text{SST}/(n - 1)}$

Adjusted r^2 used in building multiple regression models.

Solved Problems

Solved Problem 1

Judith Thompson runs a florist shop on the Gulf Coast of Texas, specializing in floral arrangements for weddings and other special events. She advertises weekly in the local newspapers and is considering increasing her advertising budget. Before doing so, she decides to evaluate the past effectiveness of these ads. Five weeks are sampled, and the advertising dollars and sales volume for each of these are shown in the following table. Develop a regression equation that would help Judith evaluate her advertising. Find the coefficient of determination for this model.

SALES ($1,000)	ADVERTISING ($100)
11	5
6	3
10	7
6	2
12	8

Solution

SALES Y	ADVERTISING X	$(X - \bar{X})^2$	$(X - \bar{X})(Y - \bar{Y})$
11	5	$(5 - 5)^2 = 0$	$(5 - 5)(11 - 9) = 0$
6	3	$(3 - 5)^2 = 4$	$(3 - 5)(6 - 9) = 6$
10	7	$(7 - 5)^2 = 4$	$(7 - 5)(10 - 9) = 2$
6	2	$(2 - 5)^2 = 9$	$(2 - 5)(6 - 9) = 9$
12	8	$(8 - 5)^2 = 9$	$(8 - 5)(12 - 9) = 9$
$\sum Y = 45$	$\sum X = 25$	$\sum(X - \bar{X})^2 = 26$	$\sum(X - \bar{X})(Y - \bar{Y}) = 26$
$\bar{Y} = 45/5$	$\bar{X} = 25/5$		
$= 9$	$= 5$		

$$b_1 = \frac{\sum(X - \bar{X})(Y - \bar{Y})}{\sum(X - \bar{X})^2} = \frac{26}{26} = 1$$

$$b_0 = \bar{Y} - b_1\bar{X} = 9 - (1)(5) = 4$$

The regression equation is

$$\hat{Y} = 4 + 1X$$

To compute r^2, we use the following table:

Y	X	$\hat{Y} = 4 + 1X$	$(\hat{Y} - \bar{Y})^2$	$(Y - \bar{Y})^2$
11	5	9	$(11 - 9)^2 = 4$	$(11 - 9)^2 = 4$
6	3	7	$(6 - 7)^2 = 1$	$(6 - 9)^2 = 9$
10	7	11	$(10 - 11)^2 = 1$	$(10 - 9)^2 = 1$
6	2	6	$(6 - 6)^2 = 0$	$(6 - 9)^2 = 9$
12	8	12	$(12 - 12)^2 = 0$	$(12 - 9)^2 = 9$
$\sum Y = 45$	$\sum X = 25$		$\sum(Y - \hat{Y})^2 = 6$	$\sum(Y - \bar{Y})^2 = 32$
$\bar{Y} = 9$	$\bar{X} = 5$		SSE	SST

The slope $(b_1 = 1)$ tells us that for each 1 unit increase in X (or \$100 in advertising), sales increase by 1 unit (or \$1,000). Also, $r^2 = 0.8125$ indicating that about 81% of the variability in sales can be explained by the regression model with advertising as the independent variable.

Solved Problem 2

Use Excel with the data in Solved Problem 1 to find the regression model. What does the F test say about this model?

Solution

Program 8 provides the Excel output for this problem. We see the equation is

$$\hat{Y} = 4 + 1X$$

The coefficient of determination (r^2) is shown to be 0.8125. The significance level for the F test is 0.0366, which is less than 0.05. This indicates the model is statistically significant. Thus, there is sufficient evidence in the data to conclude that the model is useful, and there is a relationship between X (advertising) and Y (sales).

PROGRAM 8

Excel 2013 Output for Solved Problem 2

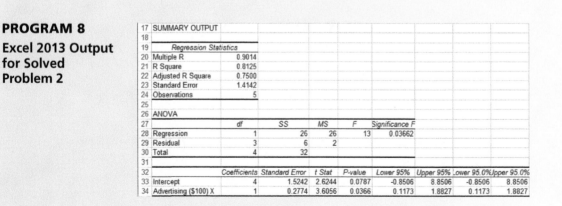

17	SUMMARY OUTPUT								
18									
19	Regression Statistics								
20	Multiple R	0.9014							
21	R Square	0.8125							
22	Adjusted R Square	0.7500							
23	Standard Error	1.4142							
24	Observations	5							
25									
26	ANOVA								
27		df	SS	MS	F	Significance F			
28	Regression	1	26	26	13	0.03662			
29	Residual	3	6	2					
30	Total	4	32						
31									
32		Coefficients	Standard Error	t Stat	P-value	Lower 95%	Upper 95%	Lower 95.0%	Upper 95.0%
33	Intercept	4	1.5242	2.6244	0.0787	-0.8506	8.8506	-0.8506	8.8506
34	Advertising ($100) X	1	0.2774	3.6056	0.0366	0.1173	1.8827	0.1173	1.8827

Self-Test

- Before taking the self-test, refer to the learning objectives at the beginning of the chapter, the notes in the margins, and the glossary at the end of the chapter.
- Use the key at the end of the chapter to correct your answers.
- Restudy pages that correspond to any questions that you answered incorrectly or material you feel uncertain about.

1. One of the assumptions in regression analysis is that
   a. the errors have a mean of 1.
   b. the errors have a mean of 0.
   c. the observations (Y) have a mean of 1.
   d. the observations (Y) have a mean of 0.
2. A graph of the sample points that will be used to develop a regression line is called
   a. a sample graph.
   b. a regression diagram.
   c. a scatter diagram.
   d. a regression plot.
3. When using regression, an error is also called
   a. an intercept.
   b. a prediction.
   c. a coefficient.
   d. a residual.
4. In a regression model, Y is called
   a. the independent variable.
   b. the dependent variable.
   c. the regression variable.
   d. the predictor variable.
5. A quantity that provides a measure of how far each sample point is from the regression line is
   a. the SSR.
   b. the SSE.
   c. the SST.
   d. the MSR.
6. The percentage of the variation in the dependent variable that is explained by a regression equation is measured by
   a. the coefficient of correlation.
   b. the MSE.
   c. the coefficient of determination.
   d. the slope.
7. In a regression model, if every sample point is on the regression line (all errors are 0), then
   a. the correlation coefficient would be 0.
   b. the correlation coefficient would be -1 or 1.
   c. the coefficient of determination would be -1.
   d. the coefficient of determination would be 0.
8. When using dummy variables in a regression equation to model a qualitative or categorical variable, the number of dummy variables should equal
   a. the number of categories.
   b. 1 more than the number of categories.
   c. 1 less than the number of categories.
   d. the number of other independent variables in the model.
9. A multiple regression model differs from a simple linear regression model because the multiple regression model has more than one
   a. independent variable.
   b. dependent variable.
   c. intercept.
   d. error.
10. The overall significance of a regression model is tested using an F test. The model is significant if
    a. the F value is low.
    b. the significance level of the F value is low.
    c. the r^2 value is low.
    d. the slope is lower than the intercept.
11. A new variable should not be added to a multiple regression model if that variable causes
    a. r^2 to decrease.
    b. the adjusted r^2 to decrease.
    c. the SST to decrease.
    d. the intercept to decrease.
12. A good regression model should have
    a. a low r^2 and a low significance level for the F test.
    b. a high r^2 and a high significance level for the F test.
    c. a high r^2 and a low significance level for the F test.
    d. a low r^2 and a high significance level for the F test.

Discussion Questions and Problems

Discussion Questions

1 What is the meaning of least squares in a regression model?

2 Discuss the use of dummy variables in regression analysis.

3 Discuss how the coefficient of determination and the coefficient of correlation are related and how they are used in regression analysis.

4 Explain how a scatter diagram can be used to identify the type of regression to use.

5 Explain how the adjusted r^2 value is used in developing a regression model.

6 Explain what information is provided by the F test.

7 What is the SSE? How is this related to the SST and the SSR?

8 Explain how a plot of the residuals can be used in developing a regression model.

Problems

9 John Smith has developed the following forecasting model:

$$\hat{Y} = 36 + 4.3X_1$$

where

$\hat{Y}$ = Demand for K10 air conditioners

X_1 = the outside temperature (°F)

(a) Forecast the demand for K10 when the temperature is 70°F.

(b) What is the demand for a temperature of 80°F?

(c) What is the demand for a temperature of 90°F?

10 The operations manager of a musical instrument distributor feels that demand for a particular type of guitar may be related to the number of YouTube views for a music video by the popular rock group Marble Pumpkins during the preceding month. The manager has collected the data shown in the following table:

YouTube VIEWS (1,000s)	GUITAR SALES
30	8
40	11
70	12
60	10
80	15
50	13

(a) Graph these data to see whether a linear equation might describe the relationship between the views on YouTube and guitar sales.

(b) Using the equations presented in this chapter, compute the SST, SSE, and SSR. Find the least-squares regression line for these data.

(c) Using the regression equation, predict guitar sales if there were 40,000 views last month.

11 Using the data in Problem 10, test to see if there is a statistically significant relationship between sales and YouTube views at the 0.05 level of significance. Use the formulas in this chapter and Appendix: F Distribution Values.

12 Using computer software, find the least-squares regression line for the data in Problem 10. Based on the F test, is there a statistically significant relationship between the demand for guitars and the number of YouTube views?

13 Students in a management science class have just received their grades on the first test. The instructor has provided information about the first test grades in some previous classes as well as the final average for the same students. Some of these grades have been sampled and are as follows:

STUDENT	1	2	3	4	5	6	7	8	9
1st test grade	98	77	88	80	96	61	66	95	69
Final average	93	78	84	73	84	64	64	95	76

(a) Develop a regression model that could be used to predict the final average in the course based on the first test grade.

(b) Predict the final average of a student who made an 83 on the first test.

(c) Give the values of r and r^2 for this model. Interpret the value of r^2 in the context of this problem.

14 Using the data in Problem 13, test to see if there is a statistically significant relationship between the grade on the first test and the final average at the 0.05 level of significance. Use the formulas in this chapter and Appendix: F Distribution Values.

15 Using computer software, find the least-squares regression line for the data in Problem 13. Based on the F test, is there a statistically significant relationship between the first test grade and the final average in the course?

16 Steve Caples, a real estate appraiser in Lake Charles, Louisiana, has developed a regression model to help appraise residential housing in the Lake Charles area. The model was developed using recently sold homes in a particular neighborhood. The price (Y) of the house is based on the square footage (X) of the house. The model is

$$\hat{Y} = 33,478 + 62.4X$$

The coefficient of correlation for the model is 0.63.

(a) Use the model to predict the selling price of a house that is 1,860 square feet.

(b) A house with 1,860 square feet recently sold for $165,000. Explain why this is not what the model predicted.

(c) If you were going to use multiple regression to develop an appraisal model, what other quantitative variables might be included in the model?

(d) What is the coefficient of determination for this model?

17 Accountants at the firm Walker and Walker believed that several traveling executives submit unusually high travel vouchers when they return from business trips. The accountants took a sample of 200 vouchers submitted from the past year; they then developed the following multiple regression equation relating expected travel cost (Y) to number of days on the road (X_1) and distance traveled (X_2) in miles:

$$\hat{Y} = \$90.00 + \$48.50X_1 + \$0.40X_2$$

Note: <img> means the problem may be solved with QM for Windows; <img> means the problem may be solved with Excel QM; and <img> means the problem may be solved with QM for Windows and/or Excel QM.

The coefficient of correlation computed was 0.68.

(a) If Thomas Williams returns from a 300-mile trip that took him out of town for 5 days, what is the expected amount that he should claim as expenses?

(b) Williams submitted a reimbursement request for $685; what should the accountant do?

(c) Comment on the validity of this model. Should any other variables be included? Which ones? Why?

18 Thirteen students entered the undergraduate business program at Rollins College 2 years ago. The following table indicates what their grade-point averages (GPAs) were after being in the program for 2 years and what each student scored on the SAT exam (maximum 2400) when he or she was in high school. Is there a meaningful relationship between grades and SAT scores? If a student scores a 1200 on the SAT, what do you think his or her GPA will be? What about a student who scores 2400?

STUDENT	SAT SCORE	GPA	STUDENT	SAT SCORE	GPA
A	1263	2.90	H	1443	2.53
B	1131	2.93	I	2187	3.22
C	1755	3.00	J	1503	1.99
D	2070	3.45	K	1839	2.75
E	1824	3.66	L	2127	3.90
F	1170	2.88	M	1098	1.60
G	1245	2.15			

19 Bus and subway ridership in Washington, D.C., during the summer months is believed to be heavily tied to the number of tourists visiting the city. During the past 12 years, the following data have been obtained:

YEAR	NUMBER OF TOURISTS (1,000,000s)	RIDERSHIP (100,000s)
1	7	15
2	2	10
3	6	13
4	4	15
5	14	25
6	15	27
7	16	24
8	12	20
9	14	27
10	20	44
11	15	34
12	7	17

(a) Plot these data and determine whether a linear model is reasonable.

(b) Develop a regression model.

(c) What is expected ridership if 10 million tourists visit the city?

(d) If there are no tourists at all, explain the predicted ridership.

20 Use computer software to develop a regression model for the data in Problem 19. Explain what this output indicates about the usefulness of this model.

21 The following data give the starting salary for students who recently graduated from a local university and accepted jobs soon after graduation. The starting salary, grade-point average (GPA), and major (business or other) are provided.

SALARY	$29,500	$46,000	$39,800	$36,500
GPA	3.1	3.5	3.8	2.9
Major	Other	Business	Business	Other

SALARY	$42,000	$31,500	$36,200
GPA	3.4	2.1	2.5
Major	Business	Other	Business

(a) Using a computer, develop a regression model that could be used to predict starting salary based on GPA and major.

(b) Use this model to predict the starting salary for a business major with a GPA of 3.0.

(c) What does the model say about the starting salary for a business major compared to a nonbusiness major?

(d) Do you believe this model is useful in predicting the starting salary? Justify your answer, using information provided in the computer output.

22 The following data give the selling price, square footage, number of bedrooms, and age of houses that have sold in a neighborhood in the past 6 months. Develop three regression models to predict the selling price based upon each of the other factors individually. Which of these is best?

SELLING PRICE ($)	SQUARE FOOTAGE	BEDROOMS	AGE (YEARS)
84,000	1,670	2	30
79,000	1,339	2	25
91,500	1,712	3	30
120,000	1,840	3	40
127,500	2,300	3	18
132,500	2,234	3	30
145,000	2,311	3	19
164,000	2,377	3	7
155,000	2,736	4	10
168,000	2,500	3	1
172,500	2,500	4	3
174,000	2,479	3	3
175,000	2,400	3	1
177,500	3,124	4	0
184,000	2,500	3	2
195,500	4,062	4	10
195,000	2,854	3	3

153

☠: 23 Use the data in Problem 22 and develop a regression model to predict selling price based on the square footage and number of bedrooms. Use this to predict the selling price of a 2,000-square-foot house with three bedrooms. Compare this model with the models in Problem 22. Should the number of bedrooms be included in the model? Why or why not?

☠: 24 Use the data in Problem 22 and develop a regression model to predict selling price based on the square footage, number of bedrooms, and age. Use this to predict the selling price of a 10-year-old, 2,000-square-foot house with three bedrooms.

☠: 25 The total expenses of a hospital are related to many factors. Two of these factors are the number of beds in the hospital and the number of admissions. Data were collected on 14 hospitals, as shown in the following table:

HOSPITAL	NUMBER OF BEDS	ADMISSIONS (100s)	TOTAL EXPENSES (MILLIONS)
1	215	77	57
2	336	160	127
3	520	230	157
4	135	43	24
5	35	9	14
6	210	155	93
7	140	53	45
8	90	6	6
9	410	159	99
10	50	18	12
11	65	16	11
12	42	29	15
13	110	28	21
14	305	98	63

Find the best regression model to predict the total expenses of a hospital. Discuss the accuracy of this model. Should both variables be included in the model? Why or why not?

☠: 26 A sample of 20 automobiles was taken, and the miles per gallon (MPG), horsepower, and total weight were recorded. Develop a linear regression model to predict MPG, using horsepower as the only independent variable. Develop another model with weight as the independent variable. Which of these two models is better? Explain.

MPG	HORSEPOWER	WEIGHT
44	67	1,844
44	50	1,998
40	62	1,752

MPG	HORSEPOWER	WEIGHT
37	69	1,980
37	66	1,797
34	63	2,199
35	90	2,404
32	99	2,611
30	63	3,236
28	91	2,606
26	94	2,580
26	88	2,507
25	124	2,922
22	97	2,434
20	114	3,248
21	102	2,812
18	114	3,382
18	142	3,197
16	153	4,380
16	139	4,036

☠: 27 Use the data in Problem 26 to develop a multiple linear regression model. How does this compare with each of the models in Problem 26?

☠: 28 Use the data in Problem 26 to find the best quadratic regression model. (There is more than one to consider.) How does this compare to the models in Problems 26 and 27?

☠: 29 A sample of nine public universities and nine private universities was taken. The total cost for the year (including room and board) and the median SAT score (maximum total is 2400) at each school were recorded. It was felt that schools with higher median SAT scores would have a better reputation and would charge more tuition as a result of that. The data are in the following table. Use regression to help answer the following questions based on this sample data. Do schools with higher SAT scores charge more in tuition and fees? Are private schools more expensive than public schools when SAT scores are taken into consideration? Discuss how accurate you believe these results are using information related to the regression models.

CATEGORY	TOTAL COST ($)	MEDIAN SAT
Public	21,700	1990
Public	15,600	1620
Public	16,900	1810
Public	15,400	1540
Public	23,100	1540
Public	21,400	1600
Public	16,500	1560
Public	23,500	1890

(Continued on next page)

CATEGORY	TOTAL COST ($)	MEDIAN SAT
Public	20,200	1620
Private	30,400	1630
Private	41,500	1840
Private	36,100	1980
Private	42,100	1930
Private	27,100	2130
Private	34,800	2010
Private	32,100	1590
Private	31,800	1720
Private	32,100	1770

30 In 2012, the total payroll for the New York Yankees was almost $200 million, while the total payroll for the Oakland Athletics (a team known for using baseball analytics or sabermetrics) was about $55 million, less than one-third of the Yankees payroll. In the following table, you will see the payrolls (in millions) and the total number of victories for the baseball teams in the American League in the 2012 season. Develop a regression model to predict the total number of victories based on the payroll. Use the model to predict the number of victories for a team with a payroll of $79 million. Based on the results of the computer output, discuss the relationship between payroll and victories.

TEAM	PAYROLL ($MILLIONS)	NUMBER OF VICTORIES
Baltimore Orioles	81.4	93
Boston Red Sox	173.2	69
Chicago White Sox	96.9	85
Cleveland Indians	78.4	68
Detroit Tigers	132.3	88
Kansas City Royals	60.9	72
Los Angeles Angels	154.5	89
Minnesota Twins	94.1	66
New York Yankees	198.0	95
Oakland Athletics	55.4	94
Seattle Mariners	82.0	75
Tampa Bay Rays	64.2	90
Texas Rangers	120.5	93
Toronto Blue Jays	75.5	73

31 The number of victories (W), earned run average (ERA), runs scored (R), batting average (AVG), and on-base percentage (OBP) for each team in the American League in the 2012 season are provided in the following table. The ERA is one measure of the effectiveness of the pitching staff, and a lower number is better. The other statistics are measures of effectiveness of the hitters, and higher numbers are better for each of these.

TEAM	W	ERA	R	AVG	OBP
Baltimore Orioles	93	3.90	712	0.247	0.311
Boston Red Sox	69	4.70	734	0.260	0.315
Chicago White Sox	85	4.02	748	0.255	0.318
Cleveland Indians	68	4.78	667	0.251	0.324
Detroit Tigers	88	3.75	726	0.268	0.335
Kansas City Royals	72	4.30	676	0.265	0.317
Los Angeles Angels	89	4.02	767	0.274	0.332
Minnesota Twins	66	4.77	701	0.260	0.325
New York Yankees	95	3.85	804	0.265	0.337
Oakland Athletics	94	3.48	713	0.238	0.310
Seattle Mariners	75	3.76	619	0.234	0.296
Tampa Bay Rays	90	3.19	697	0.240	0.317
Texas Rangers	93	3.99	808	0.273	0.334
Toronto Blue Jays	73	4.64	716	0.245	0.309

(a) Develop a regression model that could be used to predict the number of victories based on the ERA.

(b) Develop a regression model that could be used to predict the number of victories based on the runs scored.

(c) Develop a regression model that could be used to predict the number of victories based on the batting average.

(d) Develop a regression model that could be used to predict the number of victories based on the on-base percentage.

(e) Which of the four models is better for predicting the number of victories?

(f) Find the best multiple regression model to predict the number of wins. Use any combination of the variables to find the best model.

32 The closing stock price for each of two stocks was recorded over a 12-month period. The closing price for the Dow Jones Industrial Average (DJIA) was also recorded over this same time period. These values are shown in the following table:

MONTH	DJIA	STOCK 1	STOCK 2
1	11,168	48.5	32.4
2	11,150	48.2	31.7
3	11,186	44.5	31.9
4	11,381	44.7	36.6
5	11,679	49.3	36.7
6	12,081	49.3	38.7
7	12,222	46.1	39.5
8	12,463	46.2	41.2
9	12,622	47.7	43.3
10	12,269	48.3	39.4
11	12,354	47.0	40.1
12	13,063	47.9	42.1
13	13,326	47.8	45.2

(a) Develop a regression model to predict the price of stock 1 based on the Dow Jones Industrial Average.

(b) Develop a regression model to predict the price of stock 2 based on the Dow Jones Industrial Average.

(c) Which of the two stocks is most highly correlated to the Dow Jones Industrial Average over this time period?

Case Study

North–South Airline

In January 2012, Northern Airlines merged with Southeast Airlines to create the fourth largest U.S. carrier. The new North–South Airline inherited both an aging fleet of Boeing 727-300 aircraft and Stephen Ruth. Stephen was a tough former Secretary of the Navy who stepped in as new president and chairman of the board.

Stephen's first concern in creating a financially solid company was maintenance costs. It was commonly surmised in the airline industry that maintenance costs rise with the age of the aircraft. He quickly noticed that historically there had been a significant difference in the reported B727-300 maintenance costs (from ATA Form 41s) in both the airframe and engine areas between Northern Airlines and Southeast Airlines, with Southeast having the newer fleet.

On February 12, 2012, Peg Jones, vice president for operations and maintenance, was called into Stephen's office and asked to study the issue. Specifically, Stephen wanted to know whether the average fleet age was correlated to direct airframe maintenance costs, and whether there was a relationship between average fleet age and direct engine maintenance costs. Peg was to report back by February 26 with the answer, along with quantitative and graphical descriptions of the relationship.

Peg's first step was to have her staff construct the average age of Northern and Southeast B727-300 fleets, by quarter, since the introduction of that aircraft to service by each airline in late 1993 and early 1994. The average age of each fleet was calculated by first multiplying the total number of calendar days each aircraft had been in service at the pertinent point in time by the average daily utilization of the respective fleet to total fleet hours flown. The total fleet hours flown was then divided by the number of aircraft in service at that time, giving the age of the "average" aircraft in the fleet.

The average utilization was found by taking the actual total fleet hours flown on September 30, 2011, from Northern and Southeast data, and dividing by the total days in service for all aircraft at that time. The average utilization for Southeast was 8.3 hours per day, and the average utilization for Northern was 8.7 hours per day. Because the available cost data were calculated for each yearly period ending at the end of the first quarter, average fleet age was calculated at the same points in time. The fleet data are shown in the following table. Airframe cost data and engine cost data are both shown paired with fleet average age in that table.

Discussion Question

1. Prepare Peg Jones's response to Stephen Ruth.

Note: Dates and names of airlines and individuals have been changed in this case to maintain confidentiality. The data and issues described here are real.

North–South Airline Data for Boeing 727-300 Jets

| | NORTHERN AIRLINE DATA | | | | SOUTHEAST AIRLINE DATA | | |
YEAR	AIRFRAME COST PER AIRCRAFT ($)	ENGINE COST PER AIRCRAFT ($)	AVERAGE AGE (HOURS)		AIRFRAME COST PER AIRCRAFT ($)	ENGINE COST PER AIRCRAFT ($)	AVERAGE AGE (HOURS)
2001	51.80	43.49	6,512		13.29	18.86	5,107
2002	54.92	38.58	8,404		25.15	31.55	8,145
2003	69.70	51.48	11,077		32.18	40.43	7,360
2004	68.90	58.72	11,717		31.78	22.10	5,773
2005	63.72	45.47	13,275		25.34	19.69	7,150
2006	84.73	50.26	15,215		32.78	32.58	9,364
2007	78.74	79.60	18,390		35.56	38.07	8,259

Bibliography

Berenson, Mark L., David M. Levine, and Timothy C. Kriehbiel. *Basic Business Statistics*, 12th ed. Upper Saddle River, NJ: Prentice Hall, 2012.

Black, Ken. *Business Statistics: For Contemporary Decision Making*, 7th ed. John Wiley & Sons, Inc., 2012.

Draper, Norman R., and Harry Smith. *Applied Regression Analysis*, 3rd ed. New York: John Wiley & Sons, Inc., 1998.

Kutner, Michael, John Neter, and Chris J. Nachtsheim. *Applied Linear Regression Models*, 4th ed. Boston; New York: McGraw-Hill/Irwin, 2004.

Mendenhall, William, and Terry L. Sincich. *A Second Course in Statistics: Regression Analysis*, 7th ed. Upper Saddle River, NJ: Prentice Hall, 2012.

Appendix 1:   Formulas for Regression Calculations

When performing regression calculations by hand, there are other formulas that can make the task easier and are mathematically equivalent to the ones presented in the chapter. These, however, make it more difficult to see the logic behind the formulas and to understand what the results actually mean.

When using these formulas, it helps to set up a table with the columns shown in Table 7, which has the Triple A Construction Company data that were used earlier in the chapter. The sample size (n) is 6. The totals for all columns are shown, and the averages for X and Y are calculated. Once this is done, we can use the following formulas for computations in a simple linear regression model (one independent variable). The simple linear regression equation is again given as

$$\hat{Y} = b_0 + b_1 X$$

Slope of regression equation:

$$b_1 = \frac{\sum XY - n\overline{X}\,\overline{Y}}{\sum X^2 - n\overline{X}^2}$$

$$b_1 = \frac{180.5 - 6(4)(7)}{106 - 6(4^2)} = 1.25$$

Intercept of regression equation:

$$b_0 = \overline{Y} - b_1\overline{X}$$

$$b_0 = 7 - 1.25(4) = 2$$

Sum of squares of the error:

$$\text{SSE} = \sum Y^2 - b_0 \sum Y - b_1 \sum XY$$

$$\text{SSE} = 316.5 - 2(42) - 1.25(180.5) = 6.875$$

TABLE 7 Preliminary Calculations for Triple A Construction

Y	X	Y^2	X^2	XY
6	3	$6^2 = 36$	$3^2 = 9$	$3(6) = 18$
8	4	$8^2 = 64$	$4^2 = 16$	$4(8) = 32$
9	6	$9^2 = 81$	$6^2 = 36$	$6(9) = 54$
5	4	$5^2 = 25$	$4^2 = 16$	$4(5) = 20$
4.5	2	$4.5^2 = 20.25$	$2^2 = 4$	$2(4.5) = 9$
9.5	5	$9.5^2 = 90.25$	$5^2 = 25$	$5(9.5) = 47.5$
$\sum Y = 42$	$\sum X = 24$	$\sum Y^2 = 316.5$	$\sum X^2 = 106$	$\sum XY = 180.5$
$\overline{Y} = 42/6 = 7$	$\overline{X} = 24/6 = 4$			

Estimate of the error variance:

$$s^2 = \text{MSE} = \frac{\text{SSE}}{n-2}$$

$$s^2 = \frac{6.875}{6-2} = 1.71875$$

Estimate of the error standard deviation:

$$s = \sqrt{\text{MSE}}$$
$$s = \sqrt{1.71875} = 1.311$$

Coefficient of determination:

$$r^2 = 1 - \frac{\text{SSE}}{\sum Y^2 - n\bar{Y}^2}$$

$$r^2 = 1 - \frac{6.875}{316.5 - 6(7^2)} = 0.6944$$

This formula for the correlation coefficient automatically determines the sign of r. This could also be found by taking the square root of r^2 and giving it the same sign as the slope:

$$r = \frac{n\sum XY - \sum X \sum Y}{\sqrt{[n\sum X^2 - (\sum X)^2][n\sum Y^2 - (\sum Y)^2]}}$$

$$r = \frac{6(180.5) - (24)(42)}{\sqrt{[6(106) - 24^2][6(316.5) - 42^2]}} = 0.833$$

Solutions to Selected Problems

10 (b) SST = 29.5 SSE = 12 SSR = 17.5 $\hat{Y} = 6 + 0.1X$ (c) $\hat{Y} = 10$

12 (a) $\hat{Y} = 6 + 0.1X$

16 (a) \$149,542 (b) The model predicts the average price for a house this size. (c) Age, number of bedrooms, lot size (d) 0.3969

18 For $X = 1200$, $\hat{Y} = 2.35$ for $X = 2400$, $\hat{Y} = 3.67$

22 The model with just *age* is best because it has the highest r^2 (0.70).

24 (a) $\hat{Y} = 91,446.49 + 29.86X_1 + 2,116.86X_2 - 1,504.77X_3 = 142,465.16$.

26 The model with horsepower is: $\hat{Y} = 53.87 - 0.269X_1; r^2 = 0.77$
The model with weight is: $\hat{Y} = 57.53 - 0.01X_2; r^2 = 0.73$.

30 $\hat{Y} = 77.190 + 0.047X$

32 (a) $\hat{Y} = 42.43 + 0.0004X$; (b) $\hat{Y} = -31.54 + 0.0058X$

Solutions to Self-Tests

1.	b	**5.**	b	**9.**	a
2.	c	**6.**	c	**10.**	b
3.	d	**7.**	b	**11.**	b
4.	b	**8.**	c	**12.**	c

Forecasting

After completing this chapter, students will be able to:

1. Understand and know when to use various families of forecasting models.
2. Compare moving averages, exponential smoothing, and other time-series models.
3. Seasonally adjust data.
4. Understand Delphi and other qualitative decision-making approaches.
5. Compute a variety of error measures.

CHAPTER OUTLINE

From Chapter 5 of *Quantitative Analysis for Management*, Twelfth Edition. Barry Render, Ralph M. Stair, Jr., Michael E. Hanna, and Trevor S. Hale. Copyright © 2015 by Pearson Education, Inc. All rights reserved.

1 Introduction

Every day, managers make decisions without knowing what will happen in the future. Inventory is ordered though no one knows what sales will be, new equipment is purchased though no one knows the demand for products, and investments are made though no one knows what profits will be. Managers are always trying to reduce this uncertainty and to make better estimates of what will happen in the future. Accomplishing this is the main purpose of forecasting.

There are many ways to forecast the future. In numerous firms (especially smaller ones), the entire process is subjective, involving seat-of-the-pants methods, intuition, and years of experience.

There are also more formal forecasting techniques, both quantitative and qualitative in nature. The primary focus of this chapter will be understanding time-series models and determining which model works best with a particular set of data.

2 Types of Forecasting Models

Figure 1 lists some of the more common forecasting models, and these are categorized by the type of model. The first category involves qualitative models, while the others are quantitative in nature and use mathematical models to develop better forecasts.

Qualitative Models

Qualitative models are forecasting techniques based on judgmental or subjective factors. When a totally new product such as the iPad is introduced, forecasting demand is very difficult due to the lack of any historical sales data on that particular product or on similar products. The company must rely on expert opinion, individual experiences and judgment, and other subjective factors.

Here is a brief overview of four different qualitative forecasting techniques:

1. *Delphi method.* This iterative group process allows experts, who may be located in different places, to make forecasts. There are three different types of participants in the **Delphi** process: decision makers, staff personnel, and respondents. The **decision-making group** usually consists of 5 to 10 experts who will be making the actual forecast. The staff personnel assist the decision makers by preparing, distributing, collecting, and summarizing a series of questionnaires and survey results. The respondents are a group of people whose judgments are valued and are being sought. This group provides inputs to the decision makers before the forecast is made.

FIGURE 1
Forecasting Models

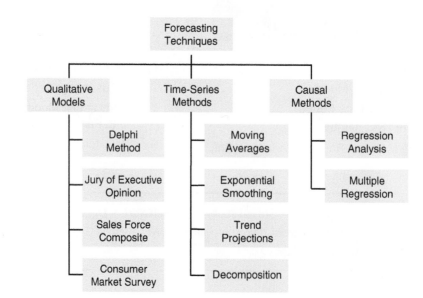

Overview of four qualitative or judgmental approaches: Delphi, jury of executive opinion, sales force composite, and consumer market survey.

In the Delphi method, when the results of the first questionnaire are obtained, the results are summarized and the questionnaire is modified. Both the summary of the results and the new questionnaire are then sent to the same respondents for a new round of responses. The respondents, upon seeing the results from the first questionnaire, may view things differently and may modify their original responses. This process is repeated with the hope that a consensus is reached.

2. *Jury of executive opinion.* This method takes the opinions of a small group of high-level managers, often in combination with statistical models, and results in a group estimate of demand.

3. *Sales force composite.* In this approach, each salesperson estimates what sales will be in his or her region; these forecasts are reviewed to ensure that they are realistic and are then combined at the district and national levels to reach an overall forecast.

4. *Consumer market survey.* This method solicits input from customers or potential customers regarding their future purchasing plans. It can help not only in preparing a forecast but also in improving product design and planning for new products.

Causal Models

A variety of quantitative forecasting models are available when past numerical data are available. Forecasting models are identified as **causal models** if the variable to be forecast is influenced by or correlated with other variables included in the model. For example, daily sales of bottled water might depend on the average temperature, the average humidity, and so on. A causal model would include factors such as these in the mathematical model. Regression models and other more complex models would be classified as causal models.

Time-Series Models

Time series are also quantitative models, and many time-series methods are available. A **time-series model** is a forecasting technique that attempts to predict the future values of a variable by using only historical data on that one variable. These models are extrapolations of past values of that series. While other factors may have influenced these past values, the impact of those other factors is captured in the previous values of the variable being predicted. Thus, if we are forecasting weekly sales for lawn mowers, we use the past weekly sales for lawn mowers in making the forecast for future sales, ignoring other factors such as the economy, competition, and even the selling price of the lawn mowers.

3 Components of a Time-Series

A time series is sequence of values recorded at successive intervals of time. The intervals can be days, weeks, months, years, or other time unit. Examples include weekly sales of HP personal computers, quarterly earnings reports of Microsoft Corporation, daily shipments of Eveready batteries, and annual U.S. consumer price indices. A time series may consist of four possible components—trend, seasonal, cyclical, and random.

The **trend** (T) **component** is the general upward or downward movement of the data over a relatively long period of time. For example, total sales for a company may be increasing consistently over time. The consumer price index, one measure of inflation, is increasing over time. While consistent upward (or downward) movements are indicative of a trend, there may be a positive (or negative) trend present in a time series and yet the values do not increase (or decrease) in every time period. There may be an occasional movement that seems inconsistent with the trend due to random or other fluctuations.

Figure 2 shows scatter diagrams for several time series. The data for all the series are quarterly, and there are four years of data. Series 3 has both trend and random components present.

The **seasonal** (S) **component** is a pattern of fluctuations above or below an average value that repeats at regular intervals. For example, with monthly sales data on snow blowers, sales tend to be high in December and January and lower in summer months and this pattern is expected to repeat every year. Quarterly sales for a consumer electronics store may be higher in the fourth quarter of every year and lower in other quarters. Daily sales in a retail store may be higher on Saturdays than on other days of the week. Hourly sales in a fast-food restaurant are usually expected to be higher around the lunch hour and the dinner hour, while other times are not as busy. Series 2 in Figure 2 illustrates seasonal variations for quarterly data.

FIGURE 2

Scatter Diagram for Four Time Series of Quarterly Data

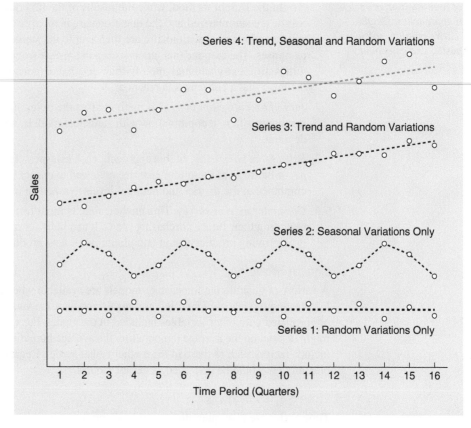

If a seasonal component is present in a set of data, the number of seasons depends on the type of data. With quarterly data, there are four seasons because there are four quarters in a year. With monthly data, there would be 12 seasons because there are 12 months in a year. With daily sales data for a retail store that is open seven days a week, there would be seven seasons. With hourly data, there could be 24 seasons if the business is open 24 hours a day.

A **cyclical** (C) **component** of a time series is a pattern in annual data that tends to repeat every several years. The cyclical component of a time series is only used when making very long-range forecasts, and it is usually associated with the business cycle. Sales or economic activity might reach a peak and then begin to recede and contract, reaching a bottom or trough. At some point after the trough is reached, activity would pick up as recovery and expansion takes place. A new peak would be reached and the cycle would begin again. Figure 3 shows 16 years of annual data for a time series that has a cyclical as well as a random component.

While a time series with cyclical variations and a time series with seasonal variations may look similar on a graph, cyclical variations tend to be irregular in length (from a few years to

FIGURE 3

Scatter Diagram of a Times Series with Cyclical and Random Components

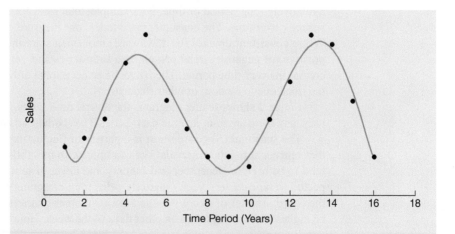

10 or more years) and magnitude, and they are very difficult to predict. Seasonal variations are very consistent in length and magnitude, are much shorter as the seasons repeat in a year or less, and are much easier to predict. The forecasting models presented in this chapter will be for short-range or medium-range forecasts and the cyclical component will not be included in these models.

The **random** (R) **component** consists of irregular, unpredictable variations in a time series. Any variation in a times series that cannot be attributed to trend, seasonal, or cyclical variations would fall into this category. If data for a time series tends to be level with no discernible trend or seasonal pattern, random variations would be the cause for any changes from one time period to the next. Series 1 in Figure 2 is an example of a time series with only a random component.

There are two general forms of time-series models in statistics. The first is a multiplicative model, which assumes that demand is the product of the four components. It is stated as follows:

$$\text{Demand} = T \times S \times C \times R$$

An additive model adds the components together to provide an estimate. Multiple regression is often used to develop additive models. This additive relationship is stated as follows:

$$\text{Demand} = T + S + C + R$$

There are other models that may be a combination of these. For example, one of the components (such as trend) might be additive while another (such as seasonality) could be multiplicative. Understanding the components of a time series will help in selecting an appropriate forecasting technique to use. The methods presented in this chapter will be grouped according to the components considered when the forecast is developed.

4   Measures of Forecast Accuracy

We discuss several different forecasting models in this chapter. To see how well one model works, or to compare that model with other models, the forecast values are compared with the actual or observed values. The **forecast error** (or **deviation**) is defined as follows:

$$\text{Forecast error} = \text{Actual value} - \text{Forecast value}$$

One measure of accuracy is the **mean absolute deviation (MAD)**. This is computed by taking the sum of the absolute values of the individual forecast errors and dividing by the numbers of errors (*n*):

$$\text{MAD} = \frac{\sum |\text{forecast error}|}{n} \tag{1}$$

TABLE 1

Computing the Mean Absolute Deviation (MAD)

MONTH	ACTUAL SALES OF WIRELESS SPEAKERS	FORECAST SALES	ABSOLUTE VALUE OF ERRORS (DEVIATION), $|$ACTUAL–FORECAST$|$
1	110	—	—
2	100	110	$|100 - 110| = 10$
3	120	100	$|120 - 100| = 20$
4	140	120	$|140 - 120| = 20$
5	170	140	$|170 - 140| = 30$
6	150	170	$|150 - 170| = 20$
7	160	150	$|160 - 150| = 10$
8	190	160	$|190 - 160| = 30$
9	200	190	$|200 - 190| = 10$
10	190	200	$|190 - 200| = 10$
11	—	190	—

Sum of $|$errors$|$ = 160

MAD = 160/9 = 17.8

To illustrate how to compute the measures of accuracy, the **naïve model** will be used to forecast one period into the future. The naïve model does not attempt to address any of the components of a time series, but it is very quick and easy to use. A naïve forecast for the next time period is the actual value that was observed in the current time period. For example, suppose someone asked you to forecast the high temperature in your city for tomorrow. If you forecast the temperature to be whatever the high temperature is today, your forecast would be a naïve forecast. This technique is often used if a forecast is needed quickly and accuracy is not a major concern.

Consider the Walker Distributors sales of wireless speakers shown in Table 1. Suppose that in the past, Walker had forecast sales for each month to be the sales that were actually achieved in the

IN ACTION

Hurricane Landfall Location Forecasts and the Mean Absolute Deviation

Scientists at the National Hurricane Center (NHC) of the National Weather Service have the very difficult job of predicting where the eye of a hurricane will hit land. Accurate forecasts are extremely important to coastal businesses and residents who need to prepare for a storm or perhaps even evacuate. They are also important to local government officials, law enforcement agencies, and other emergency responders who will provide help once a storm has passed. Over the years, the NHC has tremendously improved the forecast accuracy (measured by the mean absolute deviation [MAD]) in predicting the actual landfall location for hurricanes that originate in the Atlantic Ocean.

The NHC provides forecasts and periodic updates of where the hurricane eye will hit land. Such landfall location predictions

are recorded when a hurricane is 72 hours, 48 hours, 36 hours, 24 hours, and 12 hours away from actually reaching land. Once the hurricane has come ashore, these forecasts are compared to the actual landfall location, and the error (in miles) is recorded. At the end of the hurricane season, the errors for all the hurricanes in that year are used to calculate the MAD for each type of forecast (12 hours away, 24 hours away, etc.). The graph below shows how the landfall location forecast has improved since 1989. During the early 1990s, the landfall forecast when the hurricane was 48 hours away had an MAD close to 200 miles; in 2009, this number was down to about 75 miles. Clearly, there has been vast improvement in forecast accuracy, and this trend is continuing.

Source: Based on National Hurricane Center, http://www.nhc.noaa.gov.

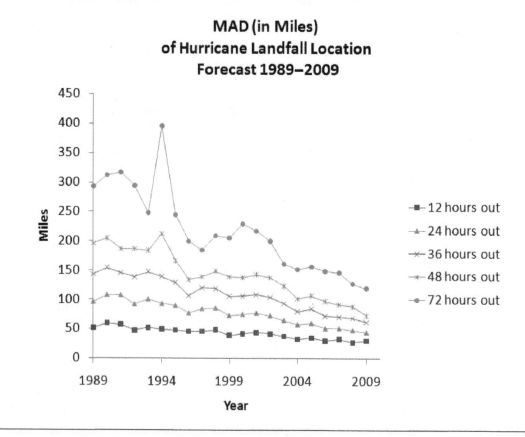

MODELING IN THE REAL WORLD
Forecasting at Tupperware International

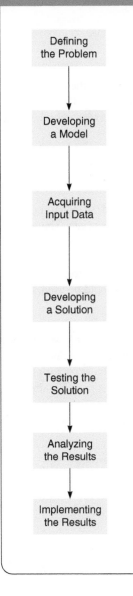

Defining the Problem

To drive production at each of Tupperware's 15 plants in the United States, Latin America, Africa, Europe, and Asia, the firm needs accurate forecasts of demand for its products.

Developing a Model

A variety of statistical models are used, including moving averages, exponential smoothing, and regression analysis. Qualitative analysis is also employed in the process.

Acquiring Input Data

At world headquarters in Orlando, Florida, huge databases are maintained that map the sales of each product, the test market results of each new product (since 20% of the firm's sales come from products less than 2 years old), and where each product falls in its own life cycle.

Developing a Solution

Each of Tupperware's 50 profit centers worldwide develops computerized monthly, quarterly, and 12-month sales projections. These are aggregated by region and then globally.

Testing the Solution

Reviews of these forecasts take place in sales, marketing, finance, and production departments.

Analyzing the Results

Participating managers analyze forecasts with Tupperware's version of a "jury of executive opinion."

Implementing the Results

Forecasts are used to schedule materials, equipment, and personnel at each plant.

Source: Interviews by the authors with Tupperware executives.

The naïve forecast for the next period is the actual value observed in the current period.

previous month. Table 1 gives these forecasts as well as the absolute value of the errors. In forecasting for the next time period (month 11), the forecast would be 190. Notice that there is no error computed for month 1 since there was no forecast for this month, and there is no error for month 11 since the actual value of this is not yet known. Thus, the number of errors (n) is 9.

From this, we see the following:

$$\text{MAD} = \frac{\Sigma \,|\,\text{forecast error}\,|}{n} = \frac{160}{9} = 17.8$$

This means that on the average, each forecast missed the actual value by 17.8 units.

Other measures of the accuracy of historical errors in forecasting are sometimes used besides the MAD. One of the most common is the **mean squared error (MSE)**, which is the average of the squared errors:[*]

$$\text{MSE} = \frac{\Sigma \,(\text{error})^2}{n} \tag{2}$$

---

[*]In regression analysis, the MSE formula is usually adjusted to provide an unbiased estimator of the error variance. Throughout this chapter, we will use the formula provided here.

Besides the MAD and MSE, the **mean absolute percent error (MAPE)** is sometimes used. The MAPE is the average of the absolute values of the errors expressed as percentages of the actual values. This is computed as follows:

$$\text{MAPE} = \frac{\sum \left| \frac{\text{error}}{\text{actual}} \right|}{n} 100\% \tag{3}$$

Three common measures of error are MAD, MSE, and MAPE. Bias gives the average error and may be positive or negative.

There is another common term associated with error in forecasting. **Bias** is the average error and tells whether the forecast tends to be too high or too low and by how much. Thus, bias may be negative or positive. It is not a good measure of the actual size of the errors because the negative errors can cancel out the positive errors.

5   Forecasting Models—Random Variations Only

If all variations in a time series are due to random variations, with no trend, seasonal, or cyclical component, some type of averaging or smoothing model would be appropriate. The averaging techniques in this chapter are moving average, weighted moving average, and exponential smoothing. These methods will smooth out the forecasts and not be too heavily influenced by random variations. However, if there is a trend or seasonal pattern present in the data, then a technique which incorporates that particular component into the forecast should be used.

Moving Averages

Moving averages smooth out variations when forecasting demands are fairly steady.

Moving averages are useful if we can assume that market demands will stay fairly steady over time. For example, a four-month moving average is found simply by summing the demand during the past four months and dividing by 4. With each passing month, the most recent month's data are added to the sum of the previous three months' data, and the earliest month is dropped. This tends to smooth out short-term irregularities in the data series.

An *n*-period moving average forecast, which serves as an estimate of the next period's demand, is expressed as follows:

$$\text{Moving average forecast} = \frac{\text{Sum of demands in previous } n \text{ periods}}{n} \tag{4}$$

Mathematically, this is written as

$$F_{t+1} = \frac{Y_t + Y_{t-1} + \cdots + Y_{t-n+1}}{n} \tag{5}$$

where

$$F_{t+1} = \text{forecast for time period } t + 1$$
$$Y_t = \text{actual value in time period } t$$
$$n = \text{number of periods to average}$$

A 4-month moving average has $n = 4$; a 5-month moving average has $n = 5$.

WALLACE GARDEN SUPPLY EXAMPLE   Storage shed sales at Wallace Garden Supply are shown in the middle column of Table 2. A 3-month moving average is indicated on the right. The forecast for the next January, using this technique, is 16. Were we simply asked to find a forecast for next January, we would only have to make this one calculation. The other forecasts are necessary only if we wish to compute the MAD or another measure of accuracy.

Weighted Moving Averages

Weights can be used to put more emphasis on recent periods.

A simple moving average gives the same weight $(1/n)$ to each of the past observations being used to develop the forecast. On the other hand, a **weighted moving average** allows different weights to be assigned to the previous observations. As the weighted moving average method typically assigns greater weight to more recent observations, this forecast is more responsive to changes in the pattern of the data that occur. However, this is also a potential drawback to this method because the heavier weight would also respond just as quickly to random fluctuations.

TABLE 2
Wallace Garden Supply Shed Sales

MONTH	ACTUAL SHED SALES	3-MONTH MOVING AVERAGE
January	10	
February	12	
March	13	
April	16	$(10 + 12 + 13)/3 = 11.67$
May	19	$(12 + 13 + 16)/3 = 13.67$
June	23	$(13 + 16 + 19)/3 = 16.00$
July	26	$(16 + 19 + 23)/3 = 19.33$
August	30	$(19 + 23 + 26)/3 = 22.67$
September	28	$(23 + 26 + 30)/3 = 26.33$
October	18	$(26 + 30 + 28)/3 = 28.00$
November	16	$(30 + 28 + 18)/3 = 25.33$
December	14	$(28 + 18 + 16)/3 = 20.67$
January	—	$(18 + 16 + 14)/3 = 16.00$

A *weighted moving average* may be expressed as

$$F_{t+1} = \frac{\sum (\text{Weight in period } i)(\text{Actual value in period } i)}{\sum (\text{Weights})} \quad (6)$$

Mathematically, this is

$$F_{t+1} = \frac{w_1 Y_t + w_2 Y_{t-1} + \cdots + w_n Y_{t-n+1}}{w_1 + w_2 + \cdots + w_n} \quad (7)$$

where

$$w_i = \text{ weight for } i\text{th observation}$$

Wallace Garden Supply decides to use a 3-month weighted moving average forecast with weights of 3 for the most recent observation, 2 for the next observation, and 1 for the most distant observation. This would be implemented as follows:

WEIGHTS APPLIED	PERIOD
3	Last month
2	2 months ago
1	3 months ago

③ × Sales last month +② × Sales 2 months ago +① × Sales 3 months ago

⑥ → Sum of the weights

The results of the Wallace Garden Supply weighted average forecast are shown in Table 3. In this particular forecasting situation, you can see that weighting the latest month more heavily provides a much more accurate projection, and calculating the MAD for each of these would verify this.

Choosing the weights obviously has an important impact on the forecasts. One way to choose weights is to try various combinations of weights, calculate the MAD for each, and select the set of weights that results in the lowest MAD. Some forecasting software has an option to search for the best set of weights, and forecasts using these weights are then provided. The best set of weights can also be found by using nonlinear programming.

TABLE 3

Weighted Moving Average Forecast for Wallace Garden Supply

MONTH	ACTUAL SHED SALES	3-MONTH WEIGHTED MOVING AVERAGE
January	10	
February	12	
March	13	
April	16	$[(3 \times 13) + (2 \times 12) + (10)]/6 = 12.17$
May	19	$[(3 \times 16) + (2 \times 13) + (12)]/6 = 14.33$
June	23	$[(3 \times 19) + (2 \times 16) + (13)]/6 = 17.00$
July	26	$[(3 \times 23) + (2 \times 19) + (16)]/6 = 20.5$
August	30	$[(3 \times 26) + (2 \times 23) + (19)]/6 = 23.83$
September	28	$[(3 \times 30) + (2 \times 26) + (23)]/6 = 27.5$
October	18	$[(3 \times 28) + (2 \times 30) + (26)]/6 = 28.33$
November	16	$[(3 \times 18) + (2 \times 28) + (30)]/6 = 23.33$
December	14	$[(3 \times 16) + (2 \times 18) + (28)]/6 = 18.67$
January	—	$[(3 \times 14) + (2 \times 16) + (18)]/6 = 15.33$

Some software packages require that the weights add to 1, and this would simplify Equation 7 because the denominator would be 1. Forcing the weights to sum to 1 is easily achieved by dividing each of the weights by the sum of the weights. In the Wallace Garden Supply example in Table 3, the weights are 3, 2, and 1, which add to 6. These weights could be revised to the new weights 3/6, 2/6, and 1/6, which add to 1. Using these weights gives the same forecasts shown in Table 4.

Both simple and weighted moving averages are effective in smoothing out sudden fluctuations in the demand pattern in order to provide stable estimates. Moving averages do, however, have two problems. First, increasing the size of n (the number of periods averaged) does smooth out fluctuations better, but it makes the method less sensitive to *real* changes in the data should they occur. Second, moving averages cannot pick up trends very well. Because they are averages, they will always stay within past levels and will not predict a change to either a higher or a lower level.

Moving averages have two problems: the larger number of periods may smooth out real changes, and they don't pick up trend.

Exponential Smoothing

Exponential smoothing is a forecasting method that is easy to use and is handled efficiently by computers. Although it is a type of moving average technique, it involves little record keeping of past data. The basic exponential smoothing formula can be shown as follows:

$$\text{New forecast} = \text{Last period's forecast} \qquad (8)$$
$$+ \alpha(\text{Last period's actual demand} - \text{Last period's forecast})$$

where α is a weight (or **smoothing constant**) that has a value between 0 and 1, inclusive.

Equation 8 can also be written mathematically as

$$F_{t+1} = F_t + \alpha(Y_t - F_t) \qquad (9)$$

where

$$F_{t+1} = \text{new forecast (for time period } t + 1)$$
$$F_t = \text{previous forecast (for time period } t)$$
$$\alpha = \text{smoothing constant } (0 \leq \alpha \leq 1)$$
$$Y_t = \text{previous period's actual demand}$$

The concept here is not complex. The latest estimate of demand is equal to the old estimate adjusted by a fraction of the error (last period's actual demand minus the old estimate).

The smoothing constant, α, allows managers to assign weight to recent data.

The smoothing constant, α, can be changed to give more weight to recent data when the value is high or more weight to past data when it is low. For example, when $\alpha = 0.5$, it can be shown mathematically that the new forecast is based almost entirely on demand in the past three periods. When $\alpha = 0.1$, the forecast places little weight on any single period, even the most recent, and it takes many periods (about 19) of historic values into account.[*]

For example, in January, a demand for 142 of a certain car model for February was predicted by a dealer. Actual February demand was 153 autos, so the forecast error was $153 - 142 = 9$. Using a smoothing constant $\alpha = 0.20$, the exponential smoothing forecast for March demand would be found by adding 20% of this error to the previous forecast of 142. Substituting into the formula, we obtain

$$\text{New forecast (for March demand)} = 142 + 0.2(153 - 142)$$
$$= 144.2$$

Thus, the forecast for the demand for cars in March would be 144 after being rounded by the dealer.

Suppose that actual demand for the cars in March was 136. A forecast for the demand in April, using the exponential smoothing model with a constant of $\alpha = 0.20$, can be made:

$$\text{New forecast (for April demand)} = 144.2 + 0.2(136 - 144.2)$$
$$= 142.6, \text{ or } 143 \text{ autos}$$

GETTING STARTED The exponential smoothing approach is easy to use and has been applied successfully by banks, manufacturing companies, wholesalers, and other organizations. To develop a forecast with this method, a smoothing constant must be selected and a previous forecast must be known or assumed. If a company has been routinely using this method, there is no problem. However, if a company is just beginning to use the method, these issues must be addressed.

The appropriate value of the smoothing constant, α, can make the difference between an accurate forecast and an inaccurate forecast. In picking a value for the smoothing constant, the objective is to obtain the most accurate forecast. Several values of the smoothing constant may be tried, and the one with the lowest MAD could be selected. This is analogous to how weights are selected for a weighted moving average forecast. Some forecasting software will automatically select the best smoothing constant. QM for Windows will display the MAD that would be obtained with values of α ranging from 0 to 1 in increments of 0.01.

When the exponential smoothing model is used for the first time, there is no prior forecast for the current time period to use in developing a forecast for the next time period. Therefore, a previous value for a forecast must be assumed. It is common practice to assume a forecast for time period 1, and to use this to develop a forecast for time period 2. The time period 2 forecast is then used to forecast time period 3, and this continues until the forecast for the current time period is found. Unless there is reason to assume another value, the forecast for time period 1 is assumed to be equal to the actual value in time period 1 (*i.e.*, the error is zero). The value of the forecast for time period 1 usually has very little impact on the value of forecasts many time periods into the future.

PORT OF BALTIMORE EXAMPLE Let us apply this concept with a trial-and-error testing of two values of α in an example. The port of Baltimore has unloaded large quantities of grain from ships during the past eight quarters. The port's operations manager wants to test the use of exponential smoothing to see how well the technique works in predicting tonnage unloaded. He assumes that the forecast of grain unloaded in the first quarter was 175 tons. Two values of α are examined: $\alpha = 0.10$ and $\alpha = 0.50$. Table 4 shows the *detailed* calculations for $\alpha = 0.10$ only.

To evaluate the accuracy of each smoothing constant, we can compute the absolute deviations and MADs (see Table 5). Based on this analysis, a smoothing constant of $\alpha = 0.10$ is preferred to $\alpha = 0.50$ because its MAD is smaller.

---

[*]The term *exponential smoothing* is used because the weight of any one period's demand in a forecast decreases exponentially over time. See an advanced forecasting book for algebraic proof.

TABLE 4

Port of Baltimore Exponential Smoothing Forecasts for $\alpha = 0.10$ and $\alpha = 0.50$

QUARTER	ACTUAL TONNAGE UNLOADED	FORECAST USING $\alpha = 0.10$	FORECAST USING $\alpha = 0.50$
1	180	175	175
2	168	$175.5 = 175.00 + 0.10(180 - 175)$	177.5
3	159	$174.75 = 175.50 + 0.10(168 - 175.50)$	172.75
4	175	$173.18 = 174.75 + 0.10(159 - 174.75)$	165.88
5	190	$173.36 = 173.18 + 0.10(175 - 173.18)$	170.44
6	205	$175.02 = 173.36 + 0.10(190 - 173.36)$	180.22
7	180	$178.02 = 175.02 + 0.10(205 - 175.02)$	192.61
8	182	$178.22 = 178.02 + 0.10(180 - 178.02)$	186.30
9	?	$178.60 = 178.22 + 0.10(182 - 178.22)$	184.15

TABLE 5

Absolute Deviations and MADs for the Port of Baltimore Example

QUARTER	ACTUAL TONNAGE UNLOADED	FORECAST WITH $\alpha = 0.10$	ABSOLUTE DEVIATIONS FOR $\alpha = 0.10$	FORECAST WITH $\alpha = 0.50$	DEVIATIONS ABSOLUTE FOR $\alpha = 0.50$
1	180	175	5	175	5
2	168	175.5	7.5	177.5	9.5
3	159	174.75	15.75	172.75	13.75
4	175	173.18	1.82	165.88	9.12
5	190	173.36	16.64	170.44	19.56
6	205	175.02	29.98	180.22	24.78
7	180	178.02	1.98	192.61	12.61
8	182	178.22	3.78	186.30	4.3
Sum of absolute deviations			82.45		98.63

$$\text{MAD} = \frac{\Sigma \,|\text{deviation}|}{n} = 10.31 \qquad\qquad \text{MAD} = 12.33$$

Using Software for Forecasting Time Series

The two software packages, Excel QM and QM for Windows, are very easy to use for forecasting. The previous examples will be solved using these.

In using Excel QM with Excel 2013 for forecasting, from the Excel QM ribbon, select *Alphabetical* as shown in Program 1A. Then simply select whichever method you wish to use, and an initialization window opens to allow you to set the size of the problem. Program 1B shows this window for the Wallace Garden Supply weighted moving average example with the number of past periods and the number of periods in the weighted average already entered. Clicking OK results in the screen shown in Program 1C to appear allowing you to enter the data and the weights. Once all numbers are entered, the calculations are automatically performed as you see in Program 1C.

To use QM for Windows to forecast, under Modules select *Forecasting*. Then select *New* and *Time Series Analysis* as shown in Program 2A. This would be for all of the models presented in this chapter. In the window that opens (Program 2B), specify the number of past periods of data. For the Port of Baltimore example, this is 8. Click *OK* and an input screen appears allowing you to enter the data and select the forecasting technique as shown in Program 2C. Based on the method you choose, other windows may open to allow you to specify the necessary parameters for that model. In this example, the exponential smoothing model is selected, so the smoothing constant must be specified. After entering the data, click Solve and the output shown in Program 2D appears. From this output screen, you can select Window to see additional information such as the details of the calculations and a graph of the time series and the forecasts.

PROGRAM 1A

Selecting the Forecasting Model in Wallace Garden Supply Problem

PROGRAM 1B

Initializing Excel QM Spreadsheet for Wallace Garden Supply Problem

PROGRAM 1C

Excel QM Output for Wallace Garden Supply Problem

Enter the demand data and the weights. The calculations will automatically be performed.

	A	B	C
1	**Wallace Garden Sup**		
2			
3	**Forecasting**	Weighted moving averages - 3 period moving average	

Enter the data in the shaded area. Enter weights in INCREASING order from top to bottom

7	Data				Forecasts and Error Analysis				
8	Period	Demand	Weights		Forecast	Error	Absolute	Squared	Abs Pct Err
9	Period 1	10	1						
10	Period 2	12	2						
11	Period 3	13	3						
12	Period 4	16			12.16667	3.833333	3.833333	14.69444	23.96%
13	Period 5	19			14.33333	4.666667	4.666667	21.77778	24.56%
14	Period 6	23			17	6	6	36	26.09%
15	Period 7	26			20.5	5.5	5.5	30.25	21.15%
16	Period 8	30			23.83333	6.166667	6.166667	38.02778	20.56%
17	Period 9	28							
18	Period 10	18							
19	Period 11	16			23.33333	-7.33333	7.333333	53.77778	45.83%
20	Period 12	14			18.66667	-4.66667	4.666667	21.77778	33.33%
21						4.333333	49	323.3333	254.68%
					0.481481	5.444444	35.92593	28.30%
					Bias	MAD	MSE	MAPE
24							SE	6.796358	
25	Next period	15.3333333							

The measures of accuracy are shown here.

The forecast for the next period is here.

PROGRAM 2A

Selecting Time-Series Analysis in QM for Windows in the Forecasting Module

In the Forecasting module, click New and Time-Series Analysis.

File   Edit

1 Time Series Analysis
2 Least Squares - Simple and Multiple Regression
3 Regression Projector
4 Error Analysis

Forecasting

PROGRAM 2B

Entering Data for Port of Baltimore Example in QM for Windows

Create data set for Forecasting/Time Series Analysis

Title: Port of Baltimore   Enter a title.   Modify default title

Number of Past periods   Enter the number of past periods of data.   names   Overview

8

- Past period 1, Past period 2, Past period 3,...
- a, b, c, d, e, ...
- A, B, C, D, E, ...
- 1, 2, 3, 4, 5, ...
- January, February, March, April, ...
  Click here to set start month
- Other

Click OK.

Cancel   Help   OK

PROGRAM 2C

Selecting the Model and Entering Data for Port of Baltimore Example in QM for Windows

Method

Exponential Smoothing

Weighted Moving Averages
Exponential Smoothing
Exponential Smoothing with trend

Alpha for smoothing

.1

Click here to see the models. Other input areas appear based on the model. Select Exponential Smoothing and a window opens for you to enter the smoothing constant.

Enter the value for the smoothing constant.

Forecast

		0
		0
Past period 3	159	0
Past period 4	175	0
Past period 5	190	0
Past period 6	205	0
Past period 7		0
Past period 8		0

Enter the data. Then click Solve at the top of the page.

PROGRAM 2D

Output for Port of Baltimore Example in QM for Windows

The measures of accuracy are shown here.

The forecast for next period is here.

6 Forecasting Models—Trend and Random Variations

If there is trend present in a time series, the forecasting model must account for this and cannot simply average past values. Two very common techniques will be presented here. The first is exponential smoothing with trend, and the second is called trend projection or simply a trend line.

Exponential Smoothing with Trend

An extension of the exponential smoothing model that will explicitly adjust for trend is called the exponential smoothing with trend model. The idea is to develop an exponential smoothing forecast and then adjust this for trend. Two smoothing constants, α and β, are used in this model, and both of these values must be between 0 and 1. The level of the forecast is adjusted by multiplying the first smoothing constant, α, by the most recent forecast error and adding it to the previous forecast. The trend is adjusted by multiplying the second smoothing constant, β, by the most recent error or excess amount in the trend. A higher value gives more weight to recent observations and thus responds more quickly to changes in the patterns.

Two smoothing constants are used.

As with simple exponential smoothing, the first time a forecast is developed, a previous forecast (F_t) must be given or estimated. If none is available, often the initial forecast is assumed to be perfect. In addition, a previous trend (T_t) must be given or estimated. This is often estimated using other past data, if available, or by using subjective means, or by calculating the increase (or decrease) observed during the first few time periods of the data available. Without such an estimate available, the trend is sometimes assumed to be 0 initially, although this may lead to poor forecasts if the trend is large and β is small. Once these initial conditions have been set, the exponential smoothing forecast including trend (FIT_t) is developed using three steps:

Estimate or assume initial values for F_t and T_t

Step 1. Compute the smoothed forecast (F_{t+1}) for time period $t + 1$ using the equation

Smoothed forecast = Previous forecast including trend + α(Last error)

$$F_{t+1} = FIT_t + \alpha(Y_t - FIT_t) \tag{10}$$

Step 2. Update the trend (T_{t+1}) using the equation

Smoothed trend = Previous trend + β(Error or excess in trend)

$$T_{t+1} = T_t + \beta(F_{t+1} - FIT_t) \tag{11}$$

Step 3. Calculate the trend-adjusted exponential smoothing forecast (FIT_{t+1}) using the equation

Forecast including trend (FIT_{t+1}) = Smoothed forecast (F_{t+1}) + Smoothed trend (T_{t+1})

$$FIT_{t+1} = F_{t+1} + T_{t+1} \tag{12}$$

where

$$T_t = \text{smoothed trend for time period } t$$

$$F_t = \text{smoothed forecast for time period } t$$

$$FIT_t = \text{forecast including trend for time period } t$$

$$\alpha = \text{smoothing constant for forecasts}$$

$$\beta = \text{smoothing constant for trend}$$

Consider the case of Midwestern Manufacturing Company, which has a demand for electrical generators over the period 2007 to 2013 as shown in Table 6. To use the trend-adjusted exponential smoothing method, first set initial conditions (previous values for F and T) and choose α and β. Assuming that F_1 is perfect and T_1 is 0, and picking 0.3 and 0.4 for the smoothing constants, we have

$$F_1 = 74 \quad T_1 = 0 \quad \alpha = 0.3 \quad \beta = 0.4$$

This results in

$$FIT_1 = F_1 + T_1 = 74 + 0 = 74$$

Following the three steps to get the forecast for 2008 (time period 2), we have

Step 1. Compute F_{t+1} using the equation

$$F_{t+1} = FIT_t + \alpha(Y_t - FIT_t)$$
$$F_2 = FIT_1 + 0.3(Y_1 - FIT_1) = 74 + 0.3(74 - 74) = 74$$

Step 2. Update the trend (T_{t+1}) using the equation

$$T_{t+1} = T_t + \beta(F_{t+1} - FIT_t)$$
$$T_2 = T_1 + 0.4(F_2 - FIT_1) = 0 + 0.4(74 - 74) = 0$$

Step 3. Calculate the trend-adjusted exponential smoothing forecast (FIT_{t+1}) using the equation

$$FIT_2 = F_2 + T_2 = 74 + 0 = 74$$

For 2009 (time period 3) we have

Step 1.

$$F_3 = FIT_2 + 0.3(Y_2 - FIT_2) = 74 + 0.3(79 - 74) = 75.5$$

Step 2.

$$T_3 = T_2 + 0.4(F_3 - FIT_2) = 0 + 0.4(75.5 - 74) = 0.6$$

Step 3.

$$FIT_3 = F_3 + T_3 = 75.5 + 0.6 = 76.1$$

The other results are shown in Table 7. The forecast for 2014 would be about 131.35.

TABLE 6

Midwestern Manufacturing's Demand

YEAR	ELECTRICAL GENERATORS SOLD
2007	74
2008	79
2009	80
2010	90
2011	105
2012	142
2013	122

TABLE 7 **Midwestern Manufacturing Exponential Smoothing with Trend Forecasts**

TIME (t)	DEMAND (Y_t)	$F_{t+1} = FIT_t + 0.3(Y_t - FIT_t)$	$T_{t+1} = T_t + 0.4(F_{t+1} - FIT_t)$	$FIT_{t+1} = F_{t+1} + T_{t+1}$
1	74	74	0	74
2	79	$74 = 74 + 0.3(74 - 74)$	$0 = 0 + 0.4(74 - 74)$	$74 = 74 + 0$
3	80	$75.5 = 74 + 0.3(79 - 74)$	$0.6 = 0 + 0.4(75.5 - 74)$	$76.1 = 75.5 + 0.6$
4	90	77.270 $= 76.1 + 0.3(80 - 76.1)$	1.068 $= 0.6 + 0.4(77.27 - 76.1)$	$78.338 = 77.270 + 1.068$
5	105	81.837 $= 78.338 + 0.3(90 - 78.338)$	2.468 $= 1.068 + 0.4(81.837 - 78.338)$	$84.305 = 81.837 + 2.468$
6	142	90.514 $= 84.305 + 0.3(105 - 84.305)$	4.952 $= 2.468 + 0.4(90.514 - 84.305)$	$95.466 = 90.514 + 4.952$
7	122	109.426 $= 95.466 + 0.3(142 - 95.466)$	10.536 $= 4.952 + 0.4(109.426 - 95.466)$	$119.962 = 109.426 + 10.536$
8		120.573 $= 119.962 + 0.3(122 - 119.962)$	10.780 $= 10.536 + 0.4(120.573 - 119.962)$	$131.353 = 120.573 + 10.780$

To have Excel QM perform the calculations in Excel 2013, from the Excel QM ribbon, select the alphabetical list of techniques and choose *Forecasting* and then *Trend Adjusted Exponential Smoothing*. After specifying the number of past observations, enter the data and the values for α and β as shown in Program 3.

Trend Projections

A trend line is a regression equation with time as the independent variable.

Another method for forecasting time series with trend is called **trend projection**. This technique fits a trend line to a series of historical data points and then projects the line into the future for medium- to long-range forecasts. There are several mathematical trend equations that can be developed (e.g., exponential and quadratic), but in this section we look at linear (straight line) trends only. A trend line is simply a linear regression equation in which the independent

PROGRAM 3
Output from Excel QM in Excel 2013 for Trend Adjusted Exponential Smoothing Example

	A	B	C	D	E	F	G	H	I	J
1	Midwestern Manufacturing Company Example									
2										
3	Forecasting			Trend adjusted exponential smoothing						
4		Enter alpha and beta (between 0 and 1), enter the past demands in the shaded column then enter								
5		a starting forecast. If the starting forecast is not in the first period then delete the error analysis for								
6										
7	Alpha	0.3								
8	Beta	0.4								
9	Data			Forecasts and Error Analysis						
10	Period	Demand		Smoothed Forecast, F_t	Smoothed Trend, T_t	Forecast Including Trend, FIT_t	Error	Absolute	Squared	Abs Pct Err
11	Period 1	74		74		74	0	0	0	00.00%
12	Period 2	79		74	0	74	5	5	25	06.33%
13	Period 3	80		75.5	0.6	76.1	3.9	3.9	15.21	04.88%
14	Period 4	90		77.27	1.068	78.338	11.662	11.662	136.0022	12.96%
15	Period 5	105		81.8366	2.46744	84.30404	20.69596	20.696	428.3228	19.71%
16	Period 6	142		90.512828	4.950955	95.4637832	46.53622	46.5362	2165.619	32.77%
17	Period 7	122		109.4246482	10.5353	119.959949	2.040051	2.04005	4.161806	0.016722
18		Next period		120.5719646	10.78011	131.352072				
19				Total			89.83423	89.8342	2774.316	78.32%
20							12.83346	12.8335	396.3309	11.19%
21		The forecast for next period is here.					Bias	MAD	MSE	MAPE
22								SE	23.55554	

variable (X) is the time period. The first time period will be time period 1. The second time period will be time period 2, and so forth. The last time period will be time period n. The form of this is

$$\hat{Y} = b_0 + b_1 X$$

where

$\hat{Y}$ = predicted value
b_0 = intercept
b_1 = slope of the line
X = time period (i.e., $X = 1, 2, 3, \ldots, n$)

The **least squares** regression method may be applied to find the coefficients that minimize the sum of the squared errors, thereby also minimizing the mean squared error (MSE). In this section, we use computer software to perform the calculations.

Let us consider the case of Midwestern Manufacturing's demand for generators that was presented in Table 6. A trend line can be used to predict demand (Y) based on the time period using a regression equation. For the first time period, which was 2007, we let $X = 1$. For 2008, we let $X = 2$, and so forth. Using computer software to develop a regression equation, we get the following equation:

$$\hat{Y} = 56.71 + 10.54X$$

To project demand in 2014, we first denote the year 2014 in our new coding system as $X = 8$:

$$\text{(sales in 2014)} = 56.71 + 10.54(8)$$
$$= 141.03, \text{ or } 141 \text{ generators}$$

We can estimate demand for 2015 by inserting $X = 9$ in the same equation:

$$\text{(sales in 2015)} = 56.71 + 10.54(9)$$
$$= 151.57, \text{ or } 152 \text{ generators}$$

Program 4 provides output from Excel QM in Excel 2013. To run this model, from the Excel QM ribbon, select *Alphabetical* to see the techniques. Then select *Forecasting* and *Regression/Trend Analysis*. When the input window opens, enter the number of past observations (7), and the spreadsheet is initialized allowing you to input the seven Y values and the seven X values as shown in Program 4.

PROGRAM 4

Output from Excel QM in Excel 2013 for Trend Line Example

PROGRAM 5

Output from QM for Windows in Excel 2013 for Trend Line Example

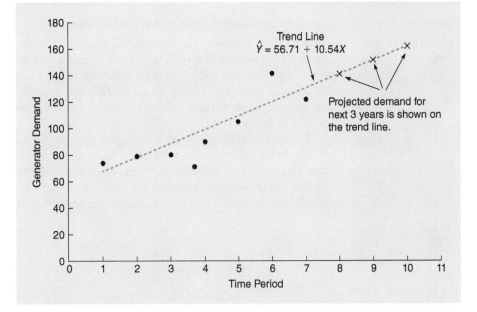

Forecasting Results				
Midwestern Manufacturing Company Summary				
Measure			Future Period	Forecast
Error Measures			8	141
Bias (Mean Error)		0	9	151.536
MAD (Mean Absolute Deviation)		8.582	10	162.071
MSE (Mean Squared Error)		110.403	11	172.607
Standard Error (denom=n-2=5)		12.432	12	183.143
MAPE (Mean Absolute Percent		8.224%	13	193.679
Regression line			14	204.214
Demand(y) = 56.714			15	214.75
+ 10.536 * Time(x)			16	225.286
Statistics				235.822
Correlation coefficient				246.357
Coefficient of determination (r^2)				256.893
			20	267.429
			21	277.964

Forecasts for future time periods are shown here.

The trend line is shown over two lines.

FIGURE 4

Generator Demand and Projections for Next Three Years Based on Trend Line

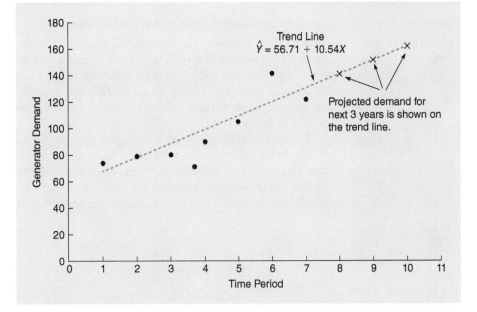

Trend Line
$\hat{Y} = 56.71 + 10.54X$

Projected demand for next 3 years is shown on the trend line.

This problem could also be solved using QM for Windows. To do this, select the *Forecasting* module, and then enter a new problem by selecting *New – Time Series Analysis*. When the next window opens, enter the number of observations (7) and press *OK*. Enter the values (Y) for the seven past observations when the input window opens. It is not necessary to enter the values for X (1, 2, 3, . . . , 7) because QM for Windows will automatically use these numbers. Then click *Solve* to see the results shown in Program 5.

Figure 4 provides a scatter diagram and a trend line for this data. The projected demand in each of the next three years is also shown on the trend line.

7 Adjusting for Seasonal Variations

Time-series forecasting such as that in the example of Midwestern Manufacturing involves looking at the *trend* of data over a series of time observations. Sometimes, however, recurring variations at certain seasons of the year make a *seasonal* adjustment in the trend line forecast necessary. Demand for coal and fuel oil, for example, usually peaks during cold winter months.

Demand for golf clubs or suntan lotion may be highest in summer. Analyzing data in monthly or quarterly terms usually makes it easy to spot seasonal patterns. A seasonal index is often used in multiplicative time-series forecasting models to make an adjustment in the forecast when a seasonal component exists. An alternative is to use an additive model such as a regression model.

Seasonal Indices

A **seasonal index** indicates how a particular season (e.g., month or quarter) compares with an average season. An index of 1 for a season would indicate that the season is average. If the index is higher than 1, the values of the time series in that season tend to be higher than average. If the index is lower than 1, the values of the time series in that season tend to be lower than average.

Seasonal indices are used with multiplicative forecasting models in two ways. First, each observation in a time series are divided by the appropriate seasonal index to remove the impact of seasonality. The resulting values are called **deseasonalized data**. Using these deseasonalized values, forecasts for future values can be developed using a variety of forecasting techniques. Once the forecasts of future deseasonalized values have been developed, they are multiplied by the seasonal indices to develop the final forecasts, which now include variations due to seasonality.

There are two ways to compute seasonal indices. The first method, based on an overall average, is easy and may be used when there is no trend present in the data. The second method, based on a centered-moving-average approach, is more difficult but it must be used when there is trend present.

Calculating Seasonal Indices with No Trend

An average season has an index of 1.

When no trend is present, the index can be found by dividing the average value for a particular season by the average of all the data. Thus, an index of 1 means the season is average. For example, if the average sales in January were 120 and the average sales in all months were 200, the seasonal index for January would be 120/200 = 0.60, so January is below average. The next example illustrates how to compute seasonal indices from historical data and to use these in forecasting future values.

Monthly sales of one brand of telephone answering machine at Eichler Supplies are shown in Table 8, for the two most recent years. The average demand in each month is computed, and these values are divided by the overall average (94) to find the seasonal index for each month. We then use the seasonal indices from Table 8 to adjust future forecasts. For example, suppose we expected the third year's annual demand for answering machines to be 1,200 units, which is

TABLE 8
Answering Machine Sales and Seasonal Indices

MONTH	SALES DEMAND YEAR 1	SALES DEMAND YEAR 2	AVERAGE 2-YEAR DEMAND	MONTHLY DEMAND[a]	AVERAGE SEASONAL INDEX[b]
January	80	100	90	94	0.957
February	85	75	80	94	0.851
March	80	90	85	94	0.904
April	110	90	100	94	1.064
May	115	131	123	94	1.309
June	120	110	115	94	1.223
July	100	110	105	94	1.117
August	110	90	100	94	1.064
September	85	95	90	94	0.957
October	75	85	80	94	0.851
November	85	75	80	94	0.851
December	80	80	80	94	0.851

Total average demand = 1,128

[a] Average monthly demand $= \dfrac{1,128}{12 \text{ months}} = 94$

[b] Seasonal index $= \dfrac{\text{Average 2 year demand}}{\text{Average monthly demand}}$

100 per month. We would not forecast each month to have a demand of 100, but we would adjust these based on the seasonal indices as follows:

Jan.	$\frac{1,200}{12} \times 0.957 = 96$		July	$\frac{1,200}{12} \times 1.117 = 112$
Feb.	$\frac{1,200}{12} \times 0.851 = 85$		Aug.	$\frac{1,200}{12} \times 1.064 = 106$
Mar.	$\frac{1,200}{12} \times 0.904 = 90$		Sept.	$\frac{1,200}{12} \times 0.957 = 96$
Apr.	$\frac{1,200}{12} \times 1.064 = 106$		Oct.	$\frac{1,200}{12} \times 0.851 = 85$
May	$\frac{1,200}{12} \times 1.309 = 131$		Nov.	$\frac{1,200}{12} \times 0.851 = 85$
June	$\frac{1,200}{12} \times 1.223 = 122$		Dec.	$\frac{1,200}{12} \times 0.851 = 85$

Calculating Seasonal Indices with Trend

Centered moving averages are used to compute seasonal indices when there is trend.

When both trend and seasonal components are present in a time series, a change from one month to the next could be due to a trend, to a seasonal variation, or simply to random fluctuations. To help with this problem, the seasonal indices should be computed using a **centered moving average** (CMA) approach whenever trend is present. Using this approach prevents a variation due to trend from being incorrectly interpreted as a variation due to the season. Consider the following example.

Quarterly sales figures for Turner Industries are shown in Table 9. Notice that there is a definite trend as the total is increasing each year, and there is an increase for each quarter from one year to the next as well. The seasonal component is obvious as there is a definite drop from the fourth quarter of one year to the first quarter of the next. A similar pattern is observed in comparing the third quarters to the fourth quarters immediately following.

If a seasonal index for quarter 1 were computed using the overall average, the index would be too low and misleading, since this quarter has less trend than any of the others in the sample. If the first quarter of year 1 were omitted and replaced by the first quarter of year 4 (if it were available), the average for quarter 1 (and consequently the seasonal index for quarter 1) would be considerably higher. To derive an accurate seasonal index, we should use a CMA.

Consider quarter 3 of year 1 for the Turner Industries example. The actual sales in that quarter were 150. To determine the magnitude of the seasonal variation, we should compare this with an average quarter centered at that time period. Thus, we should have a total of four quarters (1 year of data) with an equal number of quarters before and after quarter 3 so the trend is averaged out. Thus, we need 1.5 quarters before quarter 3 and 1.5 quarters after it. To obtain the CMA, we take quarters 2, 3, and 4 of year 1, plus one-half of quarter 1 for year 1 and one-half of quarter 1 for year 2. The average will be

$$\text{CMA (quarter 3 of year 1)} = \frac{0.5(108) + 125 + 150 + 141 + 0.5(116)}{4} = 132.00$$

We compare the actual sales in this quarter to the CMA and we have the following seasonal ratio:

$$\text{Seasonal ratio} = \frac{\text{Sales in quarter 3}}{\text{CMA}} = \frac{150}{132.00} = 1.136$$

TABLE 9
Quarterly Sales ($1,000,000s) for Turner Industries

QUARTER	YEAR 1	YEAR 2	YEAR 3	AVERAGE
1	108	116	123	115.67
2	125	134	142	133.67
3	150	159	168	159.00
4	141	152	165	152.67
Average	131.00	140.25	149.50	140.25

TABLE 10

Centered Moving Averages and Seasonal Ratios for Turner Industries

YEAR	QUARTER	SALES ($1,000,000s)	CMA	SEASONAL RATIO
1	1	108		
	2	125		
	3	150	132.000	1.136
	4	141	134.125	1.051
2	1	116	136.375	0.851
	2	134	138.875	0.965
	3	159	141.125	1.127
	4	152	143.000	1.063
3	1	123	145.125	0.848
	2	142	147.875	0.960
	3	168		
	4	165		

Thus, sales in quarter 3 of year 1 are about 13.6% higher than an average quarter at this time. All of the CMAs and the seasonal ratios are shown in Table 10.

Since there are two seasonal ratios for each quarter, we average these to get the seasonal index. Thus,

$$\text{Index for quarter } 1 = I_1 = (0.851 + 0.848)/2 = 0.85$$
$$\text{Index for quarter } 2 = I_2 = (0.965 + 0.960)/2 = 0.96$$
$$\text{Index for quarter } 3 = I_3 = (1.136 + 1.127)/2 = 1.13$$
$$\text{Index for quarter } 4 = I_4 = (1.051 + 1.063)/2 = 1.06$$

The sum of these indices should be the number of seasons (4) since an average season should have an index of 1. In this example, the sum is 4. If the sum were not 4, an adjustment would be made. We would multiply each index by 4 and divide this by the sum of the indices.

Steps Used to Compute Seasonal Indices Based on CMAs

1. Compute a CMA for each observation (where possible).
2. Compute seasonal ratio = Observation/CMA for that observation.
3. Average seasonal ratios to get seasonal indices.
4. If seasonal indices do not add to the number of seasons, multiply each index by (Number of seasons)/(Sum of the indices).

The seasonal indices found using the CMAs will be used to remove the impact of seasonal so that the trend is easier to identify. Later, the seasonal indices will be used again to adjust the trend forecast based on the seasonal variations.

8 Forecasting Models—Trend, Seasonal, and Random Variations

When both trend and seasonal components are present in a time series, the forecasting model selected must address these. The decomposition method, which uses seasonal indices, is a very common approach. Multiple regression models are also common, with dummy variables used to adjust for seasonal variations in an additive time-series model.

The Decomposition Method

The process of isolating linear trend and seasonal factors to develop more accurate forecasts is called **decomposition**. The first step is to compute seasonal indices for each season as we have done with the Turner Industries data. Then, the data are deseasonalized by dividing each number

TABLE 5.11
Deseasonalized Data for Turner Industries

SALES ($1,000,000s)	SEASONAL INDEX	DESEASONALIZED SALES ($1,000,000s)
108	0.85	127.059
125	0.96	130.208
150	1.13	132.743
141	1.06	133.019
116	0.85	136.471
134	0.96	139.583
159	1.13	140.708
152	1.06	143.396
123	0.85	144.706
142	0.96	147.917
168	1.13	148.673
165	1.06	155.660

by its seasonal index, as shown in Table 11. Figure 5 provides a graph of the original data as well as a graph of the deseasonalized data. Notice how smooth the deseasonalized data is.

A trend line is then found using the deseasonalized data. Using computer software with this data, we have[*]

$$b_1 = 2.34$$
$$b_0 = 124.78$$

The trend equation is

$$\hat{Y} = 124.78 + 2.34X$$

where

$$X = \text{time}$$

FIGURE 5
Scatterplot of Turner Industries's Original Sales Data and Deseasonalized Data

[*]If you do the calculations by hand, the numbers may differ slightly from these due to rounding.

TABLE 12 Turner Industry Forecasts for Four Quarters of Year 4

YEAR	QUARTER	TIME PERIOD (X)	TREND FORECAST $\hat{Y} = 124.78 + 2.34X$	SEASONAL INDEX	FINAL (ADJUSTED) FORECAST
4	1	13	155.20	0.85	131.92
	2	14	157.54	0.96	151.24
	3	15	159.88	1.13	180.66
	4	16	162.22	1.06	171.95

This equation is used to develop the forecast based on trend, and the result is multiplied by the appropriate seasonal index to make a seasonal adjustment. For the Turner Industries data, the forecast for the first quarter of year 4 (time period $X = 13$ and seasonal index $I_1 = 0.85$) would be found as follows:

$$\hat{Y} = 124.78 + 2.34X$$
$$= 124.78 + 2.34(13)$$
$$= 155.2 \text{ (forecast before adjustment for seasonality)}$$

We multiply this by the seasonal index for quarter 1 and we get

$$\hat{Y} \times I_1 = 155.2 \times 0.85 = 131.92$$

Using the same procedure, we find the forecasts for quarters 2, 3, and 4 of the next year. Table 12 shows the unadjusted forecast based on the trend line, for each of the four quarters of year 4. The last column of this table gives the final forecasts that were found by multiplying each trend forecast by the appropriate seasonal index. A scatter diagram showing the original data and the deseasonalized data as well as the unadjusted forecast and the final forecast for these next four quarters is provided in Figure 6.

Steps to Develop a Forecast Using the Decomposition Method

1. Compute seasonal indices using CMAs.
2. Deseasonalize the data by dividing each number by its seasonal index.
3. Find the equation of a trend line using the deseasonalized data.
4. Forecast for future periods using the trend line.
5. Multiply the trend line forecast by the appropriate seasonal index.

FIGURE 6

Scatterplot of Turner Industries Original Sales Data and Deseasonalized Data with Unadjusted and Adjusted Forecasts

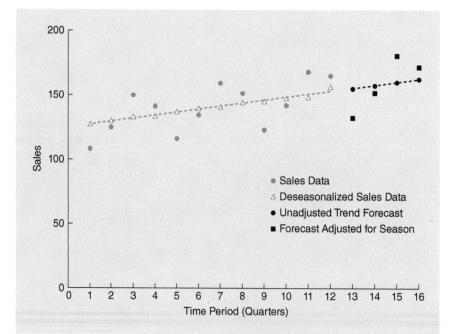

Most forecasting software, including Excel QM and QM for Windows, includes the decomposition method as one of the available techniques. This will automatically compute the CMAs, deseasonalize the data, develop the trend line, make the forecast using the trend equation, and adjust the final forecast for seasonality.

Software for Decomposition

Program 6A shows the QM for Windows input screen that appears after selecting the Forecasting Module, selecting New-Time Series, and specifying 12 past observations. The multiplicative decomposition method is selected, and you can see the inputs that are used for this problem. When this is solved, the output screen in Program 6B appears. Additional output is available by selecting details or graph from the Windows drop-down menu (not shown in Program 6B) that appears after the problem is solved. The forecasts are slightly different from the ones shown in Table 12 due to round-off error.

Excel QM can be used in Excel 2013 for this problem also. From the QM Ribbon, select the menus *By Chapter* and select *Chapter 5-Forecasting-Decomposition*. Specify there are 12 past observations, 4 seasons, and use a centered moving average.

PROGRAM 6A

QM for Windows Input Screen for Turner Industries Example

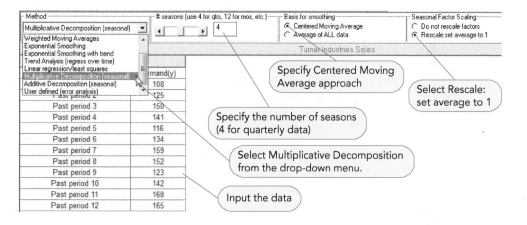

PROGRAM 6B

QM for Windows Output Screen for Turner Industries Example

Using Regression with Trend and Seasonal Components

Multiple regression can be used to develop an additive decomposition model.

Multiple regression may be used to forecast with both trend and seasonal components present in a time series. One independent variable is time, and other independent variables are dummy variables to indicate the season. If we forecast quarterly data, there are four categories (quarters) so we would use three dummy variables. The basic model is an additive decomposition model and is expressed as follows:

$$\hat{Y} = a + b_1X_1 + b_2X_2 + b_3X_3 + b_4X_4$$

where

$$X_1 = \text{time period}$$
$$X_2 = 1 \text{ if quarter 2}$$
$$= 0 \text{ otherwise}$$
$$X_3 = 1 \text{ if quarter 3}$$
$$= 0 \text{ otherwise}$$
$$X_4 = 1 \text{ if quarter 4}$$
$$= 0 \text{ otherwise}$$

If $X_2 = X_3 = X_4 = 0$, then the quarter would be quarter 1. It is an arbitrary choice as to which of the quarters would not have a specific dummy variable associated with it. The forecasts will be the same regardless of which quarter does not have a specific dummy variable.

Using Excel QM in Excel 2013 to develop the regression model, from the Excel QM ribbon, we select the menu for *Chapter 5—Forecasting*, and then choose the *Multiple Regression* method. The input screen in Program 7A appears, and the number of observations (12) and the number of independent variables (4) are entered. An initialized spreadsheet appears and the values for all the variables are entered in columns B through F as shown in Program 7B. Once this has been done, the regression coefficients appear. The regression equation (with rounded coefficients) is

$$\hat{Y} = 104.1 + 2.3X_1 + 15.7X_2 + 38.7X_3 + 30.1X_4$$

If this is used to forecast sales in the first quarter of the next year, we get

$$\hat{Y} = 104.1 + 2.3(13) + 15.7(0) + 38.7(0) + 30.1(0) = 134$$

For quarter 2 of the next year, we get

$$\hat{Y} = 104.1 + 2.3(14) + 15.7(1) + 38.7(0) + 30.1(0) = 152$$

Notice these are not the same values we obtained using the multiplicative decomposition method. We could compare the MAD or MSE for each method and choose the one that is better.

PROGRAM 7A

Excel QM Multiple Regression Initialization Screen for Turner Industries

IN ACTION   Forecasting at Disney World

When the Disney chairman receives a daily report from his main theme parks in Orlando, Florida, the report contains only two numbers: the *forecast* of yesterday's attendance at the parks (Magic Kingdom, Epcot, Fort Wilderness, Hollywood Studios (formerly MGM Studios), Animal Kingdom, Typhoon Lagoon, and Blizzard Beach) and the actual attendance. An error close to zero (using MAPE as the measure) is expected. The chairman takes his forecasts very seriously.

The forecasting team at Disney World doesn't just do a daily prediction, however, and the chairman is not its only customer. It also provides daily, weekly, monthly, annual, and 5-year forecasts to the labor management, maintenance, operations, finance, and park scheduling departments. It uses judgmental models, econometric models, moving average models, and regression analysis. The team's annual forecast of total volume, conducted in 1999 for the year 2000, resulted in a MAPE of 0.

With 20% of Disney World's customers coming from outside the United States, its econometric model includes such variables as consumer confidence and the gross domestic product of seven countries. Disney also surveys one million people each year to examine their future travel plans and their experiences at the parks. This helps forecast not only attendance, but behavior at each ride (how long people will wait and how many times they will ride). Inputs to the monthly forecasting model include airline specials, speeches by the chair of the Federal reserve, and Wall Street trends. Disney even monitors 3,000 school districts inside and outside the United States for holiday/vacation schedules.

Source: Based on J. Newkirk and M. Haskell. "Forecasting in the Service Sector," presentation at the 12th Annual Meeting of the Production and Operations Management Society. April 1, 2001, Orlando, FL.

PROGRAM 7B

Excel QM Multiple Regression Output Screen for Turner Industries

	A	B	C	D	E	F
1	**Turner Industries**					
2						
3	Forecasting	Mu	Enter the values of			
4			Y and X1–X4 as shown.			
5	Enter the data in the shad					
6						
7	Data					
8		Y	X 1	X 2	X 3	X 4
9	Period 1	108	1	0	0	0
10	Period 2	125	2	1	0	0
11	Period 3	150	3	0	1	0
12	Period 4	141				
13	Period 5	116	The regression coefficients			
14	Period 6	134	are shown here.			
15	Period 7	159				
16	Period 8	152	8	0	0	1
17				0	0	
	Enter the values of the variables				0	0
	to obtain any forecast.				1	0
					0	1
21						
22	Coefficients	104.104	2.313	15.688	38.708	30.063
23						
24						
25	Forecast	134.167	13	0	0	0

---

9   Monitoring and Controlling Forecasts

A tracking signal measures how well predictions fit actual data.

After a forecast has been completed, it is important that it not be forgotten. No manager wants to be reminded when his or her forecast is horribly inaccurate, but a firm needs to determine why the actual demand (or whatever variable is being examined) differed significantly from that projected.[*]

One way to monitor forecasts to ensure that they are performing well is to employ a **tracking signal**. A tracking signal is a measurement of how well the forecast is predicting actual values. As forecasts are updated every week, month, or quarter, the newly available demand data are compared to the forecast values.

---

[*]If the forecaster is accurate, he or she usually makes sure that everyone is aware of his or her talents. Very seldom does one read articles in *Fortune*, *Forbes*, or the *Wall Street Journal*, however, about money managers who are consistently off by 25% in their stock market forecasts.

The tracking signal is computed as the **running sum of the forecast errors (RSFE)** divided by the mean absolute deviation:

$$\text{Tracking signal} = \frac{\text{RSFE}}{\text{MAD}} \tag{13}$$

$$= \frac{\sum(\text{forecast error})}{\text{MAD}}$$

where

$$\text{MAD} = \frac{\sum|\text{forecast error}|}{n}$$

as seen earlier in Equation 1.

Positive tracking signals indicate that demand is greater than the forecast. Negative signals mean that demand is less than forecast. A good tracking signal—that is, one with a low RSFE—has about as much positive error as it has negative error. In other words, small deviations are okay, but the positive and negative deviations should balance so that the tracking signal centers closely around zero.

Setting tracking limits is a matter of setting reasonable values for upper and lower limits.

When tracking signals are calculated, they are compared with predetermined control limits. When a tracking signal exceeds an upper or lower limit, a signal is tripped. This means that there is a problem with the forecasting method, and management may want to reevaluate the way it forecasts demand. Figure 7 shows the graph of a tracking signal that is exceeding the range of acceptable variation. If the model being used is exponential smoothing, perhaps the smoothing constant needs to be readjusted.

How do firms decide what the upper and lower tracking limits should be? There is no single answer, but they try to find reasonable values—in other words, limits not so low as to be triggered with every small forecast error and not so high as to allow bad forecasts to be regularly overlooked. George Plossl and Oliver Wight, two inventory control experts, suggested using maximums of ± 4 MADs for high-volume stock items and ± 8 MADs for lower-volume items.[*]

Other forecasters suggest slightly lower ranges. One MAD is equivalent to approximately 0.8 standard deviation, so that ± 2 MADs = 1.6 standard deviations, ± 3 MADs = 2.4 standard deviations, and ± 4 MADs = 3.2 standard deviations. This suggests that for a forecast to be "in control," 89% of the errors are expected to fall within ± 2 MADs, 98% within ± 3 MADs, or 99.9% within ± 4 MADs whenever the errors are approximately normally distributed.[**]

FIGURE 7
Plot of Tracking Signals

<hr>

[*]See G. W. Plossl and O. W. Wight. *Production and Inventory Control.* Upper Saddle River, NJ: Prentice Hall, 1967.
[**]To prove these three percentages to yourself, just set up a normal curve for ± 1.6 standard deviations (Z values). From a table for a standard normal curve, you find that the area under the curve is 0.89. This represents ± 2 MADs. Similarly, ± 3 MADs = 2.4 standard deviations encompasses 98% of the area, and so on for ± 4 MADs.

Here is an example that shows how the tracking signal and RSFE can be computed. Kimball's Bakery's quarterly sales of croissants (in thousands), as well as forecast demand and error computations, are in the following table. The objective is to compute the tracking signal and determine whether forecasts are performing adequately.

TIME PERIOD	FORECAST DEMAND	ACTUAL DEMAND	ERROR	RSFE	FORECAST ERROR	CUMULATIVE ERROR	MAD	TRACKING SIGNAL
1	100	90	−10	−10	10	10	10.0	−1
2	100	95	−5	−15	5	15	7.5	−2
3	100	115	+15	0	15	30	10.0	0
4	110	100	−10	−10	10	40	10.0	−1
5	110	125	+15	+5	15	55	11.0	+0.5
6	110	140	+30	+35	30	85	14.2	+2.5

In period 6, the calculations are

$$\text{MAD} = \frac{\Sigma\,|\text{forecast error}|}{n} = \frac{85}{6}$$

$$= 14.2$$

$$\text{Tracking signal} = \frac{\text{RSFE}}{\text{MAD}} = \frac{35}{14.2}$$

$$= 2.5\,\text{MADs}$$

This tracking signal is within acceptable limits. We see that it drifted from −2.0 MADs to +2.5 MADs.

Adaptive Smoothing

A lot of research has been published on the subject of adaptive forecasting. This refers to computer monitoring of tracking signals and self-adjustment if a signal passes its preset limit. In exponential smoothing, the α and β coefficients are first selected based on values that minimize error forecasts and are then adjusted accordingly whenever the computer notes an errant tracking signal. This is called **adaptive smoothing**.

Summary

Forecasts are a critical part of a manager's function. Demand forecasts drive the production, capacity, and scheduling systems in a firm and affect the financial, marketing, and personnel planning functions.

In this chapter we introduced three types of forecasting models: time series, causal, and qualitative. Moving averages, exponential smoothing, trend projection, and decomposition time-series models were developed. Regression and multiple regression models were recognized as causal models. Four qualitative models were briefly discussed. In addition, we

explained the use of scatter diagrams and measures of forecasting accuracy.

As we learned in this chapter, no forecasting method is perfect under all conditions. Even when management has found a satisfactory approach, it must still monitor and control its forecasts to make sure that errors do not get out of hand. Forecasting can often be a very challenging but rewarding part of managing.

Glossary

Adaptive Smoothing   The process of automatically monitoring and adjusting the smoothing constants in an exponential smoothing model.

Bias   A technique for determining the accuracy of a forecasting model by measuring the average error and its direction.

Causal Models   Models that forecast using variables and factors in addition to time.

Centered Moving Average   An average of the values centered at a particular point in time. This is used to compute seasonal indices when trend is present.

Cyclical Component   A component of a time series is a pattern in annual data that tends to repeat every several years.

Decision-Making Group   A group of experts in a Delphi technique that has the responsibility of making the forecast.

Decomposition   A forecasting model that decomposes a time series into its seasonal and trend components.

Delphi   A judgmental forecasting technique that uses decision makers, staff personnel, and respondents to determine a forecast.

Deseasonalized Data   Time-series data in which each value has been divided by its seasonal index to remove the effect of the seasonal component.

Deviation   A term used in forecasting for error.

Error   The difference between the actual value and the forecast value.

Exponential Smoothing   A forecasting method that is a combination of the last forecast and the last observed value.

Least Squares   A procedure used in trend projection and regression analysis to minimize the squared distances between the estimated straight line and the observed values.

Mean Absolute Deviation (MAD)   A technique for determining the accuracy of a forecasting model by taking the average of the absolute deviations.

Mean Absolute Percent Error (MAPE)   A technique for determining the accuracy of a forecasting model by taking the average of the absolute errors as a percentage of the observed values.

Mean Squared Error (MSE)   A technique for determining the accuracy of a forecasting model by taking the average of the squared error terms for a forecasting model.

Moving Average   A forecasting technique that averages past values in computing the forecast.

Naïve Model   A time-series forecasting model in which the forecast for next period is the actual value for the current period.

Qualitative Models   Models that forecast using judgments, experience, and qualitative and subjective data.

Random Component   The irregular, unpredictable variations in a time series.

Running Sum of Forecast Errors (RSFE)   Used to develop a tracking signal for time-series forecasting models, this is a running total of the errors and may be positive or negative.

Seasonal Component   A pattern of fluctuations in a time series above or below an average value that repeats at regular intervals.

Seasonal Index   An index number that indicates how a particular season compares with an average time period (with an index of 1 indicating an average season).

Smoothing Constant   A value between 0 and 1 that is used in an exponential smoothing forecast.

Time-series Model   A forecasting technique that predicts the future values of a variable by using only historical data on that one variable.

Tracking Signal   A measure of how well the forecast is predicting actual values.

Trend Component   The general upward or downward movement of the data in a time series over relatively long period of time.

Trend Projection   The use of a trend line to forecast a time-series with trend present. A linear trend line is a regression line with time as the independent variable.

Weighted Moving Average   A moving average forecasting method that places different weights on past values.

Key Equations

(1) $\text{MAD} = \dfrac{\Sigma |\text{forecast error}|}{n}$

A measure of overall forecast error called mean absolute deviation.

(2) $\text{MSE} = \dfrac{\Sigma (\text{error})^2}{n}$

A measure of forecast accuracy called mean squared error.

(3) $\text{MAPE} = \dfrac{\Sigma \left| \dfrac{\text{error}}{\text{actual}} \right|}{n} 100\%$

A measure of forecast accuracy called mean absolute percent error.

(4) $\begin{array}{l}\text{Moving} \\ \text{average} \\ \text{forecast}\end{array} = \dfrac{\text{Sum of demands in previous } n \text{ periods}}{n}$

An equation for computing a moving average forecast.

(5) $F_{t+1} = \dfrac{Y_t + Y_{t-1} + \cdots + Y_{t-n+1}}{n}$

A mathematical expression for a moving average forecast.

(6) $F_{t+1} = \dfrac{\Sigma(\text{Weight in period } i)(\text{Actual value in period } i)}{\Sigma(\text{Weights})}$

An equation for computing a weighted moving average forecast.

(7) $F_{t+1} = \dfrac{w_1 Y_t + w_2 Y_{t-1} + \cdots + w_n Y_{t-n+1}}{w_1 + w_2 + \cdots + w_n}$

A mathematical expression for a weighted moving average forecast.

(8) New forecast = Last period's forecast + α(Last period's actual demand − Last period's forecast)

An equation for computing an exponential smoothing forecast.

(9) $F_{t+1} = F_t + \alpha(Y_t - F_t)$

Equation 8 rewritten mathematically.

(10) $F_{t+1} = FIT_t + \alpha(Y_t - FIT_t)$

Equation to update the smoothed forecast (F_{t+1}) used in the trend-adjusted exponential smoothing model.

(11) $T_{t+1} = T_t + \beta(F_{t+1} - FIT_t)$

Equation to update the smoothed trend value (T_{t+1}) used in the trend-adjusted exponential smoothing model.

(12) $FIT_{t+1} = F_{t+1} + T_{t+1}$

Equation to develop forecast including trend (FIT) in the trend-adjusted exponential smoothing model.

(13) Tracking signal $= \dfrac{RSFE}{MAD}$

$= \dfrac{\Sigma(\text{forecast error})}{MAD}$

An equation for monitoring forecasts with a tracking signal.

Solved Problems

Solved Problem 1

Demand for patient surgery at Washington General Hospital has increased steadily in the past few years, as seen in the following table:

YEAR	OUTPATIENT SURGERIES PERFORMED
1	45
2	50
3	52
4	56
5	58
6	—

The director of medical services predicted six years ago that demand in year 1 would be 42 surgeries. Using exponential smoothing with a weight of $\alpha = 0.20$, develop forecasts for years 2 through 6. What is the MAD?

Solution

YEAR	ACTUAL	FORECAST (SMOOTHED)	ERROR	|ERROR|
1	45	42	+3	3
2	50	42.6 = 42 + 0.2(45 − 42)	+7.4	7.4
3	52	44.1 = 42.6 + 0.2(50 − 42.6)	+7.9	7.9
4	56	45.7 = 44.1 + 0.2(52 − 44.1)	+10.3	10.3
5	58	47.7 = 45.7 + 0.2(56 − 45.7)	+10.3	10.3
6	—	49.8 = 47.7 + 0.2(58 − 47.7)	—	—
		MAD $= \dfrac{\Sigma \|\text{errors}\|}{n} = \dfrac{38.9}{5} = 7.78$		38.9

Solved Problem 2

Quarterly demand for Jaguar XJ8 at a New York auto dealership is forecast with the equation

$$\hat{Y} = 10 + 3X$$

where

$$X = \text{time period (quarter): quarter 1 of last year} = 0$$
$$\text{quarter 2 of last year} = 1$$
$$\text{quarter 3 of last year} = 2$$
$$\text{quarter 4 of last year} = 3$$
$$\text{quarter 1 of this year} = 4, \text{and so on}$$

and

$$\hat{Y} = \text{predicted quarterly demand}$$

The demand for luxury sedans is seasonal, and the indices for quarters 1, 2, 3, and 4 are 0.80, 1.00, 1.30, and 0.90, respectively. Using the trend equation, forecast the demand for each quarter of next year. Then adjust each forecast to adjust for seasonal (quarterly) variations.

Solution

Quarter 2 of this year is coded $X = 5$; quarter 3 of this year, $X = 6$; and quarter 4 of this year, $X = 7$. Hence, quarter 1 of next year is coded $X = 8$; quarter 2, $X = 9$; and so on.

$$\hat{Y} \text{ (next year quarter 1)} = 10 + (3)(8) = 34 \quad \text{Adjusted forecast} = (0.80)(34) = 27.2$$
$$\hat{Y} \text{ (next year quarter 2)} = 10 + (3)(9) = 37 \quad \text{Adjusted forecast} = (1.00)(37) = 37$$
$$\hat{Y} \text{ (next year quarter 3)} = 10 + (3)(10) = 40 \quad \text{Adjusted forecast} = (1.30)(40) = 52$$
$$\hat{Y} \text{ (next year quarter 4)} = 10 + (3)(11) = 43 \quad \text{Adjusted forecast} = (0.90)(43) = 38.7$$

Self-Test

- Before taking the self-test, refer to the learning objectives at the beginning of the chapter, the notes in the margins, and the glossary at the end of the chapter.
- Use the key at the end of the chapter to correct your answers.
- Restudy pages that correspond to any questions that you answered incorrectly or material you feel uncertain about.

1. Qualitative forecasting models include
   a. regression analysis.
   b. Delphi.
   c. time-series models.
   d. trend lines.
2. A forecasting model that only uses historical data for the variable being forecast is called a
   a. time-series model.
   b. causal model.
   c. Delphi model.
   d. variable model.
3. One example of a causal model is
   a. exponential smoothing.
   b. trend projections.
   c. moving averages.
   d. regression analysis.
4. Which of the following is a time-series model?
   a. the Delphi model
   b. regression analysis

   c. exponential smoothing
   d. multiple regression
5. Which of the following is not a component of a time series?
   a. seasonality
   b. causal variations
   c. trend
   d. random variations
6. Which of the following may be negative?
   a. MAD
   b. bias
   c. MAPE
   d. MSE
7. When comparing several forecasting models to determine which one best fits a particular set of data, the model that should be selected is the one
   a. with the highest MSE.
   b. with the MAD closest to 1.
   c. with a bias of 0.
   d. with the lowest MAD.

8. In exponential smoothing, if you wish to give a significant weight to the most recent observations, then the smoothing constant should be
   a. close to 0.
   b. close to 1.
   c. close to 0.5.
   d. less than the error.

9. A trend equation is a regression equation in which
   a. there are multiple independent variables.
   b. the intercept and the slope are the same.
   c. the dependent variable is time.
   d. the independent variable is time.

10. Sales for a company are typically higher in the summer months than in the winter months. This variation would be called a
    a. trend.
    b. seasonal factor.
    c. random factor.
    d. cyclical factor.

11. An exponential smoothing forecast with a smoothing constant of 1 would result in the same forecast as
    a. a trend line forecast.
    b. an exponential smoothing forecast with a smoothing constant of 0.
    c. a naïve forecast.
    d. a 2-period moving average forecast.

12. If the seasonal index for January is 0.80, then
    a. January sales tend to be 80% higher than an average month.
    b. January sales tend to be 20% higher than an average month.
    c. January sales tend to be 80% lower than an average month.
    d. January sales tend to be 20% lower than an average month.

13. If both trend and seasonal components are present in a time-series, then the seasonal indices
    a. should be computed based on an overall average.
    b. should be computed based on CMAs.
    c. will all be greater than 1.
    d. should be ignored in developing the forecast.

14. Which of the following is used to alert the user of a forecasting model that a significant error occurred in one of the periods?
    a. a seasonal index
    b. a smoothing constant
    c. a tracking signal
    d. a regression coefficient

15. If the multiplicative decomposition model is used to forecast daily sales for a retail store, how many seasons will there be?
    a. 4
    b. 7
    c. 12
    d. 365

Discussion Questions and Problems

Discussion Questions

1 Describe briefly the steps used to develop a forecasting system.

2 What is a time-series forecasting model?

3 What is the difference between a causal model and a time-series model?

4 What is a qualitative forecasting model, and when is it appropriate?

5 What are some of the problems and drawbacks of the moving average forecasting model?

6 What effect does the value of the smoothing constant have on the weight given to the past forecast and the past observed value?

7 Describe briefly the Delphi technique.

8 What is MAD, and why is it important in the selection and use of forecasting models?

9 Explain how the number of seasons is determined when forecasting with a seasonal component.

10 A seasonal index may be less than one, equal to one, or greater than one. Explain what each of these values would mean.

11 How is the impact of seasonality removed from a time series?

12 In using the decomposition method, the forecast based on trend is found using the trend line. How is the seasonal index used to adjust this forecast based on trend?

13 Explain what would happen if the smoothing constant in an exponential smoothing model was equal to zero. Explain what would happen if the smoothing constant was equal to one.

14 Explain when a CMA (rather than an overall average) should be used in computing a seasonal index. Explain why this is necessary.

Problems

15 Develop a four-month moving average forecast for Wallace Garden Supply and compute the MAD. A three-month moving average forecast was developed in the section on moving averages in Table 2.

16 Using MAD, determine whether the forecast in Problem 15 or the forecast in the section concerning Wallace Garden Supply is more accurate.

Note: ♨ means the problem may be solved with QM for Windows; ✕ means the problem may be solved with Excel QM; and ♨ means the problem may be solved with QM for Windows and/or Excel QM.

17 Data collected on the yearly demand for 50-pound bags of fertilizer at Wallace Garden Supply are shown in the following table. Develop a 3-year moving average to forecast sales. Then estimate demand again with a weighted moving average in which sales in the most recent year are given a weight of 2 and sales in the other 2 years are each given a weight of 1. Which method do you think is best?

DEMAND FOR FERTILIZER	
YEAR	(1,000s OF BAGS)
1	4
2	6
3	4
4	5
5	10
6	8
7	7
8	9
9	12
10	14
11	15

18 Develop a trend line for the demand for fertilizer in Problem 17, using any computer software.

19 In Problems 17 and 18, three different forecasts were developed for the demand for fertilizer. These three forecasts are a 3-year moving average, a weighted moving average, and a trend line. Which one would you use? Explain your answer.

20 Use exponential smoothing with a smoothing constant of 0.3 to forecast the demand for fertilizer given in Problem 17. Assume that last period's forecast for year 1 is 5,000 bags to begin the procedure. Would you prefer to use, the exponential smoothing model or the weighted average model developed in Problem 17? Explain your answer.

21 Sales of Cool-Man air conditioners have grown steadily during the past 5 years:

YEAR	SALES
1	450
2	495
3	518
4	563
5	584
6	?

The sales manager had predicted, before the business started, that year 1's sales would be 410 air conditioners. Using exponential smoothing with a weight of $\alpha = 0.30$, develop forecasts for years 2 through 6.

22 Using smoothing constants of 0.6 and 0.9, develop forecasts for the sales of Cool-Man air conditioners (see Problem 21).

23 What effect did the smoothing constant have on the forecast for Cool-Man air conditioners? (See Problems 21 and 22.) Which smoothing constant gives the most accurate forecast?

24 Use a three-year moving average forecasting model to forecast the sales of Cool-Man air conditioners (see Problem 21).

25 Using the trend projection method, develop a forecasting model for the sales of Cool-Man air conditioners (see Problem 21).

26 Would you use exponential smoothing with a smoothing constant of 0.3, a 3-year moving average, or a trend to predict the sales of Cool-Man air conditioners? Refer to Problems 21, 24, and 25.

27 Sales of industrial vacuum cleaners at R. Lowenthal Supply Co. over the past 13 months are as follows:

SALES ($1,000s)	MONTH	SALES ($1,000s)	MONTH
11	January	14	August
14	February	17	September
16	March	12	October
10	April	14	November
15	May	16	December
17	June	11	January
11	July		

(a) Using a moving average with three periods, determine the demand for vacuum cleaners for next February.

(b) Using a weighted moving average with three periods, determine the demand for vacuum cleaners for February. Use 3, 2, and 1 for the weights of the most recent, second most recent, and third most recent periods, respectively. For example, if you were forecasting the demand for February, November would have a weight of 1, December would have a weight of 2, and January would have a weight of 3.

(c) Evaluate the accuracy of each of these methods.

(d) What other factors might R. Lowenthal consider in forecasting sales?

28 Passenger miles flown on Northeast Airlines, a commuter firm serving the Boston hub, are as follows for the past 12 weeks:

WEEK	ACTUAL PASSENGER MILES (1,000s)	WEEK	ACTUAL PASSENGER MILES (1,000s)
1	17	7	20
2	21	8	18
3	19	9	22
4	23	10	20
5	18	11	15
6	16	12	22

(a) Assuming an initial forecast for week 1 of 17,000 miles, use exponential smoothing to compute miles for weeks 2 through 12. Use $\alpha = 0.2$.

(b) What is the MAD for this model?

(c) Compute the RSFE and tracking signals. Are they within acceptable limits?

29 Emergency calls to Winter Park, Florida's 911 system, for the past 24 weeks are as follows:

WEEK	CALLS	WEEK	CALLS	WEEK	CALLS
1	50	9	35	17	55
2	35	10	20	18	40
3	25	11	15	19	35
4	40	12	40	20	60
5	45	13	55	21	75
6	35	14	35	22	50
7	20	15	25	23	40
8	30	16	55	24	65

(a) Compute the exponentially smoothed forecast of calls for each week. Assume an initial forecast of 50 calls in the first week and use $\alpha = 0.1$. What is the forecast for the 25th week?

(b) Reforecast each period using $\alpha = 0.6$.

(c) Actual calls during the 25th week were 85. Which smoothing constant provides a superior forecast?

30 How would the forecast for week 25 of the previous problem change if the initial forecast was 40 instead of 50? How would the forecast for week 25 change if the forecast for week 1 were assumed to be 60?

31 Consulting income at Kate Walsh Associates for the period February–July has been as follows:

MONTH	INCOME ($1,000s)
February	70.0
March	68.5
April	64.8
May	71.7
June	71.3
July	72.8

Use exponential smoothing to forecast August's income. Assume that the initial forecast for February is $65,000. The smoothing constant selected is $\alpha = 0.1$.

32 Resolve Problem 31 with $\alpha = 0.3$. Using MAD, which smoothing constant provides a better forecast?

33 A major source of revenue in Texas is a state sales tax on certain types of goods and services. Data are compiled and the state comptroller uses them to project future revenues for the state budget. One particular category of goods is classified as Retail Trade. Four years of quarterly data (in $millions) for one particular area of southeast Texas follow:

QUARTER	YEAR 1	YEAR 2	YEAR 3	YEAR 4
1	218	225	234	250
2	247	254	265	283
3	243	255	264	289
4	292	299	327	356

(a) Compute seasonal indices for each quarter based on a CMA.

(b) Deseasonalize the data and develop a trend line on the deseasonalized data.

(c) Use the trend line to forecast the sales for each quarter of year 5.

(d) Use the seasonal indices to adjust the forecasts found in part (c) to obtain the final forecasts.

34 Using the data in Problem 33, develop a multiple regression model to predict sales (both trend and seasonal components), using dummy variables to incorporate the seasonal factor into the model. Use this model to predict sales for each quarter of the next year. Comment on the accuracy of this model.

35 Trevor Harty, an avid mountain biker, always wanted to start a business selling top-of-the-line mountain bikes and other outdoor supplies. A little over 6 years ago, he and a silent partner opened a store called Hale and Harty Trail Bikes and Supplies. Growth was rapid in the first 2 years, but since that time, growth in sales has slowed a bit, as expected. The quarterly sales (in $1,000s) for the past 4 years are shown in the table below:

	YEAR 1	YEAR 2	YEAR 3	YEAR 4
QUARTER 1	274	282	282	296
QUARTER 2	172	178	182	210
QUARTER 3	130	136	134	158
QUARTER 4	162	168	170	182

(a) Develop a trend line using the data in the table. Use this to forecast sales for each quarter of year 5. What does the slope of this line indicate?

(b) Use the multiplicative decomposition model to incorporate both trend and seasonal components into the forecast. What does the slope of this line indicate?

(c) Compare the slope of the trend line in part (a) to the slope in the trend line for the decomposition model that was based on the deseasonalized sales figures. Discuss why these are so different and explain which one is best to use.

36 The unemployment rates in the United States during a 10-year period are given in the following table. Use exponential smoothing to find the best forecast for next year. Use smoothing constants of 0.2, 0.4, 0.6, and 0.8. Which one had the lowest MAD?

YEAR	1	2	3	4	5	6	7	8	9	10
Unemployment rate (%)	7.2	7.0	6.2	5.5	5.3	5.5	6.7	7.4	6.8	6.1

37 Management of Davis's Department Store has used time-series extrapolation to forecast retail sales for the next four quarters. The sales estimates are $100,000, $120,000, $140,000, and $160,000 for the respective quarters before adjusting for seasonality. Seasonal indices for the four quarters have been found to be 1.30, 0.90, 0.70, and 1.10, respectively. Compute a seasonalized or adjusted sales forecast.

38 In the past, Judy Holmes's tire dealership sold an average of 1,000 radials each year. In the past two years, 200 and 250, respectively, were sold in fall, 350 and 300 in winter, 150 and 165 in spring, and 300 and 285 in summer. With a major expansion planned, Judy projects sales next year to increase to 1,200 radials. What will the demand be each season?

39 The following table provides the Dow Jones Industrial Average (DJIA) opening index value on the first working day of 1994–2013:

Develop a trend line and use it to predict the opening DJIA index value for years 2014, 2015, and 2016. Find the MSE for this model.

YEAR	DJIA	YEAR	DJIA
2013	13,104	2003	8,342
2012	12,392	2002	10,022
2011	11,577	2001	10,791
2010	10,431	2000	11,502
2009	8,772	1999	9,213
2008	13,262	1998	7,908
2007	12,460	1997	6,448
2006	10,718	1996	5,117
2005	10,784	1995	3,834
2004	10,453	1994	3,754

40 Using the DJIA data in Problem 39, use exponential smooth with trend adjustment to forecast the opening DJIA value for 2014. Use $\alpha = 0.8$ and $\beta = 0.2$. Compare the MSE for this technique with the MSE for the trend line.

41 Refer to the DJIA data in Problem 39.

(a) Use an exponential smoothing model with a smoothing constant of 0.4 to predict the opening DJIA index value for 2014. Find the MSE for this.

(b) Use QM for Windows or Excel and find the smoothing constant that would provide the lowest MSE.

42 The following table gives the average monthly exchange rate between the U.S. dollar and the euro for 2009. It shows that 1 euro was equivalent to 1.289 U.S. dollars in January 2009. Develop a trend line that could be used to predict the exchange rate for 2010. Use this model to predict the exchange rate for January 2010 and February 2010.

MONTH	EXCHANGE RATE
January	1.289
February	1.324
March	1.321
April	1.317
May	1.280
June	1.254
July	1.230
August	1.240
September	1.287
October	1.298
November	1.283
December	1.311

43 For the data in Problem 42, develop an exponential smoothing model with a smoothing constant of 0.3. Using the MSE, compare this with the model in Problem 42.

Internet Homework Problems

See our Internet home page, at www.pearsonhighered.com/render, for additional homework problems, Problems 44 to 52.

Case Study

Forecasting Attendance at SWU Football Games

Southwestern University (SWU), a large state college in Stephenville, Texas, 30 miles southwest of the Dallas/Fort Worth metroplex, enrolls close to 20,000 students. In a typical town–gown relationship, the school is a dominant force in the small city, with more students during fall and spring than permanent residents.

A longtime football powerhouse, SWU is a member of the Big Eleven conference and is usually in the top 20 in college football rankings. To bolster its chances of reaching the elusive and long-desired number-one ranking, in 2008 SWU hired the legendary Billy Bob Taylor as its head coach. Although

the number-one ranking remained out of reach, attendance at the five Saturday home games each year increased. Prior to Taylor's arrival, attendance generally averaged 25,000 to 29,000 per game. Season ticket sales bumped up by 10,000 just with the announcement of the new coach's arrival. Stephenville and SWU were ready to move to the big time!

The immediate issue facing SWU, however, was not NCAA ranking. It was capacity. The existing SWU stadium, built in 1953, has seating for 54,000 fans. The following table indicates attendance at each game for the past six years.

One of Taylor's demands upon joining SWU had been a stadium expansion, or possibly even a new stadium. With attendance increasing, SWU administrators began to face the issue head-on. Taylor had wanted dormitories solely for his athletes in the stadium as an additional feature of any expansion.

SWU's president, Dr. Marty Starr, decided it was time for his vice president of development to forecast when the existing stadium would "max out." He also sought a revenue projection, assuming an average ticket price of $20 in 2014 and a 5% increase each year in future prices.

Discussion Questions

1. Develop a forecasting model, justify its selection over other techniques, and project attendance through 2015.
2. What revenues are to be expected in 2014 and 2015?
3. Discuss the school's options.

Southwestern University Football Game Attendance, 2008–2013

| GAME | 2008 | | 2009 | | 2010 | |
	ATTENDEES	OPPONENT	ATTENDEES	OPPONENT	ATTENDEES	OPPONENT
1	34,200	Baylor	36,100	Oklahoma	35,900	TCU
2*	39,800	Texas	40,200	Nebraska	46,500	Texas Tech
3	38,200	LSU	39,100	UCLA	43,100	Alaska
4**	26,900	Arkansas	25,300	Nevada	27,900	Arizona
5	35,100	USC	36,200	Ohio State	39,200	Rice

| GAME | 2011 | | 2012 | | 2013 | |
	ATTENDEES	OPPONENT	ATTENDEES	OPPONENT	ATTENDEES	OPPONENT
1	41,900	Arkansas	42,500	Indiana	46,900	LSU
2*	46,100	Missouri	48,200	North Texas	50,100	Texas
3	43,900	Florida	44,200	Texas A&M	45,900	Prairie View A&M
4**	30,100	Miami	33,900	Southern	36,300	Montana
5	40,500	Duke	47,800	Oklahoma	49,900	Arizona State

*Homecoming games

**During the fourth week of each season, Stephenville hosted a hugely popular southwestern crafts festival. This event brought tens of thousands of tourists to the town, especially on weekends, and had an obvious negative impact on game attendance.

Source: J. Heizer and B. Render. *Operations Management*, 11th ed. Upper Saddle River, NJ: Pearson, 2014, p. 148.

Case Study

Forecasting Monthly Sales

For years The Glass Slipper restaurant has operated in a resort community near a popular ski area of New Mexico. The restaurant is busiest during the first 3 months of the year, when the ski slopes are crowded and tourists flock to the area.

When James and Deena Weltee built The Glass Slipper, they had a vision of the ultimate dining experience. As the view of surrounding mountains was breathtaking, a high priority was placed on having large windows and providing a spectacular view from anywhere inside the restaurant. Special attention was also given to the lighting, colors, and overall ambiance, resulting in a truly magnificent experience for all who came to enjoy gourmet dining. Since its opening, The Glass Slipper has developed and maintained a reputation as one of the "must visit" places in that region of New Mexico.

While James loves to ski and truly appreciates the mountains and all that they have to offer, he also shares Deena's dream of retiring to a tropical paradise and enjoying a more relaxed lifestyle on the beach. After some careful analysis of their financial condition, they knew that retirement was many years away. Nevertheless, they were hatching a plan to bring them closer to their dream. They decided to sell The Glass Slipper and open a bed and breakfast on a beautiful beach in

TABLE 13

Monthly Revenue (in $1,000s)

MONTH	2011	2012	2013
January	438	444	450
February	420	425	438
March	414	423	434
April	318	331	338
May	306	318	331
June	240	245	254
July	240	255	264
August	216	223	231
September	198	210	224
October	225	233	243
November	270	278	289
December	315	322	335

Mexico. While this would mean that work was still in their future, they could wake up in the morning to the sight of the palm trees blowing in the wind and the waves lapping at the shore. They also knew that hiring the right manager would allow James and Deena the time to begin a semi-retirement in a corner of paradise.

To make this happen, James and Deena would have to sell The Glass Slipper for the right price. The price of the business would be based on the value of the property and equipment, as well as projections of future income. A forecast of sales for the next year is needed to help in the determination of the value of the restaurant. Monthly sales for each of the past 3 years are provided in Table 13.

Discussion Questions

1. Prepare a graph of the data. On this same graph, plot a 12-month moving average forecast. Discuss any apparent trend and seasonal patterns.
2. Use regression to develop a trend line that could be used to forecast monthly sales for the next year. Is the slope of this line consistent with what you observed in question 1? If not, discuss a possible explanation.
3. Use the multiplicative decomposition model on these data. Use this model to forecast sales for each month of the next year. Discuss why the slope of the trend equation with this model is so different from that of the trend equation in question 2.

---

www   Internet Case Study

See our Internet home page, at www.pearsonhighered.com/render, for the additional case study on **Akron Zoological Park**. This case involves forecasting attendance at Akron's zoo.

Bibliography

Billah, Baki, Maxwell L. King, Ralph D. Snyder, and Anne B. Koehler. "Exponential Smoothing Model Selection for Forecasting," *International Journal of Forecasting* 22, 2, (April–June 2006): 239–247.

Black, Ken. *Business Statistics: For Contemporary Decision Making*, 7th ed. John Wiley & Sons, Inc., 2012.

Diebold, F. X. *Elements of Forecasting*, 4th ed. Cincinnati: Cengage College Publishing, 2007.

Gardner, Everette Jr. "Exponential Smoothing: The State of the Art—Part II," *International Journal of Forecasting* 22, 4 (October 2006): 637–666.

Granger, Clive W., and J. M. Hashem Pesaran. "Economic and Statistical Measures of Forecast Accuracy," *Journal of Forecasting* 19, 7 (December 2000): 537–560.

Hanke, J. E., and D. W. Wichern. *Business Forecasting*, 9th ed. Upper Saddle River, NJ: Prentice Hall, 2009.

Heizer, J., and B. Render. *Operations Management*, 9th ed. Upper Saddle River, NJ: Prentice Hall, 2008.

Hyndman, Rob J. "The Interaction Between Trend and Seasonality," *International Journal of Forecasting* 20, 4 (October–December 2004): 561–563.

Hyndman, Rob J., and Anne B. Koehler. "Another Look at Measures of Forecast Accuracy," *International Journal of Forecasting* 22, 4 (October 2006): 679–688.

Levine, David M., David F. Stephan, and Kathryn A. Szabat. *Statistics for Managers Using Microsoft Excel*, 7th ed. Upper Saddle River, NJ: Pearson, 2014.

Meade, Nigel. "Evidence for the Selection of Forecasting Methods," *Journal of Forecasting* 19, 6 (November 2000): 515–535.

Snyder, Ralph D., and Roland G. Shami. "Exponential Smoothing of Seasonal Data: A Comparison," *Journal of Forecasting* 20, 3 (April 2001): 197–202.

Yurkiewicz, J. "Forecasting Software Survey," *OR/MS Today* 39, 3 (June 2012): 52–61.

Solutions to Selected Problems

16 MAD = 6.48 for 3-month moving average; MAD = 7.78 for 4-month moving average

18 $Y = 2.22 + 1.05X$

20 Forecast for year 12 is 11.789; MAD = 2.437

22 Forecasts for year 6 are 565.6 and 581.4

24 Forecast for year 6 is 555

26 MAD = 5.6 for trend line; MAD = 74.56 for exponential smoothing; MAD = 67 for moving average

28 (b) MAD = 2.60; RSFE = 5.11 at week 10

32 MAD = 3.34

36 $F_{11} = 6.26$; MAD = 0.58 for $\alpha = 0.8$ is lowest.

38 270, 390, 189, 351

Solutions to Self-Tests

1.	b	**6.**	b	**11.**	c
2.	a	**7.**	d	**12.**	d
3.	d	**8.**	b	**13.**	b
4.	c	**9.**	d	**14.**	c
5.	b	**10.**	b	**15.**	b

Linear Programming Models: Graphical and Computer Methods

LEARNING OBJECTIVES

After completing this chapter, students will be able to:

1. Understand the basic assumptions and properties of linear programming (LP).

2. Graphically solve any LP problem that has only two variables by both the corner point and isoprofit line methods.

3. Understand special issues in LP such as infeasibility, unboundedness, redundancy, and alternative optimal solutions.

4. Understand the role of sensitivity analysis.

5. Use Excel spreadsheets to solve LP problems.

Summary • Glossary • Solved Problems • Self-Test • Discussion Questions and Problems • Internet Homework Problems • Case Study: Mexicana Wire Works • Internet Case Study • Bibliography

From Chapter 7 of *Quantitative Analysis for Management*, Twelfth Edition. Barry Render, Ralph M. Stair, Jr., Michael E. Hanna, and Trevor S. Hale. Copyright © 2015 by Pearson Education, Inc. All rights reserved.

1 Introduction

Linear programming is a technique that helps in resource allocation decisions.

Many management decisions involve trying to make the most effective use of an organization's resources. Resources typically include machinery, labor, money, time, warehouse space, and raw materials. These resources may be used to make products (such as machinery, furniture, food, or clothing) or services (such as schedules for airlines or production, advertising policies, or investment decisions). **Linear programming (LP)** is a widely used mathematical modeling technique designed to help managers in planning and decision making relative to resource allocation.

Despite its name, LP and the more general category of techniques called **"mathematical" programming** have very little to do with computer programming. In the world of management science, *programming* refers to modeling and solving a problem mathematically. Computer programming has, of course, played an important role in the advancement and use of LP. Real-life LP problems are too cumbersome to solve by hand or with a calculator.

2 Requirements of a Linear Programming Problem

In the past 60 years, LP has been applied extensively to military, industrial, financial, marketing, accounting, and agricultural problems. Even though these applications are diverse, all LP problems have several properties and assumptions in common.

Problems seek to maximize or minimize an objective.

All problems seek to *maximize* or *minimize* some quantity, usually profit or cost. We refer to this property as the **objective function** of an LP problem. The major objective of a typical manufacturer is to maximize dollar profits. In the case of a trucking or railroad distribution system, the objective might be to minimize shipping costs. In any event, this objective must be stated clearly and defined mathematically. It does not matter, by the way, whether profits and costs are measured in cents, dollars, or millions of dollars.

Constraints limit the degree to which the objective can be obtained.

The second property that LP problems have in common is the presence of restrictions, or **constraints**, that limit the degree to which we can pursue our objective. For example, deciding how many units of each product in a firm's product line to manufacture is restricted by available personnel and machinery. Selection of an advertising policy or a financial portfolio is limited by the amount of money available to be spent or invested. We want, therefore, to maximize or minimize a quantity (the objective function) subject to limited resources (the constraints).

There must be alternatives available.

There must be alternative courses of action to choose from. For example, if a company produces three different products, management may use LP to decide how to allocate among them its limited production resources (of personnel, machinery, and so on). Should it devote all manufacturing capacity to make only the first product, should it produce equal amounts of each product, or should it allocate the resources in some other ratio? If there were no alternatives to select from, we would not need LP.

Mathematical relationships are linear.

The objective and constraints in LP problems must be expressed in terms of *linear* equations or inequalities. Linear mathematical relationships just mean that all terms used in the objective function and constraints are of the first degree (i.e., not squared, or to the third or higher power, or appearing more than once). Hence, the equation $2A + 5B = 10$ is an acceptable linear function, while the equation $2A^2 + 5B^3 + 3AB = 10$ is not linear because the variable A is squared, the variable B is cubed, and the two variables appear again as a product of each other.

The term *linear* implies both proportionality and additivity. Proportionality means that if production of 1 unit of a product uses 3 hours, production of 10 units would use 30 hours. Additivity means that the total of all activities equals the sum of the individual activities. If the production of one product generated $3 profit and the production of another product generated $8 profit, the total profit would be the sum of these two, which would be $11.

We assume that conditions of *certainty* exist: that is, number in the objective and constraints are known with certainty and do not change during the period being studied.

We make the *divisibility* assumption that solutions need not be in whole numbers (integers). Instead, they are divisible and may take any fractional value. In production problems, we often define variables as the number of units produced per week or per month, and a fractional value

TABLE 1
LP Properties and Assumptions

PROPERTIES OF LINEAR PROGRAMS
1. One objective function
2. One or more constraints
3. Alternative courses of action
4. Objective function and constraints are linear—proportionality and divisibility
5. Certainty
6. Divisibility
7. Nonnegative variables

(e.g., 0.3 chair) would simply mean that there is work in process. Something that was started in one week can be finished in the next. However, in other types of problems, fractional values do not make sense. If a fraction of a product cannot be purchased (for example, one-third of a submarine), an integer programming problem exists.

Finally, we assume that all answers or variables are *nonnegative*. Negative values of physical quantities are impossible; you simply cannot produce a negative number of chairs, shirts, lamps, or computers. However, there are some variables that can have negative values, such as profit, where a negative value indicates a loss. A simple mathematical operation can transform such a variable into two nonnegative variables, and that process can be found in books on linear programming. Table 1 summarizes these properties and assumptions.

3 Formulating LP Problems

Formulating a linear program involves developing a mathematical model to represent the managerial problem. Thus, in order to formulate a linear program, it is necessary to completely understand the managerial problem being faced. Once this is understood, we can begin to develop the mathematical statement of the problem. The steps in formulating a linear program follow:

1. Completely understand the managerial problem being faced.
2. Identify the objective and the constraints.
3. Define the decision variables.
4. Use the decision variables to write mathematical expressions for the objective function and the constraints.

Product mix problems use LP to decide how much of each product to make, given a series of resource restrictions.

One of the most common LP applications is the **product mix problem**. Two or more products are usually produced using limited resources such as personnel, machines, raw materials, and so on. The profit that the firm seeks to maximize is based on the profit contribution per unit of each product. (Profit contribution, you may recall, is just the selling price per unit minus the variable cost per unit.*) The company would like to determine how many units of each product it should produce so as to maximize overall profit given its limited resources. A problem of this type is formulated in the following example.

Flair Furniture Company

The Flair Furniture Company produces inexpensive tables and chairs. The production process for each is similar in that both require a certain number of hours of carpentry work and a certain number of labor hours in the painting and varnishing department. Each table takes 4 hours of carpentry and 2 hours in the painting and varnishing shop. Each chair requires 3 hours in carpentry and 1 hour in painting and varnishing. During the current production period, 240 hours of carpentry time are available and 100 hours in painting and varnishing time are available. Each table sold yields a profit of $70; each chair produced is sold for a $50 profit.

---

*Technically, we maximize total contribution margin, which is the difference between unit selling price and costs that vary in proportion to the quantity of the item produced. Depreciation, fixed general expense, and advertising are excluded from calculations.

Flair Furniture's problem is to determine the best possible combination of tables and chairs to manufacture in order to reach the maximum profit. The firm would like this production mix situation formulated as an LP problem.

We begin by summarizing the information needed to formulate and solve this problem (see Table 2). This helps us understand the problem being faced. Next we identify the objective and the constraints. The objective is

Maximize profit

The constraints are

1. The hours of carpentry time used cannot exceed 240 hours per week.
2. The hours of painting and varnishing time used cannot exceed 100 hours per week.

The **decision variables** that represent the actual decisions we will make are defined as

$$T = \text{number of tables to be produced per week}$$
$$C = \text{number of chairs to be produced per week}$$

Now we can create the LP objective function in terms of T and C. The objective function is Maximize profit $= \$70T + \$50C$.

Our next step is to develop mathematical relationships to describe the two constraints in this problem. One general relationship is that the amount of a resource used is to be less than or equal to ($\leq$) the amount of resource *available*.

In the case of the carpentry department, the total time used is

$$(4 \text{ hours per table})(\text{Number of tables produced})$$
$$+ (3 \text{ hours per chair})(\text{Number of chairs produced})$$

TABLE 2
Flair Furniture
Company Data

DEPARTMENT	HOURS REQUIRED TO PRODUCE 1 UNIT		AVAILABLE HOURS THIS WEEK
	(T) TABLES	(C) CHAIRS	
Carpentry	4	3	240
Painting and varnishing	2	1	100
Profit per unit	$70	$50	

The resource constraints put limits on the carpentry labor resource and the painting labor resource mathematically.

So the first constraint may be stated as follows:

Carpentry time used $\leq$ Carpentry time available

$$4T + 3C \leq 240 \text{ (hours of carpentry time)}$$

Similarly, the second constraint is as follows:

Painting and varnishing time used $\leq$ Painting and varnishing time available

$$②T + 1C \leq 100 \text{ (hours of painting and varnishing time)}$$

(This means that each table produced takes two hours of the painting and varnishing resource.)

Both of these constraints represent production capacity restrictions and, of course, affect the total profit. For example, Flair Furniture cannot produce 80 tables during the production period because if $T = 80$, both constraints will be violated. It also cannot make $T = 50$ tables and $C = 10$ chairs. Why? Because this would violate the second constraint that no more than 100 hours of painting and varnishing time be allocated.

To obtain meaningful solutions, the values for T and C must be nonnegative numbers. That is, all potential solutions must represent real tables and real chairs. Mathematically, this means that

$$T \geq 0 \text{ (number of tables produced is greater than or equal to 0)}$$

$$C \geq 0 \text{ (number of chairs produced is greater than or equal to 0)}$$

The complete problem may now be restated mathematically as

$$\text{Maximize profit} = \$70T + \$50C$$

Here is a complete mathematical statement of the LP problem.

subject to the constraints

$$
\begin{array}{ll}
4T + 3C \leq 240 & \text{(carpentry constraint)} \\
2T + 1C \leq 100 & \text{(painting and varnishing constraint)} \\
T \geq 0 & \text{(first nonnegativity constraint)} \\
C \geq 0 & \text{(second nonnegativity constraint)}
\end{array}
$$

While the nonnegativity constraints are technically separate constraints, they are often written on a single line with the variables separated by commas. In this example, this would be written as

$$T, C \geq 0$$

4 Graphical Solution to an LP Problem

The graphical method works only when there are two decision variables, but it provides valuable insight into how larger problems are structured.

The easiest way to solve a small LP problem such as that of the Flair Furniture Company is with the graphical solution approach. The graphical procedure is useful only when there are two decision variables (such as number of tables to produce, T, and number of chairs to produce, C) in the problem. When there are more than two variables, it is not possible to plot the solution on a two-dimensional graph and we must turn to more complex approaches. But the graphical method is invaluable in providing us with insights into how other approaches work. For that reason alone, it is worthwhile to spend the rest of this chapter exploring graphical solutions.

Graphical Representation of Constraints

To find the optimal solution to an LP problem, we must first identify a set, or region, of feasible solutions. The first step in doing so is to plot each of the problem's constraints on a graph. The variable T (tables) is plotted as the horizontal axis of the graph and the variable C (chairs) is plotted as the vertical axis. The notation (T, C) is used to identify the points on the graph. The *Nonnegativity constraints mean* $T \geq 0$ *and* $C \geq 0$. **nonnegativity constraints** mean that we are always working in the first (or northeast) quadrant of a graph (see Figure 1).

To represent the first constraint graphically, $4T + 3C \leq 240$, we must first graph the equality portion of this, which is

$$4T + 3C = 240$$

FIGURE 1

**Quadrant Containing
All Positive Values**

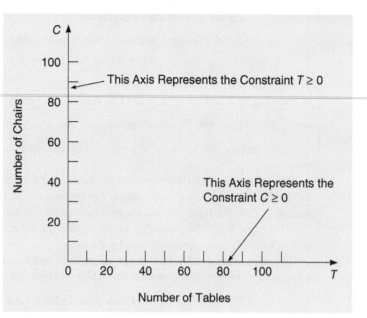

Plotting the first constraint involves finding points at which the line intersects the T *and* C *axes.*

As you may recall from elementary algebra, a linear equation in two variables is a straight line. The easiest way to plot the line is to find any two points that satisfy the equation, then draw a straight line through them.

The two easiest points to find are generally the points at which the line intersects the T and C axes.

When Flair Furniture produces no tables, namely $T = 0$, it implies that

$$4(0) + 3C = 240$$

or

$$3C = 240$$

or

$$C = 80$$

In other words, if *all* of the carpentry time available is used to produce chairs, 80 chairs *could* be made. Thus, this constraint equation crosses the vertical axis at 80.

To find the point at which the line crosses the horizontal axis, we assume that the firm makes no chairs, that is, $C = 0$. Then

$$4T + 3(0) = 240$$

or

$$4T = 240$$

or

$$T = 60$$

Hence, when $C = 0$, we see that $4T = 240$ and that $T = 60$.

The carpentry constraint is illustrated in Figure 2. It is bounded by the line running from point $(T = 0, C = 80)$ to point $(T = 60, C = 0)$.

Recall, however, that the actual carpentry constraint was the **inequality** $4T + 3C \leq 240$. How can we identify all of the solution points that satisfy this constraint? It turns out that there are three possibilities. First, we know that any point that lies on the line $4T + 3C = 240$ satisfies the constraint. Any combination of tables and chairs on the line will use up all 240 hours of carpentry time.* Now we must find the set of solution points that would use less than

_____

*Thus, what we have done is to plot the constraint equation in its most binding position, that is, using all of the carpentry resource.

FIGURE 2

Graph of Carpentry Constraint Equation $4T + 3C = 240$

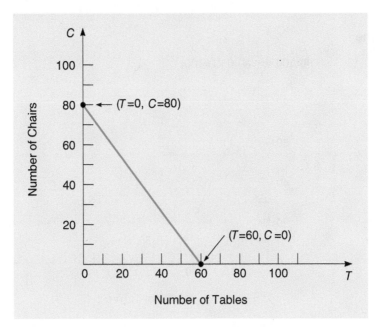

the 240 hours. The points that satisfy the $<$ portion of the constraint (i.e., $4T + 3C < 240$) will be all the points on one side of the line, while all the points on the other side of the line will not satisfy this condition. To determine which side of the line this is, simply choose any point on either side of the constraint line shown in Figure 2 and check to see if it satisfies this condition. For example, choose the point (30, 20), as illustrated in Figure 3:

$$4(30) + 3(20) = 180$$

Since $180 < 240$, this point satisfies the constraint, and all points on this side of the line will also satisfy the constraint. This set of points is indicated by the shaded region in Figure 3.

To see what would happen if the point did not satisfy the constraint, select a point on the other side of the line, such as (70, 40). This constraint would not be met at this point as

$$4(70) + 3(40) = 400$$

Since $400 > 240$, this point and every other point on that side of the line would not satisfy this constraint. Thus, the solution represented by the point (70, 40) would require more than the 240 hours that are available. There are not enough carpentry hours to produce 70 tables and 40 chairs.

FIGURE 3

Region That Satisfies the Carpentry Constraint

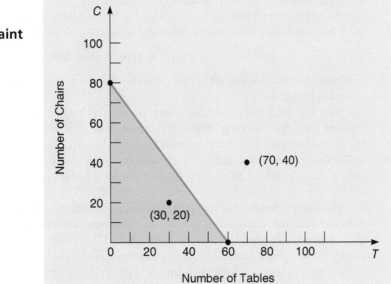

FIGURE 4

Region That Satisfies the Painting and Varnishing Constraint

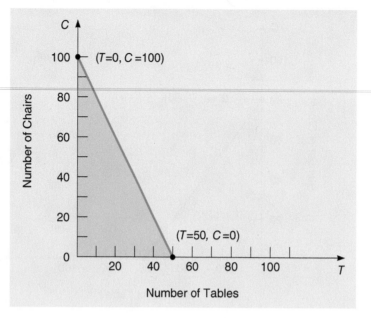

Next, let us identify the solution corresponding to the second constraint, which limits the time available in the painting and varnishing department. That constraint was given as $2T + 1C \leq 100$. As before, we start by graphing the equality portion of this constraint, which is

$$2T + 1C = 100$$

To find two points on the line, select $T = 0$ and solve for C:

$$2(0) + 1C = 100$$
$$C = 100$$

So, one point on the line is $(0, 100)$. To find the second point, select $C = 0$ and solve for T:

$$2T + 1(0) = 100$$
$$T = 50$$

The second point used to graph the line is $(50, 0)$. Plotting this point, $(50, 0)$, and the other point, $(0, 100)$, results in the line representing all the solutions in which exactly 100 hours of painting and varnishing time are used, as shown in Figure 4.

To find the points that require less than 100 hours, select a point on either side of this line to see if the inequality portion of the constraint is satisfied. Selecting $(0, 0)$ gives us

$$2(0) + 1(0) = 0 < 100$$

This indicates that this and all the points below the line satisfy the constraint, and this region is shaded in Figure 4.

Now that each individual constraint has been plotted on a graph, it is time to move on to the next step. We recognize that to produce a chair or a table, both the carpentry and painting and varnishing departments must be used. In an LP problem we need to find that set of solution points that satisfies all of the constraints *simultaneously*. Hence, the constraints should be redrawn on one graph (or superimposed one upon the other). This is shown in Figure 5.

The shaded region now represents the area of solutions that does not exceed either of the two Flair Furniture constraints. It is known by the term *area of feasible solutions* or, more simply, the **feasible region**. The feasible region in an LP problem must satisfy *all* conditions specified by the problem's constraints, and is thus the region where all constraints overlap. Any point in the region would be a **feasible solution** to the Flair Furniture problem; any point outside the shaded area would represent an **infeasible solution**. Hence, it would be feasible to manufacture

In LP problems we are interested in satisfying all constraints at the same time.

The feasible region is the set of points that satisfy all the constraints.

FIGURE 5

Feasible Solution Region for the Flair Furniture Company Problem

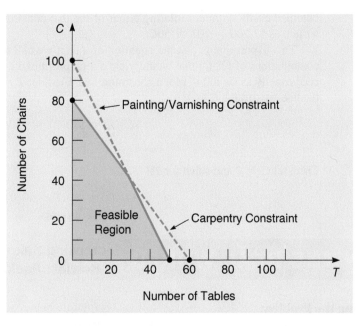

30 tables and 20 chairs ($T = 30$, $C = 20$) during a production period because both constraints are observed:

Carpentry constraint	$4T + 3C \leq 240$ hours available	
	$(4)(30) + (3)(20) = 180$ hours used	⊘
Painting constraint	$2T + 1C \leq 100$ hours available	
	$(2)(30) + (1)(20) = 80$ hours used	⊘

But it would violate both of the constraints to produce 70 tables and 40 chairs, as we see here mathematically:

Carpentry constraint	$4T + 3C \leq 240$ hours available	
	$(4)(70) + (3)(40) = 400$ hours used	⊗
Painting constraint	$2T + 1C \leq 100$ hours available	
	$(2)(70) + (1)(40) = 180$ hours used	⊗

Furthermore, it would also be infeasible to manufacture 50 tables and 5 chairs ($T = 50$, $C = 5$). Can you see why?

Carpentry constraint	$4T + 3C \leq 240$ hours available	
	$(4)(50) + (3)(5) = 215$ hours used	⊘
Painting constraint	$2T + 1C \leq 100$ hours available	
	$(2)(50) + (1)(5) = 105$ hours used	⊗

This possible solution falls within the time available in carpentry but exceeds the time available in painting and varnishing and thus falls outside the feasible region.

Isoprofit Line Solution Method

Now that the feasible region has been graphed, we may proceed to find the optimal solution to the problem. The optimal solution is the point lying in the feasible region that produces the highest profit. Yet there are many, many possible solution points in the region. How do we go about selecting the best one, the one yielding the highest profit?

The isoprofit method is the first method we introduce for finding the optimal solution.

There are a few different approaches that can be taken in solving for the optimal solution when the feasible region has been established graphically. The speediest one to apply is called the *isoprofit line method*.

We start the technique by letting profits equal some arbitrary but small dollar amount. For the Flair Furniture problem we may choose a profit of $2,100. This is a profit level that can be obtained easily without violating either of the two constraints. The objective function can be written as $2,100 = 70T + 50C$.

This expression is just the equation of a line; we call it an **isoprofit line**. It represents all combinations of (T, C) that would yield a total profit of $2,100. To plot the profit line, we proceed exactly as we did to plot a constraint line. First, let $T = 0$ and solve for the point at which the line crosses the C axis:

$$\$2,100 = \$70(0) = \$50C$$

$$C = 42 \text{ chairs}$$

Then, let $C = 0$ and solve for T:

$$\$2,100 = \$70T + 50(0)$$

$$T = 30 \text{ tables}$$

MODELING IN THE REAL WORLD — Increasing Sales at Hewlett Packard

Defining the Problem

Defining the Problem

Hewlett Packard (HP) launched HPDirect.com in the late 1990s and opened online sales of HP products including computers, printers, accessories, and supplies. In 2008, the management of HPDirect.com were told that online sales had to grow 150% in the next three years, and this had to be done without exceeding marketing budgets. To do this, they had to attract more visitors to the site, they had to convert the visitors into customers by targeted marketing efforts, and they had to retain loyal customers by providing a satisfying experience in a cost-efficient manner.

Developing a Model

Developing a Model

The massive nature of this project required the use of a variety of operations research models to achieve the objectives. Multiple regression was used to identify the key drivers of online visitors, and it was combined with time-series models (which identified seasonality and trend) to forecast the number of visits across all Web pages as well as the sales of the large variety of products. Bayesian models and Markov models were used to help predict the likelihood of a making a purchase. Linear programming was used to determine which marketing channels to use for different customers and to optimize these decisions.

Acquiring Input Data

Acquiring Input Data

Data was collected over a 2-year period not only on visitors to the website and their behavior, but also on sales and marketing activities over this same 2-year period. The data was separated into two groups: a training set to develop the model and a test set to validate the model.

Developing a Solution

Developing a Solution

The training set of data was used to develop the models that would be used in this project, including the linear programs to optimally allocate the marketing budget.

Testing the Solution

Testing the Solution

The data in the test set was then used to validate the models to make sure that the models were working as planned. When the different parts of the project were implemented, a test group of customers received customized marketing material based on their segment profile, while a control group received generic material.

Analyzing the Results

Analyzing the Results

The test group performed better than the control group on all key metrics, including average order size, conversion rate, and total sales per dollar spent on marketing. During one particular period, the conversion rate of the targeted group was 58% higher than for the control group and dollar sales per marketing item up 33%.

Implementing the Results

Implementing the Results

At the beginning of each quarter, the models are run to help the marketing team plan efforts for that quarter. The models themselves are refreshed every quarter. Since 2009, the models have been credited with increasing incremental revenue by $117 million, increasing order size, and reducing overall inventory cost.

Source: Based on R. Randon et al., "Hewlett Packard: Delivering Profitable Growth for HPDirect.com Using Operations Research," *Interfaces* 43, 1 (January–February 2013): 48–61.

FIGURE 6

Profit Line of $2,100 Plotted for the Flair Furniture Company

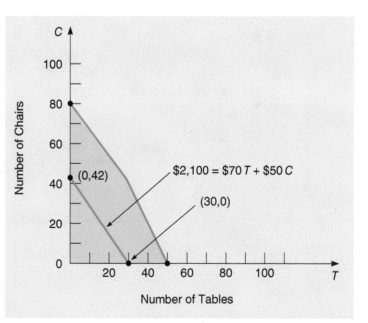

We can now connect these two points with a straight line. This profit line is illustrated in Figure 6. All points on the line represent feasible solutions that produce a profit of $2,100.*

Isoprofit involves graphing parallel profit lines.

Now, obviously, the isoprofit line for $2,100 does not produce the highest possible profit to the firm. In Figure 7 we try graphing two more lines, each yielding a higher profit. The middle equation, $2,800 = $70T + $50C$, was plotted in the same fashion as the lower line. When $T = 0$,

$$\$2,800 = \$70(0) + \$50C$$
$$C = 56$$

When $C = 0$,

$$\$2,800 = \$70T + \$50(C)$$
$$T = 40$$

FIGURE 7

Four Isoprofit Lines Plotted for the Flair Furniture Company

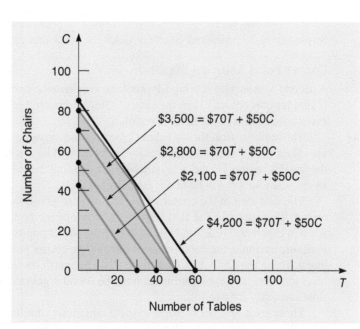

*Iso means "equal" or "similar." Thus, an isoprofit line represents a line with all profits the same, in this case $2,100.

209

FIGURE 8
Optimal Solution to the Flair Furniture Problem

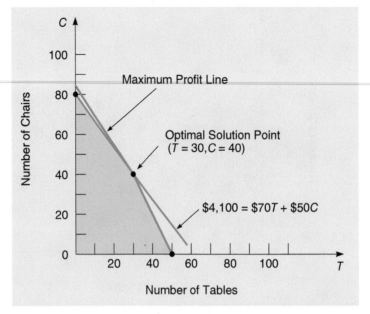

We draw a series of parallel isoprofit lines until we find the highest isoprofit line, that is, the one with the optimal solution.

Again, any combination of tables (T) and chairs (C) on this isoprofit line produces a total profit of $2,800. Note that the third line generates a profit of $3,500, even more of an improvement. The farther we move from the origin, the higher our profit will be. Another important point is that these isoprofit lines are parallel. We now have two clues as to how to find the optimal solution to the original problem. We can draw a series of parallel lines (by carefully moving our ruler in a plane parallel to the first profit line). The highest profit line that still touches some point of the feasible region pinpoints the optimal solution. Notice that the fourth line ($4,200) is too high to be considered.

The last point that an isoprofit line would touch in this feasible region is the corner point where the two constraint lines intersect, so this point will result in the maximum possible profit. To find the coordinates of this point, solve the two equations simultaneously (as detailed in the next section). This results in the point (30, 40) as shown in Figure 8. Calculating the profit at this point, we get

$$\text{Profit} = 70T + 50C = 70(30) + 50(40) = \$4,100$$

So producing 30 tables and 40 chairs yields the maximum profit of $4,100.

Corner Point Solution Method

A second approach to solving LP problems employs the **corner point method**. This technique is simpler conceptually than the isoprofit line approach, but it involves looking at the profit at every corner point of the feasible region.

The mathematical theory behind LP is that the optimal solution must lie at one of the corner points in the feasible region.

The mathematical theory behind LP states that an optimal solution to any problem (that is, the values of T, C that yield the maximum profit) will lie at a **corner point**, or **extreme point**, of the feasible region. Hence, it is only necessary to find the values of the variables at each corner; an optimal solution will lie at one (or more) of them.

The first step in the corner point method is to graph the constraints and find the feasible region. This was also the first step in the isoprofit method, and the feasible region is shown again in Figure 9. The second step is to find the corner points of the feasible region. For the Flair Furniture example, the coordinates of three of the corner points are obvious from observing the graph. These are (0, 0), (50, 0), and (0, 80). The fourth corner point is where the two constraint lines intersect, and the coordinates must be found algebraically by solving the two equations simultaneously for two variables.

There are a number of ways to solve equations simultaneously, and any of these may be used. We will illustrate the elimination method here. To begin the elimination method, select a variable to be eliminated. We will select T in this example. Then multiply or divide one equation

FIGURE 9

Four Corner Points of the Feasible Region

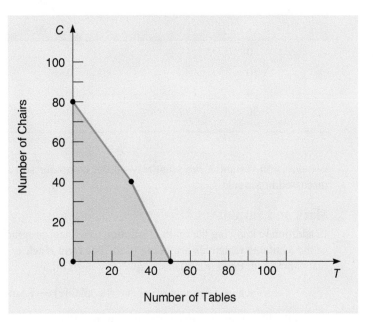

by a number so that the coefficient of that variable (T) in one equation will be the negative of the coefficient of that variable in the other equation. The two constraint equations are

$$4T + 3C = 240 \quad (\text{carpentry})$$
$$2T + 1C = 100 \quad (\text{painting})$$

To eliminate T, we multiply the second equation by -2:

$$-2(2T + 1C = 100) = -4T - 2C = -200$$

and then add it to the first equation:

$$\frac{+4T + 3C = \quad 240}{+ 1C = \quad 40}$$

or

$$C = 40$$

Doing this has enabled us to eliminate one variable, T, and to solve for C. We can now substitute 40 for C in either of the original equations and solve for T. Let's use the first equation. When $C = 40$, then

$$4T + (3)(40) = 240$$
$$4T + 120 = 240$$

or

$$4T = 120$$
$$T = 30$$

Thus, the last corner point is (30, 40).

The next step is to calculate the value of the objective function at each of the corner points. The final step is to select the corner with the best value, which would be the highest profit in this example. Table 3 lists these corners points with their profits. The highest profit is found to be $4,100, which is obtained when 30 tables and 40 chairs are produced. This is exactly what was obtained using the isoprofit method.

Table 4 provides a summary of both the isoprofit method and the corner point method. Either of these can be used when there are two decision variables. If a problem has more than

211

TABLE 3

Feasible Corner Points and Profits for Flair Furniture

NUMBER OF TABLES (T)	NUMBER OF CHAIRS (C)	Profit = $70T + $50C
0	0	$0
50	0	$3,500
0	80	$4,000
30	40	$4,100

two decision variables, we must rely on the computer software or use the simplex algorithm discussed in Module 7.

Slack and Surplus

The term slack is associated with ≤ constraints.

In addition to knowing the optimal solution to a linear program, it is helpful to know whether all of the available resources are being used. The term **slack** is used for the amount of a resource that is not used. For a less-than-or-equal to constraint,

$$\text{Slack} = (\text{Amount of resource available}) - (\text{Amount of resource used})$$

In the Flair Furniture example, there were 240 hours of carpentry time available. If the company decided to produce 20 tables and 25 chairs instead of the optimal solution, the amount of carpentry time used $(4T + 3C)$ would be $4(20) + 3(25) = 155$. So,

$$\text{Slack time in carpentry} = 240 - 155 = 85$$

For the optimal solution $(30, 40)$ to the Flair Furniture problem, the slack is 0 since all 240 hours are used.

The term surplus is associated with ≥ constraints.

The term **surplus** is used with greater-than-or-equal-to constraints to indicate the amount by which the right-hand side of a constraint is exceeded. For a greater-than-or-equal-to constraint,

$$\text{Surplus} = (\text{Actual amount}) - (\text{Minimum amount})$$

Suppose there had been a constraint in the example that required the total number of tables and chairs combined to be at least 42 units (i.e., $T + C \geq 42$), and the company decided to produce 20 tables and 25 chairs. The total amount produced would be $20 + 25 = 45$, so the surplus would be

$$\text{Surplus} = 45 - 42 = 3$$

meaning that 3 units more than the minimum were produced. For the optimal solution $(30, 40)$ in the Flair Furniture problem, if this constraint had been in the problem, the surplus would be $70 - 42 = 28$.

TABLE 4

Summaries of Graphical Solution Methods

ISOPROFIT METHOD

1. Graph all constraints and find the feasible region.
2. Select a specific profit (or cost) line and graph it to find the slope.
3. Move the objective function line in the direction of increasing profit (or decreasing cost) while maintaining the slope. The last point it touches in the feasible region is the optimal solution.
4. Find the values of the decision variables at this last point and compute the profit (or cost).

CORNER POINT METHOD

1. Graph all constraints and find the feasible region.
2. Find the corner points of the feasible region.
3. Compute the profit (or cost) at each of the feasible corner points.
4. Select the corner point with the best value of the objective function found in step 3. This is the optimal solution.

So the slack and surplus represent the difference between the left-hand side (LHS) and the right-hand side (RHS) of a constraint. The term *slack* is used when referring to less-than-or-equal-to constraints, and the term *surplus* is used when referring to greater-than-or-equal-to constraints. Most computer software for linear programming will provide the amount of slack and surplus that exist for each constraint in the optimal solution.

A constraint that has zero slack or surplus for the optimal solution is called a **binding constraint**. A constraint with positive slack or surplus for the optimal solution is called a **nonbinding constraint**. Some computer outputs will specify whether a constraint is binding or nonbinding.

5 Solving Flair Furniture's LP Problem Using QM for Windows, Excel 2013, and Excel QM

Almost every organization has access to computer programs that are capable of solving enormous LP problems. Although each computer program is slightly different, the approach each takes toward handling LP problems is basically the same. The format of the input data and the level of detail provided in output results may differ from program to program and computer to computer, but once you are experienced in dealing with computerized LP algorithms, you can easily adjust to minor changes.

Using QM for Windows

Let us begin by demonstrating QM for Windows on the Flair Furniture Company problem. To use QM for Windows, select the Linear Programming module. Then specify the number of constraints (other than the nonnegativity constraints, as it is assumed that the variables must be nonnegative), the number of variables, and whether the objective is to be maximized or minimized. For the Flair Furniture Company problem, there are two constraints and two variables. Once these numbers are specified, the input window opens as shown in Program 1A. Then you can enter the coefficients for the objective function and the constraints. Placing the cursor over the X1 or X2 and typing a new name such as *T* and *C* will change the variable names. The constraint names can be similarly modified. Program 1B shows the QM for Windows screen after the data has been input and before the problem is solved. When you click the *Solve* button, you get the output shown in Program 1C.

PROGRAM 1A

QM for Windows Linear Programming Input Screen

The equations will automatically appear as you enter the coefficients in the other columns.

Type over X1 and X2 to change the names of the Variables.

Input the coefficients in the appropriate columns.

	X1	X2		RHS	Equation form
Maximize	0	0			Max
Constraint 1	0	0	<=	0	<= 0
Constraint 2	0	0	<=	0	<= 0

PROGRAM 1B

QM for Windows Data Input for Flair Furniture Problem

Click here to change the type of constraint.

Click Solve after entering the data.

Flair Furniture Company

	T	C		RHS	Equation form
Maximize	70	50			Max 70T + 50C
Constraint 1	4	3	<=	240	4T + 3C <= 240
Constraint 2	2	1	<=	100	2T + C <= 100

PROGRAM 1C

QM for Windows Output and Graph for Flair Furniture Problem

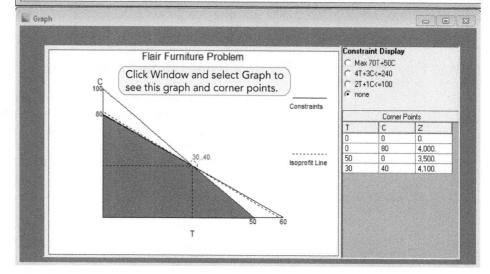

Linear Programming Results					
The values of the variables are shown here.	T	The objective function value (profit) is shown here.		RHS	Dual
Maximize	70	50			
Carpentry	4	3	<=	240	15
Painting	2	1	<=	100	5
Solution->	30	40		4,100	

Flair Furniture Problem

Click Window and select Graph to see this graph and corner points.

Constraints

30.,40.

Isoprofit Line

Constraint Display
- Max 70T+50C
- 4T+3C<=240
- 2T+1C<=100
- none

Corner Points		
T	C	Z
0	0	0.
0	80	4,000.
50	0	3,500.
30	40	4,100.

Once the problem has been solved, a graph may be displayed by selecting *Window—Graph* from the menu bar in QM for Windows. Program 1C shows the output for the graphical solution. Notice that in addition to the graph, the corner points and the original problem are also shown. Later we return to see additional information related to sensitivity analysis that is provided by QM for Windows.

Using Excel's Solver Command to Solve LP Problems

Excel 2013 (as well as earlier versions) has an add-in called Solver that can be used to solve linear programs. If this add-in doesn't appear on the Data tab in Excel 2013, it has not been activated.

PREPARING THE SPREADSHEET FOR SOLVER   The spreadsheet must be prepared with data and formulas for certain calculations before Solver can be used. Excel QM can be used to simplify this process. We will briefly describe the steps, and further discussion and suggestions will be provided when the Flair Furniture example is presented. Here is a summary of the steps to prepare the spreadsheet:

1. Enter the problem data. The problem data consist of the coefficients of the objective function and the constraints, plus the RHS values for each of the constraints. It is best to organize this in a logical and meaningful way. The coefficients will be used when writing formulas in steps 3 and 4, and the RHS will be entered into Solver.
2. Designate specific cells for the values of the decision variables. Later, these cell addresses will be input into Solver.
3. Write a formula to calculate the value of the objective function, using the coefficients for the objective function (from step 1) that you have entered and the cells containing the values of the decision variables (from step 2). Later, this cell address will be input into Solver.
4. Write a formula to calculate the value of the LHS of each constraint, using the coefficients for the constraints (from step 1) that you have entered and the cells containing the values of the decision variables (from step 2). Later, these cell addresses and the cell addresses for the corresponding RHS value will be input into Solver.

PROGRAM 2A

Excel Data Input for Flair Furniture Example

These cells are selected to contain the values of the decision variables. Solver will enter the optimal solution here, but you may enter numbers here also.

The signs for the constraints are entered here for reference only.

	A	B	C	D	E	F
1	Flair Furniture					
2						
3	Variables	T (Tables)	C (Chairs)			
4	Units Produced			Profit		
5	Objective function	70	50	0		
6						
7	Constraints			LHS (Hours used)		RHS
8	Carpentry	4	3	0	≤	240
9	Painting	2	1	0	≤	100

PROGRAM 2B

Formulas for Flair Furniture Example

	D
4	Profit
5	=SUMPRODUCT($B$4:$C$4,B5:C5)
6	
7	LHS (Hours used)
8	=SUMPRODUCT($B$4:$C$4,B8:C8)
9	=SUMPRODUCT($B$4:$C$4,B9:C9)

PROGRAM 2C

Excel Spreadsheet for Flair Furniture Example

Because there is a 1 in each of these cells, the LHS values can be calculated very easily to see if a mistake has been made.

You can change these values to see how the profit and resource utilization change.

	A	B	C	D	E	F
1	Flair Furniture					
2						
3	Variables	T (Tables)	C (Chairs)			
4	Units Produced	1	1	Profit		
5	Objective function	70	50	120		
6						
7	Constraints			LHS (Hours used)		RHS
8	Carpentry	4	3	7	≤	240
9	Painting	2	1	3	≤	100

These four steps must be completed in some way with all linear programs in Excel. Additional information may be put into the spreadsheet for clarification purposes. Let's illustrate these with an example.

1. Program 2A provides the input data for the Flair Furniture example. You should enter the numbers in the cells shown. The words can be any description that you choose. The "≤" symbols are entered for reference only. They are not specifically used by Excel Solver.
2. The cells designated for the values of the variables are B4 for T (tables) and C4 for C (chairs). These cell addresses will be entered into Solver as the *By Changing Variable Cells*. Solver will change the values in these cells to find the optimal solution. It is sometimes helpful to enter a 1 in each of these to help identify any obvious errors when the formulas for the objective and the constraints are written.
3. A formula is written in Excel for the objective function (D5), and this is displayed in Program 2B. The Sumproduct function is very helpful, although there are other ways to write this. This cell address will be entered into Solver as the *Set Objective* location.
4. The hours used in carpentry (the LHS of the carpentry constraint) is calculated with the formula in cell D8, while cell D9 calculates the hours used in painting as illustrated in Program 2B. These cells and the cells containing the RHS values will be used when the constraints are entered into Solver.

The problem is now ready for the use of Solver. However, even if the optimal solution is not found, this spreadsheet has benefits. You can enter different values for *T* and *C* into cells B4 and C4 just to see how the resource utilization (LHS) and profit change.

PROGRAM 2D

Starting Solver in Excel 2013

From the Data ribbon, click Solver.

If Solver does not appear on the Data ribbon, it has not been activated.

PROGRAM 2E Solver Parameters Dialog Box

Enter the cell address for the objective function value.

Specify Max or Min.

Enter the location of the values for the variables.

Always select Simplex LP for solution method.

Click Add to input constraints.

Check this box for nonegative variables.

Click Solve after constraints have been added.

USING SOLVER   To begin using Solver, go to the *Data* tab in Excel 2013 and click *Solver*, as shown in Program 2D. Once you click Solver, the Solver Parameters dialog box opens, as shown in Program 2E, and the following inputs should be entered, although the order is not important:

1. In the *Set Objective* box, enter the cell address for the total profit (D5).
2. In the *By Changing Variable Cells* box, enter the cell addresses for the variable values (B4:C4). Solver will allow the values in these cells to change while searching for the best value in the Set Objective cell reference.

PROGRAM 2F

Solver Add Constraint Dialog Box

Add Constraint

Enter the address for the LHS of the constraints. These may be entered one at a time or all together if they are of the same type (e.g., all < or all >).

Enter the address for the RHS of the constraints.

Ce_ll Reference: $D$8:$D$9

Co_nstraint: =$F$8:$F$9

<=

OK   Add   Cancel

Click OK when finished.

Click button to select the type of constraint relationship.

3. Click *Max* for a maximization problem and *Min* for a minimization problem.
4. Check the box for *Make Unconstrained Variables Non-Negative* since the variables *T* and *C* must be greater than or equal to zero.
5. Click the *Select Solving Method* button and select *Simplex LP* from the menu that appears.
6. Click *Add* to add the constraints. When you do this, the dialog box shown in Program 2F appears.
7. In the *Cell Reference* box, enter the cell references for the LHS values (D8:D9). Click the button to open the drop-down menu to select <=, which is for ≤ constraints. Then enter the cell references for the RHS values (F8:F9). Since these are all less-than- or-equal-to constraints, they can all be entered at one time by specifying the ranges. If there were other types of constraints, such as ≥ constraints, you could click *Add* after entering these first constraints, and the Add Constraint dialog box would allow you to enter additional constraints. When preparing the spreadsheet for Solver, it is easier if all the ≤ constraints are together and the ≥ constraints are together. After entering all the constraints, click *OK*. The Add Constraint dialog box closes, and the Solver Parameters dialog box reopens.
8. Click *Solve* on the Solver Parameters dialog box, and the solution is found. The Solver Results dialog box opens and indicates that a solution was found, as shown in Program 2G. In situations where there is no feasible solution, this box will indicate this. Additional information may be obtained from the Reports section of this as will be seen later. Program 2H shows the results of the spreadsheet with the optimal solution.

Using Excel QM

Using the Excel QM add-in can help you easily solve linear programming problems. Not only are all formulas automatically created by Excel QM, the spreadsheet preparation for the use of

PROGRAM 2G

Solver Results Dialog Box

Solver Results

Solver found a sol...   Additional information is available.   ...mality

conditions are sat...

Re_ports

Answer
Sensitivity
Limits

⊙ _Keep Solver Solution

○ _Restore Original Values

☐ _Return to Solver Parameters Dialog

☐ O_utline Reports

OK   Cancel   _Save Scenario...

Solver found a solution. All Constraints and optimality conditions are satisfied.

When the GRG engine is used, Solver has found at least a local optimal solution. When Simplex LP is used, this means Solver has found a global optimal solution.

Check this to be sure that a solution was found.

PROGRAM 2H

Flair Furniture Solution Found by Solver

	A			
1	Flair Furniture			
2				
3	Variables	T (Tables)	C (Chairs)	
4	Units Produced	30	40	Profit
5	Objective function	70	50	4100
6				
7	Constraints			LHS (Hours used)
8	Carpentry	4	3	240	≤	240
9	Painting	2	1	100	≤	100

The optimal solution is T = 30, C = 40, profit = 4,100.

The hours used are given here.

the Solver add-in is also automatically performed. We will illustrate this using the Flair Furniture example.

To begin, from the Excel QM ribbon in Excel 2013, click the *Alphabetical* menu and then select *Linear, Integer & Mixed Integer Programming* from the drop-down menu, as shown in Program 3A. The Excel QM Spreadsheet Initialization window opens, and in it you enter the problem title, the number of variables, and the number of constraints (do not count the nonnegativity constraints). Specify whether the problem is a maximization or minimization problem, and then click *OK*. When the initialization process is finished, a spreadsheet is prepared for data input, as shown in Program 3B. In this worksheet, enter the data in the section labeled Data. Specify the type of constraint (less-than, greater-than, or equal-to) and change the variable names and the constraint names, if desired. You do not have to write any formulas.

Once the data have been entered, from the *Data* tab, select *Solver*. The Solver Parameters window opens (refer back to Program 2E to see what input is normally required in a typical Solvers Parameters window), and you will see that Excel QM has made all the necessary inputs and selections. You do not enter any information, and you simply click *Solve* to find the solution. The solution is displayed in Program 3C.

Program 3A   Using Excel QM in Excel 2013 for the Flair Furniture Example

From the Excel QM ribbon, click the Alphabetical Menu, and then select Linear, Integer, and Mixed Integer Programming from the menu.

When the initialization window appears, enter the number of variables, number of constraints, and indicate maximize or minimize.

PROGRAM 3B   Excel QM Data Input for the Flair Furniture Example

After entering the problem, click the Data tab and select Solver from the Data ribbon. When the window for Solver opens, simply click Solve as all the necessary inputs have been entered by Excel QM.

Instructions to access Solver are here.

Enter the data in the appropriate cells. Do not change any other cells in the spreadsheet.

	A	B	C	D	E	F	G	H	I
1	Flair Furniture								
2	Enter the values in the shaded area. Then go to the DATA Tab on the ribbon, click on Solver in the Data Analysis								
3	Group and then click SOLVE.								
4	If SOLVER is not on the Data Tab then please see the Help file (Solver) for instructions.								
5	Signs								
6			<		less than or equal to				
7			=		equals (You need to enter an apostrophe first.)				
8			>		greater than or equal to				
9									
10	Data						Results		
11			X 1	X 2				LHS	Slack/Surplus
12	Objective	70	50	sign	RHS		0	
13	Constraint 1	4	3	<	240		0	240
14	Constraint 2	2	1	<	100		0	100
15									
16	Results								
17	Variables								
18	Objective								

PROGRAM 3C

Excel QM Output for the Flair Furniture Example

Solution is shown here.

	A	B	C	D	E	F	G	H
1	Flair Furniture							
2	Enter the values in the shaded area. Then go to the DATA Tab on the ribbon, click on Solver in the Data Analysis							
3	Group and then click SOLVE.							
4	If SOLVER is not on the Data Tab then please see the Help file (Solver) for instructions.							
5	Signs							
6			<		less than or equal to			
7			=		equals (You need to enter an apostrophe first.)			
8			>		greater than or equal to			
9								
10	Data						Results	
11			X 1	X 2				LHS	Slack/Surplus
12	Objective	70	50	sign	RHS		4100	
13	Constraint 1	4	3	<	240		240	0
14	Constraint 2	2	1	<	100		100	0
15								
16	Results							
17	Variables	30	40					
18	Objective				4100			

6   Solving Minimization Problems

Many LP problems involve minimizing an objective such as cost instead of maximizing a profit function. A restaurant, for example, may wish to develop a work schedule to meet staffing needs while minimizing the total number of employees. A manufacturer may seek to distribute its products from several factories to its many regional warehouses in such a way as to minimize total shipping costs. A hospital may want to provide a daily meal plan for its patients that meets certain nutritional standards while minimizing food purchase costs.

Minimization problems with only two variables can be solved graphically by first setting up the feasible solution region and then using either the corner point method or an isocost line approach (which is analogous to the isoprofit approach in maximization problems) to find the values of the decision variables (e.g., X_1 and X_2) that yield the minimum cost. Let's take a look at a common LP problem referred to as the diet problem. This situation is similar to the one that the hospital faces in feeding its patients at the least cost.

Holiday Meal Turkey Ranch

The Holiday Meal Turkey Ranch is considering buying two different brands of turkey feed and blending them to provide a good, low-cost diet for its turkeys. Each feed contains, in varying proportions, some or all of the three nutritional ingredients essential for fattening turkeys. Each pound of brand 1 purchased, for example, contains 5 ounces of ingredient A, 4 ounces of ingredient B, and 0.5 ounce of ingredient C. Each pound of brand 2 contains 10 ounces of ingredient A,

TABLE 5
Holiday Meal Turkey Ranch Data

INGREDIENT	COMPOSITION OF EACH POUND OF FEED (OZ.)		MINIMUM MONTHLY REQUIREMENT PER TURKEY (OZ.)
	BRAND 1 FEED	BRAND 2 FEED	
A	5	10	90
B	4	3	48
C	0.5	0	1.5
Cost per pound	2 cents	3 cents	

3 ounces of ingredient B, but no ingredient C. The brand 1 feed costs the ranch 2 cents a pound, while the brand 2 feed costs 3 cents a pound. The owner of the ranch would like to use LP to determine the lowest-cost diet that meets the minimum monthly intake requirement for each nutritional ingredient.

Table 5 summarizes the relevant information. If we let

$$X_1 = \text{number of pounds of brand 1 feed purchased}$$
$$X_2 = \text{number of pounds of brand 2 feed purchased}$$

then we may proceed to formulate this linear programming problem as follows:

$$\text{Minimize cost (in cents)} = 2X_1 + 3X_2$$

subject to these constraints:

$$
\begin{aligned}
5X_1 + 10X_2 &\geq 90 \text{ ounces} \quad &\text{(ingredient A constraint)} \\
4X_1 + 3X_2 &\geq 48 \text{ ounces} \quad &\text{(ingredient B constraint)} \\
0.5\, X_1 &\geq 1.5 \text{ ounces} \quad &\text{(ingredient C constraint)} \\
X_1 &\geq 0 \quad &\text{(nonnegativity constraint)} \\
X_2 &\geq 0 \quad &\text{(nonnegativity constraint)}
\end{aligned}
$$

Before solving this problem, we want to be sure to note three features that affect its solution. First, you should be aware that the third constraint implies that the farmer *must* purchase enough brand 1 feed to meet the minimum standards for the C nutritional ingredient. Buying only brand 2 would not be feasible because it lacks C. Second, as the problem is formulated, we will be solving for the best blend of brands 1 and 2 to buy per turkey per month. If the ranch houses 5,000 turkeys in a given month, it need simply multiply the X_1 and X_2 quantities by 5,000 to decide how much feed to order overall. Third, we are now dealing with a series of greater-than-or-equal-to constraints. These cause the feasible solution area to be above the constraint lines in this example.

USING THE CORNER POINT METHOD ON A MINIMIZATION PROBLEM To solve the Holiday Meal Turkey Ranch problem, we first construct the feasible solution region. This is done by plotting each of the three constraint equations as in Figure 10. Note that the third constraint, $0.5\, X_1 \geq 1.5$, can be rewritten and plotted as $X_1 \geq 3$. (This involves multiplying both sides of the inequality by 2 but does not change the position of the constraint line in any way.) Minimization problems are often unbounded outward (i.e., on the right side and on top), but this causes no difficulty in solving them. As long as they are bounded inward (on the left side and the bottom), corner points may be established. The optimal solution will lie at one of the corners as it would in a maximization problem.

We plot the three constraints to develop a feasible solution region for the minimization problem.

Note that minimization problems often have unbounded feasible regions.

In this case, there are three corner points: *a*, *b*, and *c*. For point *a*, we find the coordinates at the intersection of the ingredient C and B constraints, that is, where the line $X_1 = 3$ crosses the line $4X_1 + 3X_2 = 48$. If we substitute $X_1 = 3$ into the B constraint equation, we get

$$4(3) + 3X_2 = 48$$

or

$$X_2 = 12$$

Thus, point *a* has the coordinates ($X_1 = 3, X_2 = 12$).

FIGURE 10

Feasible Region for the Holiday Meal Turkey Ranch Problem

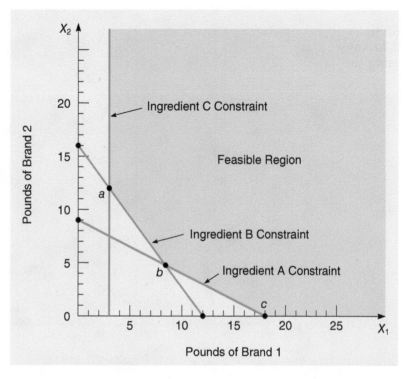

To find the coordinates of point *b* algebraically, we solve the equations $4X_1 + 3X_2 = 48$ and $5X_1 + 10X_2 = 90$ simultaneously. This yields $(X_1 = 8.4, X_2 = 4.8)$.

The coordinates at point *c* are seen by inspection to be $(X_1 = 18, X_2 = 0)$. We now evaluate the objective function at each corner point, and we get

$$\text{Cost} = 2X_1 + 3X_2$$
$$\text{Cost at point } a = 2(3) + 3(12) = 42$$
$$\text{Cost at point } b = 2(8.4) + 3(4.8) = 31.2$$
$$\text{Cost at point } c = 2(18) + 3(0) = 36$$

Hence, the minimum cost solution is to purchase 8.4 pounds of brand 1 feed and 4.8 pounds of brand 2 feed per turkey per month. This will yield a cost of 31.2 cents per turkey.

 IN ACTION

NBC Uses Linear, Integer, and Goal Programming in Selling Advertising Slots

The National Broadcasting Company (NBC) sells over $4 billion in television advertising each year. About 60% to 80% of the air time for an upcoming season is sold in a 2- to 3-week period in late May. The advertising agencies approach the networks to purchase advertising time for their clients. Included in each request are the dollar amount, the demographic (e.g., age of the viewing audience) in which the client is interested, the program mix, weekly weighting, unit-length distribution, and a negotiated cost per 1,000 viewers. NBC must then develop detailed sales plans to meet these requirements. Traditionally, NBC developed these plans manually, and this required several hours per plan. These usually had to be reworked due to the complexity involved. With more than 300 such plans to be developed and reworked in a 2- to 3-week period, this was very time intensive and did not necessarily result in the maximum possible revenue.

In 1996, a project in the area of yield management was begun. Through this effort, NBC was able to create plans that more accurately meet customers' requirements, respond to customers more quickly, make the most profitable use of its limited inventory of advertising time slots, and reduce rework. The success of this system led to the development of a full-scale optimization system based on linear, integer, and goal programming. It is estimated that sales revenue between the years 1996 and 2000 increased by over $200 million due largely to this effort. Improvements in rework time, sales force productivity, and customer satisfaction were also benefits of this system.

Source: Based on Srinivas Bollapragada, et al. "NBC's Optimization Systems Increase Revenues and Productivity," *Interfaces* 32, 1 (January–February 2002): 47–60.

FIGURE 11

Graphical Solution to the Holiday Meal Turkey Ranch Problem Using the Isocost Line

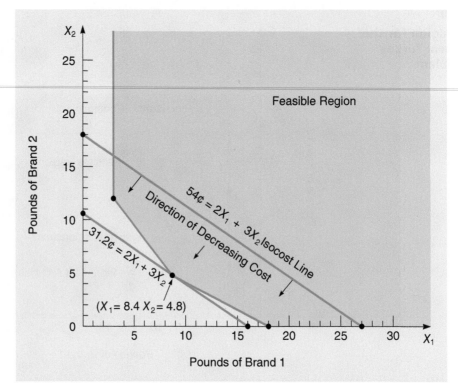

The isocost line method is analogous to the isoprofit line method we used in maximization problems.

ISOCOST LINE APPROACH As mentioned before, the **isocost line** approach may also be used to solve LP minimization problems such as that of the Holiday Meal Turkey Ranch. As with isoprofit lines, we need not compute the cost at each corner point, but instead draw a series of parallel cost lines. The lowest cost line (i.e., the one closest toward the origin) to touch the feasible region provides us with the optimal solution corner.

For example, we start in Figure 11 by drawing a 54-cent cost line, namely $54 = 2X_1 + 3X_2$. Obviously, there are many points in the feasible region that would yield a lower total cost. We proceed to move our isocost line toward the lower left, in a plane parallel to the 54-cent solution line. The last point we touch while still in contact with the feasible region is the same as corner point *b* of Figure 10. It has the coordinates $(X_1 = 8.4, X_2 = 4.8)$ and an associated cost of 31.2 cents.

This could be solved using QM for Windows by selecting the *Linear Programming* Module and selecting *New* problem. Specify that there are 2 variables and 3 constraints. When the input window opens, enter the data and click *Solve*. The output is shown in Program 4.

To solve this in Excel 2013, determine the cells where the solution will be, enter the coefficients from the objective function and the constraints, and write formulas for the total cost and the total of each ingredient (constraint). The input values and solution are shown in Program 5A, with Column D containing the formulas. These formulas are shown in Program 5B. When the Solver Parameters window opens, the *Set Objective* cell is D5; the *By Changing Variable Cells* are B4:C4; the Simplex LP method is used; the box for variables to be nonnegative is checked; and Min is selected because this is a minimization problem.

PROGRAM 4

Solution to the Holiday Meal Turkey Ranch Problem in QM for Windows

Holiday Meal Solution						
	X1	X2			RHS	Dual
Minimize	2	3				
Ingredient A	5	10	>=		90	-0.24
Ingredient B	4	3	>=		48	-0.2
Ingredient C	0.5	0	>=		1.5	0
Solution->	8.4	4.8			31.2	

PROGRAM 5A

Excel 2013 Solution for Holiday Meal Turkey Ranch Problem

Formulas are written to find the values in column D.

	A	B				
1	Holiday Meal Turkey Ran					
2						
3	Variables	Brand 1	Brand 2			
4	Units Produced	8.4	4.8	Cost		
5	Objective function	2	3	31.2		
6						
7	Constraints			LHS (Amt. of Ing.)		RHS
8	Ingredient A	5	10	90	≥	90
9	Ingredient B	4	3	48	≥	48
10	Ingredient C	0.5	0	4.2	≥	1.5

PROGRAM 5B

Excel 2013 Formulas for Holiday Meal Turkey Ranch Problem

	D
4	Cost
5	=SUMPRODUCT($B$4:$C$4,B5:C5)
6	
7	LHS (Amt. of Ing.)
8	=SUMPRODUCT($B$4:$C$4,B8:C8)
9	=SUMPRODUCT($B$4:$C$4,B9:C9)
10	=SUMPRODUCT($B$4:$C$4,B10:C10)

7 Four Special Cases in LP

Four special cases and difficulties arise at times when using the graphical approach to solving LP problems: (1) infeasibility, (2) unboundedness, (3) redundancy, and (4) alternate optimal solutions.

No Feasible Solution

Lack of a feasible solution region can occur if constraints conflict with one another.

When there is no solution to an LP problem that satisfies all of the constraints given, then no feasible solution exists. Graphically, it means that no feasible solution region exists—a situation that might occur if the problem was formulated with conflicting constraints. This, by the way, is a frequent occurrence in real-life, large-scale LP problems that involve hundreds of constraints. For example, if one constraint is supplied by the marketing manager who states that at least 300 tables must be produced (namely, $X_1 \geq 300$) to meet sales demand, and a second restriction is supplied by the production manager, who insists that no more than 220 tables be produced (namely, $X_1 \leq 220$) because of a lumber shortage, no feasible solution region results. When the operations research analyst coordinating the LP problem points out this conflict, one manager or the other must revise his or her inputs. Perhaps more raw materials could be procured from a new source, or perhaps sales demand could be lowered by substituting a different model table to customers.

As a further graphic illustration of this, let us consider the following three constraints:

$$X_1 + 2X_2 \leq 6$$
$$2X_1 + X_2 \leq 8$$
$$X_1 \geq 7$$

As seen in Figure 12, there is no feasible solution region for this LP problem because of the presence of conflicting constraints.

Unboundedness

When the profit in a maximization problem can be infinitely large, the problem is unbounded and is missing one or more constraints.

Sometimes a linear program will not have a finite solution. This means that in a maximization problem, for example, one or more solution variables, and the profit, can be made infinitely large without violating any constraints. If we try to solve such a problem graphically, we will note that the feasible region is open ended.

FIGURE 12

A Problem with No Feasible Solution

Let us consider a simple example to illustrate the situation. A firm has formulated the following LP problem:

$$\text{Maximize profit} = \$3X_1 + \$5X_2$$
$$\text{subject to} \qquad X_1 \qquad \geq 5$$
$$X_2 \leq 10$$
$$X_1 + 2X_2 \geq 10$$
$$X_1, X_2 \geq 0$$

As you see in Figure 13, because this is a maximization problem and the feasible region extends infinitely to the right, there is **unboundedness**, or an unbounded solution. This implies that the problem has been formulated improperly. It would indeed be wonderful for the company to be able to produce an infinite number of units of X_1 (at a profit of $3 each!), but obviously no firm has infinite resources available or infinite product demand.

Redundancy

A redundant constraint is one that does not affect the feasible solution region.

The presence of redundant constraints is another common situation that occurs in large LP formulations. **Redundancy** causes no major difficulties in solving LP problems graphically, but you should be able to identify its occurrence. A redundant constraint is simply one that does

FIGURE 13

A Feasible Region That Is Unbounded to the Right

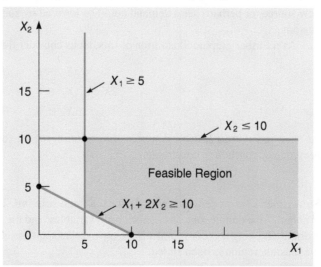

FIGURE 14

Example of a Redundant Constraint

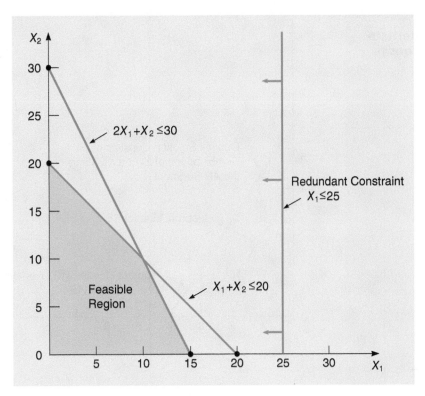

not affect the feasible solution region. In other words, other constraints may be more binding or restrictive than the redundant constraint.

Let's look at the following example of an LP problem with three constraints:

$$\text{Maximize profit} = \$1X_1 + \$2X_2$$
$$\text{subject to} \quad X_1 + X_2 \le 20$$
$$2X_1 + X_2 \le 30$$
$$X_1 \le 25$$
$$X_1, X_2 \ge 0$$

The third constraint, $X_1 \le 25$, is less binding but the first two constraints are indeed more restrictive constraints (see Figure 14).

Alternate Optimal Solutions

Multiple optimal solutions are possible in LP problems.

An LP problem may, on occasion, have two or more **alternate optimal solutions**. Graphically, this is the case when the objective function's isoprofit or isocost line runs perfectly parallel to one of the problem's constraints—in other words, when they have the same slope.

Management of a firm noticed the presence of more than one optimal solution when they formulated this simple LP problem:

$$\text{Maximize profit} = \$3X_1 + \$2X_2$$
$$\text{subject to} \quad 6X_1 + 4X_2 \le 24$$
$$X_1 \le 3$$
$$X_1, X_2 \ge 0$$

As we see in Figure 15, our first isoprofit line of \$8 runs parallel to the first constraint equation. At a profit level of \$12, the isoprofit line will rest directly on top of the segment of the first constraint line. This means that any point along the line between A and B provides an optimal X_1 and X_2 combination. Far from causing problems, the existence of more than one optimal solution

FIGURE 15

Example of Alternate Optimal Solutions

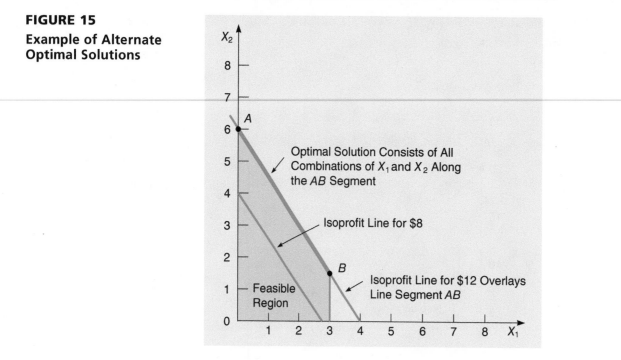

allows management great flexibility in deciding which combination to select. The profit remains the same at each alternate solution.

8 Sensitivity Analysis

How sensitive is the optimal solution to changes in profits, resources, or other input parameters?

Optimal solutions to LP problems have thus far been found under what are called *deterministic assumptions*. This means that we assume complete certainty in the data and relationships of a problem—namely, prices are fixed, resources known, time needed to produce a unit exactly set. But in the real world, conditions are dynamic and changing. How can we handle this apparent discrepancy?

One way we can do so is by continuing to treat each particular LP problem as a deterministic situation. However, when an optimal solution is found, we recognize the importance of seeing just how *sensitive* that solution is to model assumptions and data. For example, if a firm realizes that profit per unit is not $5 as estimated but instead is closer to $5.50, how will the final solution mix and total profit change? If additional resources, such as 10 labor hours or 3 hours of machine time, should become available, will this change the problem's answer? Such analyses are used to examine the effects of changes in three areas: (1) contribution rates for each variable, (2) technological coefficients (the numbers in the constraint equations), and (3) available resources (the right-hand-side quantities in each constraint). This task is alternatively called **sensitivity analysis**, *postoptimality analysis*, *parametric programming*, or *optimality analysis*.

An important function of sensitivity analysis is to allow managers to experiment with values of the input parameters.

Sensitivity analysis also often involves a series of what-if? questions. What if the profit on product 1 increases by 10%? What if less money is available in the advertising budget constraint? What if workers each stay one hour longer every day at 1½-time pay to provide increased production capacity? What if new technology will allow a product to be wired in one-third the time it used to take? So we see that sensitivity analysis can be used to deal not only with errors in estimating input parameters to the LP model but also with management's experiments with possible future changes in the firm that may affect profits.

There are two approaches to determining just how sensitive an optimal solution is to changes. The first is simply a trial-and-error approach. This approach usually involves resolving the entire problem, preferably by computer, each time one input data item or parameter is changed. It can take a long time to test a series of possible changes in this way.

Postoptimality analysis means examining changes after the optimal solution has been reached.

The approach we prefer is the analytic postoptimality method. After an LP problem has been solved, we attempt to determine a range of changes in problem parameters that will not affect the optimal solution or change the variables in the solution. This is done without resolving the whole problem.

Let's investigate sensitivity analysis by developing a small production mix problem. Our goal will be to demonstrate graphically and through the simplex tableau how sensitivity analysis can be used to make linear programming concepts more realistic and insightful.

High Note Sound Company

The High Note Sound Company manufactures quality speakers and stereo receivers. Each of these products requires a certain amount of skilled artisanship, of which there is a limited weekly supply. The firm formulates the following LP problem in order to determine the best production mix of speakers (X_1) and receivers (X_2):

$$\text{Maximize profit} = \$50X_1 + \$120X_2$$

subject to

$$2X_1 + 4X_2 \le 80 \quad \text{(hours of electricians' time available)}$$
$$3X_1 + 1X_2 \le 60 \quad \text{(hours of audio technicians' time available)}$$
$$X_1, X_2 \ge 0$$

The solution to this problem is illustrated graphically in Figure 16. Given this information and deterministic assumptions, the firm should produce only stereo receivers (20 of them), for a weekly profit of $2,400.

For the optimal solution, $(0, 20)$, the electrician hours used are

$$2X_1 + 4X_2 = 2(0) + 4(20) = 80$$

and this equals the amount available, so there is 0 slack for this constraint. Thus, it is a binding constraint. If a constraint is binding, obtaining additional units of that resource will usually result in higher profits. The audio technician hours used for the optimal solution $(0, 20)$ are

$$3X_1 + 1X_2 = 3(0) + 1(20) = 20$$

but the hours available are 60. Thus, there is a slack of $60 - 20 = 40$ hours. Because there are extra hours available that are not being used, this is a nonbinding constraint. For a nonbinding constraint, obtaining additional units of that resource will not result in higher profits and will only increase the slack.

FIGURE 16

High Note Sound Company Graphical Solution

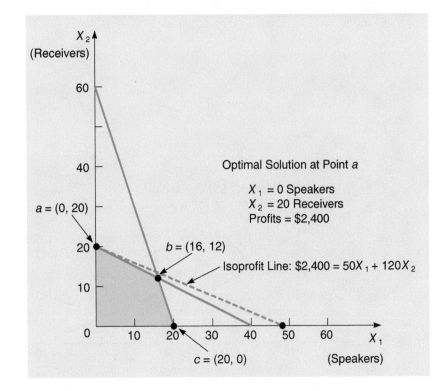

227

Changes in the Objective Function Coefficient

Changes in contribution rates are examined first.

In real-life problems, contribution rates (usually profit or cost) in the objective functions fluctuate periodically, as do most of a firm's expenses. Graphically, this means that although the feasible solution region remains exactly the same, the slope of the isoprofit or isocost line will change. It is easy to see in Figure 17 that the High Note Sound Company's profit line is optimal at point a. But what if a technical breakthrough just occurred that raised the profit per stereo receiver (X_2) from \$120 to \$150? Is the solution still optimal? The answer is definitely yes, for in this case the slope of the profit line accentuates the profitability at point a. The new profit is $\$3,000 = 0(\$50) + 20(\$150)$.

On the other hand, if X_2's profit coefficient was overestimated and should only have been \$80, the slope of the profit line changes enough to cause a new corner point (b) to become optimal. Here the profit is $\$1,760 = 16(\$50) + 12(\$80)$.

A new corner point becomes optimal if an objective function coefficient is decreased or increased too much.

This example illustrates a very important concept about changes in objective function coefficients. We can increase or decrease the objective function coefficient (profit) of any variable, and the current corner point may remain optimal if the change is not too large. However, if we increase or decrease this coefficient by too much, then the optimal solution would be at a different corner point. How much can the objective function coefficient change before another corner point becomes optimal? Both QM for Windows and Excel provide the answer.

QM for Windows and Changes in Objective Function Coefficients

The current solution remains optimal unless an objective function coefficient is increased to a value above the upper bound or decreased to a value below the lower bound.

The QM for Windows input for the High Note Sound Company example is shown in Program 6A. When the solution has been found, selecting *Window* and *Ranging* allows us to see additional information on sensitivity analysis. Program 6B provides the output related to sensitivity analysis.

From Program 6B, we see the profit on speakers was \$50, which is indicated as the original value in the output. This objective function coefficient has a lower bound of negative infinity

Figure 17 Changes in the Receiver Contribution Coefficients

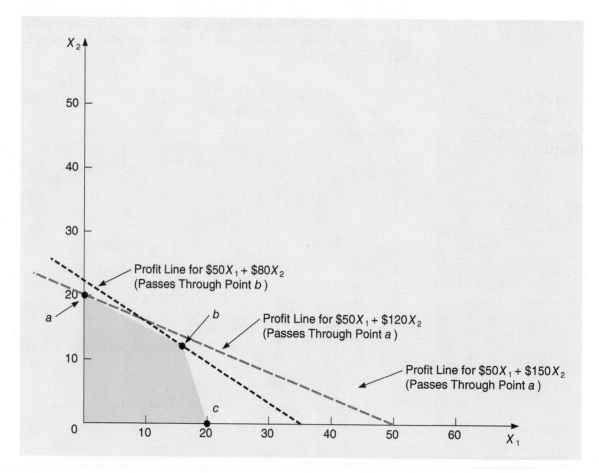

PROGRAM 6A

Input to QM for Windows High Note Sound Company Data

Objective ⊙ Maximize ○ Minimize	Instruction Use these option buttons to set the objective.				
		High Note Sound Company			
	X1	X2		RHS	Equation form
Maximize	50	120			Max 50X1 + 120X2
Electrician hours	2	4	<=	80	2X1 + 4X2 <= 80
Audio technician hours	3	1	<=	60	3X1 + X2 <= 60

PROGRAM 6B

High Note Sound Company Sensitivity Analysis Output

◈ Ranging					— ◻ ✕
	High Note Sound Company Solution				
Variable	Value	Reduced Cost	Original Val	Lower Bound	Upper Bound
X1	0	10	50	-Infinity	60
X2	20	0	120	100	Infinity
Constraint	Dual Value	Slack/Surplus	Original Val	Lower Bound	Upper Bound
Electrician hours	30	0	80	0	240
Audio technician hours	0	40	60	20	Infinity

and an upper bound of $60. This means that the current corner point solution remains optimal as long as the profit on speakers does not go above $60. If it equals $60, there would be two optimal solutions as the objective function would be parallel to the first constraint. The points (0, 20) and (16, 12) would both give a profit of $2,400. The profit on speakers may decrease any amount as indicated by the negative infinity, and the optimal corner point does not change. This negative infinity is logical because currently there are no speakers being produced because the profit is too low. Any decrease in the profit on speakers would make them less attractive relative to the receivers, and we certainly would not produce any speakers because of this.

The profit on receivers has an upper bound of infinity (it may increase by any amount) and a lower bound of $100. If this profit equaled $100, then the corner points (0, 20) and (16, 12) would both be optimal. The profit at each of these would be $2,000.

The upper and lower bounds relate to changing only one coefficient at a time.

In general, a change can be made to one (and only one) objective function coefficient, and the current optimal corner point remains optimal as long as the change is between the Upper and Lower Bounds. If two or more coefficients are changed simultaneously, then the problem should be solved with the new coefficients to determine whether or not this current solution remains optimal.

Excel Solver and Changes in Objective Function Coefficients

Program 7A illustrates how the Excel 2013 spreadsheet for this example is set up for Solver. When *Solver* is selected from the *Data* tab, the appropriate inputs are made, and *Solve* is clicked in the Solver dialog box, the solution and the Solver Results window will appear as in Program 7B. Selecting *Sensitivity* from the reports area of this window will provide a Sensitivity Report on a new worksheet, with results as shown in Program 7C. Note how the cells are named based on the text from Program 7A. Notice that Excel does not provide lower bounds and upper bounds for the objective function coefficients. Instead, it gives the allowable increases and

PROGRAM 7A

Excel 2013 Spreadsheet for High Note Sound Company

> The By Changing Variable Cells in the Solver Dialog Box are B4:C4.

	A	B	C	D	E	F
1	High Note Sound					
2		Speakers		The Set Objective cell in the Solver Dialog Box is D5.		
3	Variables	X1	X2			
4	Units Produced	0	20	Profit		
5	Objective function	50	120	=SUMPRODUCT($B$4:$C$4,B5:C5)		
6						
7	Constraints			LHS (Hrs. Used)		RHS
8	Electrician Hours	2	4	=SUMPRODUCT($B$4:$C$4,B8:C8)	≤	80
9	Audio Tech Hours	3	1	=SUMPRODUCT($B$4:$C$4,B9:C9)	≤	60

> The constraints added into Solver will be D8:D9 <=F8:F9.

PROGRAM 7B   Excel 2013 Solution and Solver Results Window for High Note Sound Company

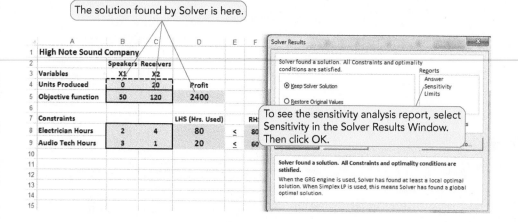

The solution found by Solver is here.

To see the sensitivity analysis report, select Sensitivity in the Solver Results Window. Then click OK.

PROGRAM 7C

Excel 2013 Sensitivity Report for High Note Sound Company

The names presented in the Sensitivity Report combine the text in column A and the text above the data, unless the cells have been named using the Name Manager from the Formulas tab.

The profit on speakers may change by these amounts and the current corner point will remain optimal.

The resources used are here. The RHS can change by these amounts, and the shadow price will still be relevant.

Excel solver gives allowable increases and decreases rather than upper and lower bounds.

decreases for these. By adding the allowable increase to the current value, we may obtain the upper bound. For example, the allowable increase on the profit (objective coefficient) for speakers is 10, which means that the upper bound on this profit is $50 + $10 = $60. Similarly, we may subtract the allowable decrease from the current value to obtain the lower bound.

Changes in the Technological Coefficients

Changes in technological coefficients affect the shape of the feasible solution region.

Changes in what are called the **technological coefficients** often reflect changes in the state of technology. If fewer or more resources are needed to produce a product such as a speaker or stereo receiver, coefficients in the constraint equations will change. These changes will have no effect on the objective function of an LP problem, but they can produce a significant change in the shape of the feasible solution region, and hence in the optimal profit or cost.

Figure 18 illustrates the original High Note Sound Company graphical solution as well as two separate changes in technological coefficients. In Figure 18, Part (a), we see that the optimal solution lies at point a, which represents $X_1 = 0, X_2 = 20$. You should be able to prove to yourself that point a remains optimal in Figure 18, Part (b) despite a constraint change from $3X_1 + 1X_2 \leq 60$ to $2X_1 + 1X_2 \leq 60$. Such a change might take place when the firm discovers that it no longer demands three hours of audio technicians' time to produce a speaker, but only two hours.

FIGURE 18 Change in the Technological Coefficients for the High Note Sound Company

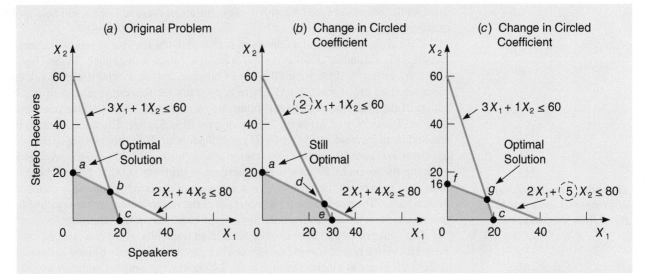

In Figure 18, Part (c), however, a change in the other constraint changes the shape of the feasible region enough to cause a new corner point (*g*) to become optimal. Before moving on, see if you reach an objective function value of $1,954 profit at point *g* (versus a profit of $1,920 at point *f*).*

Changes in the Resources or Right-Hand-Side Values

The right-hand-side values of the constraints often represent resources available to the firm. The resources could be labor hours or machine time or perhaps money or production materials available. In the High Note Sound Company example, the two resources are hours available of electricians' time and hours of audio technicians' time. If additional hours were available, a higher

 IN ACTION   **Swift & Company Uses LP to Schedule Production**

Based in Greeley, Colorado, Swift & Company has annual sales over $8 billion, with beef and related products making up the vast majority of this. Swift has five processing plants, which handle over 6 billion pounds of beef each year. Each head of beef is cut into two sides, which yield the chuck, the brisket, the loins, the ribs, the round, the plate, and the flank. With some cuts in greater demand than others, the customer service representatives (CSRs) try to meet the demand for customers while providing discounts when necessary to clear out some cuts that might be in excess supply. It is important that the CSRs have accurate information on product availability in close to real time so they can react quickly to changing demand.

With the cost of raw material being as high as 85%, and with a very thin profit margin, it is essential that the company operate efficiently. Swift started a project in March 2001 to develop a mathematical programming model that would optimize the supply chain. Ten full-time employees worked with four operations research consultants from Aspen Technology on what was called Project Phoenix. At the heart of the final model are 45 integrated LP models that enable the company to dynamically schedule its operations in real time as orders are received.

With Project Phoenix, not only did profit margins increase, but the improvements in forecasting, cattle procurement, and manufacturing improved relations with customers and enhanced the reputation of Swift & Company in the marketplace. The company is better able to deliver products according to customer specification. While the model cost over $6 million to develop, in the first year of operation, it generated a benefit of $12.7 million.

Source: Based on Ann Bixby, Brian Downs, and Mike Self. "A Scheduling and Capable-to-Promise Application for Swift & Company," *Interfaces* 36, 1 (January–February 2006): 69–86.

---

*Note that the values of X_1 and X_2 at point *g* are fractions. Although the High Note Sound Company cannot produce 0.67, 0.75, or 0.90 of a speaker or stereo, we can assume that the firm can *begin* a unit one week and complete it the next. As long as the production process is fairly stable from week to week, this raises no major problems. If solutions *must* be whole numbers each period, integer programming method should be followed to handle the situation.

total profit could be realized. How much should the company be willing to pay for additional hours? Is it profitable to have some electricians work overtime? Should we be willing to pay for more audio technician time? Sensitivity analysis about these resources will help us answer these questions.

If the right-hand side of a constraint is changed, the feasible region will change (unless the constraint is redundant), and often the optimal solution will change. In the High Note Sound Company example, there were 80 hours of electrician time available each week and the maximum possible profit was $2,400. There is no slack for this constraint, so it is a binding constraint. If the available electricians' hours are increased to 100 hours, the new optimal solution seen in Figure 19, part (a) is (0, 25) and the profit is $3,000. Thus, the extra 20 hours of time resulted in an increase in profit of $600 or $30 per hour. If the hours were decreased to 60 hours as shown in Figure 19, part (b), the new optimal solution is (0, 15) and the profit is $1,800. Thus, reducing the hours by 20 results in a decrease in profit of $600 or $30 per hour. This $30 per hour change in profit that resulted from a change in the hours available is called the dual price or dual value. The **dual price** for a constraint is the improvement in the objective function value that results from a one-unit increase in the right-hand side of the constraint.

The value of one additional unit of a scarce resource may be found from the dual price.

The dual price of $30 per hour of electrician time tells us we can increase profit if we have more electrician hours. However, there is a limit to this as there is limited audio technician time. If the total hours of electrician time were 240 hours, the optimal solution would be (0, 60) as shown in Figure 19, part (c) and the profit would be $7,200. Again, this is an increase of $30 profit per hour (the dual price) for each of the 160 hours that were added to the original amount. If the number of hours increased beyond 240, then profit would no longer increase and the optimal solution would still be (0, 60) as shown in Figure 19, part (c). There would simply be excess (slack) hours of electrician time and all of the audio technician time would be used. Thus, the dual price is relevant only within limits. Both QM for Windows and Excel Solver provide these limits.

QM for Windows and Changes in Right-Hand-Side Values

The QM for Windows sensitivity analysis output was shown in Program 6B. The dual value for the electrician hours constraint is given as 30, and the lower bound is zero while the upper bound is 240. This means that each additional hour of electrician time, up to a total of 240 hours, will increase the maximum possible profit by $30. Similarly, if the available electrician time is decreased, the maximum possible profit will decrease by $30 per hour until the available time is decreased to the lower bound of 0. If the amount of electrician time (the right-hand-side value for this constraint) is outside this range (0 to 240), then the dual value is no longer relevant and the problem should be resolved with the new right-hand-side value.

Dual prices will change if the amount of the resource (the right-hand side of the constraint) goes above the upper bound or below the lower bound given in the Ranging section of the QM for Windows output.

In Program 6B, the dual value for audio technician hours is shown to be $0 and the slack is 40, so it is a nonbinding constraint. There are 40 hours of audio technician time that are not being used despite the fact that they are currently available. If additional hours were made available they would not increase profit but would simply increase the amount of slack. This dual value of zero is relevant as long as the right-hand side does not go below the lower bound of 20. The upper limit is infinity indicating that adding more hours would simply increase the amount of slack.

Excel Solver and Changes in Right-Hand-Side Values

The Sensitivity report from Excel Solver was shown in Program 7C. Notice that Solver gives the shadow price instead of the dual price. A **shadow price** is the change in the objective function value (e.g., profit or cost) that results from a one-unit increase in the right-hand-side of a constraint.

The shadow price is the same as the dual price in maximization problems.

Since an improvement in the objective function value in a maximization problem is the same as a positive change (increase), the dual price and the shadow price are exactly the same for maximization problems. For a minimization problem, an improvement in the objective function value is a decrease, which is a negative change. So for minimization problems, the shadow price will be the negative of the dual price.

FIGURE 19

Changes in the Electricians' Time Resource for the High Note Sound Company

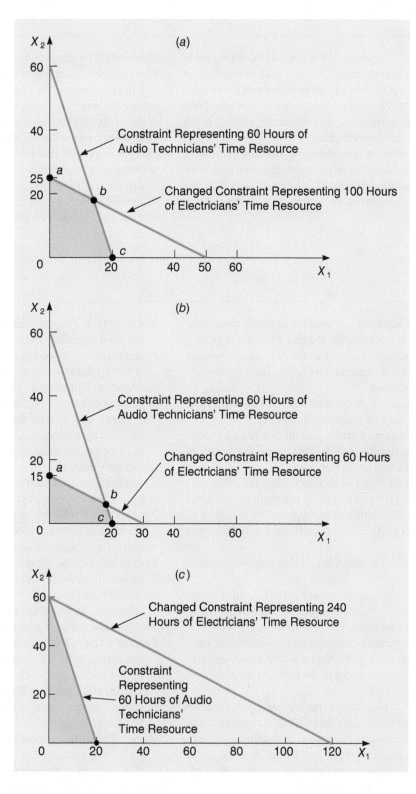

The Allowable Increase and Allowable Decrease for the right-hand side of each constraint is provided, and the shadow price is relevant for changes within these limits. For the electrician hours, the right-hand-side value of 80 may be increased by 160 (for a total of 240) or decreased by 80 (for a total of 0) and the shadow price remains relevant. If a change is made that exceeds these limits, then the problem should be resolved to find the impact of the change.

Summary

In this chapter, we introduce a mathematical modeling technique called linear programming (LP). It is used in reaching an optimum solution to problems that have a series of constraints binding the objective. We use both the corner point method and the isoprofit/isocost approaches for graphically solving problems with only two decision variables.

The graphical solution approaches of this chapter provide a conceptual basis for tackling larger, more complex problems. To solve real-life LP problems with numerous variables and constraints, we need a solution procedure such as the simplex algorithm. The simplex algorithm is the method that QM for Windows and Excel use to tackle LP problems.

In this chapter, we also present the important concept of sensitivity analysis. Sometimes referred to as postoptimality analysis, sensitivity analysis is used by management to answer a series of what-if? questions about LP model parameters. It also tests just how sensitive the optimal solution is to changes in profit or cost coefficients, technological coefficients, and right-hand-side resources. We explored sensitivity analysis graphically (i.e., for problems with only two decision variables) and with computer output.

Glossary

Alternate Optimal Solution   A situation in which more than one optimal solution is possible. It arises when the slope of the objective function is the same as the slope of a constraint.

Binding Constraint   A constraint with zero slack or surplus for the optimal solution.

Constraint   A restriction on the resources available to a firm (stated in the form of an inequality or an equation).

Corner Point, or **Extreme Point**   A point that lies on one of the corners of the feasible region. This means that it falls at the intersection of two constraint lines.

Corner Point Method   The method of finding the optimal solution to an LP problem by testing the profit or cost level at each corner point of the feasible region. The theory of LP states that the optimal solution must lie at one of the corner points.

Decision Variable   A variable whose value may be chosen by the decision maker.

Dual Price (value)   The improvement in the objective function value that results from a one-unit increase in the right-hand side of that constraint.

Feasible Region   The area satisfying all of the problem's resource restrictions; that is, the region where all constraints overlap. All possible solutions to the problem lie in the feasible region.

Feasible Solution   A point lying in the feasible region. Basically, it is any point that satisfies all of the problem's constraints.

Inequality   A mathematical expression containing a greater-than-or-equal-to relation ($\geq$) or a less-than-or-equal-to relation ($\leq$) used to indicate that the total consumption of a resource must be $\geq$ or $\leq$ some limiting value.

Infeasible Solution   Any point lying outside the feasible region. It violates one or more of the stated constraints.

Isocost Line   A straight line representing all combinations of X_1 and X_2 for a particular cost level.

Isoprofit Line   A straight line representing all nonnegative combinations of X_1 and X_2 for a particular profit level.

Linear Programming (LP)   A mathematical technique used to help management decide how to make the most effective use of an organization's resources.

Mathematical Programming   The general category of mathematical modeling and solution techniques used to allocate resources while optimizing a measurable goal. LP is one type of programming model.

Nonbinding Constraint   A constraint with a positive amount of slack or surplus for the optimal solution.

Nonnegativity Constraints   A set of constraints that requires each decision variable to be nonnegative; that is, each X_i must be greater than or equal to 0.

Objective Function   A mathematical statement of the goal of an organization, stated as an intent to maximize or to minimize some important quantity such as profits or costs.

Product Mix Problem   A common LP problem involving a decision as to which products a firm should produce given that it faces limited resources.

Redundancy   The presence of one or more constraints that do not affect the feasible solution region.

Sensitivity Analysis   The study of how sensitive an optimal solution is to model assumptions and to data changes. It is often referred to as postoptimality analysis.

Shadow Price   The increase in the objective function value that results from a one-unit increase in the right-hand side of that constraint.

Simultaneous Equation Method   The algebraic means of solving for the intersection point of two or more linear constraint equations.

Slack   The difference between the left-hand side and the right-hand side of a less-than-or-equal-to constraint. Often this is the amount of a resource that is not being used.

Surplus   The difference between the left-hand side and the right-hand side of a greater-than-or-equal-to constraint. Often this represents the amount by which a minimum quantity is exceeded.

Technological Coefficients   Coefficients of the variables in the constraint equations. The coefficients represent the amount of resources needed to produce one unit of the variable.

Unboundedness   A condition that exists when a solution variable and the profit can be made infinitely large without violating any of the problem's constraints in a maximization process.

Solved Problems

Solved Problem 1

Personal Mini Warehouses is planning to expand its successful Orlando business into Tampa. In doing so, the company must determine how many storage rooms of each size to build. Its objective and constraints follow:

$$\text{Maximize monthly earnings} = 50X_1 + 20X_2$$

subject to

$$20X_1 + 40X_2 \leq 4{,}000 \quad \text{(advertising budget available)}$$
$$100X_1 + 50X_2 \leq 8{,}000 \quad \text{(square footage required)}$$
$$X_1 \qquad\qquad \leq 60 \quad \text{(rental limit expected)}$$
$$X_1, X_2 \geq 0$$

where

X_1 = number of large spaces developed

X_2 = number of small spaces developed

Solution

An evaluation of the five corner points of the accompanying graph indicates that corner point C produces the greatest earnings. Refer to the graph and table.

CORNER POINT	VALUES OF X_1, X_2	OBJECTIVE FUNCTION VALUE ($)
A	(0, 0)	0
B	(60, 0)	3,000
C	(60, 40)	3,800
D	(40, 80)	3,600
E	(0, 100)	2,000

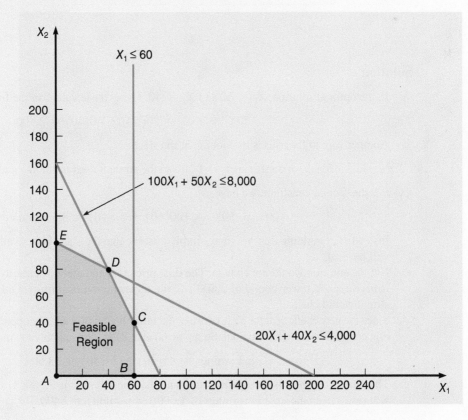

235

Solved Problem 2

The solution obtained with QM for Windows for Solved Problem 1 is given in the following program. Use this to answer the following questions.

a. For the optimal solution, how much of the advertising budget is spent?
b. For the optimal solution, how much square footage will be used?
c. Would the solution change if the budget were only $3,000 instead of $4,000?
d. What would the optimal solution be if the profit on the large spaces were reduced from $50 to $45?
e. How much would earnings increase if the square footage requirement were increased from 8,000 to 9,000?

Linear Programming Results

Solved Problem 7-2 Solution

	X1	X2		RHS	Dual
Maximize	50	20			
Constraint 1	20	40	<=	4,000	0
Constraint 2	100	50	<=	8,000	0.4
Constraint 3	1	0	<=	60	10
Solution->	60	40		3,800	

Ranging

Solved Problem 7-2 Solution

Variable	Value	Reduced	Original Val	Lower Bound	Upper Bound
X1	60	0	50	40	Infinity
X2	40	0	20	0	25
Constraint	Dual Value	Slack/Surplus	Original Val	Lower Bound	Upper Bound
Constraint 1	0	1,200	4,000	2,800	Infinity
Constraint 2	0.4	0	8,000	6,000	9,500
Constraint 3	10	0	60	40	80

Solution

a. In the optimal solution, $X_1 = 60$ and $X_2 = 40$. Using these values in the first constraint gives us

$$20X_1 + 40X_2 = 20(60) + 40(40) = 2,800$$

Another way to find this is by looking at the slack:

Slack for constraint $1 = 1,200$ so the amount used is $4,000 - 1,200 = 2,800$

b. For the second constraint we have

$$100X_1 + 50X_2 = 100(60) + 50(40) = 8,000 \text{ square feet}$$

Instead of computing this, you may simply observe that the slack is 0, so all of the 8,000 square feet will be used.

c. No, the solution would not change. The dual price is 0 and there is slack available. The value 3,000 is between the lower bound of 2,800 and the upper bound of infinity. Only the slack for this constraint would change.

d. Since the new coefficient for X_1 is between the lower bound (40) and the upper bound (infinity), the current corner point remains optimal. So $X_1 = 60$ and $X_2 = 40$, and only the monthly earnings change.

$$\text{Earnings} = 45(60) + 20(40) = \$3,500$$

e. The dual price for this constraint is 0.4, and the upper bound is 9,500. The increase of 1,000 units will result in an increase in earnings of $1,000(0.4 \text{ per unit}) = \$400$.

Solved Problem 3

Solve the following LP formulation graphically, using the isocost line approach:

$$\text{Minimize costs} = 24X_1 + 28X_2$$

$$\begin{aligned}
\text{subject to} \quad 5X_1 + 4X_2 &\leq 2{,}000 \\
X_1 &\geq 80 \\
X_1 + X_2 &\geq 300 \\
X_2 &\geq 100 \\
X_1, X_2 &\geq 0
\end{aligned}$$

Solution

A graph of the four constraints follows. The arrows indicate the direction of feasibility for each constraint. The next graph illustrates the feasible solution region and plots of two possible objective function cost lines. The first, $10,000, was selected arbitrarily as a starting point. To find the optimal corner point, we need to move the cost line in the direction of lower cost, that is, down and to the left. The last point where a cost line touches the feasible region as it moves toward the origin is corner point D. Thus D, which represents $X_1 = 200$, $X_2 = 100$, and a cost of $7,600, is optimal.

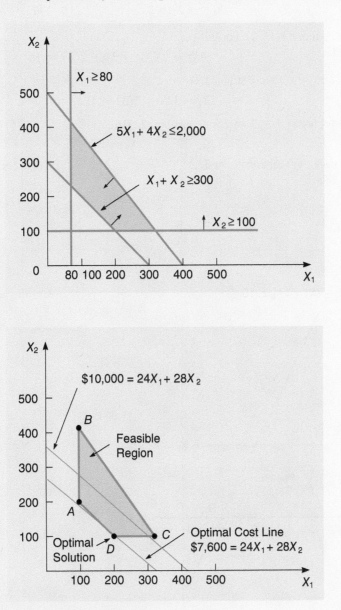

Solved Problem 4

Solve the following problem, using the corner point method. For the optimal solution, how much slack or surplus is there for each constraint?

$$\text{Maximize profit} = 30X_1 + 40X_2$$
$$\text{subject to} \qquad 4X_1 + 2X_2 \leq 16$$
$$2X_1 - X_2 \geq 2$$
$$X_2 \leq 2$$
$$X_1, X_2 \geq 0$$

Solution

The graph appears next with the feasible region shaded.

CORNER POINT	COORDINATES	PROFIT ($)
A	$X_1 = 1, X_2 = 0$	30
B	$X_1 = 4, X_2 = 0$	120
C	$X_1 = 3, X_2 = 2$	170
D	$X_1 = 2, X_2 = 2$	140

The optimal solution is $(3, 2)$. For this point,

$$4X_1 + 2X_2 = 4(3) + 2(2) = 16$$

Therefore, slack = 0 for constraint 1. Also,

$$2X_1 - 1X_2 = 2(3) - 1(2) = 4 > 2$$

Therefore, surplus = $4 - 2 = 2$ for constraint 2. Also,

$$X_2 = 2$$

Therefore, slack = 0 for constraint 3.

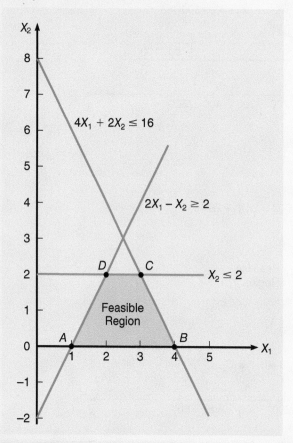

The optimal profit of $170 is at corner point C.

Self-Test

- Before taking the self-test, refer to the learning objectives at the beginning of the chapter, the notes in the margins, and the glossary at the end of the chapter.
- Use the key at the end of the chapter to correct your answers.
- Restudy pages that correspond to any questions that you answered incorrectly or material you feel uncertain about.

1. When using a graphical solution procedure, the region bounded by the set of constraints is called the
   a. solution.
   b. feasible region.
   c. infeasible region.
   d. maximum profit region.
   e. none of the above.

2. In an LP problem, at least one corner point must be an optimal solution if an optimal solution exists.
   a. True
   b. False

3. An LP problem has a bounded feasible region. If this problem has an equality ($=$) constraint, then
   a. this must be a minimization problem.
   b. the feasible region must consist of a line segment.
   c. the problem must be degenerate.
   d. the problem must have more than one optimal solution.

4. Which of the following would cause a change in the feasible region?
   a. Increasing an objective function coefficient in a maximization problem
   b. Adding a redundant constraint
   c. Changing the right-hand side of a nonredundant constraint
   d. Increasing an objective function coefficient in a minimization problem

5. If a nonredundant constraint is removed from an LP problem, then
   a. the feasible region will get larger.
   b. the feasible region will get smaller.
   c. the problem would become nonlinear.
   d. the problem would become infeasible.

6. In the optimal solution to a linear program, there are 20 units of slack for a constraint. From this we know that
   a. the dual price for this constraint is 20.
   b. the dual price for this constraint is 0.
   c. this constraint must be redundant.
   d. the problem must be a maximization problem.

7. A linear program has been solved and sensitivity analysis has been performed. The ranges for the objective function coefficients have been found. For the profit on X_1, the upper bound is 80, the lower bound is 60, and the current value is 75. Which of the following must be true if the profit on this variable is lowered to 70 and the optimal solution is found?
   a. A new corner point will become optimal.
   b. The maximum possible total profit may increase.
   c. The values for all the decision variables will remain the same.
   d. All of the above are possible.

8. A graphical method should only be used to solve an LP problem when
   a. there are only two constraints.
   b. there are more than two constraints.
   c. there are only two variables.
   d. there are more than two variables.

9. In LP, variables do not have to be integer valued and may take on any fractional value. This assumption is called
   a. proportionality.
   b. divisibility.
   c. additivity.
   d. certainty.

10. In solving a linear program, no feasible solution exists. To resolve this problem we might
    a. add another variable.
    b. add another constraint.
    c. remove or relax a constraint.
    d. try a different computer program.

11. If the feasible region gets larger due to a change in one of the constraints, the optimal value of the objective function
    a. must increase or remain the same for a maximization problem.
    b. must decrease or remain the same for a maximization problem.
    c. must increase or remain the same for a minimization problem.
    d. cannot change.

12. When alternate optimal solutions exist in an LP problem, then
    a. the objective function will be parallel to one of the constraints.
    b. one of the constraints will be redundant.
    c. two constraints will be parallel.
    d. the problem will also be unbounded.

13. If a linear program is unbounded, the problem probably has not been formulated correctly. Which of the following would most likely cause this?
    a. A constraint was inadvertently omitted.
    b. An unnecessary constraint was added to the problem.
    c. The objective function coefficients are too large.
    d. The objective function coefficients are too small.

14. A feasible solution to an LP problem
    a. must satisfy all of the problem's constraints simultaneously.
    b. need not satisfy all of the constraints, only some of them.
    c. must be a corner point of the feasible region.
    d. must give the maximum possible profit.

Discussion Questions and Problems

Discussion Questions

1 Discuss the similarities and differences between minimization and maximization problems using the graphical solution approaches of LP.

2 It is important to understand the assumptions underlying the use of any quantitative analysis model. What are the assumptions and requirements for an LP model to be formulated and used?

3 It has been said that each LP problem that has a feasible region has an infinite number of solutions. Explain.

4 You have just formulated a maximization LP problem and are preparing to solve it graphically. What criteria should you consider in deciding whether it would be easier to solve the problem by the corner point method or the isoprofit line approach?

5 Under what condition is it possible for an LP problem to have more than one optimal solution?

6 Develop your own set of constraint equations and inequalities and use them to illustrate graphically each of the following conditions:

(a) an unbounded problem
(b) an infeasible problem
(c) a problem containing redundant constraints

7 The production manager of a large Cincinnati manufacturing firm once made the statement, "I would like to use LP, but it's a technique that operates under conditions of certainty. My plant doesn't have that certainty; it's a world of uncertainty. So LP can't be used here." Do you think this statement has any merit? Explain why the manager may have said it.

8 The mathematical relationships that follow were formulated by an operations research analyst at the Smith–Lawton Chemical Company. Which ones are invalid for use in an LP problem, and why?

$$\text{Maximize profit} = 4X_1 + 3X_1X_2 + 8X_2 + 5X_3$$

$$
\begin{aligned}
\text{subject to} \quad 2X_1 \phantom{{}+{}} &+ X_2 + 2X_3 \le 50 \\
X_1 &- 4X_2 \phantom{{}+ 2X_3} \ge 6 \\
1.5X_1^2 &+ 6X_2 + 3X_3 \ge 21 \\
&19X_2 - 0.35X_3 = 17 \\
5X_1 &+ 4X_2 + 3\sqrt{X_3} \le 80 \\
-X_1 &- X_2 + X_3 = 5
\end{aligned}
$$

9 Discuss the role of sensitivity analysis in LP. Under what circumstances is it needed, and under what conditions do you think it is not necessary?

10 A linear program has the objective of maximizing profit $= 12X + 8Y$. The maximum profit is $8,000. Using a computer we find the upper bound for profit on X is 20 and the lower bound is 9. Discuss the changes to the optimal solution (the values of the variables and the profit) that would occur if the profit on X were increased to $15. How would the optimal solution change if the profit on X were increased to $25?

11 A linear program has a maximum profit of $600. One constraint in this problem is $4X + 2Y \le 80$. Using a computer we find the dual price for this constraint is 3, and there is a lower bound of 75 and an upper bound of 100. Explain what this means.

12 Develop your own original LP problem with two constraints and two real variables.

(a) Explain the meaning of the numbers on the right-hand side of each of your constraints.
(b) Explain the significance of the technological coefficients.
(c) Solve your problem graphically to find the optimal solution.
(d) Illustrate graphically the effect of increasing the contribution rate of your first variable (X_1) by 50% over the value you first assigned it. Does this change the optimal solution?

13 Explain how a change in a technological coefficient can affect a problem's optimal solution. How can a change in resource availability affect a solution?

Problems

♀. 14 The Electrocomp Corporation manufactures two electrical products: air conditioners and large fans. The assembly process for each is similar in that both require a certain amount of wiring and drilling. Each air conditioner takes 3 hours of wiring and 2 hours of drilling. Each fan must go through 2 hours of wiring and 1 hour of drilling. During the next production period, 240 hours of wiring time are available and up to 140 hours of drilling time may be used. Each air conditioner sold yields a profit of $25. Each fan assembled may be sold for a $15 profit. Formulate and solve this LP production mix situation to find the best combination of air conditioners and fans that yields the highest profit. Use the corner point graphical approach.

♀. 15 Electrocomp's management realizes that it forgot to include two critical constraints (see Problem 14). In particular, management decides that there should be a minimum number of air conditioners produced in

Note: ♀ means the problem may be solved with QM for Windows; ✕ means the problem may be solved with Excel; and ♀ means the problem may be solved with QM for Windows and/or Excel.

240

order to fulfill a contract. Also, due to an oversupply of fans in the preceding period, a limit should be placed on the total number of fans produced.

(a) If Electrocomp decides that at least 20 air conditioners should be produced but no more than 80 fans should be produced, what would be the optimal solution? How much slack or surplus is there for each of the four constraints?

(b) If Electrocomp decides that at least 30 air conditioners should be produced but no more than 50 fans should be produced, what would be the optimal solution? How much slack or surplus is there for each of the four constraints at the optimal solution?

16 A candidate for mayor in a small town has allocated $40,000 for last-minute advertising in the days preceding the election. Two types of ads will be used: radio and television. Each radio ad costs $200 and reaches an estimated 3,000 people. Each television ad costs $500 and reaches an estimated 7,000 people. In planning the advertising campaign, the campaign manager would like to reach as many people as possible, but she has stipulated that at least 10 ads of each type must be used. Also, the number of radio ads must be at least as great as the number of television ads. How many ads of each type should be used? How many people will this reach?

17 The Outdoor Furniture Corporation manufactures two products, benches and picnic tables, for use in yards and parks. The firm has two main resources: its carpenters (labor force) and a supply of redwood for use in the furniture. During the next production cycle, 1,200 hours of labor are available under a union agreement. The firm also has a stock of 3,500 board feet of good-quality redwood. Each bench that Outdoor Furniture produces requires 4 labor hours and 10 board feet of redwood; each picnic table takes 6 labor hours and 35 board feet of redwood. Completed benches will yield a profit of $9 each, and tables will result in a profit of $20 each. How many benches and tables should Outdoor Furniture produce to obtain the largest possible profit? Use the graphical LP approach.

18 The dean of the Western College of Business must plan the school's course offerings for the fall semester. Student demands make it necessary to offer at least 30 undergraduate and 20 graduate courses in the term. Faculty contracts also dictate that at least 60 courses be offered in total. Each undergraduate course taught costs the college an average of $2,500 in faculty wages, and each graduate course costs $3,000. How many undergraduate and graduate courses should be taught in the fall so that total faculty salaries are kept to a minimum?

19 MSA Computer Corporation manufactures two models of minicomputers, the Alpha 4 and the Beta 5. The firm employs five technicians, working 160 hours each per month, on its assembly line. Management insists that full employment (i.e., *all* 160 hours of time) be maintained for each worker during next month's operations. It requires 20 labor hours to assemble each Alpha 4 computer and 25 labor hours to assemble each Beta 5 model. MSA wants to see at least 10 Alpha 4s and at least 15 Beta 5s produced during the production period. Alpha 4s generate $1,200 profit per unit, and Beta 5s yield $1,800 each. Determine the most profitable number of each model of minicomputer to produce during the coming month.

20 A winner of the Texas Lotto has decided to invest $50,000 per year in the stock market. Under consideration are stocks for a petrochemical firm and a public utility. Although a long-range goal is to get the highest possible return, some consideration is given to the risk involved with the stocks. A risk index on a scale of 1–10 (with 10 being the most risky) is assigned to each of the two stocks. The total risk of the portfolio is found by multiplying the risk of each stock by the dollars invested in that stock.

The following table provides a summary of the return and risk:

STOCK	ESTIMATED RETURN	RISK INDEX
Petrochemical	12%	9
Utility	6%	4

The investor would like to maximize the return on the investment, but the average risk index of the investment should not be higher than 6. How much should be invested in each stock? What is the average risk for this investment? What is the estimated return for this investment?

21 Referring to the Texas Lotto situation in Problem 20, suppose the investor has changed his attitude about the investment and wishes to give greater emphasis to the risk of the investment. Now the investor wishes to minimize the risk of the investment as long as a return of at least 8% is generated. Formulate this as an LP problem and find the optimal solution. How much should be invested in each stock? What is the average risk for this investment? What is the estimated return for this investment?

22 Solve the following LP problem using the corner point graphical method. At the optimal solution, calculate the slack for each constraint:

$$\text{Maximize profit} = 4X + 4Y$$

subject to
$$3X + 5Y \leq 150$$
$$X - 2Y \leq 10$$
$$5X + 3Y \leq 150$$
$$X, Y \geq 0$$

23 Consider this LP formulation:

$$\text{Minimize cost} = \$X + 2Y$$
$$\text{subject to} \quad X + 3Y \geq 90$$
$$8X + 2Y \geq 160$$
$$3X + 2Y \geq 120$$
$$Y \leq 70$$
$$X, Y \geq 0$$

Graphically illustrate the feasible region and apply the isocost line procedure to indicate which corner point produces the optimal solution. What is the cost of this solution?

24 The stock brokerage firm of Blank, Leibowitz, and Weinberger has analyzed and recommended two stocks to an investors' club of college professors. The professors were interested in factors such as short-term growth, intermediate growth, and dividend rates. These data on each stock are as follows:

FACTOR	STOCK ($)	
	LOUISIANA GAS AND POWER	TRIMEX INSULATION COMPANY
Short-term growth potential, per dollar invested	0.36	0.24
Intermediate growth potential (over next three years), per dollar invested	1.67	1.50
Dividend rate potential	4%	8%

Each member of the club has an investment goal of (1) an appreciation of no less than $720 in the short term, (2) an appreciation of at least $5,000 in the next three years, and (3) a dividend income of at least $200 per year. What is the smallest investment that a professor can make to meet these three goals?

25 Woofer Pet Foods produces a low-calorie dog food for overweight dogs. This product is made from beef products and grain. Each pound of beef costs $0.90, and each pound of grain costs $0.60. A pound of the dog food must contain at least 9 units of Vitamin 1 and 10 units of Vitamin 2. A pound of beef contains 10 units of Vitamin 1 and 12 units of Vitamin 2. A pound of grain contains 6 units of Vitamin 1 and 9 units of Vitamin 2. Formulate this as an LP problem to minimize the cost of the dog food. How many pounds of beef and grain should be included in each pound of dog food? What is the cost and vitamin content of the final product?

26 The seasonal yield of olives in a Piraeus, Greece, vineyard is greatly influenced by a process of branch pruning. If olive trees are pruned every two weeks, output is increased. The pruning process, however, requires considerably more labor than permitting the olives to grow on their own and results in a smaller size olive. It also, though, permits olive trees to be spaced closer together. The yield of 1 barrel of olives by pruning requires 5 hours of labor and 1 acre of land. The production of a barrel of olives by the normal process requires only 2 labor hours but takes 2 acres of land. An olive grower has 250 hours of labor available and a total of 150 acres for growing. Because of the olive size difference, a barrel of olives produced on pruned trees sells for $20, whereas a barrel of regular olives has a market price of $30. The grower has determined that because of uncertain demand, no more than 40 barrels of pruned olives should be produced. Use graphical LP to find

(a) the maximum possible profit.
(b) the best combination of barrels of pruned and regular olives.
(c) the number of acres that the olive grower should devote to each growing process.

27 Consider the following four LP formulations. Using a graphical approach, determine

(a) which formulation has more than one optimal solution.
(b) which formulation is unbounded.
(c) which formulation has no feasible solution.
(d) which formulation is correct as is.

Formulation 1

$$\text{Maximize } 10X_1 + 10X_2$$
$$\text{subject to} \quad 2X_1 \qquad \leq 10$$
$$2X_1 + 4X_2 \leq 16$$
$$4X_2 \leq 8$$
$$X_1 \qquad = 6$$

Formulation 2

$$\text{Maximize } X_1 + 2X_2$$
$$\text{subject to } X_1 \qquad \leq 1$$
$$2X_2 \leq 2$$
$$X_1 + 2X_2 \leq 2$$

Formulation 3

$$\text{Maximize } 3X_1 + 2X_2$$
$$\text{subject to} \quad X_1 + X_2 \geq 5$$
$$X_1 \qquad \geq 2$$
$$2X_2 \geq 8$$

Formulation 4

$$\text{Maximize } 3X_1 + 3X_2$$
$$\text{subject to } 4X_1 + 6X_2 \leq 48$$
$$4X_1 + 2X_2 \leq 12$$
$$3X_2 \geq 3$$
$$2X_1 \qquad \geq 2$$

28 Graph the following LP problem and indicate the optimal solution point:

$$\text{Maximize profit} = \$3X + \$2Y$$
$$\text{subject to} \quad 2X + Y \leq 150$$
$$2X + 3Y \leq 300$$

(a) Does the optimal solution change if the profit per unit of X changes to $4.50?
(b) What happens if the profit function should have been $3X + $3Y?

29 Graphically analyze the following problem:

Maximize profit = $4X + $6Y

subject to $\quad\quad X + 2Y \leq 8$ hours

$\quad\quad\quad\quad\quad 6X + 4Y \leq 24$ hours

(a) What is the optimal solution?

(b) If the first constraint is altered to $X + 3Y \leq 8$, does the feasible region or optimal solution change?

30 Examine the LP formulation in Problem 29. The problem's second constraint reads

$6X + 4Y \leq 24$ hours $\quad$ (time available on machine 2)

If the firm decides that 36 hours of time can be made available on machine 2 (namely, an additional 12 hours) at an additional cost of $10, should it add the hours?

31 Consider the following LP problem:

Maximize profit = $5X + 6Y$

subject to $\quad\quad 2X + Y \leq 120$

$\quad\quad\quad\quad 2X + 3Y \leq 240$

$\quad\quad\quad\quad\quad X, Y \geq 0$

(a) What is the optimal solution to this problem? Solve it graphically.

(b) If a technical breakthrough occurred that raised the profit per unit of X to $8, would this affect the optimal solution?

(c) Instead of an increase in the profit coefficient X to $8, suppose that profit was overestimated and should only have been $3. Does this change the optimal solution?

32 Consider the LP formulation given in Problem 31. If the second constraint is changed from $2X + 3Y \leq 240$ to $2X + 4Y \leq 240$, what effect will this have on the optimal solution?

33 The computer output given below is for Problem 31. Use this to answer the following questions.

(a) How much could the profit on X increase or decrease without changing the values of X and Y in the optimal solution?

(b) If the right-hand side of constraint 1 were increased by 1 unit, how much would the profit increase?

(c) If the right-hand side of constraint 1 were increased by 10 units, how much would the profit increase?

34 The computer output on the next page is for a product mix problem in which there are two products and three resource constraints. Use the output to help you answer the following questions. Assume that you wish to maximize profit in each case.

(a) How many units of product 1 and product 2 should be produced?

(b) How much of each of the three resources is being used? How much slack is there for each constraint? Which of the constraints are binding, and which are nonbinding?

(c) What are the dual prices for each resource?

(d) If you could obtain more of one of the resources, which one should you obtain? How much should you be willing to pay for this?

(e) What would happen to profit if, with the original output, management decided to produce one more unit of product 2?

35 Graphically solve the following problem:

Maximize profit = $8X_1 + 5X_2$

subject to $\quad\quad X_1 + X_2 \leq 10$

$\quad\quad\quad\quad X_1 \quad\quad \leq 6$

$\quad\quad\quad\quad X_1, X_2 \geq 0$

(a) What is the optimal solution?

(b) Change the right-hand side of constraint 1 to 11 (instead of 10) and resolve the problem. How much did the profit increase as a result of this?

Linear Programming Results					
Problem 33 Solution					
	X	Y		RHS	Dual
Maximize	5	6			
const 1	2	1	<=	120	0.75
const 2	2	3	<=	240	1.75
Solution->	30	60		510	

Ranging					
Problem 33 Solution					
Variable	Value	Reduced Cost	Original Val	Lower Bound	Upper Bound
X	30	0	5	4	12
Y	60	0	6	2.5	7.5
Constraint	Dual Value	Slack/Surplus	Original Val	Lower Bound	Upper Bound
const 1	0.75	0	120	80	240
const 2	1.75	0	240	120	360

Linear Programming Results

Problem 34 Solution

	X1	X2		RHS	Dual
Maximize	50	20			
Constraint 1	1	2	<=	45	0
Constraint 2	3	3	<=	87	0
Constraint 3	2	1	<=	50	25
Solution->	25	0		1,250	

Ranging

Problem 34 Solution

Variable	Value	Reduced Cost	Original Val	Lower Bound	Upper Bound
X1	25	0	50	40	Infinity
X2	0	5	20	-Infinity	25
Constraint	Dual Value	Slack/Surplus	Original Val	Lower Bound	Upper Bound
Constraint 1	0	20	45	25	Infinity
Constraint 2	0	12	87	75	Infinity
Constraint 3	25	0	50	0	58

Linear Programming Results

Problem 35 Solution

	X1	X2		RHS	Dual
Maximize	8	5			
Constraint 1	1	1	<=	10	5
Constraint 2	1	0	<=	6	3
Solution->	6	4		68	

Ranging

Problem 35 Solution

Variable	Value	Reduced	Original Val	Lower Bound	Upper Bound
X1	6	0	8	5	Infinity
X2	4	0	5	0	8
Constraint	Dual Value	Slack/Surplus	Original Val	Lower Bound	Upper Bound
Constraint 1	5	0	10	6	Infinity
Constraint 2	3	0	6	0	10

(c) Change the right-hand side of constraint 1 to 6 (instead of 10) and resolve the problem. How much did the profit decrease as a result of this? Looking at the graph, what would happen if the right-hand-side value were to go below 6?

(d) Change the right-hand-side value of constraint 1 to 5 (instead of 10) and resolve the problem. How much did the profit decrease from the original profit as a result of this?

(e) Using the computer output on this page, what is the dual price of constraint 1? What is the lower bound on this?

(f) What conclusions can you draw from this regarding the bounds of the right-hand-side values and the dual price?

36 Serendipity*

The three princes of Serendip
Went on a little trip.
They could not carry too much weight;
More than 300 pounds made them hesitate.
They planned to the ounce. When they returned to Ceylon
They discovered that their supplies were just about gone
When, what to their joy, Prince William found
A pile of coconuts on the ground.
"Each will bring 60 rupees," said Prince Richard with a grin

---

*The word *serendipity* was coined by the English writer Horace Walpole after a fairy tale titled *The Three Princes of Serendip*. Source of problem is unknown.

As he almost tripped over a lion skin.

"Look out!" cried Prince Robert with glee

As he spied some more lion skins under a tree.

"These are worth even more—300 rupees each

If we can just carry them all down to the beach."

Each skin weighed fifteen pounds and each coconut, five,

But they carried them all and made it alive.

The boat back to the island was very small

15 cubic feet baggage capacity—that was all.

Each lion skin took up one cubic foot

While eight coconuts the same space took.

With everything stowed they headed to sea

And on the way calculated what their new wealth might be.

"Eureka!" cried Prince Robert, "Our worth is so great

That there's no other way we could return in this state.

Any other skins or nut that we might have brought

Would now have us poorer. And now I know what—

I'll write my friend Horace in England, for surely

Only he can appreciate our serendipity."

Formulate and solve **Serendipity** by graphical LP in order to calculate "what their new wealth might be."

37 Bhavika Investments, a group of financial advisors and retirement planners, has been requested to provide advice on how to invest $200,000 for one of its clients. The client has stipulated that the money must be put into either a stock fund or a money market fund, and the annual return should be at least $14,000. Other conditions related to risk have also

been specified, and the following linear program was developed to help with this investment decision:

Minimize risk $= 12S + 5M$

subject to

$$S + M = 200,000 \quad \text{total investment is } \$200,000$$

$$0.10S + 0.05M \geq 14,000 \quad \text{return must be at least } \$14,000$$

$$M \geq 40,000 \quad \text{at least } \$40,000 \text{ must be in money market fund}$$

$$S, M \geq 0$$

where

$S = $ dollars invested in stock fund

$M = $ dollars invested in money market fund

The QM for Windows output is shown below.

(a) How much money should be invested in the money market fund and the stock fund? What is the total risk?

(b) What is the total return? What rate of return is this?

(c) Would the solution change if risk measure for each dollar in the stock fund were 14 instead of 12?

(d) For each additional dollar that is available, how much does the risk change?

(e) Would the solution change if the amount that must be invested in the money market fund were changed from $40,000 to $50,000?

38 Refer to the Bhavika Investments (Problem 37) situation once again. It has been decided that, rather than minimize risk, the objective should be to maximize return while placing restriction on the amount of risk.

Linear Programming Results

Problem 37 Solution	S	M		RHS	Dual
Minimize	12	5			
Constraint 1	1	1	=	200,000	2
Constraint 2	0.1	0.05	>=	14,000	-140
Constraint 3	0	1	>=	40,000	0
Solution->	80,000	120,000.0		1,560,000	

Ranging

Problem 37 Solution					
Variable	Value	Reduced Cost	Original Val	Lower Bound	Upper Bound
S	80,000	0	12	5	Infinity
M	120,000.0	0	5	-Infinity	12
Constraint	Dual Value	Slack/Surplus	Original Val	Lower Bound	Upper Bound
Constraint 1	2	0	200,000	160,000	280,000
Constraint 2	-140	0	14,000	10,000	18,000
Constraint 3	0	80,000.01	40,000	-Infinity	120,000.0

Linear Programming Results

Problem 38 Solution

	S	M		RHS	Dual
Maximize	0.1	0.05			
Constraint 1	1	1	=	200,000	0.1
Constraint 2	12	5	<=	2,200,000	0
Constraint 3	0	1	>=	40,000	-0.05
Solution->	160,000	40,000		18,000	

Ranging

Problem 38 Solution

Variable	Value	Reduced Cost	Original Val	Lower Bound	Upper Bound
S	160,000	0	0.1	0.05	Infinity
M	40,000	0	0.05	-Infinity	0.1
Constraint	Dual Value	Slack/Surplus	Original Val	Lower Bound	Upper Bound
Constraint 1	0.1	0	200,000	40,000	206,666.7
Constraint 2	0	80,000	2,200,000	2,120,000	Infinity
Constraint 3	-0.05	0	40,000	28,571.43	200,000

The average risk should be no more than 11 (with a total risk of 2,200,000 for the $200,000 invested). The linear program was reformulated, and the QM for Windows output is shown above.

(a) How much money should be invested in the money market fund and the stock fund? What is the total return? What rate of return is this?

(b) What is the total risk? What is the average risk?

(c) Would the solution change if return for each dollar in the stock fund were 0.09 instead of 0.10?

(d) For each additional dollar that is available, what is the marginal rate of return?

(e) How much would the total return change if the amount that must be invested in the money market fund were changed from $40,000 to $50,000?

Problems 39 to 44 test your ability to formulate LP problems that have more than two variables. They cannot be solved graphically but will give you a chance to set up a larger problem.

39 The Feed 'N Ship Ranch fattens cattle for local farmers and ships them to meat markets in Kansas City and Omaha. The owners of the ranch seek to determine the amounts of cattle feed to buy so that minimum nutritional standards are satisfied, and at the same time total feed costs are minimized. The feed mix can be made up of the three grains that contain the following ingredients per pound of feed:

	FEED (OZ.)		
INGREDIENT	STOCK X	STOCK Y	STOCK Z
A	3	2	4
B	2	3	1
C	1	0	2
D	6	8	4

The cost per pound of stocks X, Y, and Z are $2, $4, and $2.50, respectively. The minimum requirement per cow per month is 4 pounds of ingredient A, 5 pounds of ingredient B, 1 pound of ingredient C, and 8 pounds of ingredient D.

The ranch faces one additional restriction: it can only obtain 500 pounds of stock Z per month from the feed supplier regardless of its need. Because there are usually 100 cows at the Feed 'N Ship Ranch at any given time, this means that no more than 5 pounds of stock Z can be counted on for use in the feed of each cow per month.

(a) Formulate this as an LP problem.

(b) Solve using LP software.

40 The Weinberger Electronics Corporation manufactures four highly technical products that it supplies to aerospace firms that hold NASA contracts. Each of the products must pass through the following departments before they are shipped: wiring, drilling, assembly, and inspection. The time requirement in hours for each unit produced and its corresponding profit value are summarized in the following table:

	DEPARTMENT				UNIT PROFIT
PRODUCT	WIRING	DRILLING	ASSEMBLY	INSPECTION	($)
XJ201	0.5	0.3	0.2	0.5	9
XM897	1.5	1	4	1	12
TR29	1.5	2	1	0.5	15
BR788	1	3	2	0.5	11

The production available in each department each month, and the minimum monthly production requirement to fulfill contracts, are as follows:

DEPARTMENT	CAPACITY (HOURS)	PRODUCT	MINIMUM PRODUCTION LEVEL
Wiring	15,000	XJ201	150
Drilling	17,000	XM897	100
Assembly	26,000	TR29	300
Inspection	12,000	BR788	400

The production manager has the responsibility of specifying production levels for each product for the coming month. Help him by formulating (that is, setting up the constraints and objective function) Weinberger's problem using LP.

41 Outdoor Inn, a camping equipment manufacturer in southern Utah, is developing a production schedule for a popular type of tent, the Double Inn. Orders have been received for 180 of these to be delivered at the end of this month, 220 to be delivered at the end of next month, and 240 to be delivered at the end of the month after that. This tent may be produced at a cost of $120, and the maximum number of tents that can be produced in a month is 230. The company may produce some extra tents in one month and keep them in storage until the next month. The cost for keeping these in inventory for 1 month is estimated to be $6 per tent for each tent left at the end of the month. Formulate this as an LP problem to minimize cost while meeting demand and not exceeding the monthly production capacity. Solve it using any computer software. (*Hint:* Define variables to represent the number of tents left over at the end of each month.)

42 Outdoors Inn (see Problem 41) expanded its tent-making operations later in the year. While still making the Double Inn tent, it is also making a larger tent, the Family Rolls, which has four rooms. The company can produce up to a combined total of 280 tents per month. The following table provides the demand that must be met and the production costs for the next 3 months. Note that the costs will increase in month 2. The holding cost for keeping a tent in inventory at the end of the month for use in the next month is estimated to be $6 per tent for the Double Inn and $8 per tent for the Family Rolls. Develop a linear program to minimize the total cost. Solve it using any computer software.

MONTH	DEMAND FOR DOUBLE INN	COST TO PRODUCE DOUBLE INN	DEMAND FOR FAMILY ROLLS	COST TO PRODUCE FAMILY ROLLS
1	185	$120	60	$150
2	205	$130	70	$160
3	225	$130	65	$160

43 Modem Corporation of America (MCA) is the world's largest producer of modem communication devices for microcomputers. MCA sold 9,000 of the regular model and 10,400 of the smart ("intelligent") model this September. Its income statement for the month is shown in the Table for Problem 43. Costs presented are typical of prior months and are expected to remain at the same levels in the near future.

The firm is facing several constraints as it prepares its November production plan. First, it has experienced a tremendous demand and has been unable to keep any significant inventory in stock. This situation is not expected to change. Second, the firm is located in a small Iowa town from which additional labor is not readily available. Workers can be shifted from production of one modem to another, however. To produce the 9,000 regular modems in September required 5,000 direct labor hours. The 10,400 intelligent modems absorbed 10,400 direct labor hours.

Third, MCA is experiencing a problem affecting the intelligent modems model. Its component supplier is able to guarantee only 8,000 microprocessors for November delivery. Each intelligent modem requires one of these specially made microprocessors. Alternative suppliers are not available on short notice.

TABLE FOR PROBLEM 43

MCA Income Statement Month Ended September 30

	REGULAR MODEMS	INTELLIGENT MODEMS
Sales	$450,000	$640,000
Less: Discounts	10,000	15,000
Returns	12,000	9,500
Warranty replacements	4,000	2,500
Net sales	$424,000	$613,000
Sales costs		
Direct labor	60,000	76,800
Indirect labor	9,000	11,520
Materials cost	90,000	128,000
Depreciation	40,000	50,800
Cost of sales	$199,000	$267,120
Gross profit	$225,000	$345,880
Selling and general expenses		
General expenses—variable	30,000	35,000
General expenses—fixed	36,000	40,000
Advertising	28,000	25,000
Sales commissions	31,000	60,000
Total operating cost	$125,000	$160,000
Pretax income	$100,000	$185,880
Income taxes (25%)	25,000	46,470
Net income	$ 75,000	$139,410

MCA wants to plan the optimal mix of the two modem models to produce in November to maximize profits for MCA.

(a) Formulate, using September's data, MCA's problem as a linear program.

(b) Solve the problem graphically.

(c) Discuss the implications of your recommended solution.

44 Working with chemists at Virginia Tech and George Washington Universities, landscape contractor Kenneth Golding blended his own fertilizer, called "Golding-Grow." It consists of four chemical compounds, C-30, C-92, D-21, and E-11. The cost per pound for each compound is indicated as follows:

CHEMICAL COMPOUND	COST PER POUND ($)
C-30	0.12
C-92	0.09
D-21	0.11
E-11	0.04

The specifications for Golding-Grow are as follows: (1) E-11 must constitute at least 15% of the blend; (2) C-92 and C-30 must together constitute at least 45% of the blend; (3) D-21 and C-92 can together constitute no more than 30% of the blend; and (4) Golding-Grow is packaged and sold in 50-pound bags.

(a) Formulate an LP problem to determine what blend of the four chemicals will allow Golding

to minimize the cost of a 50-pound bag of the fertilizer.

(b) Solve using a computer to find the best solution.

45 Raptor Fuels produces three grades of gasoline—Regular, Premium, and Super. All of these are produced by blending two types of crude oil—Crude A and Crude B. The two types of crude contain specific ingredients which help in determining the octane rating of gasoline. The important ingredients and the costs are contained in the following table:

	CRUDE A	CRUDE B
Cost per gallon	$0.42	$0.47
Ingredient 1	40%	52%
Other ingredients	60%	48%

In order to achieve the desired octane ratings, at least 41% of Regular gasoline should be Ingredient 1; at least 44% of Premium gasoline must be Ingredient 1, and at least 48% of Super gasoline must be Ingredient 1. Due to current contract commitments, Raptor Fuels must produce as least 20,000 gallons of Regular, at least 15,000 gallons of Premium, and at least 10,000 gallons of Super. Formulate a linear program that could be used to determine how much of Crude A and Crude B should be used in each of the gasolines to meet the demands at the minimum cost. What is the minimum cost? How much of Crude A and Crude B are used in each gallon of the different types of gasoline?

Internet Homework Problems

See our Internet home page, at www.pearsonhighered.com/render, for additional homework problems, Problems 46 to 50.

Case Study

Mexicana Wire Works

Ron Garcia felt good about his first week as a management trainee at Mexicana Wire Winding, Inc. He had not yet developed any technical knowledge about the manufacturing process, but he had toured the entire facility, located in the suburbs of Mexico City, and had met many people in various areas of the operation.

Mexicana, a subsidiary of Westover Wire Works, a Texas firm, is a medium-sized producer of wire windings used in making electrical transformers. José Arroyo, the production control manager, described the windings to Garcia as being of standardized design. Garcia's tour of the plant, laid out by process type (see Figure 20), followed the manufacturing sequence for the windings: drawing, extrusion, winding, inspection, and

packaging. After inspection, good product is packaged and sent to finished product storage; defective product is stored separately until it can be reworked.

On March 8, Vivian Espania, Mexicana's general manager, stopped by Garcia's office and asked him to attend a staff meeting at 1:00 P.M.

"Let's get started with the business at hand," Vivian said, opening the meeting. "You all have met Ron Garcia, our new management trainee. Ron studied operations management in his MBA program in southern California, so I think he is competent to help us with a problem we have been discussing for a long time without resolution. I'm sure that each of you on my staff will give Ron your full cooperation."

FIGURE 20

Mexicana Wire Winding, Inc.

Vivian turned to José Arroyo, production manager. "José, why don't you describe the problem we are facing?"

"Well," José said, "business is very good right now. We are booking more orders than we can fill. We will have some new equipment on line within the next several months, which will take care of our capacity problems, but that won't help us in April. I have located some retired employees who used to work in the drawing department, and I am planning to bring them in as temporary employees in April to increase capacity there. Because we are planning to refinance some of our long-term debt, Vivian wants our profits to look as good as possible in April. I'm having a hard time figuring out which orders to run and which to back order so that I can make the bottom line look as good as possible. Can you help me with this?"

Garcia was surprised and apprehensive to receive such an important, high-profile assignment so early in his career. Recovering quickly, he said, "Give me your data and let me work with it for a day or two."

April Orders

Product W0075C	1,400 units
Product W0033C	250 units
Product W0005X	1,510 units
Product W0007X	1,116 units

Note: Vivian Espania has given her word to a key customer that we will manufacture 600 units of product W0007X and 150 units of product W0075C for him during April

Standard Cost

PRODUCT	MATERIAL	LABOR	OVERHEAD	SELLING PRICE
W0075C	$33.00	$ 9.90	$23.10	$100.00
W0033C	25.00	7.50	17.50	80.00
W0005X	35.00	10.50	24.50	130.00
W0007X	75.00	11.25	63.75	175.00

Selected Operating Data

Average output per month = 2,400 units

Average machine utilization = 63%

Average percentage of production set to rework department = 5% (mostly from Winding Department)

Average no. of rejected units awaiting rework = 850 (mostly from Winding Department)

Plant Capacity (Hours)

DRAWING	EXTRUSION	WINDING	PACKAGING
4,000	4,200	2,000	2,300

Note: Inspection capacity is not a problem; we can work overtime, as necessary, to accommodate any schedule.

Bill of Labor (Hours/Unit)

PRODUCT	DRAWING	EXTRUSION	WINDING	PACKAGING
W0075C	1.0	1.0	1.0	1.0
W0033C	2.0	1.0	3.0	0.0
W0005X	0.0	4.0	0.0	3.0
W0007X	1.0	1.0	0.0	2.0

Discussion Questions

1. What recommendations should Ron Garcia make, with what justification? Provide a detailed analysis with charts, graphs, and computer printouts included.
2. Discuss the need for temporary workers in the drawing department.
3. Discuss the plant layout.

Source: Professor Victor E. Sower, Sam Houston State University. This case material is based on an actual situation, with names and data altered for confidentiality.

Bibliography

Bassamboo, Achal, J. Michael Harrison, and Assaf Zeevi. "Design and Control of a Large Call Center: Asymptotic Analysis of an LP-Based Method," *Operations Research* 54, 3 (May–June 2006): 419–435.

Behjat, Laleh, Anthony Vannelli, and William Rosehart. "Integer Linear Programming Model for Global Routing," *INFORMS Journal on Computing* 18, 2 (Spring 2006): 137–150.

Bixby, Robert E. "Solving Real-World Linear Programs: A Decade and More of Progress," *Operations Research* 50, 1 (January–February 2002): 3–15.

Bodington, C. E., and T. E. Baker. "A History of Mathematical Programming in the Petroleum Industry," *Interfaces* 20, 4 (July–August 1990): 117–132.

Boros, E., L. Fedzhora, P. B. Kantor, K. Saeger, and P. Stroud. "A Large-Scale Linear Programming Model For Finding Optimal Container Inspection Strategies," *Naval Research Logistics* 56, 5 (August 2009): 404–420.

Chakravarti, N. "Tea Company Steeped in OR," *OR/MS Today* 27, 2 (April 2000): 32–34.

Ching, Wai-Ki, Wai-On Yuen, Michael K. Ng, and Shu-Qin Zhang. "A Linear Programming Approach for Determining Optimal Advertising Policy," *IMA Journal of Management Mathematics* 17, 1 (2006): 83–96.

Dantzig, George B. "Linear Programming Under Uncertainty," *Management Science* 50, 12 (December 2004): 1764–1769.

Degbotse, Alfred, Brian T. Denton, Kenneth Fordyce, R. John Milne, Robert Orzell, and Chi-Tai Wang. "IBM Blends Heuristics and Optimization to Plan Its Semiconductor Supply Chain," *Interfaces* 43 (March/April 2013): 130–141.

Gass, Saul I. "The First Linear-Programming Shoppe," *Operations Research* 50, 1 (January–February 2002): 61–68.

Greenberg, H. J. "How to Analyze the Results of Linear Programs—Part 1: Preliminaries," *Interfaces* 23, 4 (July–August 1993): 56–68.

Greenberg, H. J. "How to Analyze the Results of Linear Programs—Part 3: Infeasibility Diagnosis," *Interfaces* 23, 6 (November–December 1993): 120–139.

Hafizoğlu, A. B., and M Azizoğlu. "Linear Programming Based Approaches for the Discrete Time/Cost Trade-off Problem in Project Networks," *Journal of the Operational Research Society* 61 (April 2010): 676–685.

Higle, Julia L., and Stein W. Wallace. "Sensitivity Analysis and Uncertainty in Linear Programming," *Interfaces* 33, 4 (July–August 2003): 53–60.

Marszalkowski, Jakub and Drozdowski Maciej. "Optimization of Column Width in Website Layout for Advertisement Fit," *European Journal of Operational Research* 226, 3 (May 2013): 592–601.

Murphy, Frederic H. "ASP, the Art and Science of Practice: Elements of a Theory of the Practice of Operations Research: Expertise in Practice," *Interfaces* 35, 4 (July–August 2005): 313–322.

Orden, A. "LP from the '40s to the '90s," *Interfaces* 23, 5 (September–October 1993): 2–12.

Pazour, Jennifer A. and Lucas C. Neubert. "Routing and Scheduling of Cross-Town Drayage Operations at J.B. Hunt Transport," *Interfaces* 43, (March/April 2013): 117–129.

Romeijn, H. Edwin, Ravindra K. Ahuja, James F. Dempsey, and Arvind Kumar. "A New Linear Programming Approach to Radiation Therapy Treatment Planning Problems," *Operations Research* 54, 2 (March–April 2006): 201–216.

Rubin, D. S., and H. M. Wagner. "Shadow Prices: Tips and Traps for Managers and Instructors," *Interfaces* 20, 4 (July–August 1990): 150–157.

Wendell, Richard E. "Tolerance Sensitivity and Optimality Bounds in Linear Programming," *Management Science* 50, 6 (June 2004) 797–803.

Solutions to Selected Problems

14 40 air conditioners, 60 fans, profit = $1,900

16 175 radio ads, 10 TV ads

18 40 undergraduate, 20 graduate, $160,000

20 $20,000 Petrochemical; $30,000 Utilities; return = $4,200; risk = 6

22 $X = 18.75$, $Y = 18.75$, profit = $150

24 (1358.7, 1820.6), $3,179.30

26 (a) profit = $2,375   (b) 25 barrels pruned, 62.5 barrels regular   (c) 25 acres pruned, 125 acres regular

28 (a) Yes   (b) Doesn't change

34 (a) 25 units product 1, 0 units product 2   (b) 25 units of resource 1 is used, slack = 20; 75 units of resource 2 is used, slack = 12; 50 units of resource 3 is used, slack = 0; constraint 3 is binding and others are not.   (c) 0, 0, and 25   (d) Resource 3. Up to $25 (dual price)   (e) Total profit would decrease by 5 (value of reduced cost).

36 24 coconuts, 12 skins; profit = 5,040 rupees

42 Use 7.5 lb of C-30, 15 lb of C-92, 0 lb of D-21, and 27.5 lb of E-11; cost = $3.35 per lb

Solutions to Self-Tests

1.	b	**6.**	b	**11.**	a		
2.	a	**7.**	c	**12.**	a		
3.	b	**8.**	c	**13.**	a		
4.	c	**9.**	b	**14.**	a		
5.	a	**10.**	c				

Linear Programming Applications

LEARNING OBJECTIVES

After completing this chapter, students will be able to:

1. Model a wide variety of medium to large LP problems.
2. Understand major application areas, including marketing, production, labor scheduling, fuel blending, and finance.
3. Gain experience in solving LP problems with Excel Solver software.

Summary • Self-Test • Problems • Internet Homework Problems • Case Study: Cable & Moore • Bibliography

From Chapter 8 of *Quantitative Analysis for Management*, Twelfth Edition. Barry Render, Ralph M. Stair, Jr., Michael E. Hanna, and Trevor S. Hale. Copyright © 2015 by Pearson Education, Inc. All rights reserved.

1 Introduction

The graphical method of linear programming (LP) is useful for understanding how to formulate and solve small LP problems. The purpose of this chapter is to go one step further and show how a large number of real-life problems can be modeled using LP. We do this by presenting examples of models in the areas of marketing research, media selection, production mix, labor scheduling, production scheduling, ingredient mix, and financial portfolio selection. We will solve many of these LP problems using Excel's Solver and QM for Windows.

Although some of these models are relatively small numerically, the principles developed here are definitely applicable to larger problems. Moreover, this practice in "paraphrasing" LP model formulations should help develop your skills in applying the technique to other, less common applications.

2 Marketing Applications

Media Selection

Media selection problems can be approached with LP from two perspectives. The objective can be to maximize audience exposure or to minimize advertising costs.

Linear programming models have been used in the advertising field as a decision aid in selecting an effective media mix. Sometimes the technique is employed in allocating a fixed or limited budget across various media, which might include radio or television commercials, newspaper ads, direct mailings, magazine ads, and so on. In other applications, the objective is the maximization of audience exposure. Restrictions on the allowable media mix might arise through contract requirements, limited media availability, or company policy. An example follows.

The Win Big Gambling Club promotes gambling junkets from a large Midwestern city to casinos in the Bahamas. The club has budgeted up to $8,000 per week for local advertising. The money is to be allocated among four promotional media: TV spots, newspaper ads, and two types of radio advertisements. Win Big's goal is to reach the largest possible high-potential audience through the various media. The following table presents the number of potential gamblers reached by making use of an advertisement in each of the four media. It also provides the cost per advertisement placed and the maximum number of ads that can be purchased per week.

MEDIUM	AUDIENCE REACHED PER AD	COST PER AD ($)	MAXIMUM ADS PER WEEK
TV spot (1 minute)	5,000	800	12
Daily newspaper (full-page ad)	8,500	925	5
Radio spot (30 seconds, prime time)	2,400	290	25
Radio spot (1 minute, afternoon)	2,800	380	20

Win Big's contractual arrangements require that at least five radio spots be placed each week. To ensure a broad-scoped promotional campaign, management also insists that no more than $1,800 be spent on radio advertising every week.

In formulating this as an LP, the first step is to completely understand the problem. Sometimes asking "what if" questions will help understand the situation. In this example, what would happen if exactly five ads of each type were used? What would this cost? How many people would it reach? Certainly the use of a spreadsheet for the calculations can help with this since formulas can be written to calculate the cost and the number of people reached. Once the situation is understood, the objective and the constraints are stated:

Objective:

Maximize number of people (audience) reached

LINEAR PROGRAMMING APPLICATIONS

Constraints:

(1) No more than 12 TV ads can be used. (2) No more than 5 newspaper ads can be used. (3) No more than 25 of the 30-second radio ads can be used. (4) No more than 20 of the 1-minute radio ads can be used. (5) Total amount spent cannot exceed $8,000. (6) Total number of radio ads must be at least 5. (7) Total amount spent on radio ads must not exceed $1,800.

Next, define the decision variables. The decisions being made here are the number of ads of each type to use. Once these are known, they can be used to calculate the amount spent and the number of people reached. Let

X_1 = number of 1-minute TV spots taken each week

X_2 = number of full-page daily newspaper ads taken each week

X_3 = number of 30-second prime-time radio spots taken each week

X_4 = number of 1-minute afternoon radio spots taken each week

Next, using these variables, write the mathematical expression for the objective and the constraint that were identified. The nonnegativity constraints are also explicitly stated.

Objective:

$$\text{Maximize audience coverage} = 5{,}000X_1 + 8{,}500X_2 + 2{,}400X_3 + 2{,}800X_4$$

subject to

$X_1 \le 12$ (maximum TV spots/week)

$X_2 \le 5$ (maximum newspaper ads/week)

$X_3 \le 25$ (maximum 30-second radio spots/week)

$X_4 \le 20$ (maximum 1-minute radio spots/week)

$800X_1 + 925X_2 + 290X_3 + 380X_4 \le \$8{,}000$ (weekly advertising budget)

$X_3 + X_4 \ge 5$ (minimum radio spots contracted)

$290X_3 + 380X_4 \le \$1{,}800$ (maximum dollars spent on radio)

$X_1, X_2, X_3, X_4 \ge 0$

The solution to this can be found using Excel's Solver. Program 1 gives the inputs to the Solver Parameter dialog box, the formula that must be written in the cell for the objective function value, and the cells where this formula should be copied. The results are shown in the spreadsheet. This solution is

$X_1 = 1.97$ TV spots

$X_2 = 5$ newspaper ads

$X_3 = 6.2$ 30-second radio spots

$X_4 = 0$ one-minute radio spots

This produces an audience exposure of 67,240 contacts. Because X_1 and X_3 are fractional, Win Big would probably round them to 2 and 6, respectively.

Marketing Research

Linear programming has also been applied to marketing research problems and the area of consumer research. The next example illustrates how statistical pollsters can reach strategy decisions with LP.

Management Sciences Associates (MSA) is a marketing and computer research firm based in Washington, D.C., that handles consumer surveys. One of its clients is a national press service that periodically conducts political polls on issues of widespread interest. In a survey for the press service, MSA determines that it must fulfill several requirements in order to draw statistically valid conclusions on the sensitive issue of new U.S. immigration laws:

1. Survey at least 2,300 U.S. households in total.
2. Survey at least 1,000 households whose heads are 30 years of age or younger.

PROGRAM 1

Win Big Solution in Excel 2013

	A	B	C	D	E	F	G	H
1	Win Big Gambling Club							
2				Radio	Radio			
3		TV	Newspaper	30 sec.	1 min.			
4	Variables	X1	X2	X3	X4			
5	Solution	1.9688	5	6.2069	0	Total Audience		
6	Audience per ad	5000	8500	2400	2800	67240.3017		
7								
8	Constraints					LHS		RHS
9	Max. TV	1				1.9688	≤	12
10	Max. Newspaper		1			5	≤	5
11	Max. 30-sec. radio			1		6.2069	≤	25
12	Max. 1 min. radio				1	0	≤	20
13	Cost	800	925	290	380	8000	≤	8000
14	Radio dollars			290	380	1800	≤	1800
15	Radio spots			1	1	6.2069	≥	5

Solver Parameter Inputs and Selections

Set Objective: F6

By Changing cells: B5:E5

To: Max

Subject to the Constraints:

> F9:F14 <= H9:H14

> F15 >= H15

Solving Method: Simplex LP

☑ **Make Variables Non-Negative**

Key Formulas

	F
5	Total Audience
6	=SUMPRODUCT($B$5:$E$5,B6:E6)

Copy F6 to F9:F15

3. Survey at least 600 households whose heads are between 31 and 50 years of age.
4. Ensure that at least 15% of those surveyed live in a state that borders on Mexico.
5. Ensure that no more than 20% of those surveyed who are 51 years of age or over live in a state that borders on Mexico.

MSA decides that all surveys should be conducted in person. It estimates that the costs of reaching people in each age and region category are as follows:

REGION	COST PER PERSON SURVEYED ($)		
	AGE ≤ 30	AGE 31–50	AGE ≥ 51
State bordering Mexico	$7.50	$6.80	$5.50
State not bordering Mexico	$6.90	$7.25	$6.10

MSA would like to meet the five sampling requirements at the least possible cost.

In formulating this as an LP, the objective is to minimize cost. The five requirements about the number of people to be sampled with specific characteristics result in five constraints. The decision variables come from the decisions that must be made, which are the number of people sampled from each of the two regions in each of the three age categories. Thus, the six variables are

X_1 = number surveyed who are 30 or younger and live in a border state

X_2 = number surveyed who are 31–50 and live in a border state

X_3 = number surveyed who are 51 or older and live in a border state

X_4 = number surveyed who are 30 or younger and do not live in a border state

X_5 = number surveyed who are 31–50 and do not live in a border state

X_6 = number surveyed who are 51 or older and do not live in a border state

Objective function:

$$\text{Minimize total interview costs} = \$7.50X_1 + \$6.80X_2 + \$5.50X_3$$
$$+ \$6.90X_4 + \$7.25X_5 + \$6.10X_6$$

subject to

$$X_1 + X_2 + X_3 + X_4 + X_5 + X_6 \geq 2,300 \quad \text{(total households)}$$
$$X_1 + \quad\quad\quad X_4 \quad\quad\quad \geq 1,000 \quad \text{(households 30 or younger)}$$
$$X_2 + \quad\quad\quad X_5 \quad \geq 600 \quad \text{(households 31–50 in age)}$$
$$X_1 + X_2 + X_3 \geq 0.15(X_1 + X_2 + X_3 + X_4 + X_5 + X_6) \quad \text{(border states)}$$
$$X_3 \leq 0.2(X_3 + X_6) \quad \text{(limit on age group 51+ who live in border state)}$$
$$X_1, X_2, X_3, X_4, X_5, X_6 \geq 0$$

The computer solution to MSA's problem costs $15,166 and is presented in the following table and in Program 2, which presents the input and output from Excel 2013. Note that the variables in the constraints are moved to the left-hand side of the inequality.

REGION	AGE $\leq$ 30	AGE 31–50	AGE $\geq$ 51
State bordering Mexico	0	600	140
State not bordering Mexico	1,000	0	560

PROGRAM 2
MSA Solution in Excel 2013

	A	B	C	D	E	F	G	H	I	J
1	Management Science Associates									
2										
3	Variable	X1	X2	X3	X4	X5	X6			
4	Solution	0	600	140	1000	0	560	Total Cost		
5	Min. Cost	7.5	6.8	5.5	6.9	7.25	6.1	15166		
6										
7	Constraints							LHS		RHS
8	Total Households	1	1	1	1	1	1	2300	$\geq$	2,300
9	30 and Younger	1	0	0	1	0	0	1000	$\geq$	1,000
10	31-50	0	1	0	0	1	0	600	$\geq$	600
11	Border States	0.85	0.85	0.85	-0.15	-0.15	-0.15	395	$\geq$	0
12	51+ Border States	0	0	0.8	0	0	-0.2	0	$\leq$	0

Solver Parameter Inputs and Selections

Set Objective: H5

By Changing cells: B4:G4

To: Min

Subject to the Constraints:

    H8:H11 <= J8:J11

    H12 >= J12

Solving Method: Simplex LP

☑ **Make Variables Non-Negative**

Key Formulas

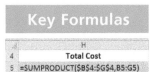

	H
4	Total Cost
5	=SUMPRODUCT($B$4:$G$4,B5:G5)

Copy H5 to H8:H12

3 Manufacturing Applications

Production Mix

A fertile field for the use of LP is in planning for the optimal mix of products to manufacture. A company must meet a myriad of constraints, ranging from financial concerns to sales demand to material contracts to union labor demands. Its primary goal is to generate the largest profit possible.

Fifth Avenue Industries, a nationally known manufacturer of menswear, produces four varieties of ties. One is an expensive, all-silk tie; one is an all-polyester tie; one is a blend of polyester and cotton; and one is a blend of silk and cotton. The following table illustrates the cost and availability (per monthly production planning period) of the three materials used in the production process:

MATERIAL	COST PER YARD ($)	MATERIAL AVAILABLE PER MONTH (YARDS)
Silk	24	1,200
Polyester	6	3,000
Cotton	9	1,600

The firm has fixed contracts with several major department store chains to supply ties. The contracts require that Fifth Avenue Industries supply a minimum quantity of each tie but allow for a larger demand if Fifth Avenue chooses to meet that demand. (Most of the ties are not shipped with the name Fifth Avenue on their label, incidentally, but with "private stock" labels supplied by the stores.) Table 1 summarizes the contract demand for each of the four styles of ties, the selling price per tie, and the fabric requirements of each variety. Fifth Avenue's goal is to maximize its monthly profit. It must decide upon a policy for product mix.

In formulating this problem, the objective is to maximize profit. There are three constraints (one for each material) indicating that the amount of silk, polyester, and cotton cannot exceed the amount that is available. There are four constraints (one for each type of tie) that specify that the number of all silk ties, all polyester ties, poly–silk ties, and silk–cotton ties produced must be at least the minimum contract amount. There are four more constraints (one for each type of tie) that indicate that the number of each of these ties produced cannot exceed the monthly demand. The variables are defined as

X_1 = number of all-silk ties produced per month

X_2 = number of polyester ties

X_3 = number of blend 1 poly–cotton ties

X_4 = number of blend 2 silk–cotton ties

TABLE 1 Data for Fifth Avenue Industries

VARIETY OF TIE	SELLING PRICE PER TIE ($)	MONTHLY CONTRACT MINIMUM	MONTHLY DEMAND	MATERIAL REQUIRED PER TIE (YARDS)	MATERIAL REQUIREMENTS
All silk	19.24	5,000	7,000	0.125	100% silk
All polyester	8.70	10,000	14,000	0.08	100% polyester
Poly–cotton blend 1	9.52	13,000	16,000	0.10	50% polyester–50% cotton
Silk–cotton blend 2	10.64	5,000	8,500	0.11	60% silk–40% cotton

But first the firm must establish the profit per tie:

1. Each all-silk tie (X_1) requires 0.125 yard of silk, at a cost of $24.00 per yard. Therefore, the material cost per tie is $3.00. The selling price is $19.24, leaving a net profit of $16.24 per silk tie.
2. Each all-polyester tie (X_2) requires 0.08 yard of polyester, at a cost of $6 per yard. Therefore, the material cost per tie is $0.48. The selling price is $8.70, leaving a net profit of $8.22 per polyester tie.
3. Each poly–cotton (blend 1) tie (X_3) requires 0.05 yard of polyester, at a cost of $6 per yard, and 0.05 yard of cotton, at $9 per yard, for a cost of $0.30 + $0.45 = $0.75 per tie. The selling price is $9.52, leaving a net profit of $8.77 per poly–cotton tie.
4. Performing similar calculations will show that each silk–cotton (blend 2) tie (X_4) has a material cost per tie of $1.98 and a profit of $8.66.

The objective function may now be stated as

$$\text{Maximize profit} = \$16.24X_1 + \$8.22X_2 + \$8.77X_3 + \$8.66X_4$$

$$\begin{aligned}
\text{subject to} \quad 0.125X_1 + 0.066X_4 &\leq 1{,}200 \quad \text{(yards of silk)} \\
0.08X_2 + 0.05X_3 &\leq 3{,}000 \quad \text{(yards of polyester)} \\
0.05X_3 + 0.044X_4 &\leq 1{,}600 \quad \text{(yards of cotton)} \\
X_1 &\geq 5{,}000 \quad \text{(contract minimum for all silk)} \\
X_1 &\leq 7{,}000 \quad \text{(contract maximum)} \\
X_2 &\geq 10{,}000 \quad \text{(contract minimum for all polyester)} \\
X_2 &\leq 14{,}000 \quad \text{(contract maximum)} \\
X_3 &\geq 13{,}000 \quad \text{(contract minimum for blend 1)} \\
X_3 &\leq 16{,}000 \quad \text{(contract maximum)} \\
X_4 &\geq 5{,}000 \quad \text{(contract minimum for blend 2)} \\
X_4 &\leq 8{,}500 \quad \text{(contract maximum)} \\
X_1, X_2, X_3, X_4 &\geq 0
\end{aligned}$$

Using Excel and its Solver command, the computer-generated solution is to produce 5,112 all-silk ties each month; 14,000 all-polyester ties; 16,000 poly–cotton blend 1 ties; and 8,500 silk–cotton blend 2 ties. This produces a profit of $412,028 per production period. See Program 3 for details.

Production Scheduling

Setting a low-cost production schedule over a period of weeks or months is a difficult and important management problem in most plants. The production manager has to consider many factors: labor capacity, inventory and storage costs, space limitations, product demand, and labor relations. Because most companies produce more than one product, the scheduling process is often quite complex.

Basically, the problem resembles the product mix model for each period in the future. The objective is either to maximize profit or to minimize the total cost (production plus inventory) of carrying out the task.

Production scheduling is amenable to solution by LP because it is a problem that must be solved on a regular basis. When the objective function and constraints for a firm are established, the inputs can easily be changed each month to provide an updated schedule.

An example of production scheduling: Greenberg Motors

Greenberg Motors, Inc., manufactures two different electrical motors for sale under contract to Drexel Corp., a well-known producer of small kitchen appliances. Its model GM3A is found in many Drexel food processors, and its model GM3B is used in the assembly of blenders.

Three times each year, the procurement officer at Drexel contacts Irwin Greenberg, the founder of Greenberg Motors, to place a monthly order for each of the coming four months. Drexel's demand for motors varies each month based on its own sales forecasts, production capacity, and financial position. Greenberg has just received the January–April order and must begin his own four-month production plan. The demand for motors is shown in Table 2.

PROGRAM 3
Fifth Avenue Solution
in Excel 2013

	A	B	C	D	E	F	G	H
1	Fifth Avenue Industries							
2								
3		All silk	All poly.	Blend 1	Blend 2			
4	Variables	X1	X2	X3	X4			
5	Values	5112	14000	16000	8500	Total Profit		
6	Profit	16.24	8.22	8.77	8.66	412028.88		
7								
8	Constraints					LHS		RHS
9	Silk available	0.125			0.066	1200	≤	1200
10	Polyester available		0.08	0.05		1920	≤	3000
11	Cotton available			0.05	0.044	1174	≤	1600
12	Maximum silk	1				5112	≤	7000
13	Maximum polyester		1			14000	≤	14000
14	Maximum blend 1			1		16000	≤	16000
15	Maximum blend 2				1	8500	≤	8500
16	Minimum silk	1				5112	≥	5000
17	Minimum polyester		1			14000	≥	10000
18	Minimum blend 1			1		16000	≥	13000
19	Minimum blend 2				1	8500	≥	5000

Solver Parameter Inputs and Selections

Set Objective: F6

By Changing cells: B5:E5

To: Max

Subject to the Constraints:

F9:F15 <= H9:H15

F16:F19 >= H16:H19

Solving Method: Simplex LP

☑ Make Variables Non-Negative

Key Formulas

	F
5	Total Profit
6	=SUMPRODUCT($B$5:$E$5,B6:E6)

Copy F6 to F9:F19

TABLE 2
Four-Month Order
Schedule for Electrical
Motors

MODEL	JANUARY	FEBRUARY	MARCH	APRIL
GM3A	800	700	1,000	1,100
GM3B	1,000	1,200	1,400	1,400

Production planning at Greenberg Motors must consider several factors:

1. The company must meet the demand for each of the two products in each of the four months (see Table 2). Also, the company would like to have 450 units of the GM3A and 300 units of the GM3B in inventory at the end of April, as demand in May is expected to be somewhat higher than demand in the previous months.
2. There is a carrying, or holding, cost for any inventory left at the end of the month. So producing too many extra units of either product may not be desirable. The carrying cost assigned to the GM3A is $0.36 per unit per month, while the carrying cost for the GM3B is $0.26 per unit per month.
3. The company has been able to maintain a no-layoff policy, and it would like to continue with this. This is easier if the labor hours used do not fluctuate too much from month to month. Maintaining a production schedule that would require from 2,240 to 2,560 labor hours per month is desired. The GM3A requires 1.3 labor hours per unit, while the GM3B requires only 0.9 labor hours.

4. Warehouse limitations cannot be exceeded without great additional costs. There is room at the end of the month for only 3,300 units of the GM3A and GM3B combined.

Although these factors sometimes conflict, Greenberg has found that linear programming is an effective tool in setting up a production schedule that will minimize total cost. Production costs are currently $20 per unit for the GM3A and $15 per unit for the GM3B. However, each of these is due to increase by 10% on March 1 as a new labor agreement goes into effect.

In formulating this as a linear program, it is important to understand how all the important factors are related, how the costs are calculated, how the labor hours per month are calculated, and how demand is met with both production and inventory on hand. To help with understanding this, try to determine the number of labor hours used, the number of units left in inventory at the end of each month for each product, and the total cost if exactly 1,000 of the GM3A and exactly 1,200 of the GM3B were produced each month.

To begin formulating the linear program for the Greenberg production problem, the objective and the constraints are:

Objective:

Minimize total cost (production cost plus carrying cost)

Constraints:

4 demand constraints (1 constraint for each of 4 months) for GM3A

4 demand constraints (1 constraint for each of 4 months) for GM3B

2 constraints (1 for GM3A and 1 for GM3B) for the inventory at the end of April

4 constraints for minimum labor hours (1 constraint for each month)

4 constraints for maximum labor hours (1 constraint for each month)

4 constraints for inventory storage capacity each month

The decisions involve determining how many units of each of 2 products to produce in each of 4 months, so there will be 8 variables. But, since the objective is to minimize cost, and there are costs associated not only with the units produced each month but also with the number of units of each left in inventory, it would be best to define variables for these also. Let

A_i = number of units of GM3A produced in month i (i = 1, 2, 3, 4 for January–April)

B_i = number of units of GM3B produced in month i (i = 1, 2, 3, 4 for January–April)

IA_i = units of GM3A left in inventory at end of month i (i = 1, 2, 3, 4 for January–April)

IB_i = units of GM3B left in inventory at end of month i (i = 1, 2, 3, 4 for January–April)

The objective function in the LP model is

$$\text{Minimize cost} = 20A_1 + 20A_2 + 22A_3 + 22A_4 + 15B_1 + 15B_2 + 16.50B_3$$
$$+ 16.50B_4 + 0.36IA_1 + 0.36IA_2 + 0.36IA_3 + 0.36IA_4$$
$$+ 0.26IB_1 + 0.26IB_2 + 0.26IB_3 + 0.26IB_4$$

Inventory constraints set the relationship between closing inventory this month, closing inventory last month, this month's production, and sales this month.

In setting up the constraints, we must recognize the relationship between last month's ending inventory, the current month's production, and the sales to Drexel this month. The inventory at the end of a month is

$$\begin{pmatrix} \text{Inventory} \\ \text{at the} \\ \text{end of} \\ \text{this month} \end{pmatrix} = \begin{pmatrix} \text{Inventory} \\ \text{at the} \\ \text{end of} \\ \text{last month} \end{pmatrix} + \begin{pmatrix} \text{Current} \\ \text{month's} \\ \text{production} \end{pmatrix} - \begin{pmatrix} \text{Sales} \\ \text{to Drexel} \\ \text{this month} \end{pmatrix}$$

While the constraints could be written in this form, inputting the problem into the computer requires all variables to be on the left-hand side of the constraint. Rearranging the terms to do this results in

$$\begin{pmatrix} \text{Inventory} \\ \text{at the} \\ \text{end of} \\ \text{last month} \end{pmatrix} + \begin{pmatrix} \text{Current} \\ \text{month's} \\ \text{production} \end{pmatrix} - \begin{pmatrix} \text{Inventory} \\ \text{at the} \\ \text{end of} \\ \text{this month} \end{pmatrix} = \begin{pmatrix} \text{Sales} \\ \text{to Drexel} \\ \text{this month} \end{pmatrix}$$

Using this, the demand constraints are:

$$A_1 - IA_1 = 800 \qquad \text{(demand for GM3A in January)}$$
$$IA_1 + A_2 - IA_2 = 700 \qquad \text{(demand for GM3A in February)}$$
$$IA_2 + A_3 - IA_3 = 1{,}000 \qquad \text{(demand for GM3A in March)}$$
$$IA_3 + A_4 - IA_4 = 1{,}100 \qquad \text{(demand for GM3A in April)}$$
$$B_1 - IB_1 = 1{,}000 \qquad \text{(demand for GM3B in January)}$$
$$IB_1 + B_2 - IB_2 = 1{,}200 \qquad \text{(demand for GM3B in February)}$$
$$IB_2 + B_3 - IB_3 = 1{,}400 \qquad \text{(demand for GM3B in March)}$$
$$IB_3 + B_4 - IB_4 = 1{,}400 \qquad \text{(demand for GM3B in April)}$$
$$IA_4 = 450 \qquad \text{(inventory of GM3A at end of April)}$$
$$IB_4 = 300 \qquad \text{(inventory of GM3B at end of April)}$$

Employment constraints are set for each month.

The constraints for the minimum and maximum number of labor hours each month are:

$$1.3A_1 + 0.9B_1 \geq 2{,}240 \qquad \text{(minimum labor hours in January)}$$
$$1.3A_2 + 0.9B_2 \geq 2{,}240 \qquad \text{(minimum labor hours in February)}$$
$$1.3A_3 + 0.9B_3 \geq 2{,}240 \qquad \text{(minimum labor hours in March)}$$
$$1.3A_4 + 0.9B_4 \geq 2{,}240 \qquad \text{(minimum labor hours in April)}$$
$$1.3A_1 + 0.9B_1 \leq 2{,}560 \qquad \text{(maximum labor hours in January)}$$
$$1.3A_2 + 0.9B_2 \leq 2{,}560 \qquad \text{(maximum labor hours in February)}$$
$$1.3A_3 + 0.9B_3 \leq 2{,}560 \qquad \text{(maximum labor hours in March)}$$
$$1.3A_4 + 0.9B_4 \leq 2{,}560 \qquad \text{(maximum labor hours in April)}$$

The storage capacity constraints are:

$$IA_1 + IB_1 \leq 3{,}300 \qquad \text{(storage capacity in January)}$$
$$IA_2 + IB_2 \leq 3{,}300 \qquad \text{(storage capacity in February)}$$
$$IA_3 + IB_3 \leq 3{,}300 \qquad \text{(storage capacity in March)}$$
$$IA_4 + IB_4 \leq 3{,}300 \qquad \text{(storage capacity in April)}$$
$$\text{All variables} \geq 0 \qquad \text{(nonnegativity constraints)}$$

The solution was obtained using Solver in Excel 2013, as shown in Program 4. Some of the variables are not integers, but this is not a problem because work in process can be carried over from one month to the next. Table 3 summarizes the solution with the values rounded. The total cost is about $169,295. Greenberg can use this model to develop production schedules again in the future by letting the subscripts on the variables represent new months and making minor changes to the problem. The only things in the model that would have to be changed are the RHS values for the demand constraints (and inventory desired at the end of the fourth month) and the objective function coefficients (costs) if they should change.

PROGRAM 4

Greenberg Motors Solution in Excel 2013

	A1	A2	A3	A4	B1	B2	B3	B4	IA1	IA2	IA3	IA4	IB1	IB2	IB3	IB4			
Greenberg Motors																			
Variable	A1	A2	A3	A4	B1	B2	B3	B4	IA1	IA2	IA3	IA4	IB1	IB2	IB3	IB4	Total Cost		
Solution	1276.9	223.1	1757.7	792.3	1000	2522.2	77.8	1700	476.9	0	757.7	450	0	1322.2	0	300			
Min. Cost	20	20	22	22	15	15	16.5	16.5	0.36	0.36	0.36	0.36	0.26	0.26	0.26	0.26	169294.9		
																	LHS	Sign	RHS
Demand Constraints																			
Jan. GM3A	1								-1								800	=	800
Feb. GM3A		1							1	-1							700	=	700
Mar. GM3A			1							1	-1						1000	=	1000
Apr. GM3A				1							1	-1					1100	=	1100
Jan. GM3B					1								-1				1000	=	1000
Feb. GM3B						1							1	-1			1200	=	1200
Mar. GM3B							1							1	-1		1400	=	1400
Apr. GM3B								1							1	-1	1400	=	1400
Inv.GM3A Apr.												1					450	=	450
Inv.GM3B Apr.																1	300	=	300
Labor Hour Constraints																			
Hrs Min. Jan.	1.3				0.9												2560	≥	2240
Hrs Min. Feb.		1.3				0.9											2560	≥	2240
Hrs Min. Mar.			1.3				0.9										2355	≥	2240
Hrs Min. Apr.				1.3				0.9									2560	≥	2240
Hrs Max. Jan.	1.3				0.9												2560	≤	2560
Hrs Max. Feb.		1.3				0.9											2560	≤	2560
Hrs Max.Mar.			1.3				0.9										2355	≤	2560
Hrs Max. Apr.				1.3				0.9									2560	≤	2560
Storage Constraints																			
Jan. Inv. Limit									1				1				476.92	≤	3300
Feb. Inv. Limit										1				1			1322.22	≤	3300
Mar. Inv. Limit											1				1		757.69	≤	3300
Apr. Inv. Limit												1				1	750	≤	3300

Solver Parameter Inputs and Selections

Set Objective: F5

By Changing cells: B4:Q4

To: Min

Subject to the Constraints:

  R19:R22 >= T19:T22

  R23:R26 <= T23:T26

  R28:R31 <= T28:T31

  R8:R17 = T8:T17

Solving Method: Simplex LP

☑ Make Variables Non-Negative

Key Formulas

	R
4	Total Cost
5	=SUMPRODUCT($B$4:$Q$4,B5:Q5)

Copy formula in R5 to R8:R17
Copy formula in R5 to R19:R26
Copy formula in R5 to R28:R31

TABLE 3

Solution to Greenberg Motors Problem

PRODUCTION SCHEDULE	JANUARY	FEBRUARY	MARCH	APRIL
Units of GM3A produced	1,277	223	1,758	792
Units of GM3B produced	1,000	2,522	78	1,700
Inventory of GM3A carried	477	0	758	450
Inventory of GM3B carried	0	1,322	0	300
Labor hours required	2,560	2,560	2,355	2,560

4 Employee Scheduling Applications

Labor Planning

Labor planning problems address staffing needs over a specific time period. They are especially useful when managers have some flexibility in assigning workers to jobs that require overlapping or interchangeable talents. Large banks frequently use LP to tackle their labor scheduling.

TABLE 4

Hong Kong Bank of Commerce and Industry

TIME PERIOD	NUMBER OF TELLERS REQUIRED
9 A.M.–10 A.M.	10
10 A.M.–11 A.M.	12
11 A.M.–Noon	14
Noon–1 P.M.	16
1 P.M.–2 P.M.	18
2 P.M.–3 P.M.	17
3 P.M.–4 P.M.	15
4 P.M.–5 P.M.	10

Hong Kong Bank of Commerce and Industry is a busy bank that has requirements for between 10 and 18 tellers, depending on the time of day. The lunch time, from noon to 2 P.M., is usually heaviest. Table 4 indicates the workers needed at various hours that the bank is open.

The bank now employs 12 full-time tellers, but many people are on its roster of available part-time employees. A part-time employee must put in exactly four hours per day but can start anytime between 9 A.M. and 1 P.M. Part-timers are a fairly inexpensive labor pool, since no retirement or lunch benefits are provided for them. Full-timers, on the other hand, work from 9 A.M. to 5 P.M. but are allowed 1 hour for lunch. (Half of the full-timers eat at 11 A.M., the other half at noon.) Full-timers thus provide 35 hours per week of productive labor time.

By corporate policy, the bank limits part-time hours to a maximum of 50% of the day's total requirement. Part-timers earn $8 per hour (or $32 per day) on average, and full-timers earn $100 per day in salary and benefits, on average. The bank would like to set a schedule that would minimize its total personnel costs. It will release one or more of its full-time tellers if it is profitable to do so.

In formulating this as an LP, the objective is to minimize cost. There is a constraint for each hour of the day, stating that the number of people working at the bank during that hour should be at least the minimum number shown in Table 4, so there are eight of these constraints. Another constraint will limit the total number of full-time workers to be no more than 12. The last constraint will specify that the number of part-time hours must not exceed 50% of the total hours.

The bank must decide how many full-time tellers to use, so there will be one decision variable for that. Similarly, the bank must decide about using part-time tellers, but this is more complex as the part-time workers can start at different times of the day while all full-time workers start at the beginning of the day. Thus, there must be a variable indicating the number of part-time workers starting at each hour of the day from 9 A.M. until 1 P.M. Any worker who starts at 1 P.M. will work until closing, so there is no need to consider having any part-time workers start after that. Let

$$F = \text{full-time tellers}$$
$$P_1 = \text{part-timers starting at 9 A.M (leaving at 1 P.M.)}$$
$$P_2 = \text{part-timers starting at 10 A.M (leaving at 2 P.M.)}$$
$$P_3 = \text{part-timers starting at 11 A.M (leaving at 3 P.M.)}$$
$$P_4 = \text{part-timers starting at noon (leaving at 4 P.M.)}$$
$$P_5 = \text{part-timers starting at 1 P.M (leaving at 5 P.M.)}$$

Objective function:

$$\text{Minimize total daily personnel cost} = \$100F + \$32(P_1 + P_2 + P_3 + P_4 + P_5)$$

Constraints:

For each hour, the available labor hours must be at least equal to the required labor hours.

$$F + P_1 \geq 10 \quad \text{(9 A.M.–10 A.M. needs)}$$
$$F + P_1 + P_2 \geq 12 \quad \text{(10 A.M.–11 A.M. needs)}$$
$$0.5F + P_1 + P_2 + P_3 \geq 14 \quad \text{(11 A.M.–noon needs)}$$
$$0.5F + P_1 + P_2 + P_3 + P_4 \geq 16 \quad \text{(noon–1 P.M. needs)}$$
$$F + P_2 + P_3 + P_4 + P_5 \geq 18 \quad \text{(1 P.M.–2 P.M. needs)}$$
$$F + P_3 + P_4 + P_5 \geq 17 \quad \text{(2 P.M.–3 P.M. needs)}$$
$$F + P_4 + P_5 \geq 15 \quad \text{(3 P.M.–4 P.M. needs)}$$
$$F + P_5 \geq 10 \quad \text{(4 P.M.–5 P.M. needs)}$$

Only 12 full-time tellers are available, so

$$F \leq 12$$

Part-time worker hours cannot exceed 50% of total hours required each day, which is the sum of the tellers needed each hour:

$$4(P_1 + P_2 + P_3 + P_4 + P_5) \leq 0.50(10 + 12 + 14 + 16 + 18 + 17 + 15 + 10)$$

or

$$4P_1 + 4P_2 + 4P_3 + 4P_4 + 4P_5 \leq 0.50(112)$$
$$F, P_1, P_2, P_3, P_4, P_5 \geq 0$$

Alternate optimal solutions are common in many LP problems. The sequence in which you enter the constraints into QM for Windows can affect the solution found.

Program 5 gives the solution to this, found using Solver in Excel 2013. There are several alternate optimal schedules that Hong Kong Bank can follow. The first is to employ only 10 full-time tellers ($F = 10$) and to start 7 part-timers at 10 A.M. ($P_2 = 7$), 2 part-timers at 11 A.M. ($P_3 = 2$), and 5 part-timers at noon ($P_4 = 5$). No part-timers would begin at 9 A.M. or 1 P.M.

A second solution also employs 10 full-time tellers, but starts 6 part-timers at 9 A.M. ($P_1 = 6$), 1 part-timer at 10 A.M. ($P_2 = 1$), 2 part-timers at 11 A.M. and 5 at noon ($P_3 = 2$ and $P_4 = 5$), and 0 part-timers at 1 P.M. ($P_5 = 0$). The cost of either of these two policies is $1,448 per day.

5 Financial Applications

Portfolio Selection

Maximizing return on investment subject to a set of risk constraints is a popular financial application of LP.

A problem frequently encountered by managers of banks, mutual funds, investment services, and insurance companies is the selection of specific investments from among a wide variety of alternatives. The manager's overall objective is usually to maximize expected return on investment, given a set of legal, policy, or risk restraints.

For example, the International City Trust (ICT) invests in short-term trade credits, corporate bonds, gold stocks, and construction loans. To encourage a diversified portfolio, the board of directors has placed limits on the amount that can be committed to any one type of investment. ICT has $5 million available for immediate investment and wishes to do two things: (1) maximize the return on the investments made over the next six months and (2) satisfy the diversification requirements as set by the board of directors.

PROGRAM 5

Labor Planning Solution in Excel 2013

	A	B	C	D	E	F	G	H	I	J
1	Labor Planning Example									
2										
3										
4	Variables	F	P1	P2	P3	P4	P5			
5	Values	10	0	7	2	5	0	Total Cost		
6	Cost	100	32	32	32	32	32	1448		
7										
8	Constraints							LHS	Sign	RHS
9	9 a.m. - 10 a.m.	1	1					10	≥	10
10	10 a.m. - 11 a.m.	1	1	1				17	≥	12
11	11 a.m. - noon	0.5	1	1	1			14	≥	14
12	noon - 1 p.m.	0.5	1	1	1	1		19	≥	16
13	1 p.m. - 2 p.m.	1		1	1	1	1	24	≥	18
14	2 p.m. - 3 p.m.	1			1	1	1	17	≥	17
15	3 p.m. - 4 p.m.	1				1	1	15	≥	15
16	4 p.m. - 5 p.m.	1					1	10	≥	10
17	Max. Full time	1						10	≤	12
18	Total PT hours		4	4	4	4	4	56	≤	56

Solver Parameter Inputs and Selections

Set Objective: H6

By Changing cells: B5:G5

To: Min

Subject to the Constraints:

   H9:H16 >= J9:J16

   H17:H18 <= J17:J18

Solving Method: Simplex LP

☑ **Make Variables Non-Negative**

Key Formulas

	H
5	Total Cost
6	=SUMPRODUCT($B$5:$G$5,B6:G6)

Copy H6 to H9:H18

The specifics of the investment possibilities are as follows:

INVESTMENT	INTEREST RETURN	MAXIMUM INVESTMENT ($ MILLIONs)
Trade credit	7%	1.0
Corporate bonds	11%	2.5
Gold stocks	19%	1.5
Construction loans	15%	1.8

In addition, the board specifies that at least 55% of the funds invested must be in gold stocks and construction loans, and that no less than 15% be invested in trade credit.

In formulating this as an LP, the objective is to maximize the return. There are four separate constraints limiting the maximum amount in each investment option to the maximum given in the table. The fifth constraint specifies that the total amount in gold stocks and construction loans must be at least 55% of the total amount invested, and the next constraint specifies that the total amount in trade credit must be at least 15% of the total amount invested. The final constraint stipulates that the total amount invested cannot exceed $5 million (it could be less). Define the variables as

X_1 = dollars invested in trade credit

X_2 = dollars invested in corporate bonds

X_3 = dollars invested in gold stocks

X_4 = dollars invested in construction loans

The total amount invested is $X_1 + X_2 + X_3 + X_4$, which may be less than $5 million. This is important when calculating 55% of the total amount invested and 15% of the total amount invested in two of the constraints.

Objective:

$$\text{Maximize dollars of interest earned} = 0.07X_1 + 0.11X_2 + 0.19X_3 + 0.15X_4$$

$$\begin{aligned}
\text{subject to} \quad X_1 &\leq 1{,}000{,}000 \\
X_2 &\leq 2{,}500{,}000 \\
X_3 &\leq 1{,}500{,}000 \\
X_4 &\leq 1{,}800{,}000 \\
X_3 + X_4 &\geq 0.55(X_1 + X_2 + X_3 + X_4) \\
X_1 &\geq 0.15(X_1 + X_2 + X_3 + X_4) \\
X_1 + X_2 + X_3 + X_4 &\leq 5{,}000{,}000 \\
X_1, X_2, X_3, X_4 &\geq 0
\end{aligned}$$

IN ACTION Optimization at UPS

On an average day, UPS delivers 13 million packages to almost 8 million customers in 200 countries and territories. Deliveries are classified as same-day air, next-day air, and second-day air. The next-day air operations average more than 1.1 million packages per day and generate annual revenue of over $5 billion. The company has 256 aircraft and many more on order. During the busiest time of year, between Thanksgiving and New Year's Day, the company leases additional aircraft to meet the demand. The size of its fleet makes UPS the 9th-largest commercial airline in the United States and the 11th-largest commercial airline in the world.

In the next-day delivery operation, the pickup and delivery of packages by UPS involves several stages. Packages are carried by truck to ground centers. From there, the packages are taken to the airport, and then they are flown to one of the airport hubs with at most one stop at another airport to pick up more packages. At the hub, the packages are sorted and loaded onto planes and flown to the destination. Packages are then loaded on large trucks and taken to ground centers. At the ground centers, additional sorting is done, packages are put on smaller trucks, and the packages are delivered to their final destinations before 10:30 A.M. The same aircraft are used in the second-day

deliveries as well, so these two types of operations must be coordinated.

A team from UPS and Massachusetts Institute of Technology worked together to develop an optimization-based planning system called VOLCANO (Volume, Location, and Aircraft Network Optimizer) that is used for planning and managing operations. This group developed optimization methods to minimize overall cost (ownership and operating) while meeting capacity and service standard constraints. Mathematical models are used to determine the minimum cost set of routes, fleet assignments, and package flows. Constraints include the number of aircraft, landing restrictions at airports, and aircraft operating characteristics (such as speed, capacity, and range).

The VOLCANO system is credited with saving over $87 million from late in 2000 to the end of 2002. It is expected that $189 million will be saved over the next decade. This optimizer is also used to identify the needed fleet composition and recommend future aircraft acquisitions.

Source: Based on Andrew P. Armacost, Cynthia Barnhart, Keith A. Ware, and Alysia M. Wilson. "UPS Optimizes Its Air Network," *Interfaces* 34, 1 (January–February 2004): 15–25.

PROGRAM 6

ICT Portfolio Solution in Excel 2013

	A	B	C	D	E	F	G	H
1	ICT Portfolio Selection							
2								
3	Variable	X1	X2	X3	X4			
4	Solution	750000	950000	1500000	1800000	Total Return		
5	Max. Return	0.07	0.11	0.19	0.15	712000		
6								
7						LHS		RHS
8	Trade	1				750000	≤	1,000,000
9	Bonds		1			950000	≤	2,500,000
10	Gold			1		1500000	≤	1,500,000
11	Construction				1	1800000	≤	1,800,000
12	Min. Gold+Const	-0.55	-0.55	0.45	0.45	550000	≥	0
13	Min. Trade	0.85	-0.15	-0.15	-0.15	0	≥	0
14	Total Invested	1	1	1	1	5000000	≤	5000000

Solver Parameter Inputs and Selections

Set Objective: F5

By Changing cells: B4:E4

To: Min

Subject to the Constraints:

F8:F11 <= H8:H11

F12:F13 >= H12:H13

F14 <= H14

Solving Method: Simplex LP

☑ Make Variables Non-Negative

Key Formulas

	F
4	Total Return
5	=SUMPRODUCT($B$4:$E$4,B5:E5)

Copy F5 to F8:F14

Program 6 shows the solution found using Solver in Excel. ICT maximizes its interest earned by making the following investment: $X_1 = \$750,000$, $X_2 = \$950,000$, $X_3 = \$1,500,000$, and $X_4 = \$1,800,000$, and the total interest earned is $712,000.

Truck Loading Problem

The truck loading problem involves deciding which items to load on a truck so as to maximize the value of a load shipped. As an example, we consider Goodman Shipping, an Orlando firm owned by Steven Goodman. One of his trucks, with a capacity of 10,000 pounds, is about to be loaded.* Awaiting shipment are the following items:

ITEM	VALUE ($)	WEIGHT (POUNDS)
1	22,500	7,500
2	24,000	7,500
3	8,000	3,000
4	9,500	3,500
5	11,500	4,000
6	9,750	3,500

*Adapted from an example in S. L. Savage. *What's Best!* Oakland, CA: General Optimization, Inc., and Holden-Day, 1985.

Each of these six items, we see, has an associated dollar value and weight.

The objective is to maximize the total value of the items loaded onto the truck without exceeding the truck's weight capacity. We let X_i be the proportion of each item i loaded on the truck:

$$\text{Maximize load value} = \$22{,}500X_1 + \$24{,}000X_2 + \$8{,}000X_3 + \$9{,}500X_4 \\ + \$11{,}500X_5 + \$9{,}750X_6$$

$$\text{subject to} \quad 7{,}500X_1 + 7{,}500X_2 + 3{,}000X_3 + 3{,}500X_4 + 4{,}000X_5 \\ + 3{,}500X_6 \leq 10{,}000 \text{ lb capacity}$$

$$X_1 \leq 1$$
$$X_2 \leq 1$$
$$X_3 \leq 1$$
$$X_4 \leq 1$$
$$X_5 \leq 1$$
$$X_6 \leq 1$$
$$X_1, X_2, X_3, X_4, X_5, X_6 \geq 0$$

These final six constraints reflect the fact that at most one "unit" of an item can be loaded onto the truck. In effect, if Goodman can load a *portion* of an item (say, item 1 is a batch of 1,000 folding chairs, not all of which need be shipped together), the X_is will all be proportions ranging from 0 (nothing) to 1 (all of that item loaded).

To solve this LP problem, we turn to Excel's Solver. Program 7 shows Goodman's Excel formulation, input data, and the solution, which yields a total load value of $31,500.

What does Goodman do if fractional values of items cannot be loaded? For example, if luxury cars were the items being loaded, we clearly cannot ship one-third of a Maserati.

PROGRAM 7

Goodman Truck Loading Solution in Excel

	A	B	C	D	E	F	G	H	I	J
1	Goodman Shipping									
2										
3	Variables	X1	X2	X3	X4	X5	X6			
4	Values	0.3333	1	0	0	0	0	Total Value		
5	Load Value $	22500	24000	8000	9500	11500	9750	31500		
6										
7	Constraints							LHS	Sign	RHS
8	Total weight	7500	7500	3000	3500	4000	3500	10000	≤	10000
9	% Item 1	1						0.3333333	≤	1
10	% Item 2		1					1	≤	1
11	% Item 3			1				0	≤	1
12	% Item 4				1			0	≤	1
13	% Item 5					1		0	≤	1
14	% Item 6						1	0	≤	1

Solver Parameter Inputs and Selections

Set Objective: H5

By Changing cells: B4:G4

To: Min

Subject to the Constraints:

H8:H14 <= J8:J14

Solving Method: Simplex LP

☑ **Make Variables Non-Negative**

Key Formulas

	H
4	Total Value
5	=SUMPRODUCT($B$4:$G$4,B5:G5)

Copy H5 to H8:H14

If the proportion of item 1 was rounded up to 1.00, the weight of the load would increase to 15,000 pounds. This would violate the 10,000 pounds maximum weight constraint. Therefore, the fraction of item 1 must be rounded down to zero. This would drop the value of the load to 7,500 pounds, leaving 2,500 pounds of the load capacity unused. Because no other item weighs less than 2,500 pounds, the truck cannot be filled up further.

Thus, we see that by using regular LP and rounding the fractional weights, the truck would carry only item 2, for a load weight of 7,500 pounds and a load value of $24,000.

QM for Windows and spreadsheet optimizers such as Excel's Solver are capable of dealing with *integer programming* problems as well; that is, LP problems requiring integer solutions. Using Excel, the integer solution to Goodman's problem is to load items 3, 4, and 6, for a total weight of 10,000 pounds and load value of $27,250.

6 Ingredient Blending Applications

Diet Problems

The diet problem, one of the earliest applications of LP, was originally used by hospitals to determine the most economical diet for patients. Known in agricultural applications as the feed mix problem, the diet problem involves specifying a food or feed ingredient combination that satisfies stated nutritional requirements at a minimum cost level.

The Whole Food Nutrition Center uses three bulk grains to blend a natural cereal that it sells by the pound. The cost of each bulk grain and the protein, riboflavin, phosphorus, and magnesium units per pound of each are shown in Table 5.

On the packaging for each of its products, Whole Food indicates the nutritional content in each bowl of cereal when eaten with 0.5 cup of milk. The USRDA (U.S. Recommended Dietary Allowance) and the more recent DRI (Dietary Reference Intake) were consulted to establish recommended amounts of certain vitamins and minerals for an average adult. Based on these figures and the desired amounts for labeling on the package, Whole Food has determined that each 2-ounce serving of the cereal should contain 3 units of protein, 2 units of riboflavin, 1 unit of phosphorous, and 0.425 unit of magnesium.

In modeling this as an LP, the objective is to minimize cost. There will be four constraints (one each for protein, riboflavin, phosphorous, and magnesium) stipulating that the number of units must be at least the minimum amount specified. Since these requirements are for each 2 ounce serving, the last constraint must say that the total amount of the grains used will be 2 ounces, or 0.125 pound.

In defining the variables, notice that the cost is expressed per pound of the three grains. Thus, in order to calculate the total cost, we must know the number of pounds of the grains used in one serving of the cereal. Also, the numbers in Table 5 are expressed in units per pound of grain, so defining variables as the number of pounds of the grains makes it easier to calculate the amounts of protein, riboflavin, phosphorous, and magnesium. We let

X_A = pounds of grain A in one 2-ounce serving of cereal

X_B = pounds of grain B in one 2-ounce serving of cereal

X_C = pounds of grain C in one 2-ounce serving of cereal

TABLE 5 Whole Food's Natural Cereal Requirements

GRAIN	COST PER POUND (CENTS)	PROTEIN (UNITS/LB)	RIBOFLAVIN (UNITS/LB)	PHOSPHORUS (UNITS/LB)	MAGNESIUM (UNITS/LB)
A	33	22	16	8	5
B	47	28	14	7	0
C	38	21	25	9	6

Objective function:

Minimize total cost of mixing a 2-ounce serving = $\$0.33X_A + \$0.47X_B + \$0.38X_C$
subject to

$$22X_A + 28X_B + 21X_C \geq 3 \qquad \text{(protein units)}$$
$$16X_A + 14X_B + 25X_C \geq 2 \qquad \text{(riboflavin units)}$$
$$8X_A + 7X_B + 9X_C \geq 1 \qquad \text{(phosphorus units)}$$
$$5X_A + 0X_B + 6X_C \geq 0.425 \quad \text{(magnesium units)}$$
$$X_A + X_B + X_C = 0.125 \quad \text{(total mix is 2 ounces or 0.125 pound)}$$
$$X_A, X_B, X_C \geq 0$$

The solution to this problem requires mixing together 0.025 lb of grain A, 0.050 lb of grain B, and 0.050 lb of grain C. Another way of stating the solution is in terms of the proportion of the 2-ounce serving of each grain, namely, 0.4 ounce of grain A, 0.8 ounce of grain B, and 0.8 ounce of grain C in each serving. The cost per serving is $0.05. Program 8 illustrates this solution using Solver in Excel 2013.

Ingredient Mix and Blending Problems

Diet and feed mix problems are actually special cases of a more general class of LP problems known as *ingredient* or *blending problems*. Blending problems arise when a decision must be made regarding the blending of two or more resources to produce one or more products. Resources, in this case, contain one or more essential ingredients that must be blended so that each final product contains specific percentages of each ingredient. The following example deals with an application frequently seen in the petroleum industry, the blending of crude oils to produce refinable gasoline.

PROGRAM 8
Whole Food Diet Solution in Excel 2013

	A	B	C	D	E	F	G
1	Whole Foods Nutrition Problem						
2							
3		Grain A	Grain B	Grain C			
4	Variable	Xa	Xb	Xc			
5	Solution	0.025	0.05	0.05	Total Cost		
6	Minimize	0.33	0.47	0.38	0.05075		
7							
8	Constraints				LHS	Sign	RHS
9	Protein	22	28	21	3	≥	3
10	Riboflavin	16	14	25	2.35	≥	2
11	Phosphorus	8	7	9	1	≥	1
12	Magnesium	5	0	6	0.425	≥	0.425
13	Total Weight	1	1	1	0.125	=	0.125

Solver Parameter Inputs and Selections

Set Objective: E6

By Changing cells: B5:D5

To: Min

Subject to the Constraints:

  E9:E12 <= G9:G12

  E13 = G13

Solving Method: Simplex LP

☑ **Make Variables Non-Negative**

Key Formulas

	E
5	Total Cost
6	=SUMPRODUCT($B$5:$D$5,B6:D6)

Copy E6 to E9:E13

The Low Knock Oil Company produces two grades of cut-rate gasoline for industrial distribution. The grades, regular and economy, are produced by refining a blend of two types of crude oil, type X100 and type X220. Each crude oil differs not only in cost per barrel, but in composition as well. The following table indicates the percentage of crucial ingredients found in each of the crude oils and the cost per barrel for each:

CRUDE OIL TYPE	INGREDIENT A (%)	INGREDIENT B (%)	COST/BARREL ($)
X100	35	55	30.00
X220	60	25	34.80

Weekly demand for the regular grade of Low Knock gasoline is at least 25,000 barrels, and demand for the economy is at least 32,000 barrels per week. *At least* 45% of each barrel of regular must be ingredient A. *At most* 50% of each barrel of economy should contain ingredient B. While the gasoline yield from one barrel of crude depends on the type of crude and the type of processing used, we will assume for the sake of this example that one barrel of crude oil will yield one barrel of gasoline.

The Low Knock management must decide how many barrels of each type of crude oil to buy each week for blending to satisfy demand at minimum cost. In modeling this as an LP, the objective is to minimize cost. Each of the two types of gasoline has a demand constraint, and each of the two types of gasoline has a constraint restricting the amount of the ingredients. Thus, there are four constraints. The decisions involve the amount of each type of crude to use in each type of gasoline, so these will be the decision variables. Let

$$X_1 = \text{barrels of crude X100 blended to produce the refined regular}$$
$$X_2 = \text{barrels of crude X100 blended to produce the refined economy}$$
$$X_3 = \text{barrels of crude X220 blended to produce the refined regular}$$
$$X_4 = \text{barrels of crude X220 blended to produce the refined economy}$$

This problem can be formulated as follows:

Objective:

$$\text{Minimize cost} = \$30X_1 + \$30X_2 + \$34.80X_3 + \$34.80X_4$$

subject to

$$X_1 + X_3 \geq 25,000 \quad \text{(demand for regular)}$$
$$X_2 + X_4 \geq 32,000 \quad \text{(demand for economy)}$$

At least 45% of each barrel of regular must be ingredient A:

$$(X_1 + X_3) = \text{total amount of crude blended to produce the refined regular}$$
$$\text{gasoline demand}$$

Thus,

$$0.45(X_1 + X_3) = \text{minimum amount of ingredient A required}$$

But

$$0.35X_1 + 0.60X_3 = \text{amount of ingredient A in refined regular gas}$$

So

$$0.35X_1 + 0.60X_3 \geq 0.45X_1 + 0.45X_3$$

or

$$-0.10X_1 + 0.15X_3 \geq 0 \quad \text{(ingredient A in regular constraint)}$$

Similarly, at most 50% of each barrel of economy should be ingredient B:

$$X_2 + X_4 = \text{total amount of crude blended to produce the refined economy gasoline demanded}$$

Thus,

$$0.50(X_2 + X_4) = \text{maximum amount of ingredient B allowed}$$

But

$$0.55X_2 + 0.25X_4 = \text{amount of ingredient B in refined economy gas}$$

So

$$0.55X_2 + 0.25X_4 \leq 0.50X_2 + 0.50X_4$$

or

$$0.05X_2 - 0.25X_4 \leq 0 \text{ (ingredient B in economy constraint)}$$

Here is the entire LP formulation:

$$\text{Minimize cost} = 30X_1 + 30X_2 + 34.80X_3 + 34.80X_4$$

$$
\begin{aligned}
\text{subject to} \quad X_1 \qquad\quad + \quad X_3 \qquad\qquad &\geq 25{,}000 \\
X_2 + \qquad\qquad X_4 &\geq 32{,}000 \\
-0.10X_1 \qquad\quad + \; 0.15X_3 \qquad\qquad &\geq 0 \\
0.05X_2 \qquad\quad - \; 0.25X_4 &\leq 0 \\
X_1, X_2, X_3, X_4 &\geq 0
\end{aligned}
$$

Using Excel, the solution to Low Knock Oil's formulation was found to be

$$X_1 = 15{,}000 \text{ barrels of X100 into regular}$$
$$X_2 = 26{,}666.67 \text{ barrels of X100 into economy}$$
$$X_3 = 10{,}000 \text{ barrels of X220 into regular}$$
$$X_4 = 5{,}333.33 \text{ barrels of X220 into economy}$$

The cost of this mix is $1,783,600. Refer to Program 9 for details.

7 Other Linear Programming Applications

There are many other types of linear programming applications. One particular application was first developed and used by American Airlines in the early 1990s, and it is called revenue management. This was designed to use differential pricing for seats so that additional revenue could be obtained. Some customers who were willing to book with certain restrictions, such as 14-day advance purchase or with a stay over a Saturday night, would receive lower fares. However, if all seats are sold at this reduced cost, then higher paying passengers, often business travelers who might try to book seats at the last minute, would not be able to do so. The extra revenue generated from these passengers is then lost. A revenue management system was developed to determine how many seats to make available to each type of passenger. Linear programs would have an objective of maximizing the total revenue, while constraints would be based on the number of total seats available on the plane and the number of seats allocated to each category. Companies have reported dramatic increases in revenues as a result of this.

Given the success of revenue management systems in the airlines industry, similar systems were also adopted by many hotel chains. The airline industry and the hotel industry have products with similar characteristics—a limited inventory of a very perishable

PROGRAM 9

Low Knock Oil Solution in Excel 2013

	A	B	C	D	E	F	G	H
1	Low Knock Oil Company							
2								
3		X100 Reg	X100 Econ	X220 Reg	X220 Econ			
4	Variable	X1	X2	X3	X4			
5	Solution	15000	26666.67	10000	5333.33	Total Cost		
6	Cost	30	30	34.8	34.8	1783600		
7								
8	Constraints					LHS	Sign	RHS
9	Demand Regular	1		1		25000	≥	25000
10	Demand Economy		1		1	32000	≥	32000
11	Ing. A in Regular	-0.1		0.15		0	≥	0
12	Ing. B in Economy		0.05		-0.25	0	≤	0

Solver Parameter Inputs and Selections

Set Objective: F6

By Changing cells: B5:E5

To: Min

Subject to the Constraints:

> **F9:F11 >= H9:H11**

> **F12 <= H12**

Solving Method: Simplex LP

☑ **Make Variables Non-Negative**

Key Formulas

	F
5	Total Cost
6	=SUMPRODUCT($B$5:$E$5,B6:E6)

Copy F6 to F9:F12

product. A plane has a limited number of seats, and when the plane takes off, any empty seats can no longer be sold and the revenue is lost. A hotel has a limited number of rooms, and once a particular date has passed, an empty room on that date cannot be sold and the revenue is lost.

Another common type of application is data envelopment analysis (DEA). This is sometimes used to measure the efficiency of several similar operating units such as hospitals or schools. It is often used with nonprofit entities where measuring the success of a particular unit is difficult as there is no single objective, such as profit, that is to be optimized. In developing the LP, the inputs and outputs of the particular system must be identified. For a hospital system, the inputs might be the number of doctors working, the number of nurses working, the number of bed-day available per year, and the total payroll. The outputs might be the number of patient-days in the hospital, the number of nurses trained, the number of surgeries performed, the number of outpatient procedures performed, and the number of doctors trained. Constraints are developed for each of these inputs and outputs for each unit in the system. The objective is basically to minimize the resources needed to generate specific levels of output. The results indicate whether fewer resources could have been used to generate the same level of outputs when compared to a typical unit in the system. Efforts can then be made to identify specific areas that are deemed to be potentially inefficient, and improvements can be targeted for these areas.

Transportation problems, transshipment problems, and assignment problems are very widely used in business. These are so common that special purpose algorithms have been developed to solve these more quickly than the current procedures used for other type of linear programming problems.

Q.A. IN ACTION — Harrah's Cherokee Casino Uses Linear Programming for Revenue Management

Identifying the customers who would generate the most revenue is usually very difficult, but Harrah's Cherokee Casino has benefited from a unique way of placing customers into particular market segments based on spending habits. Harrah's encourages casino customers to join their Total Rewards club. Points in this club are earned each time the member plays a casino game or spends money in a restaurant, spa, gift shop, or hotel facility. Earning points entitles players to receive benefits such as free or discounted rooms, meals, show tickets, and other things. Tracking the size of the bets as well as the number of bets allows Harrah's to place the players in segments based on the amount that they typically play when visiting the casinos. The best revenue generators are guests who typically gamble more money during each day of their stay. When a player tries to reserve a room, a low-spending player might be told there are no rooms available, while a high-spending customer will get to reserve the room. To promote goodwill, the customer in the lower-spending segment might be offered a free room at a nearby hotel. The additional revenue that will be obtained by reserving the room for a high-roller will more than offset this cost.

An LP is used to maximize the revenue generated subject to the total number of rooms available and the total number of rooms that are allocated to each segment of customers. The variables include the number of rooms to make available for each segment. The shadow prices of the constraints indicate how much extra revenue will be generated if one additional room is made available to the different segments. The model is frequently updated based on the number of rooms still available, the number of days remaining until the date of the reservation, and other factors. Based on results from this model, marketing efforts are targeted for very specific Total Rewards members when it appears that hotel traffic might be light on a particular day.

While revenue management implementations typically increase revenue by 3–7%, Harrah's has experienced a 15% increase in revenues from the revenue management systems throughout its many hotels and casinos. At Harrah's Cherokee Casino, the hotel opened with the system already in place so there is no basis for comparison. However, the profit margin of this particular property is 60% on gross revenue, which is twice the industry average.

Source: Based on Metters, Richard, et al. "The 'Killer Application' of Revenue Management: Harrah's Cherokee Casino & Hotel," *Interfaces* 38, 3 (May–June 2008): 161–175.

Summary

In this chapter we discussed linear programming models. The basic steps for formulating a linear program were followed for a variety of problems. These included applications in marketing, production scheduling, finance, and ingredient blending.

Attention was paid to understanding the problem, identifying the objective and the constraints, defining the decision variables, and developing the mathematical model from these.

Self-Test

- Before taking the self-test, refer to the learning objectives at the beginning of the chapter, the notes in the margins, and the glossary at the end of the chapter.
- Use the key at the end of the chapter to correct your answers.
- Restudy pages that correspond to any questions that you answered incorrectly or material you feel uncertain about.

1. Linear programming can be used to select effective media mixes, allocate fixed or limited budgets across media, and maximize audience exposure.
   a. True
   b. False
2. Using LP to maximize audience exposure in an advertising campaign is an example of the type of LP application known as
   a. marketing research.
   b. media selection.
   c. portfolio assessment.
   d. media budgeting.
   e. all of the above.
3. Which of the following *does not* represent a factor manager might consider when employing LP for production scheduling:
   a. labor capacity
   b. space limitations
   c. product demand
   d. risk assessment
   e. inventory costs

4. When applying LP to diet problems, the objective function is usually designed to
   a. maximize profits from blends of nutrients.
   b. maximize ingredient blends.
   c. minimize production losses.
   d. maximize the number of products to be produced.
   e. minimize the costs of nutrient blends.
5. The diet problem is
   a. also called the feed mix problem in agriculture.
   b. a special case of the ingredient mix problem.

c. a special case of the blending problem.
d. all of the above.
6. The selection of specific investments from among a wide variety of alternatives is the type of LP problem known as
   a. the product mix problem.
   b. the investment banker problem.
   c. the portfolio selection problem.
   d. the Wall Street problem.
   e. none of the above.

Problems

1 **(Production problem)** Winkler Furniture manufactures two different types of china cabinets: a French Provincial model and a Danish Modern model. Each cabinet produced must go through three departments: carpentry, painting, and finishing. The table below contains all relevant information concerning production times per cabinet produced and production capacities for each operation per day, along with net revenue per unit produced. The firm has a contract with an Indiana distributor to produce a minimum of 300 of each cabinet per week (or 60 cabinets per day). Owner Bob Winkler would like to determine a product mix to maximize his daily revenue.
(a) Formulate as an LP problem.
(b) Solve using an LP software program or spreadsheet.

2 **(Investment decision problem)** The Heinlein and Krampf Brokerage firm has just been instructed by one of its clients to invest $250,000 of her money obtained recently through the sale of land holdings in Ohio. The client has a good deal of trust in the investment house, but she also has her own ideas about the distribution of the funds being invested. In particular, she requests that the firm select whatever stocks and bonds they believe are well rated, but within the following guidelines:

(a) Municipal bonds should constitute at least 20% of the investment.
(b) At least 40% of the funds should be placed in a combination of electronic firms, aerospace firms, and drug manufacturers.
(c) No more than 50% of the amount invested in municipal bonds should be placed in a high-risk, high-yield nursing home stock.

Subject to these restraints, the client's goal is to maximize projected return on investments. The analysts at Heinlein and Krampf, aware of these guidelines, prepare a list of high-quality stocks and bonds and their corresponding rates of return:

INVESTMENT	PROJECTED RATE OF RETURN (%)
Los Angeles municipal bonds	5.3
Thompson Electronics, Inc.	6.8
United Aerospace Corp.	4.9
Palmer Drugs	8.4
Happy Days Nursing Homes	11.8

(a) Formulate this portfolio selection problem using LP.
(b) Solve this problem.

Data for Problem 1

CABINET STYLE	CARPENTRY (HOURS/ CABINET)	PAINTING (HOURS/ CABINET)	FINISHING (HOURS/ CABINET)	NET REVENUE/ CABINET ($)
French Provincial	3	1.5	0.75	28
Danish Modern	2	1	0.75	25
Department capacity (hours)	360	200	125	

Note: ☯ means the problem may be solved with QM for Windows; ✕ means the problem may be solved with Excel; and ☯ means the problem may be solved with QM for Windows and/or Excel.

276

3 *(Restaurant work scheduling problem).* The famous Y. S. Chang Restaurant is open 24 hours a day. Waiters and busboys report for duty at 3 A.M., 7 A.M., 11 A.M., 3 P.M., 7 P.M., or 11 P.M., and each works an 8-hour shift. The following table shows the minimum number of workers needed during the six periods into which the day is divided. Chang's scheduling problem is to determine how many waiters and busboys should report for work at the start of each time period to minimize the total staff required for one day's operation. (*Hint:* Let X_i equal the number of waiters and busboys beginning work in time period i, where $i = 1, 2, 3, 4, 5, 6.$)

PERIOD	TIME	NUMBER OF WAITERS AND BUSBOYS REQUIRED
1	3 A.M.–7 A.M.	3
2	7 A.M.–11 A.M.	12
3	11 A.M.–3 P.M.	16
4	3 P.M.–7 P.M.	9
5	7 P.M.–11 P.M.	11
6	11 P.M.–3 A.M.	4

4 *(Animal feed mix problem)* The Battery Park Stable feeds and houses the horses used to pull tourist-filled carriages through the streets of Charleston's historic waterfront area. The stable owner, an ex-racehorse trainer, recognizes the need to set a nutritional diet for the horses in his care. At the same time, he would like to keep the overall daily cost of feed to a minimum.

The feed mixes available for the horses' diet are an oat product, a highly enriched grain, and a mineral product. Each of these mixes contains a certain amount of five ingredients needed daily to keep the average horse healthy. The table on this page shows these minimum requirements, units of each ingredient per pound of feed mix, and costs for the three mixes.

In addition, the stable owner is aware that an overfed horse is a sluggish worker. Consequently, he determines that 6 pounds of feed per day are the most that any horse needs to function properly. Formulate this problem and solve for the optimal daily mix of the three feeds.

5 The Kleenglass Corporation makes a dishwasher that has excellent cleaning power. This dishwasher uses less water than most competitors, and it is extremely quiet. Orders have been received from several retails stores for delivery at the end of each of the next 3 months, as shown below:

MONTH	NUMBER OF UNITS
June	195
July	215
August	205

Due to limited capacity, only 200 of these can be made each month on regular time, and the cost is $300 each. However, an extra 15 units per month can be produced if overtime is used, but the cost goes up to $325 each. Also, if there are any dishwashers produced in a month that are not sold in that month, there is a $20 cost to carry this item to the next month. Use linear programming to determine how many units to produce in each month on regular time and on overtime to minimize the total cost while meeting the demands.

6 Eddie Kelly is running for reelection as mayor of a small town in Alabama. Jessica Martinez, Kelly's campaign manager during this election, is planning the marketing campaign, and there is some stiff competition. Martinez has selected four ways to advertise: television ads, radio ads, billboards,

Data for Problem 4

DIET REQUIREMENT (INGREDIENTS)	OAT PRODUCT (UNITS/LB)	ENRICHED GRAIN (UNITS/LB)	MINERAL PRODUCT (UNITS/LB)	MINIMUM DAILY REQUIREMENT (UNITS)
A	2	3	1	6
B	0.5	1	0.5	2
C	3	5	6	9
D	1	1.5	2	8
E	0.5	0.5	1.5	5
Cost/lb	$0.09	$0.14	$0.17	

and newspaper ads. The costs of these, the audience reached by each type of ad, and the maximum number available is shown in the following table:

TYPE OF AD	COST PER AD	AUDIENCE REACHED/AD	MAXIMUM NUMBER
TV	$800	30,000	10
Radio	$400	22,000	10
Billboards	$500	24,000	10
Newspapers	$100	8,000	10

In addition, Martinez has decided that there should be at least six ads on TV or radio or some combination of those two. The amount spent on billboards and newspapers together must not exceed the amount spent on TV ads. While fundraising is still continuing, the monthly budget for advertising has been set at $15,000. How many ads of each type should be placed to maximize the total number of people reached?

7 **(Media selection problem)** The advertising director for Diversey Paint and Supply, a chain of four retail stores on Chicago's North Side, is considering two media possibilities. One plan is for a series of half-page ads in the Sunday *Chicago Tribune* newspaper, and the other is for advertising time on Chicago TV. The stores are expanding their lines of do-it-yourself tools, and the advertising director is interested in an exposure level of at least 40% within the city's neighborhoods and 60% in northwest suburban areas.

The TV viewing time under consideration has an exposure rating per spot of 5% in city homes and 3% in the northwest suburbs. The Sunday newspaper has corresponding exposure rates of 4% and 3% per ad. The cost of a half-page *Tribune* advertisement is $925; a television spot costs $2,000.

Diversey Paint would like to select the least costly advertising strategy that would meet desired exposure levels.
(a) Formulate using LP.
(b) Solve the problem.

8 **(Automobile leasing problem)** Sundown Rent-a-Car, a large automobile rental agency operating in the Midwest, is preparing a leasing strategy for the next six months. Sundown leases cars from an automobile manufacturer and then rents them to the public on a daily basis. A forecast of the demand for Sundown's cars in the next six months follows:

MONTH	MARCH	APRIL	MAY	JUNE	JULY	AUGUST
Demand	420	400	430	460	470	440

Cars may be leased from the manufacturer for either three, four, or five months. These are leased on the first day of the month and are returned on the last day of the month. Every six months the automobile

manufacturer is notified by Sundown about the number of cars needed during the next six months. The automobile manufacturer has stipulated that at least 50% of the cars leased during a six-month period must be on the five-month lease. The cost per month on each of the three types of leases are $420 for the three-month lease, $400 for the four-month lease, and $370 for the five-month lease.

Currently, Sundown has 390 cars. The lease on 120 cars expires at the end of March. The lease on another 140 cars expires at the end of April, and the lease on the rest of these expires at the end of May.

Use LP to determine how many cars should be leased in each month on each type of lease to minimize the cost of leasing over the six-month period. How many cars are left at the end of August?

9 Management of Sundown Rent-a-Car (see Problem 8) has decided that perhaps the cost during the six-month period is not the appropriate cost to minimize because the agency may still be obligated to additional months on some leases after that time. For example, if Sundown had some cars delivered at the beginning of the sixth month, Sundown would still be obligated for two additional months on a three-month lease. Use LP to determine how many cars should be leased in each month on each type of lease to minimize the cost of leasing over the entire life of these leases.

10 **(High school busing problem)** The Arden County, Maryland, superintendent of education is responsible for assigning students to the *three* high schools in his county. He recognizes the need to bus a certain number of students, for several sectors of the county are beyond walking distance to a school. The superintendent partitions the county into *five* geographic sectors as he attempts to establish a plan that will minimize the total number of student miles traveled by bus. He also recognizes that if a student happens to live in a certain sector and is assigned to the high school in that sector, there is no need to bus that student because he or she can walk to school. The three schools are located in sectors B, C, and E.

The following table reflects the number of high-school-age students living in each sector and the busing distance in miles from each sector to each school:

	DISTANCE TO SCHOOL			
SECTOR	SCHOOL IN SECTOR B	SCHOOL IN SECTOR C	SCHOOL IN SECTOR E	NUMBER OF STUDENTS
A	5	8	6	700
B	0	4	12	500
C	4	0	7	100
D	7	2	5	800
E	12	7	0	400
				2,500

Each high school has a capacity of 900 students. Set up the objective function and constraints of this problem using LP so that the total number of student miles traveled by bus is minimized. Then solve the problem.

11 **(Pricing and marketing strategy problem)** The I. Kruger Paint and Wallpaper Store is a large retail distributor of the Supertrex brand of vinyl wallcoverings. Kruger will enhance its citywide image in Miami if it can outsell other local stores in total number of rolls of Supertrex next year. It is able to estimate the demand function as follows:

Number of rolls of Supertrex sold = 20 × Dollars spent on advertising + 6.8 × Dollars spent on in-store displays + 12 × Dollars invested in on-hand wallpaper inventory − 65,000 × Percentage markup taken above wholesale cost of a roll

The store budgets a total of $17,000 for advertising, in-store displays, and on-hand inventory of Supertrex for next year. It decides it must spend at least $3,000 on advertising; in addition, at least 5% of the amount invested in on-hand inventory should be devoted to displays. Markups on Supertrex seen at other local stores range from 20% to 45%. Kruger decides that its markup had best be in this range as well.
(a) Formulate as an LP problem.
(b) Solve the problem.
(c) What is the difficulty with the answer?
(d) What constraint would you add?

12 **(College meal selection problem)** Kathy Roniger, campus dietitian for a small Idaho college, is responsible for formulating a nutritious meal plan for students. For an evening meal, she feels that the following five meal-content requirements should be met: (1) between 900 and 1,500 calories; (2) at least 4 milligrams of iron; (3) no more than 50 grams of fat; (4) at least 26 grams of protein; and (5) no more than 50 grams of carbohydrates. On a particular day, Roniger's food stock includes seven items that can be prepared and served for supper to meet these requirements. The cost per pound for each food item and the contribution to each of the five nutritional requirements are given in the table below.

What combination and amounts of food items will provide the nutrition Roniger requires at the least total food cost?
(a) Formulate as an LP problem.
(b) What is the cost per meal?
(c) Is this a well-balanced diet?

13 **(High-tech production problem)** Quitmeyer Electronics Incorporated manufactures the following six microcomputer peripheral devices: internal modems, external modems, graphics circuit boards, CD drives, hard disk drives, and memory expansion boards. Each of these technical products requires time, in minutes, on three types of electronic testing equipment, as shown in the table below.

The first two test devices are available 120 hours per week. The third (device 3) requires more preventive maintenance and may be used only

Data for Problem 12

TABLE OF FOOD VALUES AND COSTS

FOOD ITEM	CALORIES/ LB	IRON (MG/LB)	FAT (GM/LB)	PROTEIN (GM/LB)	CARBOHYDRATES (GM/LB)	COST/ LB ($)
Milk	295	0.2	16	16	22	0.60
Ground meat	1216	0.2	96	81	0	2.35
Chicken	394	4.3	9	74	0	1.15
Fish	358	3.2	0.5	83	0	2.25
Beans	128	3.2	0.8	7	28	0.58
Spinach	118	14.1	1.4	14	19	1.17
Potatoes	279	2.2	0.5	8	63	0.33

Source: Pennington, Jean A. T., and Judith S. Douglass. Bowes and Church's Food Values of Portions Commonly Used, 18th ed., Philadelphia: Lippincott Williams & Wilkins, 2004, pp. 100–130.

Data for Problem 13

	INTERNAL MODEM	EXTERNAL MODEM	CIRCUIT BOARD	CD DRIVES	HARD DRIVES	MEMORY BOARDS
Test device 1	7	3	12	6	18	17
Test device 2	2	5	3	2	15	17
Test device 3	5	1	3	2	9	2

100 hours each week. The market for all six computer components is vast, and Quitmeyer Electronics believes that it can sell as many units of each product as it can manufacture. The table that follows summarizes the revenues and material costs for each product:

DEVICE	REVENUE PER UNIT SOLD ($)	MATERIAL COST PER UNIT ($)
Internal modem	200	35
External modem	120	25
Graphics circuit board	180	40
CD drive	130	45
Hard disk drive	430	170
Memory expansion board	260	60

In addition, variable labor costs are $15 per hour for test device 1, $12 per hour for test device 2, and $18 per hour for test device 3. Quitmeyer Electronics wants to maximize its profits.
(a) Formulate this problem as an LP model.
(b) Solve the problem by computer. What is the best product mix?
(c) What is the value of an additional minute of time per week on test device 1? Test device 2? Test device 3? Should Quitmeyer Electronics add more test device time? If so, on which equipment?

14 (*Nuclear plant staffing problem*) South Central Utilities has just announced the August 1 opening of its second nuclear generator at its Baton Rouge, Louisiana, nuclear power plant. Its personnel department has been directed to determine how many nuclear technicians need to be hired and trained over the remainder of the year.

The plant currently employs 350 fully trained technicians and projects the following personnel needs:

MONTH	PERSONNEL HOURS NEEDED
August	40,000
September	45,000
October	35,000
November	50,000
December	45,000

By Louisiana law, a reactor employee can actually work no more than 130 hours per month. (Slightly over 1 hour per day is used for check-in and check-out, recordkeeping, and daily radiation health scans.) Policy at South Central Utilities also dictates that layoffs are not acceptable in those months when the nuclear plant is overstaffed. So, if more trained employees are available than are

needed in any month, each worker is still fully paid, even though he or she is not required to work the 130 hours.

Training new employees is an important and costly procedure. It takes one month of one-on-one classroom instruction before a new technician is permitted to work alone in the reactor facility. Therefore, South Central must hire trainees one month before they are actually needed. Each trainee teams up with a skilled nuclear technician and requires 90 hours of that employee's time, meaning that 90 hours less of the technician's time are available that month for actual reactor work.

Personnel department records indicate a turnover rate of trained technicians at 5% per month. In other words, about 5% of the skilled employees at the start of any month resign by the end of that month. A trained technician earns an average monthly salary of $2,000 (regardless of the number of hours worked, as noted earlier). Trainees are paid $900 during their one month of instruction.
(a) Formulate this staffing problem using LP.
(b) Solve the problem. How many trainees must begin each month?

15 (*Agricultural production planning problem*) Margaret Black's family owns five parcels of farmland broken into a southeast sector, north sector, northwest sector, west sector, and southwest sector. Margaret is involved primarily in growing wheat, alfalfa, and barley crops and is currently preparing her production plan for next year. The Pennsylvania Water Authority has just announced its yearly water allotment, with the Black farm receiving 7,400 acre-feet. Each parcel can only tolerate a specified amount of irrigation per growing season, as specified in the following table:

PARCEL	AREA (ACRES)	WATER IRRIGATION LIMIT (ACRE-FEET)
Southeast	2,000	3,200
North	2,300	3,400
Northwest	600	800
West	1,100	500
Southwest	500	600

Each of Margaret's crops needs a minimum amount of water per acre, and there is a projected limit on sales of each crop. Crop data follow:

CROP	MAXIMUM SALES	WATER NEEDED PER ACRE (ACRE-FEET)
Wheat	110,000 bushels	1.6
Alfalfa	1,800 tons	2.9
Barley	2,200 tons	3.5

Margaret's best estimate is that she can sell wheat at a net profit of $2 per bushel, alfalfa at $40 per ton, and barley at $50 per ton. One acre of land yields an average of 1.5 tons of alfalfa and 2.2 tons of barley. The wheat yield is approximately 50 bushels per acre.

(a) Formulate Margaret's production plan.

(b) What should the crop plan be, and what profit will it yield?

(c) The Water Authority informs Margaret that for a special fee of $6,000 this year, her farm will qualify for an additional allotment of 600 acre-feet of water. How should she respond?

16 *(Material blending problem)* Amalgamated Products has just received a contract to construct steel body frames for automobiles that are to be produced at the new Japanese factory in Tennessee. The Japanese auto manufacturer has strict quality control standards for all of its component subcontractors and has informed Amalgamated that each frame must have the following steel content:

MATERIAL	MINIMUM PERCENTAGE	MAXIMUM PERCENTAGE
Manganese	2.1	2.3
Silicon	4.3	4.6
Carbon	5.05	5.35

Amalgamated mixes batches of eight different available materials to produce one ton of steel used in the body frames. The table on this page details these materials.

Formulate and solve the LP model that will indicate how much each of the eight materials should be blended into a 1-ton load of steel so that Amalgamated meets its requirements while minimizing costs.

17 Refer to Problem 16. Find the cause of the difficulty and recommend how to adjust it. Then solve the problem again.

18 *(Hospital expansion problem)* Mt. Sinai Hospital in New Orleans is a large, private, 600-bed facility, complete with laboratories, operating rooms, and x-ray equipment. In seeking to increase revenues, Mt. Sinai's administration has decided to make a 90-bed addition on a portion of adjacent land currently used for staff parking. The administrators feel that the labs, operating rooms, and x-ray department are not being fully utilized at present and do not need to be expanded to handle additional patients. The addition of 90 beds, however, involves deciding how many beds should be allocated to the medical staff for medical patients and how many to the surgical staff for surgical patients.

The hospital's accounting and medical records departments have provided the following pertinent information. The average hospital stay for a medical patient is 8 days, and the average medical patient generates $2,280 in revenues. The average surgical patient is in the hospital 5 days and receives a $1,515 bill. The laboratory is capable of handling 15,000 tests per year more than it was handling. The average medical patient requires 3.1 lab tests and the average surgical patient takes 2.6 lab tests. Furthermore, the average medical patient uses one x-ray, whereas the average surgical patient requires two x-rays. If the hospital was expanded by 90 beds, the x-ray department could handle up to 7,000 x-rays without significant additional cost. Finally, the administration estimates that up to 2,800 additional operations could be performed in existing operating room facilities. Medical patients, of course, do not require surgery, whereas each surgical patient generally has one surgery performed.

Formulate this problem so as to determine how many medical beds and how many surgical beds should be added to maximize revenues. Assume that the hospital is open 365 days a year. Then solve the problem.

19 Prepare a written report to the CEO of Mt. Sinai Hospital in Problem 18 on the expansion of the hospital. Round off your answers to the nearest *integer*. The format of presentation of results is important. The CEO is a busy person and wants to be able to find your optimal solution quickly in your report.

Data for Problem 16

MATERIAL AVAILABLE	MANGANESE (%)	SILICON (%)	CARBON (%)	POUNDS AVAILABLE	COST PER POUND ($)
Alloy 1	70.0	15.0	3.0	No limit	0.12
Alloy 2	55.0	30.0	1.0	300	0.13
Alloy 3	12.0	26.0	0	No limit	0.15
Iron 1	1.0	10.0	3.0	No limit	0.09
Iron 2	5.0	2.5	0	No limit	0.07
Carbide 1	0	24.0	18.0	50	0.10
Carbide 2	0	25.0	20.0	200	0.12
Carbide 3	0	23.0	25.0	100	0.09

Cover all the areas given in the following sections, but do not mention any variables or shadow prices.

(a) What is the maximum revenue per year, how many medical patients/year are there, and how many surgical patients/year are there? How many medical beds and how many surgical beds of the 90-bed addition should be added?

(b) Are there any empty beds with this optimal solution? If so, how many empty beds are there? Discuss the effect of acquiring more beds if needed.

(c) Are the laboratories being used to their capacity? Is it possible to perform more lab tests/year? If so, how many more? Discuss the effect of acquiring more lab space if needed.

(d) Is the x-ray facility being used to its maximum? Is it possible to do more x-rays/year? If so, how many more? Discuss the effect of acquiring more x-ray facilities if needed.

(e) Is the operating room being used to capacity? Is it possible to do more operations/year? If so, how many more? Discuss the effect of acquiring more operating room facilities if needed. (**Source:** Professor Chris Vertullo.)

20 In the Low Knock Oil Company blending problem, it was assumed that one barrel of crude would result in one barrel of gasoline as the final product. In processing one barrel of crude, a typical gasoline yield is about 0.46 barrels, although it could be higher or lower than this, depending on the particular crude and processing used. However, other products such as diesel, jet fuel, home fuel oil, and asphalt also come from that same barrel. Assuming that only 46% of the crude turns into gasoline, modify the Low Knock Oil Company linear programming example to account for this. Solve the resulting LP problem, using any computer software.

21 A paper mill produces rolls of paper that are 10 inches wide and 100 feet long. These rolls are used for creating narrower rolls of paper that are used in cash registers, automatic teller machines (ATMs), and other devices. The narrower widths (2, 2.5, and 3 inches) needed for these devices are obtained by cutting the 10-inch rolls using pre-specified cutting patterns. Cutting pattern #1 will cut the 10-inch roll into four rolls that are 2.5 inches each. Cutting pattern #2 results in three rolls that are each 3 inches wide (leaving 1 inch of waste on the end). Cutting pattern #3 results in one roll that is 3 inches wide and two rolls that are 3.5 inches wide. Cutting pattern #4 results in one of the 2.5-inch rolls, one of the 3-inch rolls, and one of the 3.5-inch rolls (leaving 1 inch of waste). Cutting pattern #5 results in 1 roll that is 2.5 inches wide and two rolls that are 3.5 inches wide (leaving 0.5 inches of waste on the end). An order has been received for 2,000 of the 2.5-inch rolls,

4,000 of the 3-inch rolls, and 5,000 of the 3.5 inch rolls. How many rolls should be cut on each pattern if the company wants to minimize the total number of 10-inch rolls used? How many rolls should be cut on each pattern if the company wants to minimize the total waste?

22 (**Portfolio selection problem**) Daniel Grady is the financial advisor for a number of professional athletes. An analysis of the long-term goals for many of these athletes has resulted in a recommendation to purchase stocks with some of their income that is set aside for investments. Five stocks have been identified as having very favorable expectations for future performance. Although the expected return is important in these investments, the risk, as measured by the beta of the stock, is also important. (A high value of beta indicates that the stock has a relatively high risk.) The expected return and the betas for five stocks are as follows:

STOCK	1	2	3	4	5
Expected return (%)	11.0	9.0	6.5	15.0	13.0
Beta	1.20	0.85	0.55	1.40	1.25

Daniel would like to minimize the beta of the stock portfolio (calculated using a weighted average of the amounts put into the different stocks) while maintaining an expected return of at least 11%. Since future conditions may change, Daniel has decided that no more than 35% of the portfolio should be invested in any one stock.

(a) Formulate this as a linear program. (*Hint*: Define the variables to be the proportion of the total investment that would be put in each stock. Include a constraint that restricts the sum of these variables to be 1.)

(b) Solve this problem. What are the expected return and beta for this portfolio?

23 (**Airline fuel problem**) Coast-to-Coast Airlines is investigating the possibility of reducing the cost of fuel purchases by taking advantage of lower fuel costs in certain cities. Since fuel purchases represent a substantial portion of operating expenses for an airline, it is important that these costs be carefully monitored. However, fuel adds weight to an airplane, and consequently, excess fuel raises the cost of getting from one city to another. In evaluating one particular flight rotation, a plane begins in Atlanta, flies from Atlanta to Los Angeles, from Los Angeles to Houston, from Houston to New Orleans, and from New Orleans to Atlanta. When the plane arrives in Atlanta, the flight rotation is said to have been completed, and then it starts again. Thus, the fuel on board when the flight arrived in Atlanta must be taken into consideration when the flight begins.

Data for Problem 23

LEG	MINIMUM FUEL REQUIRED (1,000 GAL.)	MAXIMUM FUEL ALLOWED (1,000 GAL.)	REGULAR FUEL CONSUMPTION (1,000 GAL.)	FUEL PRICE PER GALLON
Atlanta–Los Angeles	24	36	12	$4.15
Los Angeles–Houston	15	23	7	$4.25
Houston–New Orleans	9	17	3	$4.10
New Orleans–Atlanta	11	20	5	$4.18

Along each leg of this route, there is a minimum and a maximum amount of fuel that may be carried. This and additional information is provided in the table above.

The regular fuel consumption is based on the plane carrying the minimum amount of fuel. If more than this is carried, the amount of fuel consumed is higher. Specifically, for each 1,000 gallons of fuel above the minimum, 5% (or 50 gallons per 1,000 gallons of extra fuel) is lost due to excess fuel consumption. For example, if 25,000 gallons of fuel were on board when the plane takes off from Atlanta, the fuel consumed on this route would be $12 + 0.05 = 12.05$ thousand gallons. If 26 thousand gallons were on board, the fuel consumed would be increased by another 0.05 thousand, for a total of 12.1 thousand gallons.

Formulate this as an LP problem to minimize the cost. How many gallons should be purchased in each city? What is the total cost of this?

---

www Internet Homework Problems

See our Internet home page, at www.pearsonhighered.com/render, for additional homework problems, Problems 24 to 26.

Case Study

Cable & Moore

With the company expanding into several new markets in the coming months, Cable & Moore was anticipating a large increase in sales revenue. The future looked bright for this provider of television, telephone, and Internet services. However, management of Cable & Moore was well aware of the importance of customer service in new markets. If the public had problems with new service and could not quickly and efficiently have their problems solved, demand would quickly erode and it might take years to recover from the bad publicity. Therefore, management was adamant that there would be enough well-trained customer service representatives to handle the calls from new customers and from potential customers.

Based on experience in other markets, the anticipated number of phone calls to customer service was projected. Given the average call-length, the number of hours of customer-service time from April to August was projected and is shown in the table below.

MONTH	APRIL	MAY	JUNE	JULY	AUGUST
Hours needed	21,600	24,600	27,200	28,200	29,700

Through experience, management knew that training a new employee well was essential. Each new employee was put through a 1-month training program, and was assigned to an existing employee for an entire month. Normally an existing employee would work 160 hours per month. However, when an employee was assigned to perform training of a new-hire, the productive work hours for that employee dropped to 80 hours per month.

During the training period, the trainee was paid $2,000 for the month. At the end of that time, the monthly salary increases to the standard salary for a regular customer service representative which is $3,000 per month. In the past, the company lost about 5% of the trained customer service representatives per month due to attrition. While the company is looking to improve upon this, for the next several months it is anticipated that this will continue. There will be 150 trained employees at the beginning of April. Management of the company would like to develop a schedule of hiring new employees so that there are sufficient customer service representatives to meet the demand, but this is to be done at the lowest possible cost.

Discussion Questions

1. Develop a schedule for hiring new employees. What is the total cost of this schedule?

2. Discuss any limitations that exist for this solution.

3. How would the schedule change if the attrition rate could be lowered to 3% per month instead of 5%? What would be the impact on the cost?

Internet Case Study

See out Internet home page, at www.pearsonhighered.com/render, for this additional case study: **Chase Manhattan Bank**. This case is about scheduling employees at a bank.

Bibliography

See the Bibliography at the end of Linear Programming Models: Graphical and Computer Methods.

Solutions to Selected Problems

2   (b) $50,000 in LA bonds, $175,000 in Palmer Drugs, $25,000 in Happy Days

4   1.33 pounds of oat product per horse, 0 pounds of grain, 3.33 pounds of mineral product

6   6.875 TV ads; 10 radio ads; 9 billboard ads; 10 newspaper ads

8   Use 30 of the 5-month leases starting in March, 100 5-month leases starting in April, 170 5-month leases starting in May, 160 5-month leases starting in June, and 10 5-month leases starting in July.

10   Send 400 students from sector A to school B, 300 from A to school E, 500 from B to school B, 100 from C to school C, 800 from D to school C, and 400 from E to school E.

12   (b) 0.499 lb of ground meat, 0.173 lb of chicken, 0.105 lb of spinach, and 0.762 lb of potatoes. Total cost = $1.75.

14   13.7 trainees begin in August, and 72.2 begin in October.

Solutions to Self-Tests

1. a	**3.** d	**5.** d
2. b	**4.** e	**6.** c

Integer Programming, Goal Programming, and Nonlinear Programming

Summary • Glossary • Solved Problems • Self-Test • Discussion Questions and Problems • Internet Homework Problems • Case Study: Schank Marketing Research ◆ Case Study: Oakton River Bridge • Bibliography

1 Introduction

Integer programming is the extension of LP that solves problems requiring integer solutions.

This chapter presents a series of other important mathematical programming models that arise when some of the basic assumptions of LP are made more or less restrictive. For example, one assumption of LP is that decision variables can take on fractional values such as $X_1 = 0.33, X_2 = 1.57$, or $X_3 = 109.4$. Yet a large number of business problems can be solved only if variables have *integer* values. When an airline decides how many Boeing 757s or Boeing 777s to purchase, it can't place an order for 5.38 aircraft; it must order 4, 5, 6, 7, or some other integer amount. In this chapter we present the general topic of integer programming, and we specifically consider the use of special variables that must be either 0 or 1.

Goal programming is the extension of LP that permits more than one objective to be stated.

A major limitation of LP is that it forces the decision maker to state one objective only. But what if a business has several objectives? Management may indeed want to maximize profit, but it might also want to maximize market share, maintain full employment, and minimize costs. Many of these goals can be conflicting and difficult to quantify. South States Power and Light, for example, wants to build a nuclear power plant in Taft, Louisiana. Its objectives are to maximize power generated, reliability, and safety, and to minimize cost of operating the system and the environmental effects on the community. Goal programming is an extension to LP that can permit multiple objectives such as these.

Nonlinear programming is the case in which objectives or constraints are nonlinear.

Linear programming can, of course, be applied only to cases in which the constraints and objective function are linear. Yet in many situations this is not the case. The price of various products, for example, may be a function of the number of units produced. As more units are produced, the price per unit decreases. Hence an objective function may read as follows:

$$\text{Maximize profit} = 25X_1 - 0.4X_1{}^2 + 30X_2 - 0.5X_2{}^2$$

Because of the squared terms, this is a nonlinear programming problem.

Let's examine each of these extensions of LP—integer, goal, and nonlinear programming—one at a time.

2 Integer Programming

Solution values must be whole numbers in integer programming.

An **integer programming** model is a model that has constraints and an objective function identical to that formulated by LP. The only difference is that one or more of the decision variables has to take on an integer value in the final solution. There are three types of integer programming problems:

There are three types of integer programs: pure integer programming; mixed-integer programming; and 0–1 integer programming.

1. Pure integer programming problems are cases in which all variables are required to have integer values.
2. Mixed-integer programming problems are cases in which some, but not all, of the decision variables are required to have integer values.
3. Zero–one integer programming problems are special cases in which all the decision variables must have integer solution values of 0 or 1.

Solving an integer programming problem is much more difficult than solving an LP problem. The solution time required to solve some of these may be excessive even on the fastest computer.

Harrison Electric Company Example of Integer Programming

The Harrison Electric Company, located in Chicago's Old Town area, produces two products popular with home renovators: old-fashioned chandeliers and ceiling fans. Both the chandeliers and fans require a two-step production process involving wiring and assembly. It takes about 2 hours to wire each chandelier and 3 hours to wire a ceiling fan. Final assembly of the chandeliers and fans requires 6 and 5 hours, respectively. The production capability is such that only 12 hours of wiring time and 30 hours of assembly time are available. If each chandelier produced nets the firm $7 and each fan $6, Harrison's production mix decision can be formulated using LP as follows:

$$\text{Maximize profit} = \$7X_1 + \$6X_2$$

$$\text{subject to} \quad 2X_1 + 3X_2 \leq 12 \quad \text{(wiring hours)}$$

$$6X_1 + 5X_2 \leq 30 \quad \text{(assembly hours)}$$

$$X_1, X_2 \geq 0$$

Although enumeration is feasible for some small integer programming problems, it can be difficult or impossible for large ones.

where

X_1 = number of chandeliers produced

X_2 = number of ceiling fans produced

With only two variables and two constraints, Harrison's production planner, Wes Wallace, employed the graphical LP approach (see Figure 1) to generate the optimal solution of $X_1 = 3.75$ chandeliers and $X_2 = 1.5$ ceiling fans during the production cycle. Recognizing that the company could not produce and sell a fraction of a product, Wes decided that he was dealing with an integer programming problem.

It seemed to Wes that the simplest approach was to round off the optimal fractional solutions for X_1 and X_2 to integer values of $X_1 = 4$ chandeliers and $X_2 = 2$ ceiling fans. Unfortunately, rounding can produce two problems. First, the new integer solution may not be in the feasible region and thus is not a practical answer. This is the case if we round to $X_1 = 4, X_2 = 2$. Second, even if we round off to a feasible solution, such as $X_1 = 4, X_2 = 1$, it may not be the *optimal* feasible integer solution.

Rounding off is one way to reach integer solution values, but it often does not yield the best solution.

Listing all feasible solutions and selecting the one with the best objective function value is called the *enumeration* method. Obviously this can be quite tedious for even small problems, and it is virtually impossible for large problems as the number of feasible integer solutions is extremely large.

FIGURE 1
Harrison Electric Problem

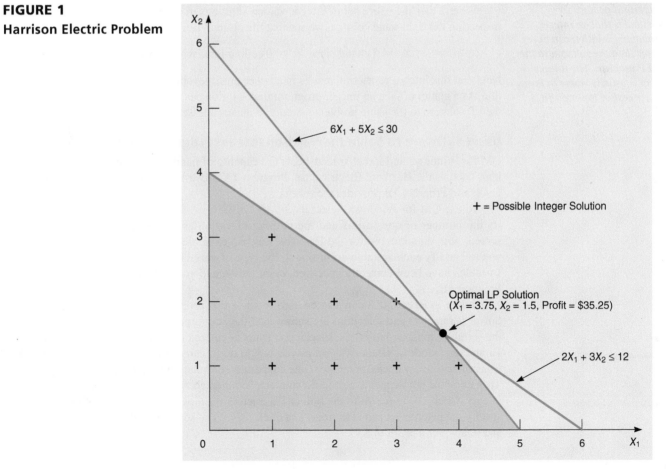

287

TABLE 1

Integer Solutions to the Harrison Electric Company Problem

CHANDELIERS (X_1)	CEILING FANS (X_2)	PROFIT ($7X_1 + 6X_2$)	
0	0	$0	
1	0	7	
2	0	14	
3	0	21	
4	0	28	
5	0	35	← Optimal solution to integer programming problem
0	1	6	
1	1	13	
2	1	20	
3	1	27	
4	1	34	← Solution if rounding is used
0	2	12	
1	2	19	
2	2	26	
3	2	33	
0	3	18	
1	3	25	
0	4	24	

An important concept to understand is that an integer programming solution can never be better than the solution to the same LP problem. The integer problem is usually worse in terms of higher cost or lower profit.

Table 1 lists the entire set of integer-valued solutions to the Harrison Electric problem. By inspecting the right-hand column, we see that the optimal *integer* solution is

$$X_1 = 5 \text{ chandeliers}, X_2 = 0 \text{ ceiling fans, with a profit} = \$35$$

Note that this integer restriction results in a lower profit level than the original optimal LP solution. As a matter of fact, an integer programming solution can *never* produce a greater profit than the LP solution to the same problem; *usually*, it means a lesser value.

Using Software to Solve the Harrison Integer Programming Problem

QM for Windows and Excel spreadsheets are capable of handling integer programming problems such as the Harrison Electric case. Program 1A illustrates the input data to QM for Windows, and Program 1B provides the results.

To use QM for Windows, select the *Integer & Mixed Integer Programming* module. Specify the number of constraints and the number of variables. Program 1A provides the input screen, with data entered for the Harrison Electric example. The last row of the table allows you to classify each variable according to the type of variable (Integer, Real, or 0/1). Once all variables have been correctly specified, click *Solve*, and you will see the output as shown in Program 1B.

Solver in Excel 2013 can also be used to solve this problem, as shown in Program 2. The Solver parameters and selections are shown, and the key formulas are displayed. To specify that the variables must be integers, a special constraint is entered in Solver. After opening the Solver Parameters window, select *Add* just as you would do to enter other constraints. When the Add Constraint window opens, enter the range containing the solution values, as shown in Program 2. Then click the tab to open the drop-down menu and then change the type of constraint to int, for integer. Click *OK* to return to the Solver Parameters window. Then enter the other constraints, specify the parameters and selections, and click *Solve*. The solution is shown to be 5 chandeliers and 0 fans, for a profit of $35.

PROGRAM 1A

QM for Windows Input
Screen for Harrison
Electric Problem

		X1	X2		RHS	Equation form
Maximize		7	6			Max 7X1 + 6X2
Constraint 1		2	3	<=	12	2X1 + 3X2 <= 12
Constraint 2		6	5	<=	30	6X1 + 5X2 <= 30
Variable type		Integ	Integer			

Maximum number of iterations: 1000
Maximum level (depth) in procedure: 50

Objective: Maximize / Minimize

Harrison Electric Integer Programming Problem

Integer
Real
0/1

PROGRAM 1B

QM for Windows
Solution Screen for
Harrison Electric Problem

Objective: Maximize / Minimize
Maximum number of iterations: 1000

Integer & Mixed Integer Programming Results

Variable	Type	Value
X1	Integer	5
X2	Integer	0
Solution value		35

PROGRAM 2

Excel 2013 Solver
Solution for Harrison
Electric Problem

	A	B	C	D			
1	Harrison Electric Integer Programming Analysis						
2		Chandeliers	Fans				
3	Variables	X1	X2				
4	Values	5	0	Total Profit			
5	Profit	7	6	35			
6							
7	Constraints			LHS	Sign	RHS	
8	Wiring hours	2	3	10	≤	12	
9	Assembly hours	6	5	30	≤	30	

Change Constraint

Cell Reference: $B$4:$C$4
Constraint: integer
= / <= / = / >= / int / bin / dif

OK   Cancel

Solver Parameter Inputs and Selections

Set Objective: D5

By Changing cells: B4:C4

To: Max

Subject to the Constraints:

D8:D9 <= F8:F9

B4:C4 = integer

Solving Method: Simplex LP

☑ Make Variables Non-Negative

Key Formulas

	D
5	=SUMPRODUCT($B$4:$C$4,B5:C5)

Copy D5 to D8:D9

Mixed-Integer Programming Problem Example

Although the Harrison Electric example was a pure integer problem, there are many situations in which some of the variables are restricted to be integers and others are not. The following is an example of such a mixed-integer programming problem.

Bagwell Chemical Company, in Jackson, Mississippi, produces two industrial chemicals. The first product, xyline, must be produced in 50-pound bags; the second, hexall, is sold by the pound in dry bulk and hence can be produced in any quantity. Both xyline and hexall are composed of three ingredients—*A*, *B*, and *C*—as follows:

AMOUNT PER 50-POUND BAG OF XYLINE (LB)	AMOUNT PER POUND OF HEXALL (LB)	AMOUNT OF INGREDIENTS AVAILABLE
30	0.5	2,000 lb—ingredient *A*
18	0.4	800 lb—ingredient *B*
2	0.1	200 lb—ingredient *C*

Bagwell sells 50-pound bags of xyline for $85 and hexall in any weight for $1.50 per pound.

MODELING IN THE REAL WORLD: Integer Programming at the USPS

Defining the Problem

Developing a Model

Acquiring Input Data

Testing the Solution

Analyzing the Results

Implementing the Results

Defining the Problem

The U.S. Postal Service (USPS) operates one of the largest transportation networks in the world, delivering one-fifth of a trillion items every year. The inherent transportation-related problems are, obviously, very large. Nevertheless, USPS's problem is how to deliver mail in the most cost-efficient manner possible.

Developing a Model

A large-scale integer program known as the Highway Corridor Analytical Program (HCAP) was developed to help solve the problem. More specifically, the HCAP solves a Vehicle Routing Problem (VRP) with known pickup and delivery locations. That is, the model takes into account all the different modes of transportation, the capacities inherent to the system, all the pickup locations, and all the delivery locations and then assigns trucks to routes as the (binary) decision variable of interest.

Acquiring Input Data

Geographic information system (GIS) data of all the pickup and delivery locations is integrated into the model. Realistic time and distance constraints were placed on the model to prevent drivers from being assigned a pickup in one area and a delivery in an area too far away.

Testing the Solution

The model was loaded into a large-scale mathematical programming solver. Several versions and models were tested.

Analyzing the Results

Decision makers found improvements in several areas. For example, one of the model outputs resulted in a 20% reduction in redundant trips.

Implementing the Results

USPS has already realized over $5 million in transportation savings due to its implementation of the HCAP integer programming optimization model. Efforts are under way to seek out additional efficiencies through the use of HCAP.

Source: Based on A. Pajunas, E. J. Matto, M. Trick, and L.F. Zuluaga. "Optimizing Highway Transportation at the United States Postal Service," *Interfaces* 37, 6 (2007): 515–525.

If we let X = number of 50-pound bags of xyline produced and Y = number of pounds of hexall (in dry bulk) mixed, Bagwell's problem can be described with mixed-integer programming:

$$\text{Maximize profit} = \$85X + \$1.50Y$$

subject to
$$30X + 0.5Y \leq 2{,}000$$
$$18X + 0.4Y \leq 800$$
$$2X + 0.1Y \leq 200$$
$$X, Y \geq 0 \text{ and } X \text{ integer.}$$

Note that Y represents bulk weight of hexall and is not required to be integer valued.

USING QM FOR WINDOWS AND EXCEL TO SOLVE BAGWELL'S INTEGER PROGRAMMING MODEL The solution to Bagwell's problem is to produce 44 bags of xyline and 20 pounds of hexall, yielding a profit of $3,770. (The optimal linear solution, by the way, is to produce 44.444 bags of xyline and 0 pounds of hexall, yielding a profit of $3,777.78.) This is first illustrated in Program 3, which uses the Mixed Integer Programming module in QM for Windows. Note that variable X is identified as Integer, while Y is Real in Program 3.

In Program 4, we use Excel to provide an alternative solution method.

PROGRAM 3

QM for Windows Solution for Bagwell Chemical Problem

Objective	Maximum number of iterations		Maximum level (depth) in procedure		Ins Oth
⦿ Maximize ○ Minimize	◄ ▐ ► 1000		◄ ▐ ► 50		

Bagwell Chemical Company Solution					
Limits are used, and the best solution available after a certain time is presented.	X	Y			RHS
Ma... *Notice that only X must be integer, while Y may be any real number.*	85	1.5			
Cons...	30	0.5	<=		2000
Constraint 2	18	0.4	<=		800
Constraint 3	2	0.1	<=		200
Variable type	Integer	Real			
Solution->	44	20	Optimal Z->		3770

IN ACTION | **Mixed-Integer Programming in the IBM Supply Chain**

The manufacture of semiconductors is a very expensive operation, often requiring investments in the billions of dollars. The IBM Systems and Technology Group has used mixed-integer programming (MIP) along with other operations research techniques to plan and optimize its semiconductor supply chain. The business of supply-chain optimization (SCO) has been deemed business critical and must incorporate a variety of planning criteria and constraints.

IBM uses a central planning engine (CPE) to balance the supply chain's resources against the semiconductor demand. The MIP is an important part of this CPE. The MIP model is a cost-minimization problem with constraints related to material flows and other aspect of the supply chain.

Some of the models involved in SCO include sourcing among multiple plants, the logistics of interplant shipping, and the development of production plans for all the plants within the system. They may involve a planning horizon of a few days, a few months, or even a few years, depending on the specific type of application. While LP is commonly used in supply-chain modeling, it is necessary to use models in which some of the variables are required to be integers. The resulting MIP models are so large (millions of variables) that they cannot be solved with even the fastest computers. Therefore, the IBM Systems and Technology Group developed heuristic methods to solve the optimization models as part of the company's advanced planning systems.

The benefits of the CPE are many. The on-time deliveries improved by 15%. A 25% to 30% reduction in inventory was observed as a result of the model. The company also observed an improvement in asset allocation of between 2% and 4% of costs. This model allowed "what-if" questions to be quickly answered—a process that was not possible in the past. Strategic planning was also facilitated by the CPE. IBM benefited greatly from the use of MIP in managing the semiconductor supply chain.

Source: Based on Brian. T. Denton, John Forrest, and R. John Milne. "IBM Solves a Mixed-Integer Program to Optimize Its Semiconductor Supply Chain," *Interfaces* 36, 5 (September–October 2006): 386–399.

PROGRAM 4

Excel 2013 Solver Solution for Bagwell Chemical Problem

	A	B	C	D	E	F
1	Bagwell Chemical Company					
2		Xyline (bags)	Hexall (lbs)			
3	Variables	X	Y			
4	Values	44	20	Total Profit		
5	Profit	85	1.5	3770		
6						
7	Constraints			LHS	sign	RHS
8	Ingredient A	30	0.5	1330	≤	2000
9	Ingredient B	18	0.4	800	≤	800
10	Ingredient C	2	0.1	90	≤	200

Solver Parameter Inputs and Selections

Set Objective: D5

By Changing cells: B4:C4

To: Max

Subject to the Constraints:

   D8:D10 <= F8:F10

   B4 = integer

Solving Method: Simplex LP

☑ Make Variables Non-Negative

Key Formulas

	D
5	=SUMPRODUCT($B$4:$C$4,B5:C5)

Copy D5 to D8:D10

3   Modeling with 0–1 (Binary) Variables

In this section we demonstrate how 0–1 variables can be used to model several diverse situations. Typically a 0–1 variable is assigned a value of 0 if a certain condition is not met and 1 if the condition is met. Another name for a 0–1 variable is a *binary variable*. A common problem of this type, the assignment problem, involves deciding which individuals to assign to a set of jobs. In this assignment problem, a value of 1 indicates a person is assigned to a specific job, and a value of 0 indicates the assignment was not made. We present other types of 0–1 problems to show the wide applicability of this modeling technique.

Capital Budgeting Example

A common capital budgeting decision involves selecting from a set of possible projects when budget limitations make it impossible to select all of these. A separate 0–1 variable can be defined for each project. We will see this in the following example.

Quemo Chemical Company is considering three possible improvement projects for its plant: a new catalytic converter, a new software program for controlling operations, and expanding the warehouse used for storage. Capital requirements and budget limitations in the next 2 years prevent the firm from undertaking all of these at this time. The net present value (the future value of the project discounted back to the present time) of each of the projects, the capital requirements, and the available funds for the next 2 years are given in Table 2.

To formulate this as an integer programming problem, we identify the objective function and the constraints as follows:

Maximize net present value of projects undertaken

subject to   Total funds used in year 1 ≤ $20,000

   Total funds used in year 2 ≤ $16,000

TABLE 2
**Quemo Chemical
Company Information**

PROJECT	NET PRESENT VALUE	YEAR 1	YEAR 2
Catalytic Converter	$25,000	$8,000	$7,000
Software	$18,000	$6,000	$4,000
Warehouse Expansion	$32,000	$12,000	$8,000
Available Funds		$20,000	$16,000

We define the decision variables as

$$X_1 = \begin{cases} 1 \text{ if catalytic converter project is funded} \\ 0 \text{ otherwise} \end{cases}$$

$$X_2 = \begin{cases} 1 \text{ if software project is funded} \\ 0 \text{ otherwise} \end{cases}$$

$$X_3 = \begin{cases} 1 \text{ if warehouse expansion project is funded} \\ 0 \text{ otherwise} \end{cases}$$

The mathematical statement of the integer programming problem becomes

$$\text{Maximize NPV} = 25,000X_1 + 18,000X_2 + 32,000X_3$$
$$\text{subject to} \quad 8,000X_1 + 6,000X_2 + 12,000X_3 \leq 20,000$$
$$7,000X_1 + 4,000X_2 + 8,000X_3 \leq 16,000$$
$$X_1, X_2, X_3 = 0 \text{ or } 1$$

Program 5 provides the Solver solution in Excel 2013. You specify the variables to be binary (0–1) by selecting bin from the Add Constraint window. The optimal solution is $X_1 = 1$,

PROGRAM 5
**Excel 2013 Solver
Solution for Quemo
Chemical Problem**

	A	B	C	D	E	F	G
1	Quemo Chemical Company						
2		Catalytic Conv.	Software	Warehouse Expan.			
3	Variables	X1	X2	X3			
4	Values	1	0	1	NPV		
5	Net Present Value	25000	18000	32000	57000		
6							
7	Constraints				LHS	sign	RHS
8	Year 1	8000	6000	12000	20000	≤	20000
9	Year 2	7000	4000	8000	15000	≤	16000

Solver Parameter Inputs and Selections

Set Objective: E5

By Changing cells: B4:D4

To: Max

Subject to the Constraints:

   E8:E9 <= G8:G9

   B4:D4 = binary

Solving Method: Simplex LP

☑ **Make Variables Non-Negative**

Key Formulas

	E
5	=SUMPRODUCT($B$4:$D$4,B5:D5)

Copy E5 to E8:E9

$X_2 = 0$, $X_3 = 1$ with an objective function value of 57,000. This means that Quemo should fund the catalytic converter project and the warehouse expansion project but not the new software project. The net present value of these investments will be $57,000.

Limiting the Number of Alternatives Selected

One common use of 0–1 variables involves limiting the number of projects or items that are selected from a group. Suppose that in the Quemo Chemical Company example, the company is required to select no more than two of the three projects *regardless* of the funds available. This could be modeled by adding the following constraint to the problem:

$$X_1 + X_2 + X_3 \leq 2$$

If we wished to force the selection of *exactly* two of the three projects for funding, the following constraint should be used:

$$X_1 + X_2 + X_3 = 2$$

This forces exactly two of the variables to have values of 1, whereas the other variable must have a value of 0.

Dependent Selections

At times the selection of one project depends in some way upon the selection of another project. This situation can be modeled with the use of 0–1 variables. Now suppose in the Quemo Chemical problem that the new catalytic converter could be purchased only if the software was also purchased. The following constraint would force this to occur:

$$X_1 \leq X_2$$

or, equivalently,

$$X_1 - X_2 \leq 0$$

Thus, if the software is not purchased, the value of X_2 is 0, and the value of X_1 must also be 0 because of this constraint. However, if the software is purchased ($X_2 = 1$), then it is possible that the catalytic converter could also be purchased ($X_1 = 1$), although this is not required.

If we wished for the catalytic converter and the software projects to either both be selected or both not be selected, we should use the following constraint:

$$X_1 = X_2$$

or, equivalently,

$$X_1 - X_2 = 0$$

Thus, if either of these variables is equal to 0, the other must also be 0. If either of these is equal to 1, the other must also be 1.

Fixed-Charge Problem Example

Often businesses are faced with decisions involving a fixed charge that will affect the cost of future operations. Building a new factory or entering into a long-term lease on an existing facility would involve a fixed cost that might vary depending upon the size of the facility and the location. Once a factory is built, the variable production costs will be affected by the labor cost in the particular city where it is located. An example follows.

Sitka Manufacturing is planning to build at least one new plant, and three cities are being considered: Baytown, Texas; Lake Charles, Louisiana; and Mobile, Alabama. Once the plant or plants have been constructed, the company wishes to have sufficient capacity to produce at least 38,000 units each year. The costs associated with the possible locations are given in Table 3.

In modeling this as an integer program, the objective function is to minimize the total of the fixed cost and the variable cost. The constraints are: (1) total production capacity is at least 38,000; (2) number of units produced at the Baytown plant is 0 if the plant is not built, and it is no more than 21,000 if the plant is built; (3) number of units produced at the Lake Charles plant is 0 if the plant is not built, and it is no more than 20,000 if the plant is built; (4) number of units

TABLE 3
Fixed and Variable Costs for Sitka Manufacturing

SITE	ANNUAL FIXED COST	VARIABLE COST PER UNIT	ANNUAL CAPACITY
Baytown, TX	$340,000	$32	21,000
Lake Charles, LA	$270,000	$33	20,000
Mobile, AL	$290,000	$30	19,000

produced at the Mobile plant is 0 if the plant is not built, and it is no more than 19,000 if the plant is built.

Then, we define the decision variables as

$$X_1 = \begin{cases} 1 \text{ if factory is built in Baytown} \\ 0 \text{ otherwise} \end{cases}$$

$$X_2 = \begin{cases} 1 \text{ if factory is built in Lake Charles} \\ 0 \text{ otherwise} \end{cases}$$

$$X_2 = \begin{cases} 1 \text{ if factory is built in Mobile} \\ 0 \text{ otherwise} \end{cases}$$

X_4 = number of units produced at Baytown plant
X_5 = number of units produced at Lake Charles plant
X_6 = number of units produced at Mobile plant

The number of units produced must be 0 if the plant is not built.

The integer programming problem formulation becomes

$$\text{Minimize cost} = 340,000X_1 + 270,000X_2 + 290,000X_3 + 32X_4 + 33X_5 + 30X_6$$

$$\text{subject to} \quad X_4 + X_5 + X_6 \geq 38,000$$
$$X_4 \leq 21,000X_1$$
$$X_5 \leq 20,000X_2$$
$$X_6 \leq 19,000X_3$$
$$X_1, X_2, X_3 = 0 \text{ or } 1; X_4, X_5, X_6 \geq 0 \text{ and integer}$$

PROGRAM 6
Excel 2013 Solver Solution for Sitka Manufacturing Problem

	A	B	C	D	E	F	G	H	I	J
1	Sitka Manufacturing Company									
2		Baytown	Lake Charles	Mobile	Baytown units	L. Charles units	Mobile units			
3	Variables	X1	X2	X3	X4	X5	X6			
4	Values	0	1	1	0	19000	19000	Cost		
5	Cost	340000	270000	290000	32	33	30	1757000		
6										
7	Constraints							LHS	Sign	RHS
8	Minimum capacity				1	1	1	38000	≥	38000
9	Maximum in Baytown	-21000			1			0	≤	0
10	Maximum in L. C.		-20000			1		-1000	≤	0
11	Maximum in Mobile			-19000			1	0	≤	0

Solver Parameter Inputs and Selections
Set Objective: H5
By Changing cells: B4:G4
To: Min
Subject to the Constraints:
H8 >= J8
H9:H11 <= J9:J11
B4:D4 = binary
E4:G4 = integer
Solving Method: Simplex LP
☑ Make Variables Non-Negative

Key Formulas

	H
5	=SUMPRODUCT($B$4:$G$4,B5:G5)

Copy H5 to H8:H11

TABLE 4
Oil Investment Opportunities

STOCK	COMPANY NAME	EXPECTED ANNUAL RETURN ($1,000s)	COST FOR BLOCK OF SHARES ($1,000s)
1	Trans-Texas Oil	50	480
2	British Petroleum	80	540
3	Dutch Shell	90	680
4	Houston Drilling	120	1,000
5	Texas Petroleum	110	700
6	San Diego Oil	40	510
7	California Petro	75	900

Notice that if $X_1 = 0$ (meaning Baytown plant is not built), then X_4 (number of units produced at Baytown plant) must also equal zero due to the second constraint. If $X_1 = 1$, then X_4 may be any integer value less than or equal to the limit of 21,000. The third and fourth constraints are similarly used to guarantee that no units are produced at the other locations if the plants are not built. The optimal solution, shown in Program 6, is

$$X_1 = 0, \quad X_2 = 1, \quad X_3 = 1, \quad X_4 = 0, \quad X_5 = 19,000, \quad X_6 = 19,000$$
$$\text{Objective function value} = 1,757,000$$

This means that factories will be built at Lake Charles and Mobile. Each of these will produce 19,000 units each year, and the total annual cost will be $1,757,000.

Financial Investment Example

Here is an example of stock portfolio analysis with 0–1 programming.

Numerous financial applications exist with 0–1 variables. A very common type of problem involves selecting from a group of investment opportunities. The following example illustrates this application.

The Houston-based investment firm of Simkin, Simkin, and Steinberg specializes in recommending oil stock portfolios for wealthy clients. One such client has made the following specifications: (1) at least two Texas oil firms must be in the portfolio, (2) no more than one investment can be made in foreign oil companies, (3) one of the two California oil stocks must be purchased. The client has up to $3 million available for investments and insists on purchasing large blocks of shares of each company that he invests in. Table 4 describes various stocks that Simkin considers. The objective is to maximize annual return on investment subject to the constraints.

To formulate this as a 0–1 integer programming problem, Simkin lets X_i be a 0–1 integer variable, where $X_i = 1$ if stock i is purchased and $X_i = 0$ if stock i is not purchased:

$$\text{Maximize return} = 50X_1 + 80X_2 + 90X_3 + 120X_4 + 110X_5 + 40X_6 + 75X_7$$
$$\text{subject to} \quad X_1 + X_4 + X_5 \geq 2 \quad \text{(Texas constraint)}$$
$$X_2 + X_3 \leq 1 \quad \text{(foreign oil constraint)}$$
$$X_6 + X_7 = 1 \quad \text{(California constraint)}$$
$$480X_1 + 540X_2 + 680X_3 + 1,000X_4 + 700X_5 + 510X_6 + 900X_7 \leq 3,000$$
$$\text{($3 million limit)}$$
$$X_i = 0 \text{ or } 1 \text{ for all } i$$

The solution from using Solver in Excel 2013 is shown is Program 7

4 Goal Programming

Firms usually have more than one goal.

In today's business environment, profit maximization or cost minimization are not always the only objectives that a firm sets forth. Often, maximizing total profit is just one of several goals, including such contradictory objectives as maximizing market share, maintaining full employment, providing quality ecological management, minimizing noise level in the neighborhood, and meeting numerous other noneconomic goals.

PROGRAM 7

Excel 2013 Solver Solution for Financial Investment Problem

	A	B	C	D	E	F	G	H	I	J	K
1	Simkin, Simkin and Steinberg										
2											
3	Variables	X1	X2	X3	X4	X5	X6	X7			
4	Values	0	0	1	1	1	1	0	Return		
5	Return ($1,000s)	50	80	90	120	110	40	75	360		
6	Constraints								LHS	Sign	RHS
7	Texas	1			1	1			2	≥	2
8	Foreign Oil		1	1					1	≤	1
9	California						1	1	1	=	1
10	$3 Million	480	540	680	1000	700	510	900	2890	≤	3000

Solver Parameter Inputs and Selections

Set Objective: I5

By Changing cells: B4:H4

To: Max

Subject to the Constraints:

  I7 >= K7

  I8 <= K8

  I9 = K9

  I10 <= K10

  B4:H4 = binary

Solving Method: Simplex LP

☑ **Make Variables Non-Negative**

Key Formulas

	I
5	=SUMPRODUCT($B$4:$H$4,B5:H5)

Copy I5 to I7:I10

The shortcoming of mathematical programming techniques such as linear and integer programming is that their objective function is measured in one dimension only. It's not possible for LP to have *multiple goals* unless they are all measured in the same units (such as dollars), a highly unusual situation. An important technique that has been developed to supplement LP is called **goal programming**.

Goal programming permits multiple goals.

Ⓠ IN ACTION | **Continental Airlines Saves $40 Million Using CrewSolver**

Airlines use state-of-the-art processes and automated tools to develop schedules that maximize profit. These schedules will assign aircraft to specific routes, and then schedule pilots and flight attendant crews to each of these aircraft. When disruptions occur, planes and personnel are often left in positions where they are unable to adhere to the next day's assignments. Airlines face schedule disruptions from a variety of unexpected reasons such as bad weather, mechanical problems, and crew unavailability.

In 1993, Continental Airlines began an effort to develop a system of dealing with disruptions in real time. Working with CALEB Technologies, Continental developed the CrewSolver and OptSolver systems (based on 0–1 integer programming models) to produce comprehensive recovery solutions for both aircraft and crews. These solutions retain revenue and promote customer satisfaction by reducing flight cancellations and minimizing delays. These crew recovery solutions are low cost while maintaining a high quality of life for pilots and flight attendants.

In late 2000 and throughout 2001, Continental and other airlines experienced four major disruptions. The first two were due to severe snowstorms in early January and in March 2001. The Houston floods caused by Tropical Storm Allison closed a major hub in June 2001 and left aircraft in locations where they were not scheduled to be. The terrorist attacks of September 11, 2001 left aircraft and crews scattered about and totally disrupted the flight schedules. The CrewSolver system provided a faster and more efficient recovery than had been possible in the past. It is estimated that the CrewSolver system saved approximately $40 million for these major disruptions in 2001. This system also saved additional money and made recovery much easier when there were minor disruptions due to local weather problems at other times throughout the year.

Source: Based on Gang Yu, Michael Arguello, Gao Song, Sandra M. McCowan, and Anna White. "A New Era for Crew Recovery at Continental Airlines," *Interfaces* 33, (January–February 2003): 5–22.

Goal programming is capable of handling decision problems involving multiple goals. It began with the work of Charnes and Cooper in 1961 and was refined and extended by Lee and Ignizio in the 1970s and 1980s (see the Bibliography).

In typical decision-making situations, the goals set by management can be achieved only at the expense of other goals. It is necessary to establish a hierarchy of importance among these goals so that lower-priority goals are tackled only after higher-priority goals are satisfied. Since it is not always possible to achieve every goal to the extent the decision maker desires, goal programming attempts to reach a satisfactory level of multiple objectives. This, of course, differs from LP, which tries to find the best possible outcome for a *single* objective. Nobel laureate Herbert A. Simon, of Carnegie-Mellon University, states that modern managers may not be able to optimize, but may instead have to "**satisfice**" or "come as close as possible" to reaching goals. This is the case with models such as goal programming.

How, specifically, does goal programming differ from LP? The objective function is the main difference. Instead of trying to maximize or minimize the objective function directly, with goal programming we try to minimize *deviations* between set goals and what we can actually achieve within the given constraints. In the LP simplex approach, such deviations are called slack and surplus variables. Because the coefficient for each of these in the objective function is zero, slack and surplus variables do not have an impact on the optimal solution. In goal programming, the deviational variables are typically the only variables in the objective function, and the objective is to minimize the total of these **deviational variables**.

When the goal programming model is formulated, the computational algorithm is almost the same as a minimization problem solved by the simplex method.

Goal programming "satisfices," as opposed to LP, which tries to "optimize." This means coming as close as possible to reaching goals.

The objective function is the main difference between goal programming and LP.

In goal programming we want to minimize deviational variables, which are the only terms in the objective function.

Example of Goal Programming: Harrison Electric Company Revisited

To illustrate the formulation of a goal programming problem, let's look back at the Harrison Electric Company case presented earlier in this chapter as an integer programming problem. That problem's LP formulation, you recall, is

$$\text{Maximize profit} = \$7X_1 + \$6X_2$$
$$\text{subject to} \quad 2X_1 + 3X_2 \leq 12 \quad \text{(wiring hours)}$$
$$6X_1 + 5X_2 \leq 30 \quad \text{(assembly hours)}$$
$$X_1, X_2 \geq 0$$

where

$X_1 = $ number of chandeliers produced

$X_2 = $ number of ceiling fans produced

We saw that if Harrison's management had a single goal, say profit, LP could be used to find the optimal solution. But let's assume that the firm is moving to a new location during a particular production period and feels that maximizing profit is not a realistic goal. Management sets a profit level, which would be satisfactory during the adjustment period, of $30. We now have a goal programming problem in which we want to find the production mix that achieves this goal as closely as possible, given the production time constraints. This simple case will provide a good starting point for tackling more complicated goal programs.

We first define two deviational variables:

$$d_1^- = \text{underachievement of the profit target}$$
$$d_1^+ = \text{overachievement of the profit target}$$

Now we can state the Harrison Electric problem as a *single-goal* programming model:

$$\text{Minimize under or overachievement of profit target} = d_1^- + d_1^+$$
$$\text{subject to} \quad \$7X_1 + \$6X_2 + d_1^- - d_1^+ = \$30 \quad \text{(profit goal constraint)}$$
$$2X_1 + 3X_2 \leq 12 \quad \text{(wiring hours constraint)}$$
$$6X_1 + 5X_2 \leq 30 \quad \text{(assembly hours constraint)}$$
$$X_1, X_2, d_1^-, d_1^+ \geq 0$$

Note that the first constraint states that the profit made, $\$7X_1 + \$6X_2$, plus any underachievement of profit minus any overachievement of profit has to equal the target of $30. For example, if $X_1 = 3$ chandeliers and $X_2 = 2$ ceiling fans, then $33 profit has been made. This exceeds $30 by $3, so d_1^+ must be equal to 3. Since the profit goal constraint was *overachieved*, Harrison did not underachieve and d_1^- will clearly be equal to zero. This problem is now ready for solution by a goal programming algorithm.

Deviational variables are zero if a goal is exactly obtained.

If the target profit of $30 is exactly achieved, we see that both d_1^+ and d_1^- are equal to zero. The objective function will also be minimized at zero. If Harrison's management was only concerned with *underachievement* of the target goal, how would the objective function change? It would be as follows: minimize underachievement $= d_1^-$. This is also a reasonable goal since the firm would probably not be upset with an overachievement of its target.

In general, once all goals and constraints are identified in a problem, management should analyze each goal to see if underachievement or overachievement of that goal is an acceptable situation. If overachievement is acceptable, the appropriate d^+ variable can be eliminated from the objective function. If underachievement is okay, the d^- variable should be dropped. If management seeks to attain a goal exactly, both d^- and d^+ must appear in the objective function.

Extension to Equally Important Multiple Goals

We need a clear definition of deviational variables, such as these.

Let's now look at the situation in which Harrison's management wants to achieve several goals, each equal in priority.

Goal 1: to produce profit of $30 if possible during the production period

Goal 2: to fully utilize the available wiring department hours

Goal 3: to avoid overtime in the assembly department

Goal 4: to meet a contract requirement to produce at least seven ceiling fans

The deviational variables can be defined as follows:

$$d_1^- = \text{underachievement of the profit target}$$
$$d_1^+ = \text{overachievement of the profit target}$$
$$d_2^- = \text{idle time in the wiring department (underutilization)}$$
$$d_2^+ = \text{overtime in the wiring department (overutilization)}$$
$$d_3^- = \text{idle time in the assembly department (underutilization)}$$
$$d_3^+ = \text{overtime in the assembly department (overutilization)}$$
$$d_4^- = \text{underachievement of the ceiling fan goal}$$
$$d_4^+ = \text{overachievement of the ceiling fan goal}$$

Management is unconcerned about whether there is overachievement of the profit goal, overtime in the wiring department, idle time in the assembly department, or more than seven ceiling fans are produced: hence, d_1^+, d_2^+, d_3^-, and d_4^+ may be omitted from the objective function. The new objective function and constraints are

$$\text{Minimize total deviation} = d_1^- + d_2^- + d_3^+ + d_4^-$$
$$\text{subject to } 7X_1 + 6X_2 + d_1^- - d_1^+ = 30 \quad \text{(profit constraint)}$$
$$2X_1 + 3X_2 + d_2^- - d_2^+ = 12 \quad \text{(wiring hours constraint)}$$
$$6X_1 + 5X_2 + d_3^- - d_3^+ = 30 \quad \text{(assembly constraint)}$$
$$X_2 + d_4^- - d_4^+ = 7 \quad \text{(ceiling fan constraint)}$$
$$\text{All } X_i, d_i \text{ variables} \geq 0.$$

Ranking Goals with Priority Levels

A key idea in goal programming is that one goal is more important than another. Priorities are assigned to each deviational variable.

In most goal programming problems, one goal will be more important than another, which in turn will be more important than a third. The idea is that goals can be ranked with respect to their importance in management's eyes. Lower-order goals are considered only after higher-order goals are met. Priorities (P_is) are assigned to each deviational variable—with the ranking that P_1 is the most important goal, P_2 the next most important, then P_3, and so on.

Let's say Harrison Electric sets the priorities shown in the following table:

GOAL	PRIORITY
Reach a profit as much above $30 as possible	P_1
Fully use wiring department hours available	P_2
Avoid assembly department overtime	P_3
Produce at least seven ceiling fans	P_4

Priority 1 is infinitely more important than Priority 2, which is infinitely more important than the next goal, and so on.

This means, in effect, that the priority of meeting the profit goal (P_1) is infinitely more important than the wiring goal (P_2), which is, in turn, infinitely more important than the assembly goal (P_3), which is infinitely more important than producing at least seven ceiling fans (P_4).

With ranking of goals considered, the new objective function becomes

$$\text{Minimize total deviation} = P_1 d_1^- + P_2 d_2^- + P_3 d_3^+ + P_4 d_4^-$$

The constraints remain identical to the previous ones.

Goal Programming with Weighted Goals

When priority levels are used in goal programming, any goal in the top priority level is infinitely more important than the goals in lower priority levels. However, there may be times when one goal is more important than another goal, but it may be only two or three times as important. Instead of placing these goals in different priority levels, they would be placed in the same priority level but with different weights. When using weighted goal programming, the coefficients in the objective function for the deviational variables include both the priority level and the weight. If all goals are in the same priority level, then simply using the weights as objective function coefficients is sufficient.

Consider the Harrison Electric example, in which the least important goal is goal 4 (produce at least seven ceiling fans). Suppose Harrison decides to add another goal of producing at least two chandeliers. The goal of seven ceiling fans is considered twice as important as this goal, so both of these should be in the same priority level. The goal of 2 chandeliers is assigned a weight of 1, while the 7 ceiling fan goal will be given a weight of 2. Both of these will be in priority level 4. A new constraint (goal) would be added:

$$X_1 + d_5^- - d_5^+ = 2 \quad \text{(chandeliers)}$$

IN ACTION | The Use of Goal Programming for Tuberculosis Drug Allocation in Manila

Allocation of resources is critical when applied to the health industry. It is a matter of life and death when neither the right supply nor the correct quantity is available to meet patient demand. This was the case faced by the Manila (Philippines) Health Center, whose drug supply to patients afflicted with Category I tuberculosis (TB) was not being efficiently allocated to its 45 regional health centers. When the TB drug supply does not reach patients on time, the disease becomes worse and can result in death. Only 74% of TB patients were being cured in Manila, 11% short of the 85% target cure rate set by the government. Unlike other diseases, TB can only be treated with four medicines and cannot be cured by alternative drugs.

Researchers at the Mapka Institute of Technology set out to create a model, using goal programming, to optimize the allocation of resources for TB treatment while considering supply constraints. The objective function of the model was to meet the target cure rate of 85% (which is the equivalent of minimizing the underachievement in the allocation of anti-TB drugs to the 45 centers). Four goal constraints considered the interrelationships among variables in the distribution system. Goal 1 was to satisfy the medication requirement (a 6-month regimen) for each patient. Goal 2 was to supply each health center with the proper allocation. Goal 3 was to satisfy the cure rate of 85%. Goal 4 was to satisfy the drug requirements of each health center.

The goal programming model successfully dealt with all of these goals and raised the TB cure rate to 88%, a 13% improvement in drug allocation over the previous distribution approach. This means that 335 lives per year were saved through this thoughtful use of goal programming.

Source: Based on G. J. C. Esmeria. "An Application of Goal Programming in the Allocation of Anti-TB Drugs in Rural Health Centers in the Philippines," *Proceedings of the 12th Annual Conference of the Production and Operations Management Society* (March 2001), Orlando, FL: 50.

PROGRAM 8A

Harrison Electric's Goal Programming Analysis Using QM for Windows: Inputs

	Wt(d+)	Prty(d+)	Wt(d-)	Prty(d-)	X1	X2		RHS
					Harrison Electric Company			
Constraint 1	0	0	1	1	7	6	=	30
Constraint 2	0	0	1	2	2	3	=	12
Constraint 3	1	3	0	0	6	5	=	30
Constraint 4	0	0	1	4	0	1	=	7

PROGRAM 8B

Summary Solution Screen for Harrison Electric's Goal Programming Problem Using QM for Windows

Item			
	Harrison Electric Company Solution		
Decision variable analysis	Value		
X1	0.		
X2	6.		
Priority analysis	Nonachievement		
Priority 1	0.		
Priority 2	0.		
Priority 3	0.		
Priority 4	1.		
Constraint Analysis	RHS	d+ (row i)	d- (row i)
Constraint 1	30.	6.	0.
Constraint 2	12.	6.	0.
Constraint 3	30.	0.	0.
Constraint 4	7.	0.	1.

The new objective function value would be

$$\text{Minimize total deviation} = P_1 d_1^- + P_2 d_2^- + P_3 d_3^+ + P_4 (2 d_4^-) + P_4 d_5^-$$

Note that the ceiling fan goal has a weight of 2. The weight for the chandelier goal is 1. Technically all of the goals in the other priority levels are assigned weights of 1 also.

USING QM FOR WINDOWS TO SOLVE HARRISON'S PROBLEM   QM for Windows goal programming module is illustrated in Programs 8A and 8B. The input screen is shown first, in Program 8A. Note in this first screen that there are two priority level columns for each constraint. For this example, the priority for either the positive or the negative deviation will be zero since the objective function does not contain both types of deviational variables for any of these goals. If a problem had a goal with both deviational variables in the objective function, both priority level columns for this goal (constraint) would contain values other than zero. Also, the weight for each deviational variable contained in the objective function is listed as 1. (It is 0 if the variable is not appearing in the objective function.) If different weights are used, they would be placed in the appropriate weight column within one priority level.

The solution with an analysis of deviations and goal achievement is shown in Program 8B. We see that the first two constraints have negative deviational variables equal to 0, indicating full achievement of those goals. In fact, the positive deviational variables both have values of 6, indicating overachievement of these goals by 6 units each. Goal (constraint) 3 has both deviational variables equal to 0, indicating complete achievement of that goal, whereas goal 4 has a negative deviational variable equal to 1, indicating underachievement by 1 unit.

5   Nonlinear Programming

Linear, integer, and goal programming all assume that a problem's objective function and constraints are linear. That means that they contain no nonlinear terms such as X_1^3, $1/X_2$, $\log X_3$, or $5X_1X_2$. Yet in many mathematical programming problems, the objective function and/or one or more of the constraints are nonlinear.

Unlike with linear programming methods, computational procedures for solving many nonlinear programming (NLP) problems do not always yield an optimal solution. In many NLP problems, a particular solution may be better than any other point nearby, but it may not be the overall best point. This is called a **local optimum**, and the overall best solution is called the **global optimum**. Thus, for a particular problem, a solution technique may indicate that an optimum solution has been found, but it is only a local optimum, so there may be a global optimum

301

that is better. The mathematics involved in solving these problems is beyond the scope of this text. We will rely on Solver in Excel to solve the nonlinear problems presented in this section.

In this section, we examine three categories of NLP problems and illustrate how Excel can be used to search for the solution to these problems. In Solved Problem 10–3, we will see how NLP in Excel can help find the best parameter to use in an exponential smoothing forecasting model.

Nonlinear Objective Function and Linear Constraints

Here is an example of a nonlinear objective function.

The Great Western Appliance Company sells two models of toaster ovens, the Microtoaster (X_1) and the Self-Clean Toaster Oven (X_2). The firm earns a profit of $28 for each Microtoaster regardless of the number sold. Profits for the Self-Clean model, however, increase as more units are sold because of fixed overhead. Profit on this model may be expressed as $21X_2 + 0.25X_2^2$.

Hence the firm's objective function is nonlinear:

$$\text{Maximize profit} = 28X_1 + 21X_2 + 0.25X_2^2$$

Great Western's profit is subject to two linear constraints on production capacity and sales time available:

$$
\begin{aligned}
X_1 + X_2 &\leq 1{,}000 \quad \text{(units of production capacity)} \\
0.5X_1 + 0.4X_2 &\leq 500 \quad \text{(hours of sales time available)} \\
X_1, X_2 &\geq 0
\end{aligned}
$$

Quadratic programming contains squared terms in the objective function.

When an objective function contains squared terms (such as $0.25X_2^2$) and the problem's constraints are linear, it is called a *quadratic programming* problem. A number of useful problems in the field of portfolio selection fall into this category. Quadratic programs can be solved by a modified method of the simplex method. Such work is outside the scope of this text but can be found in sources listed in the Bibliography.

The solution to the Great Western Appliance nonlinear programming problem is shown in Program 9. This was found using Solver in Excel 2013, and there are two important features of this spreadsheet that are different from the previous linear and integer programming examples. First, the *solving method* used for this in Solver is GRG Nonlinear instead of Simplex LP. The second change involves the objective function and the changing cells. For the sake of consistency, values for both X_2 (cell C4) and X_2^2 (cell D7) are shown in Program 9. However, cell D7 is simply cell C4 squared. Thus, when cell C4 changes, D7 will automatically change, and the Changing cells specified in Solver are B4:C4, while D7 is not included.

Both Nonlinear Objective Function and Nonlinear Constraints

An example in which the objective and constraints are both nonlinear.

The annual profit at a medium-sized (200–400 beds) Hospicare Corporation–owned hospital depends on the number of medical patients admitted (X_1) and the number of surgical patients admitted (X_2). The nonlinear objective function for Hospicare is

$$\text{Maximize profit} = \$13X_1 + \$6X_1X_2 + \$5X_2 + \$1/X_2$$

An example of nonlinear constraints.

The corporation identifies three constraints, two of which are also nonlinear, that affect operations. They are

$$
\begin{aligned}
2X_1^2 + 4X_2 &\leq 90 \quad \text{(nursing capacity, in thousands of labor–days)} \\
X_1 + X_2^3 &\leq 75 \quad \text{(x–ray capacity, in thousands)} \\
8X_1 - 2X_2 &\leq 61 \quad \text{(marketing budget limit, in thousands of \$)}
\end{aligned}
$$

Excel's Solver is capable of formulating such a problem. The optimal solution is provided in Program 10.

PROGRAM 9

Excel 2013 Solver Solution for Great Western Appliance NLP Problem

	A	B	C	D	E	F	G
1	Great Western Appliance						
2		Micro	Self-Clean				
3	Variables	X1	X2				
4	Values	0	1000				
5							
6	Terms	X1	X2	X2^2			
7	Calculated Values	0	1000	1000000	Profit		
8	Profit	28	21	0.25	271000		'
9							
10	Constraints				LHS	Sign	RHS
11	Capacity	1	1		1000	≤	1000
12	Hours Available	0.5	0.4		400	≤	500

Solver Parameter Inputs and Selections

Set Objective: E8

By Changing cells: B4:C4

To: Max

Subject to the Constraints:

　　E11:E12 <= G11:G12

Solving Method: GRG Nonlinear

☑　Make Variables Non-Negative

Key Formulas

	E
8	=SUMPRODUCT($B$7:$D$7,B8:D8)
9	
10	LHS
11	=SUMPRODUCT($B$4:$C$4,B11:C11)
12	=SUMPRODUCT($B$4:$C$4,B12:C12)

	B	C	D
7	=B4	=C4	=C4^2

PROGRAM 10

Excel 2013 Solution to the Hospicare NLP Problem

	A	B	C	D	E	F	G	H	I	J
1	Hospicare Corp									
2										
3	Variables	X1	X2							
4	Values	6.0663	4.1003							
5										
6	Terms	X1	X1^2	X1*X2	X2	X2^3	1/X2			
7	Calculated Values	6.0663	36.7995	24.8732	4.1003	68.9337	0.2439	Total Profit		
8	Profit	13	0	6	5		1	248.8457		
9										
10	Constraints							LHS	Sign	RHS
11	Nursing		2		4			90.00	≤	90
12	X-Ray	1				1		75.00	≤	75
13	Budget	8			-2			40.33	≤	61

Solver Parameter Inputs and Selections

Set Objective: H8

By Changing cells: B4:C4

To: Max

Subject to the Constraints:

　　H11:H13 <= J11:J13

Solving Method: GRG Nonlinear

☑　Make Variables Non-Negative

Key Formulas

	H
8	=SUMPRODUCT($B$7:$G$7,B8:G8)

Copy H8 to H11:H13

	B	C	D	E	F	G
7	=B4	=B4^2	=B4*C4	=C4	=C4^3	=1/C4

Linear Objective Function with Nonlinear Constraints

Thermlock Corp. produces massive rubber washers and gaskets like the type used to seal joints on the NASA Space Shuttles. To do so, it combines two ingredients: rubber (X_1) and oil (X_2). The cost of the industrial-quality rubber used is \$5 per pound and the cost of the high-viscosity oil is \$7 per pound. Two of the three constraints Thermlock faces are nonlinear. The firm's objective function and constraints are

$$\text{Minimize costs} = \$5X_1 + \$7X_2$$

$$\text{subject to} \qquad 3X_1 + 0.25X_1^2 + 4X_2 + 0.3X_2^2 \geq 125 \quad \text{(hardness contraint)}$$

$$13X_1 + X_1^3 \geq 80 \quad \text{(tensile strength)}$$

$$0.7X_1 + X_2 \geq 17 \quad \text{(elasticity)}$$

To solve this nonlinear programming, we turn again to Excel. The output is provided in Program 11.

PROGRAM 11

Excel 2013 Solution to the Thermlock NLP Problem

	A	B	C	D	E	F	G	H	I
1	Thermlock Gaskets								
2									
3	Variables	X1	X2						
4	Values	3.325	14.672	Total Cost					
5	Cost	5	7	119.333					
6									
7		X1	X1²	X1³	X2	X2²			
8	Value	3.325	11.058	36.771	14.672	215.276			
9	Constraints						LHS	Sign	RHS
10	Hardness	3	0.25		4	0.3	136.012	≥	125
11	Tensile Strengt	13		1			80	≥	80
12	Elasticity	0.7			1		17	≥	17

Solver Parameter Inputs and Selections

Set Objective: D5

By Changing cells: B4:C4

To: Min

Subject to the Constraints:

    G10:G12 >= I10:I12

Solving Method: GRG Nonlinear

☑ Make Variables Non-Negative

Key Formulas

	D
5	=SUMPRODUCT($B$4:$C$4,B5:C5)

	G
10	=SUMPRODUCT($B$8:$F$8,B10:F10)

Copy G10 to G11:G12

	B	C	D	E	F
8	=B4	=B4^2	=B4^3	=C4	=C4^2

Summary

This chapter addresses three special types of LP problems. The first, integer programming, examines LP problems that cannot have fractional answers. We also note that there are three types of integer programming problems: (1) pure or all-integer programs, (2) mixed problems, in which *some* solution variables need not be integer, and (3) 0–1 problems, in which all solutions are either 0 or 1. We also demonstrate how 0–1 variables can be used to model special situations such as fixed-charge problems. QM for Windows and Excel are used to illustrate computer approaches to these problems.

The latter part of the chapter deals with goal programming. This extension of LP allows problems to have multiple goals. Again, software such as QM for Windows is a powerful tool in solving this offshoot of LP. Finally, the advanced topic of NLP is introduced as a special mathematical programming problem. Excel is seen to be a useful tool in solving simple NLP models.

However, it is important to remember that the solution found for an NLP problem might be a local optimum and not a global optimum.

Glossary

Deviational Variables   Terms that are minimized in a goal programming problem. Like slack variables in LP, they are real. They are the only terms in the objective function.

Global Optimum   The overall best solution to a nonlinear programming problem.

Goal Programming   A mathematical programming technique that permits decision makers to set and prioritize multiple objectives.

Integer Programming   A mathematical programming technique that produces integer solutions to linear programming problems.

Local Optimum   A solution to a nonlinear programming problem which is better than any nearby point, but which may not be the global optimum.

Nonlinear Programming   A category of mathematical programming techniques that allows the objective function and/or constraints to be nonlinear.

Satisficing   The process of coming as close as possible to reaching your set of objectives.

0–1 Integer Programming   Problems in which all decision variables must have integer values of 0 or 1. This is also called a binary variable.

Solved Problems

Solved Problem 1

Consider the 0–1 integer programming problem that follows:

$$\text{Maximize} \quad 50X_1 + 45X_2 + 48X_3$$
$$\text{subject to} \quad 19X_1 + 27X_2 + 34X_3 \leq 80$$
$$22X_1 + 13X_2 + 12X_3 \leq 40$$
$$X_1, X_2, X_3 \text{ must be either 0 or 1}$$

Now reformulate this problem with additional constraints so that no more than two of the three variables can take on a value equal to 1 in the solution. Further, make sure that if $X_1 = 1$, then $X_2 = 1$ also. Then solve the new problem using Excel.

Solution

Excel can handle all-integer, mixed-integer, and 0–1 integer problems. Program 12 below shows two new constraints to handle the reformulated problem. These constraints are

$$X_1 + X_2 + X_3 \leq 2$$

and

$$X_1 - X_2 \quad \leq 0$$

The optimal solution is $X_1 = 1, X_2 = 1, X_3 = 0$, with an objective function value of 95.

PROGRAM 12

Excel 2013 Solution for Solved Problem 1

	A	B	C	D	E	F	G
1	Solved Problem 10-1						
2							
3	Variables	X1	X2	X3			
4	Values	1	1	0	Total		
5	Maximize	50	45	48	95		
6							
7	Constraints				LHS	Sign	RHS
8	Constraint 1	19	27	34	46	≤	80
9	Constraint 2	22	13	12	35	≤	40
10	Constraint 3	1	1	1	2	≤	2
11	Constraint 4	1	-1	0	0	≤	0

Solver Parameter Inputs and Selections

Set Objective: E5

By Changing cells: B4:D4

To: Max

Subject to the Constraints:

E8:E11 <= G8:G11

B4:D4 = binary

Solving Method: Simples LP

☑ **Make Variables Non-Negative**

Key Formulas

	E
5	=SUMPRODUCT($B$4:$D$4,B5:D5)

Copy E5 to E8:E11

Solved Problem 2

Recall the Harrison Electric Company goal programming problem seen in Section 4. Its LP formulation was

$$\text{Maximize profit} = \$7X_1 + \$6X_2$$
$$\text{subject to} \quad 2X_1 + 3X_2 \leq 12 \quad \text{(wiring hours)}$$
$$6X_1 + 5X_2 \leq 30 \quad \text{(assembly hours)}$$
$$X_1, X_2 \geq 0$$

where

X_1 = number of chandeliers produced

X_2 = number of ceiling fans produced

Reformulate Harrison Electrical as a goal programming model with the following goals:

Priority 1: Produce at least 4 chandeliers and 3 ceiling fans.
Priority 2: Limit overtime in the assembly department to 10 hours and in the wiring department to 6 hours.
Priority 3: Maximize profit.

Solution

$$\text{Minimize } P_1(d_1^- + d_2^-) + P_2(d_3^+ + d_4^+) + P_3 d_5^-$$
$$\text{subject to} \quad X_1 + \quad d_1^- - d_1^+ = 4 \Big\}$$
$$X_2 + d_2^- - d_2^+ = 3 \Big\} \; \textit{Priority } 1$$
$$2X_1 + 3X_2 + d_3^- - d_3^+ = 18 \Big\}$$
$$6X_1 + 5X_2 + d_4^- - d_4^+ = 40 \Big\} \; \textit{Priority } 2$$
$$7X_1 + 6X_2 + d_5^- - d_5^+ = 99{,}999 \} \; \textit{Priority } 3$$

In the priority 3 goal constraint, the 99,999 represents an unrealistically high profit. It is just a mathematical trick to use as a target so that we can get as close as possible to the maximum profit.

Solved Problem 3

Program 13A provides an example of the exponential smoothing method for forecasting time series, with the smoothing constant (α) selected to be 0.1. The forecast in time period 1 is assumed to be perfect, so the error and the absolute value of the error are both 0. The mean absolute deviation (MAD) is the measure of accuracy, and the first time period error is not used in computing this since it was simply assumed to be perfect. The MAD is very dependent on the value of α. Use Excel to find the value of α that will minimize the MAD. *Hint:* Instead of writing the entire objective function, simply use the cell already developed in Excel for the MAD. Remember, α must be between 0 and 1.

Solution

The MAD is a nonlinear function, so Solver in Excel can be used to solve this. There is only one constraint: The smoothing constant, α, must be less than or equal to 1. This can be entered directly into the *Add Constraint* window in Solver, with a 1 entered on the right-hand side of the inequality. Program 13B provides the information and the final solution for this. The value for α that minimizes the MAD is 0.3478, and this yields an MAD of 16.70.

Note: Solver can be used in a similar manner to find the best weights to use in a weighted moving average forecast.

PROGRAM 13A   Excel 2013 Spreadsheet for Solved Problem 3

	A	B	C	D	E
1	Forecasting - Exponential Smoothing				
2					
3	α =	0.1000	$F_{t+1} = F_t + \alpha(Y_t - F_t)$		
4	Time Period (t)	Demand (Y_t)	Forecast (F_t)	Error = Y_t - F_t	|error|
5	1	110	110	0	-
6	2	156	110	46.000	46.000
7	3	126	114.6	11.400	11.400
8	4	138	115.74	22.260	22.260
9	5	124	117.966	6.034	6.034
10	6	125	118.5694	6.431	6.431
11	7	160	119.21246	40.788	40.788
12	8		123.291214	MAD=	22.152
13					
14	F_1 is assumed to be a perfect forecast.				
15	MAD is based on time periods 2 through 7				

Key Formulas

	C	D	E
6	=C5+$B$3*D5	=B6-C6	=ABS(B6-C6)

Copy C6:E6 to C7:E11

	E
12	=AVERAGE(E6:E11)

PROGRAM 13B

Excel 2013 Spreadsheet Solution for Solved Problem 3

⊿	A	B	C	D	E
1	Forecasting - Exponential Smoothing				
2					
3	$\alpha =$ 0.3478		$F_{t+1} = F_t + \alpha(Y_t-F_t)$		
4	Time Period (t)	Demand (Y_t)	Forecast (F_t)	Error = Y_t - F_t	|error|
5	1	110	110	0	--
6	2	156	110	46.000	46.000
7	3	126	125.9999998	0.000	0.000
8	4	138	125.9999999	12.000	12.000
9	5	124	130.1739129	-6.174	6.174
10	6	125	128.026465	-3.026	3.026
11	7	160	126.9737815	33.026	33.026
12	8		138.4611617	MAD=	16.704
13					
14	F_1 is assumed to be a perfect forecast.				
15	MAD is based on time periods 2 through 7				

Solver Parameter Inputs and Selections

Set Objective: E12

By Changing cells: B3

To: Min

Subject to the Constraints:

   B3 <= 1

Solving Method: GRG Nonlinear

☑ **Make Variables Non-Negative**

Key Formulas

⊿	C	D	E
6	=C5+$B$3*D5	=B6-C6	=ABS(B6-C6)

Copy C6:E6 to C7:E11

⊿	E
12	=AVERAGE(E6:E11)

Self-Test

- Before taking the self-test, refer to the learning objectives at the beginning of the chapter, the notes in the margins, and the glossary at the end of the chapter.
- Use the key at the end of the chapter to correct your answers.
- Restudy pages that correspond to any questions that you answered incorrectly or material you feel uncertain about.

1. If all of the decision variables require integer solutions, the problem is
   a. a pure integer programming type of problem.
   b. a simplex method type of problem.
   c. a mixed-integer programming type of problem.
   d. a Gorsky type of problem.
2. In a mixed-integer programming problem
   a. some integers must be even and others must be odd.
   b. some decision variables must require integer results only and some variables must allow for continuous results.
   c. different objectives are mixed together even though they sometimes have relative priorities established.
3. A model containing a linear objective function and linear constraints but requiring that one or more of the decision variables take on an integer value in the final solution is called
   a. an integer programming problem.
   b. a goal programming problem.
   c. a nonlinear programming problem.
   d. a multiple objective LP problem.

4. An integer programming solution can never produce a greater profit than the LP solution to the same problem.
   a. True
   b. False
5. In goal programming, if all the goals are achieved, the value of the objective function will always be zero.
   a. True
   b. False
6. The objective in a goal programming problem with one priority level is to maximize the sum of the deviational variables.
   a. True
   b. False
7. Nobel Laureate Herbert A. Simon of Carnegie-Mellon University says that modern managers should always optimize, not satisfice.
   a. True
   b. False
8. The fixed-charge problem is typically classified as
   a. a goal programming problem.
   b. a 0–1 integer problem.

c. a quadratic programming problem.

d. an assignment problem.

9. The 0–1 integer programming problem

a. requires the decision variables to have values between 0 and 1.

b. requires that the constraints all have coefficients between 0 and 1.

c. requires that the decision variables have coefficients between 0 and 1.

d. requires the decision variables to be equal to 0 or 1.

10. Goal programming

a. requires only that you know whether the goal is direct profit maximization or cost minimization.

b. allows you to have multiple goals.

c. is an algorithm with the goal of a quicker solution to the pure integer programming problem.

d. is an algorithm with the goal of a quicker solution to the mixed-integer programming problem.

11. Nonlinear programming includes problems

a. in which the objective function is linear but some constraints are not linear.

b. in which the constraints are linear but the objective function is not linear.

c. in which both the objective function and all of the constraints are not linear.

d. solvable by quadratic programming.

e. all of the above.

Discussion Questions and Problems

Discussion Questions

1 Compare the similarities and differences of linear and goal programming.

2 A linear programming problem was developed, and the feasible region was found. If the additional restriction that all variables must be integers were added to the problem, how would the size of the feasible region change? How would the optimal value of the objective function change?

3 List the advantages and disadvantages of solving integer programming problems by (a) rounding off and (b) enumeration.

4 What is the difference between the three types of integer programming problems? Which do you think is most common, and why?

5 What is meant by "satisficing," and why is the term often used in conjunction with goal programming?

6 What are deviational variables? How do they differ from decision variables in traditional LP problems?

7 If you were the president of the college you are attending and were employing goal programming to assist in decision making, what might your goals be? What kinds of constraints would you include in your model?

8 What does it mean to rank goals in goal programming? How does this affect the problem's solution?

9 Which of the following are NLP problems, and why?

(a) Maximize profit $= 3X_1 + 5X_2 + 99X_3$

subject to $\quad X_1 \geq 10$

$\qquad X_2 \leq 5$

$\qquad X_3 \geq 18$

(b) Maximize cost $= 25X_1 + 30X_2 + 8X_1X_2$

subject to $\qquad X_1 \qquad \geq 8$

$\qquad X_1 + \quad X_2 \geq 12$

$\qquad 0.0005X_1 - \quad X_2 = 11$

(c) Maximize $Z = P_1d_1^- + P_2d_2^+ + P_3^+$

subject to $\qquad X_1 + X_2 + d_1^- - d_1^+ = 300$

$\qquad X_2 + d_2^- - d_2^+ = 200$

$\qquad X_1 + \quad d_3^- - d_3^+ = 100$

(d) Maximize profit $= 3X_1 + 4X_2$

subject to $\qquad X_1^2 - 5X_2 \geq 8$

$\qquad 3X_1 + 4X_2 \geq 12$

(e) Minimize cost $= 18X_1 + 5X_2 + X_2^2$

subject to $\qquad 4X_1 - 3X_2 \geq 8$

$\qquad X_1 + \quad X_2 \geq 18$

Are any of these quadratic programming problems?

Problems*

10 Elizabeth Bailey is the owner and general manager of Princess Brides, which provides a wedding planning service in Southwest Louisiana. She uses radio advertising to market her business. Two types of ads are available—those during prime time hours and those at other times. Each prime time ad costs $390 and reaches 8,200 people, while the offpeak ads each cost $240 and reach 5,100 people. Bailey has budgeted $1,800 per week for advertising. Based on comments from her customers, Bailey wants to have

---

Note: ☺ means the problem may be solved with QM for Windows; ✖ means the problem may be solved with Excel; and ☺ means the problem may be solved with QM for Windows and/or Excel.

at least 2 prime time ads and no more than 6 off peak ads.

(a) Formulate this as a linear program.

(b) Find a good or optimal integer solution for part (a) by rounding off or making an educated guess at the answer.

(c) Solve this as an integer programming problem using a computer.

11 A group of college students is planning a camping trip during the upcoming break. The group must hike several miles through the woods to get to the campsite, and anything that is needed on this trip must be packed in a knapsack and carried to the campsite. One particular student, Tina Shawl, has identified eight items that she would like to take on the trip, but the combined weight is too great to take all of them. She has decided to rate the utility of each item on a scale of 1 to 100, with 100 being the most beneficial. The item weights in pounds and their utility values are given below.

ITEM	1	2	3	4	5	6	7	8
WEIGHT	8	1	7	6	3	12	5	14
UTILITY	80	20	50	55	50	75	30	70

Recognizing that the hike to the campsite is a long one, a limit of 35 pounds has been set as the maximum total weight of the items to be carried.

(a) Formulate this as a 0–1 programming problem to maximize the total utility of the items carried. Solve this knapsack problem using a computer.

(b) Suppose item number 3 is an extra battery pack, which may be used with several of the other items. Tina has decided that she will only take item number 5, a CD player, if she also takes item number 3. On the other hand, if she takes item number 3, she may or may not take item number 5. Modify this problem to reflect this and solve the new problem.

12 Student Enterprises sells two sizes of wall posters, a large 3- by 4-foot poster and a smaller 2- by 3-foot poster. The profit earned from the sale of each large poster is $3; each smaller poster earns $2. The firm, although profitable, is not large; it consists of one art student, Jan Meising, at the University of Kentucky. Because of her classroom schedule, Jan has the following weekly constraints: (1) up to three large posters can be sold, (2) up to five smaller posters can be sold, (3) up to 10 hours can be spent on posters during the week, with each large poster requiring 2 hours of work and each small one taking 1 hour. With the semester almost over, Jan plans on taking a three-month summer vacation to England

and doesn't want to leave any unfinished posters behind. Find the integer solution that will maximize her profit.

13 An airline owns an aging fleet of Boeing 737 jet airplanes. It is considering a major purchase of up to 17 new Boeing model 787 and 767 jets. The decision must take into account numerous cost and capability factors, including the following: (1) the airline can finance up to $1.6 billion in purchases; (2) each Boeing 787 will cost $80 million, and each Boeing 767 will cost $110 million; (3) at least one-third of the planes purchased should be the longer-range 787; (4) the annual maintenance budget is to be no more than $8 million; (5) the annual maintenance cost per 787 is estimated to be $800,000, and it is $500,000 for each 767 purchased; and (6) each 787 can carry 125,000 passengers per year, whereas each 767 can fly 81,000 passengers annually. Formulate this as an integer programming problem to maximize the annual passenger-carrying capability. What category of integer programming problem is this? Solve this problem.

14 Trapeze Investments is a venture capital firm that is currently evaluating six different investment opportunities. There is not sufficient capital to invest in all of these, but more than one will be selected. A 0–1 integer programming model is planned to help determine which of the six opportunities to choose. Variables X_1, X_2, X_3, X_4, X_5, and X_6 represent the six choices. For each of the following situations, write a constraint (or several constraints) that would be used.

(a) At least 3 of these choices are to be selected.

(b) Either investment 1 or investment 4 must be undertaken, but not both.

(c) If investment 4 is selected, then investment 6 must also be selected. However, if investment 4 is not selected, it is still possible to select number 6.

(d) Investment 5 cannot be selected unless both investments 2 and 3 are also selected.

(e) Investment 5 must be selected if both investments 2 and 3 are also selected.

15 Horizon Wireless, a cellular telephone company, is expanding into a new era. Relay towers are necessary to provide wireless telephone coverage to the different areas of the city. A grid is superimposed on a map of the city to help determine where the towers should be located. The grid consists of 8 areas labeled A through H. Six possible tower locations (numbered 1–6) have been identified, and each location could serve several areas. The following table indicates the areas served by each of the towers.

TOWER LOCATION	1	2	3	4	5	6
AREAS SERVED	A, B, D	B, C, G	C, D, E, F	E, F, H	E, G, H	A, D, F

Formulate this as a 0–1 programming model to minimize the total number of towers required to cover all the areas. Solve this using a computer.

16 Innis Construction Company specializes in building moderately priced homes in Cincinnati, Ohio. Tom Innis has identified eight potential locations to construct new single-family dwellings, but he cannot put up homes on all of the sites because he has only $300,000 to invest in all projects. The accompanying table shows the cost of constructing homes in each area and the expected profit to be made from the sale of each home. Note that the home-building costs differ considerably due to lot costs, site preparation, and differences in the models to be built. Note also that a fraction of a home cannot be built.

LOCATION	COST OF BUILDING AT THIS SITE ($)	EXPECTED PROFIT ($)
Clifton	60,000	5,000
Mt. Auburn	50,000	6,000
Mt. Adams	82,000	10,000
Amberly	103,000	12,000
Norwood	50,000	8,000
Covington	41,000	3,000
Roselawn	80,000	9,000
Eden Park	69,000	10,000

(a) Formulate Innis's problem using 0–1 integer programming.

(b) Solve with QM for Windows or Excel.

17 A real estate developer is considering three possible projects: a small apartment complex, a small shopping center, and a mini-warehouse. Each of these requires different funding over the next two years, and the net present value of the investments also varies. The following table provides the required investment amounts (in $1,000s) and the net present value (NPV) of each (also expressed in $1,000s):

		INVESTMENT	
	NPV	YEAR 1	YEAR 2
Apartment	18	40	30
Shopping center	15	30	20
Mini-warehouse	14	20	20

The company has $80,000 to invest in year 1 and $50,000 to invest in year 2.

(a) Develop an integer programming model to maximize the NPV in this situation.

(b) Solve the problem in part (a) using computer software. Which of the three projects would be undertaken if NPV is maximized? How much money would be used each year?

18 Refer to the real estate investment situation in Problem 17.

(a) Suppose that the shopping center and the apartment would be on adjacent properties, and the shopping center would only be considered if the apartment were also built. Formulate the constraint that would stipulate this.

(b) Formulate a constraint that would force exactly two of the three projects to be undertaken.

19 Triangle Utilities provides electricity for three cities. The company has four electric generators that are used to provide electricity. The main generator operates 24 hours per day, with an occasional shutdown for routine maintenance. Three other generators (1, 2, and 3) are available to provide additional power when needed. A startup cost is incurred each time one of these generators is started. The startup costs are $6,000 for 1, $5,000 for 2, and $4,000 for 3. These generators are used in the following ways: A generator may be started at 6:00 A.M. and run for either 8 hours or 16 hours, or it may be started at 2:00 P.M. and run for 8 hours (until 10:00 P.M.). All generators except the main generator are shut down at 10:00 P.M. Forecasts indicate the need for 3,200 megawatts more than provided by the main generator before 2:00 P.M., and this need goes up to 5,700 megawatts between 2:00 and 10:00 P.M. Generator 1 may provide up to 2,400 megawatts, generator 2 may provide up to 2,100 megawatts, and generator 3 may provide up to 3,300 megawatts. The cost per megawatt used per eight hour period is $8 for 1, $9 for 2, and $7 for 3.

(a) Formulate this problem as an integer programming problem to determine the least-cost way to meet the needs of the area.

(b) Solve using computer software.

20 The campaign manager for a politician who is running for reelection to a political office is planning the campaign. Four ways to advertise have been selected: TV ads, radio ads, billboards, and newspaper ads. The cost of these are $900 for each TV ad, $500 for each radio ad, $600 for a billboard for one month, and $180 for each newspaper ad. The audience reached by each type of advertising has been

estimated to be 40,000 for each TV ad, 32,000 for each radio ad, 34,000 for each billboard, and 17,000 for each newspaper ad. The total monthly advertising budget is $16,000. The following goals have been established and ranked:

1. The number of people reached should be at least 1,500,000.
2. The total monthly advertising budget should not be exceeded.
3. Together, the number of ads on either TV or radio should be at least 6.
4. No more than 10 ads of any one type of advertising should be used.

(a) Formulate this as a goal programming problem.
(b) Solve this using computer software.
(c) Which goals are exactly met and which of them are not?

21 Geraldine Shawhan is president of Shawhan File Works, a firm that manufactures two types of metal file cabinets. The demand for her two-drawer model is up to 600 cabinets per week; demand for a three-drawer cabinet is limited to 400 per week. Shawhan File Works has a weekly operating capacity of 1,300 hours, with the two-drawer cabinet taking 1 hour to produce and the three-drawer cabinet requiring 2 hours. Each two-drawer model sold yields a $10 profit, and the profit for the large model is $15. Shawhan has listed the following goals in order of importance:

1. Attain a profit as close to $11,000 as possible each week.
2. Avoid underutilization of the firm's production capacity.
3. Sell as many two- and three-drawer cabinets as the demand indicates.

Set this up as a goal programming problem.

22 Solve Problem 21. Are any goals unachieved in this solution? Explain.

23 Hilliard Electronics produces specially coded computer chips for laser surgery in 64MB, 256MB, and 512MB sizes. (1MB means that the chip holds 1 million bytes of information.) To produce a 64MB chip requires 8 hours of labor, a 256MB chip takes 13 hours, and a 512MB chip requires 16 hours. Hilliard's monthly production capacity is 1,200 hours. Mr. Blank, the firm's sales manager, estimates that the maximum monthly sales of the 64MB, 256MB, and 512MB chips are 40, 50, and 60, respectively. The company has the following goals (ranked in order from most important to least important):

1. Fill an order from the best customer for thirty 64MB chips and thirty-five 256MB chips.
2. Provide sufficient chips to at least equal the sales estimates set by Mr. Blank.
3. Avoid underutilization of the production capacity.

Formulate this problem using goal programming.

24 An Oklahoma manufacturer makes two products: speaker telephones (X_1) and pushbutton telephones (X_2). The following goal programming model has been formulated to find the number of each to produce each day to meet the firm's goals:

Minimize $P_1 d_1^- + P_2 d_2^- + P_3 d_3^+ + P_4 d_1^+$

subject to

$$2X_1 + 4X_2 + d_1^- - d_1^+ = 80$$
$$8X_1 + 10X_2 + d_2^- - d_2^+ = 320$$
$$8X_1 + 6X_2 + d_3^- - d_3^+ = 240$$

$$\text{all } X_i, d_i \geq 0$$

Find the optimal solution using a computer.

25 Major Bill Bligh, director of the Army War College's new 6-month attaché training program, is concerned about how the 20 officers taking the course spend their precious time while in his charge. Major Bligh recognizes that there are 168 hours per week and thinks that his students have been using them rather inefficiently. Bligh lets

X_1 = number of hours of sleep needed per week

X_2 = number of personal hours (eating, personal hygiene, handling laundary, and so on)

X_3 = number of hours of class and studying

X_4 = number of hours of social time off base (dating, sports, family visits, and so on)

He thinks that students should study 30 hours a week to have time to absorb material. This is his most important goal. Bligh feels that students need at most 7 hours sleep per night on average and that this goal is number 2. He believes that goal number 3 is to provide at least 20 hours per week of social time.

(a) Formulate this as a goal programming problem.
(b) Solve the problem using computer software.

26 Mick Garcia, a certified financial planner (CFP) has been asked by a client to invest $250,000. This money may be placed in stocks, bonds, or a mutual fund in real estate. The expected return on investment is 13% for stocks, 8% for bonds, and 10% for real estate. While the client would like a very high expected return, she would be satisfied with a 10% expected return on her money. Due to risk considerations, several goals have been established to keep the risk at an acceptable level. One goal is to put at least 30% of the money in bonds. Another goal is that the amount of money in real estate should not exceed 50% of the money invested in stocks and bonds combined. In addition to these goals, there is one absolute restriction. Under no circumstances should more than $150,000 be invested in any one area.

(a) Formulate this as a goal programming problem. Assume that all of the goals are equally important.

(b) Use any available software to solve this problem. How much money should be put in each of the investment options? What is the total return? Which of the goals are not met?

27 Hinkel Rotary Engine, Ltd., produces four- and six-cylinder models of automobile engines. The firm's profit for each four-cylinder engine sold during its quarterly production cycle is $1,800 - $50X_1$, where X_1 is the number sold. Hinkel makes $2,400 - $70X_2$ for each of the larger engines sold, with X_2 equal to the number of six-cylinder engines sold. There are 5,000 hours of production time available during each production cycle. A four-cylinder engine requires 100 hours of production time, whereas six-cylinder engines take 130 hours to manufacture. Formulate this production planning problem for Hinkel.

28 Motorcross of Wisconsin produces two models of snowmobiles, the XJ6 and the XJ8. In any given production-planning week Motorcross has 40 hours available in its final testing bay. Each XJ6 requires 1 hour to test and each XJ8 takes 2 hours. The revenue (in $1,000s) for the firm is nonlinear and is stated as (Number of XJ6s)(4 − 0.1 number of XJ6s) + (Number of XJ8s)(5 − 0.2 number of XJ8s).

(a) Formulate this problem.
(b) Solve using Excel.

29 During the busiest season of the year, Green-Gro Fertilizer produces two types of fertilizers. The standard type (X) is just fertilizer, and the other type (Y) is a special fertilizer and weed-killer combination. The following model has been developed to determine how much of each type should be produced to maximize profit subject to a labor constraint:

Maximize profit $= 12X − 0.04X^2 + 15Y − 0.06Y^2$
subject to $\qquad 2X + 4Y \leq 160$ hours
$$X, Y \geq 0$$

Find the optimal solution to this problem.

30 Pat McCormack, a financial advisor for Investors R Us, is evaluating two stocks in a particular industry. He wants to minimize the variance of a portfolio consisting of these two stocks, but he wants to have an expected return of at least 9%. After obtaining historical data on the variance and returns, he develops the following nonlinear program:

Minimize portfolio variance $= 0.16X^2 + 0.2XY + 0.09Y^2$
subject to $\qquad X + Y = 1$ (all funds must be invested)
$0.11X + 0.08Y \geq 0.09$ (return on the investment)
$$X, Y \geq 0$$

where

$X =$ proportion of money invested in stock 1
$Y =$ proportion of money invested in stock 2

Solve this using Excel and determine how much to invest in each of the two stocks. What is the return for this portfolio? What is the variance of this portfolio?

31 Summertime Tees sells two very popular styles of embroidered shirts in southern Florida: a tank top and a regular T-shirt. The cost of the tank top is $6, and the cost of the T-shirt is $8. The demand for these is sensitive to the price, and historical data indicate that the weekly demands are given by

$$X_1 = 500 − 12P_1$$
$$X_2 = 400 − 15P_2$$

where

$X_1 =$ demand for tank top
$P_1 =$ price for tank top
$X_2 =$ demand for regular T-shirt
$P_2 =$ price for regular T-shirt

(a) Develop an equation for the total profit.
(b) Use Excel to find the optimal solution to the following nonlinear program. Use the profit function developed in part (a).

Maximize profit

subject to $\qquad X_1 = 500 − 12P_1$
$X_2 = 400 − 15P_2$
$P_1 \leq 20$
$P_2 \leq 25$
$X_1, P_1, X_2, P_2 \geq 0$

32 The integer programming problem on the following page has been developed to help First National Bank decide where, out of 10 possible sites, to locate four new branch offices:

where X_i represents Winter Park, Maitland, Osceola, Downtown, South Orlando, Airport, Winter Garden, Apopka, Lake Mary, Cocoa Beach, for i equals 1 to 10, respectively.

(a) Where should the four new sites be located, and what will be the expected return?
(b) If at least one new branch *must* be opened in Maitland or Osceola, will this change the answers? Add the new constraint and rerun.
(c) The expected return at Apopka was overestimated. The correct value is $160,000 per year (i.e., 160). Using the original assumptions (namely, ignoring (b)), does your answer to part (a) change?

33 In Solved Problem 3, nonlinear programming was used to find the best value for the smoothing constant, α, in an exponential smoothing forecasting problem. To see how much the MAD can vary due to the selection of the smoothing constant, use Excel and the data in Program 13A to find the value of the

smoothing constant that would maximize the MAD. Compare this MAD to the minimum MAD found in the solved problem.

 34 Using the data in Solved Problem 3, develop a spreadsheet for a 2-period weighted moving average forecast with weights of 0.6 (w_1) for the most recent period and 0.4 (w_2) for the other period.

Note these weights sum to 1, so the forecast is simply

$$\text{Forecast for next period} = w_1(\text{Value in current period}) + w_2(\text{Value in last period.})$$

Find the weights for this 2-period weighted moving average that would minimize the MAD. (*Hint:* The weights must sum to 1.)

IP for Problem 32

Maximize expected returns $= 120X_1 + 100X_2 + 110X_3 + 140X_4 + 155X_5 + 128X_6 + 145X_7 + 190X_8 + 170X_9 + 150X_{10}$

subject to

$$20X_1 + 30X_2 + 20X_3 + 25X_4 + 30X_5 + 30X_6 + 25X_7 + 20X_8 + 25X_9 + 30X_{10} \leq 110$$
$$15X_1 + 5X_2 + 20X_3 + 20X_4 + 5X_5 + 5X_6 + 10X_7 + 20X_8 + 5X_9 + 20X_{10} \leq 50$$
$$X_2 + X_6 + X_7 + X_9 + X_{10} \leq 3$$
$$X_2 + X_3 + X_5 + X_8 + X_9 \geq 2$$
$$X_1 + X_3 + X_{10} \geq 1$$
$$X_1 + X_2 + X_3 + X_4 + X_5 + X_6 + X_7 + X_8 + X_9 + X_{10} \leq 4$$

$$\text{all } X_i = 0 \text{ or } 1$$

Internet Homework Problems

See our Internet home page, at www.pearsonhighered.com/render, for additional homework problems 35 to 40.

Case Study

Schank Marketing Research

Schank Marketing Research has just signed contracts to conduct studies for four clients. At present, three project managers are free for assignment to the tasks. Although all are capable of handling each assignment, the times and cost to complete the studies depend on the experience and knowledge of each manager. Using his judgment, John Schank, the president, has been able to establish a cost for each possible assignment. These costs, which are really the salaries each manager would draw on each task, are summarized in the table on the next page.

Schank is very hesitant about neglecting NASA, which has been an important customer in the past. (NASA has employed the firm to study the public's attitude toward the Space Shuttle and proposed Space Station.) In addition, Schank has promised to try to provide Ruth a salary of at least $3,000 on his next assignment. From previous contracts, Schank also knows that Gardener does not get along well with the management at CBT Television, so he hopes to avoid assigning her to CBT. Finally, as Hines Corporation is also an old and

valued client, Schank feels that it is twice as important to assign a project manager immediately to Hines's task as it is to provide one to General Foundry, a brand-new client. Schank wants to minimize the total costs of all projects while considering each of these goals. He feels that all of these goals are important, but if he had to rank them, he would put his concern about NASA first, his worry about Gardener second, his need to keep Hines Corporation happy third, his promise to Ruth fourth, and his concern about minimizing all costs last.

Each project manager can handle, at most, one new client.

Discussion Questions

1. If Schank were not concerned about noncost goals, how would he formulate this problem so that it could be solved quantitatively?
2. Develop a formulation that will incorporate all five objectives.

PROJECT MANAGER	CLIENT			
	HINES CORP.	NASA	GENERAL FOUNDRY	CBT TELEVISION
Gardener	$3,200	$3,000	$2,800	$2,900
Ruth	2,700	3,200	3,000	3,100
Hardgraves	1,900	2,100	3,300	2,100

Case Study

Oakton River Bridge

The Oakton River had long been considered an impediment to the development of a certain medium-sized metropolitan area in the southeast. Lying to the east of the city, the river made it difficult for people living on its eastern bank to commute to jobs in and around the city and to take advantage of the shopping and cultural attractions that the city had to offer. Similarly, the river inhibited those on its western bank from access to the ocean resorts lying one hour to the east. The bridge over the Oakton River had been built prior to World War II and was grossly inadequate to handle the existing traffic, much less the increased traffic that would accompany the forecasted growth in the area. A congressional delegation from the state prevailed upon the federal government to fund a major portion of a new toll bridge over the Oakton River and the state legislature appropriated the rest of the needed monies for the project.

Progress in construction of the bridge has been in accordance with what was anticipated at the start of construction. The state highway commission, which will have operational jurisdiction over the bridge, has concluded that the opening of the bridge for traffic is likely to take place at the beginning of the next summer, as scheduled. A personnel task force has been established to recruit, train, and schedule the workers needed to operate the toll facility.

The personnel task force is well aware of the budgetary problems facing the state. They have taken as part of their mandate the requirement that personnel costs be kept as low as possible. One particular area of concern is the number of toll collectors that will be needed. The bridge is scheduling three shifts of collectors: shift A from midnight to 8 A.M., shift B from 8 A.M. to 4 P.M., and shift C from 4 P.M. to midnight. Recently, the state employees union negotiated a contract with the state which requires that all toll collectors be permanent, full-time employees. In addition, all collectors must work a five-on, two-off schedule on the same shift. Thus, for example, a worker could be assigned to work Tuesday, Wednesday, Thursday, Friday, and Saturday on shift A, followed by Sunday and Monday off. An employee could not be scheduled to work, say, Tuesday on shift A followed by Wednesday, Thursday, Friday, and Saturday on shift B or on any other mixture of shifts during a 5-day block. The

employees would choose their assignments in order of their seniority.

The task force has received projections of traffic flow on the bridge by day and hour. These projections are based on extrapolations of existing traffic patterns—the pattern of commuting, shopping, and beach traffic currently experienced with growth projections factored in. Standards data from other state-operated toll facilities have allowed the task force to convert these traffic flows into toll collector requirements, that is, the minimum number of collectors required per shift, per day, to handle the anticipated traffic load. These toll collector requirements are summarized in the following table:

Minimum Number of Toll Collectors Required per Shift

SHIFT	SUN.	MON.	TUE.	WED.	THU.	FRI.	SAT.
A	8	13	12	12	13	13	15
B	10	10	10	10	10	13	15
C	15	13	13	12	12	13	8

The numbers in the table include one or two extra collectors per shift to fill in for collectors who call in sick and to provide relief for collectors on their scheduled breaks. Note that each of the eight collectors needed for shift A on Sunday, for example, could have come from any of the A shifts scheduled to begin on Wednesday, Thursday, Friday, Saturday, or Sunday.

Discussion Questions

1. Determine the minimum number of toll collectors that would have to be hired to meet the requirements expressed in the table.
2. The union had indicated that it might lift its opposition to the mixing of shifts in a 5-day block in exchange for additional compensation and benefits. By how much could the number of toll collectors required be reduced if this is done?

Source: Based on B. Render, R. M. Stair, and I. Greenberg. *Cases and Readings in Management Science*, 2nd ed., 1990, pp. 55–56. Reprinted by permission of Prentice Hall, Upper Saddle River, NJ.

Bibliography

Aköz, Onur, and Dobrila Petrovic. "A Fuzzy Goal Programming Method with Imprecise Goal Hierarchy," *European Journal of Operational Research* 181, 3 (September 2007): 1427–1433.

Araz, Ceyhun, Pinar Mizrak Ozfirat, and Irem Ozkarahan. "An Integrated Multicriteria Decision-Making Methodology for Outsourcing Management," *Computers & Operations Research* 34, 12 (December 2007): 3738–3756.

Bertsimas, Dimitris, Christopher Darnell, and Robert Soucy. "Portfolio Construction through Mixed-Integer Programming at Grantham, Mayo, Van Otterloo and Company," *Interfaces* 29, 1 (January 1999): 49–66.

Chang, Ching-Ter. "Multi-Choice Goal Programming," *Omega* 25, 4 (August 2007): 389–396.

Charnes, A., and W. W. Cooper. *Management Models and Industrial Applications of Linear Programming*, Vols. I and II. New York: John Wiley & Sons, Inc.1961.

Dawid, Herbert, Johannes König, and Christine Strauss. "An Enhanced Rostering Model for Airline Crews," *Computers & Operations Research* 28, 7 (June 2001): 671–688.

Drees, Lawrence David, and Wilbert E. Wilhelm. "Scheduling Experiments on a Nuclear Reactor Using Mixed Integer Programming," *Computers & Operations Research* 28, 10 (September 2001): 1013–1037.

Hueter, Jackie, and William Swart. "An Integrated Labor-Management System for Taco Bell," *Interfaces* 28, 1 (January–February 1998): 75–91.

Ignizio, James P. *Introduction to Linear Goal Programming*. Beverly Hills: Sage Publications, 1985.

Katok, Elena, and Dennis Ott. "Using Mixed-Integer Programming to Reduce Label Changes in the Coors Aluminum Can Plant," *Interfaces* 30, 2 (March 2000): 1–12.

Land, Alisa, and Susan Powell. "A Survey of the Operational Use of ILP Models," *Annals of Operations Research* 149, 1 (2007): 147–156.

Lee, Sang M., and Marc J. Schniederjans. "A Multicriterial Assignment Problem: A Goal Programming Approach," *Interfaces* 13, 4 (August 1983): 75–79.

Pati, Rupesh Kumar, Prem Vrat, and Pradeep Kumar. "A Goal Programming Model for a Paper Recycling System," *Omega* 36, 3 (June 2008): 405–417.

Reyes, Pedro M., and Gregory V. Frazier. "Goal Programming Model for Grocery Shelf Space Allocation," *European Journal of Operational Research* 181, 2 (September 2007): 634–644.

Wadhwa, Vijay, and A. Ravi Ravindran. "Vendor Selection in Outsourcing," *Computers & Operations Research* 34, 12 (December 2007): 3725–3737.

Zangwill, W. I. *Nonlinear Programming: A Unified Approach*. Upper Saddle River, NJ: Prentice Hall, 1969.

Solutions to Selected Problems

10   (a) 2 prime-time ads per week, 4.25 off-peak ads per week, audience $= 38,075$ (b) 2 prime-time ads per week, 4 off-peak ads per week, audience $= 36,800$

(c) 4 prime-time ads per week, 1 off-peak ads per week, audience $= 37,900$

12   3 large posters and 4 small posters

16   Build at Mt. Auburn, Mt. Adams, Norwood, Covington, and Eden Park.

18   (a) $X_1 \geq X_2$ (b) $X_1 + X_2 + X_3 = 2$

20   (b) 0 TV, 0.73 radio, 0 billboard, and 88.86 newspaper ads

24 $X_1 = 15, X_2 = 20$

28   18.3 XJ6 and 10.8 XJ8; Revenue $= 70,420$.

30   0.333 in stock 1 and 0.667 in stock 2; variance $= 0.102$; return $= 0.09$

Solutions to Self-Tests

1.	a	**5.**	a	**9.**	d
2.	b	**6.**	b	**10.**	b
3.	a	**7.**	b	**11.**	e
4.	a	**8.**	b		

Simulation Modeling

From Chapter 13 of *Quantitative Analysis for Management*, Twelfth Edition. Barry Render, Ralph M. Stair, Jr., Michael E. Hanna, and Trevor S. Hale. Copyright © 2015 by Pearson Education, Inc. All rights reserved.

1   Introduction

We are all aware to some extent of the importance of simulation models in our world. Boeing Corporation and Airbus Industries, for example, commonly build **simulation** models of their proposed jet aircraft and then test the aerodynamic properties of the models. Your local civil defense organization may carry out rescue and evacuation practices as it simulates the natural disaster conditions of a hurricane or tornado. The U.S. Army simulates enemy attacks and defense strategies in war games played on a computer. Business students take courses that use management games to simulate realistic competitive business situations. And thousands of business, government, and service organizations develop simulation models to assist in making decisions concerning inventory control, maintenance scheduling, plant layout, investments, and sales forecasting.

As a matter of fact, simulation is one of the most widely used quantitative analysis tools. Various surveys of the largest U.S. corporations reveal that over half use simulation in corporate planning.

Simulation sounds like it may be the solution to all management problems. This is, unfortunately, by no means true. Yet we think you may find it one of the most flexible and fascinating of the quantitative techniques in your studies. Let's begin our discussion of simulation with a simple definition.

To *simulate* is to try to duplicate the features, appearance, and characteristics of a real system. In this chapter we show how to simulate a business or management system by building a *mathematical model* that comes as close as possible to representing the reality of the system. We won't build any *physical* models, as might be used in airplane wind tunnel simulation tests. But just as physical model airplanes are tested and modified under experimental conditions, our mathematical models are used to experiment and to estimate the effects of various actions. The idea behind simulation is to imitate a real-world situation mathematically, then to study its properties and operating characteristics, and, finally, to draw conclusions and make action decisions based on the results of the simulation. In this way, the real-life system is not touched until the advantages and disadvantages of what may be a major policy decision are first measured on the system's model.

The idea behind simulation is to imitate a real-world situation with a mathematical model that does not affect operations. The seven steps of simulation are illustrated in Figure 1.

Using simulation, a manager should (1) define a problem, (2) introduce the variables associated with the problem, (3) construct a simulation model, (4) set up possible courses of action for testing, (5) run the simulation experiment, (6) consider the results (possibly deciding to modify the model or change data inputs), and (7) decide what course of action to take. These steps are illustrated in Figure 1.

The problems tackled by simulation can range from very simple to extremely complex, from bank teller lines to an analysis of the U.S. economy. Although very small simulations can be conducted by hand, effective use of this technique requires some automated means of calculation, namely, a computer. Even large-scale models, simulating perhaps years of business decisions, can be handled in a reasonable amount of time by computer. Though simulation is one of the oldest

FIGURE 1
Process of Simulation

The explosion of personal computers has created a wealth of computer simulation languages and broadened the use of simulation. Now, even spreadsheet software can be used to conduct fairly complex simulations.

quantitative analysis tools (see the History below), it was not until the introduction of computers in the mid-1940s and early 1950s that it became a practical means of solving management and military problems.

We begin this chapter with a presentation of the advantages and disadvantages of simulation. An explanation of the Monte Carlo method of simulation follows. Three sample simulations, in the areas of inventory control, queuing, and maintenance planning, are presented. Other simulation models besides the Monte Carlo approach are also discussed briefly. Finally, the important role of computers in simulation is illustrated.

2 Advantages and Disadvantages of Simulation

These eight advantages of simulation make it one of the most widely used quantitative analysis techniques in corporate America.

Simulation is a tool that has become widely accepted by managers for several reasons:

1. It is relatively straightforward and flexible. It can be used to compare many different scenarios side-by-side.
2. Recent advances in software make some simulation models very easy to develop.
3. It can be used to analyze large and complex real-world situations that cannot be solved by conventional quantitative analysis models. For example, it may not be possible to build and solve a mathematical model of a city government system that incorporates important economic, social, environmental, and political factors. Simulation has been used successfully to model urban systems, hospitals, educational systems, national and state economies, and even world food systems.
4. Simulation allows what-if? types of questions. Managers like to know in advance what options are attractive. With a computer, a manager can try out several policy decisions within a matter of minutes.
5. Simulations do not interfere with the real-world system. It may be too disruptive, for example, to experiment with new policies or ideas in a hospital, school, or manufacturing plant. With simulation, experiments are done with the model, not on the system itself.
6. Simulation allows us to study the interactive effect of individual components or variables to determine which ones are important.
7. "Time compression" is possible with simulation. The effect of ordering, advertising, or other policies over many months or years can be obtained by computer simulation in a short time.
8. Simulation allows for the inclusion of real-world complications that most quantitative analysis models cannot permit. For example, some queuing models require exponential or Poisson distributions; some inventory and network models require normality. But simulation can use *any* probability distribution that the user defines; it does not require any particular distribution.

HISTORY Simulation

The history of simulation dates back over 5,000 years to Chinese war games called *weich'i*. Around 1780, the Prussians used simulation to help train their army. Since then all major military powers have used war games to test out military strategies under simulated environments.

From military gaming arose a new concept called *Monte Carlo simulation*. It was developed during the 1940s as a quantitative analysis technique by Drs. John von Neumann, Stan Ulam, and Nicholas Metropolis at Los Alamos National Laboratory (LANL; see www.lanl.gov) to solve physics problems that were too complex or too expensive to solve by hand. The first application of Monte Carlo simulation was to study neutron behavior

in fissionable materials. Because their research at LANL was Top Secret, the scientists needed a code name for their new tool. The scientists came up with "Monte Carlo" because the behavior of the neutrons reminded them of a roulette wheel and Dr. Ulam's uncle spent a lot of time gambling in Monte Carlo, Monaco.

With the advent and use of computers in the 1950s, simulation grew as a management tool. Specialized computer programming languages (e.g., GPSS and SIMSCRIPT) were developed in the 1960s to handle large-scale problems more effectively. In the 1980s, pre-written, object oriented simulation programs came onto the scene that could handle situations ranging from weather forecasting to auto parts factory analysis to ski resort design. These programs had names like SLAM, SIMAN, and Witness.

The main disadvantages of simulation are:

The four disadvantages of simulation are cost, its trial-and-error nature, the need to generate answers to tests, and uniqueness.

1. Good simulation models for complex situations can be very expensive. It is often a long, complicated process to develop a model. A corporate planning model, for example, may take months or even years to develop.
2. Simulation does not generate optimal solutions to problems as do other quantitative analysis techniques such as economic order quantity, linear programming, or PERT. It is a trial-and-error approach that can produce different solutions in repeated runs.
3. Managers must generate all of the conditions and constraints for solutions that they want to examine. The simulation model does not produce answers by itself.
4. Each simulation model is unique. Its solutions and inferences are not usually transferable to other problems.

3 Monte Carlo Simulation

When a system contains elements that exhibit chance in their behavior, the *Monte Carlo method* of simulation can be applied.

The basic idea in **Monte Carlo simulation** is to generate values for the variables making up the model being studied. There are a lot of variables in real-world systems that are probabilistic in nature and that we might want to simulate. A few examples of these variables follow:

Variables we may want to simulate abound in business problems because very little in life is certain.

1. Inventory demand on a daily or weekly basis
2. Lead time for inventory orders to arrive
3. Times between machine breakdowns
4. Times between arrivals at a service facility
5. Service times
6. Times to complete project activities
7. Number of employees absent from work each day

Some of these variables, such as the daily demand and the number of employees absent, are discrete and must be integer valued. For example, the daily demand can be 0, 1, 2, 3, and so forth. But daily demand cannot be 4.7362 or any other noninteger value. Other variables, such as those related to time, are continuous and are not required to be integers because time can be any value. When selecting a method to generate values for the random variable, this characteristic of the random variable should be considered. Examples of both will be given in the following sections.

The basis of Monte Carlo simulation is experimentation on the chance (or probabilistic) elements through random sampling. The technique breaks down into five simple steps:

Five Steps of Monte Carlo Simulation

The Monte Carlo method can be used with variables that are probabilistic.

1. Establishing probability distributions for important input variables
2. Building a cumulative probability distribution for each variable in step 1
3. Establishing an interval of random numbers for each variable
4. Generating random numbers
5. Simulating a series of trials

We will examine each of these steps and illustrate them with the following example.

Harry's Auto Tire Example

Harry's Auto Tire sells all types of tires, but a popular radial tire accounts for a large portion of Harry's overall sales. Recognizing that inventory costs can be quite significant with this product, Harry wishes to determine a policy for managing this inventory. To see what the demand would look like over a period of time, he wishes to simulate the daily demand for a number of days.

Step 1: Establishing Probability Distributions. One common way to establish a *probability distribution* for a given variable is to examine historical outcomes. The probability, or relative frequency, for each possible outcome of a variable is found by dividing the frequency of observation

TABLE 1

Historical Daily Demand for Radial Tires at Harry's Auto Tire and Probability Distribution

DEMAND FOR TIRES	FREQUENCY (DAYS)	PROBABILITY OF OCCURRENCE
0	10	$10/200 = 0.05$
1	20	$20/200 = 0.10$
2	40	$40/200 = 0.20$
3	60	$60/200 = 0.30$
4	40	$40/200 = 0.20$
5	30	$30/200 = 0.15$
	200	$200/200 = 1.00$

To establish a probability distribution for tires we assume that historical demand is a good indicator of future outcomes.

by the total number of observations. The daily demand for radial tires at Harry's Auto Tire over the past 200 days is shown in Table 1. We can convert these data to a probability distribution, if we assume that past demand rates will hold in the future, by dividing each demand frequency by the total demand, 200.

Probability distributions, we should note, need not be based solely on historical observations. Often, managerial estimates based on judgment and experience are used to create a distribution. Sometimes, a sample of sales, machine breakdowns, or service rates is used to create probabilities for those variables. And the distributions themselves can be either empirical, as in Table 1, or based on the commonly known normal, binomial, Poisson, or exponential patterns.

Step 2: Building a Cumulative Probability Distribution for Each Variable. The conversion from a regular probability distribution, such as in the right-hand column of Table 1, to a *cumulative distribution* is an easy job. A cumulative probability is the probability that a variable (demand) will be less than or equal to a particular value. A cumulative distribution lists all of the possible values and the probabilities. In Table 2 we see that the cumulative probability for each level of demand is the sum of the number in the probability column (middle column) added to the previous cumulative probability (rightmost column). The cumulative probability, graphed in Figure 2, is used in step 3 to help assign random numbers.

Step 3: Setting Random Number Intervals. After we have established a cumulative probability distribution for each variable included in the simulation, we must assign a set of numbers to represent each possible value or outcome. These are referred to as **random number intervals**. Random numbers are discussed in detail in step 4. Basically, a **random number** is a series of digits (say, two digits from 01, 02, …, 98, 99, 00) that have been selected by a totally random process.

If there is a 5% chance that demand for a product (such as Harry's radial tires) is 0 units per day, we want 5% of the random numbers available to correspond to a demand of 0 units. If a total of 100 two-digit numbers is used in the simulation (think of them as being numbered chips in a bowl), we could assign a demand of 0 units to the first five random numbers: 01, 02, 03, 04, and 05.* Then

TABLE 2

Cumulative Probabilities for Radial Tires

Cumulative probabilities are found by summing all the previous probabilities up to the current demand.

DAILY DEMAND	PROBABILITY	CUMULATIVE PROBABILITY
0	0.05	0.05
1	0.10	0.15
2	0.20	0.35
3	0.30	0.65
4	0.20	0.85
5	0.15	1.00

*Alternatively, we could have assigned the random numbers 00, 01, 02, 03, 04 to represent a demand of 0 units. The two digits 00 can be thought of as either 0 or 100. As long as 5 numbers out of 100 are assigned to the 0 demand, it doesn't make any difference which 5 they are.

FIGURE 2

Graphical Representation of the Cumulative Probability Distribution for Radial Tires

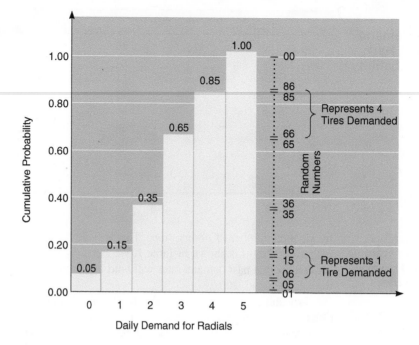

a simulated demand for 0 units would be created every time one of the numbers 01 to 05 was drawn. If there is also a 10% chance that demand for the same product is 1 unit per day, we could let the next 10 random numbers (06, 07, 08, 09, 10, 11, 12, 13, 14, and 15) represent that demand—and so on for other demand levels.

In general, using the cumulative probability distribution computed and graphed in step 2, we can set the interval of random numbers for each level of demand in a very simple fashion. You will note in Table 3 that the interval selected to represent each possible daily demand is very closely related to the cumulative probability on its left. The top end of each interval is always equal to the cumulative probability percentage.

Similarly, we can see in Figure 2 and in Table 3 that the length of each interval on the right corresponds to the probability of one of each of the possible daily demands. Hence, in assigning random numbers to the daily demand for three radial tires, the range of the random number interval (36 to 65) corresponds *exactly* to the probability (or proportion) of that outcome. A daily demand for three radial tires occurs 30% of the time. Any of the 30 random numbers greater than 35 up to and including 65 are assigned to that event.

Step 4: Generating Random Numbers.   Random numbers may be generated for simulation problems in several ways. If the problem is very large and the process being studied involves thousands of simulation trials, computer programs are available to generate the random numbers needed.

If the simulation is being done by hand, as in this text, the numbers may be selected by the spin of a roulette wheel that has 100 slots, by blindly grabbing numbered chips out of a hat, or

Random numbers can actually be assigned in many different ways—as long as they represent the correct proportion of the outcomes.

The relation between intervals and cumulative probability is that the top end of each interval is equal to the cumulative probability percentage.

There are several ways to pick random numbers—random number generators (which are a built-in feature in spreadsheets and many computer languages), tables (such as Table 4), a roulette wheel, and so on.

TABLE 3

Assignment of Random Number Intervals for Harry's Auto Tire

DAILY DEMAND	PROBABILITY	CUMULATIVE PROBABILITY	INTERVAL OF RANDOM NUMBERS
0	0.05	0.05	01 to 05
1	0.10	0.15	06 to 15
2	0.20	0.35	16 to 35
3	0.30	0.65	36 to 65
4	0.20	0.85	66 to 85
5	0.15	1.00	86 to 00

by any method that allows you to make a random selection.* The most commonly used means is to choose numbers from a table of random digits such as Table 4.

Table 4 was itself generated by a computer program. It has the characteristic that every digit or number in it has an equal chance of occurring. In a very large random number table, 10% of digits would be 1s, 10% 2s, 10% 3s, and so on. Because *everything* is random, we can select numbers from anywhere in the table to use in our simulation procedures in step 5.

Step 5: Simulating the Experiment. We can simulate outcomes of an experiment by simply selecting random numbers from Table 4. Beginning anywhere in the table, we note the interval in Table 3 or Figure 2 into which each number falls. For example, if the random number chosen is 81 and the interval 66 to 85 represents a daily demand for four tires, we select a demand of four tires.

We now illustrate the concept further by simulating 10 days of demand for radial tires at Harry's Auto Tire (see Table 5). We select the random numbers needed from Table 4, starting in the upper left-hand corner and continuing down the first column.

TABLE 4
Table of Random Numbers

52	06	50	88	53	30	10	47	99	37	66	91	35	32	00	84	57	07
37	63	28	02	74	35	24	03	29	60	74	85	90	73	59	55	17	60
82	57	68	28	05	94	03	11	27	79	90	87	92	41	09	25	36	77
69	02	36	49	71	99	32	10	75	21	95	90	94	38	97	71	72	49
98	94	90	36	06	78	23	67	89	85	29	21	25	73	69	34	85	76
96	52	62	87	49	56	59	23	78	71	72	90	57	01	98	57	31	95
33	69	27	21	11	60	95	89	68	48	17	89	34	09	93	50	44	51
50	33	50	95	13	44	34	62	64	39	55	29	30	64	49	44	30	16
88	32	18	50	62	57	34	56	62	31	15	40	90	34	51	95	26	14
90	30	36	24	69	82	51	74	30	35	36	85	01	55	92	64	09	85
50	48	61	18	85	23	08	54	17	12	80	69	24	84	92	16	49	59
27	88	21	62	69	64	48	31	12	73	02	68	00	16	16	46	13	85
45	14	46	32	13	49	66	62	74	41	86	98	92	98	84	54	33	40
81	02	01	78	82	74	97	37	45	31	94	99	42	49	27	64	89	42
66	83	14	74	27	76	03	33	11	97	59	81	72	00	64	61	13	52
74	05	81	82	93	09	96	33	52	78	13	06	28	30	94	23	37	39
30	34	87	01	74	11	46	82	59	94	25	34	32	23	17	01	58	73
59	55	72	33	62	13	74	68	22	44	42	09	32	46	71	79	45	89
67	09	80	98	99	25	77	50	03	32	36	63	65	75	94	19	95	88
60	77	46	63	71	69	44	22	03	85	14	48	69	13	30	50	33	24
60	08	19	29	36	72	30	27	50	64	85	72	75	29	87	05	75	01
80	45	86	99	02	34	87	08	86	84	49	76	24	08	01	86	29	11
53	84	49	63	26	65	72	84	85	63	26	02	75	26	92	62	40	67
69	84	12	94	51	36	17	02	15	29	16	52	56	43	26	22	08	62
37	77	13	10	02	18	31	19	32	85	31	94	81	43	31	58	33	51

Source: Excerpted from *A Million Random Digits with 100,000 Normal Deviates* (New York: The Free Press, 1955), p. 7, with permission of the RAND Corporation.

---

*One more method of generating random numbers is called the von Neumann midsquare method, developed in the 1940s. Here's how it works: (1) select any arbitrary number with n digits (e.g., $n = 4$ digits), (2) square the number, (3) extract the middle n digits as the next random number. As an example of a four-digit arbitrary number, use 3,614. The square of 3,614 is 13,060,996. The middle four digits of this new number are 0609. Thus, 0609 is the next random number and steps 2 and 3 are repeated. The midsquare method is simple and easily programmed, but sometimes the numbers repeat quickly and are *not* random. For example, try using the method starting with 6,100 as your first arbitrary number!

Simulating GM's OnStar System to Evaluate Strategic Alternatives

General Motors (GM) has a two-way vehicle communication system, OnStar, that is the leader in the telematics business of providing communications services to automobiles. Communication can be by an automated system (a virtual advisor) or with a human advisor via a cell-phone connection. This is used for such things as crash notification, navigation, Internet access, and traffic information. OnStar answers thousands of emergency calls each month, and many lives have been saved by providing a rapid emergency response.

In developing the new business model for OnStar, GM used an integrated simulation model to analyze the new telematics industry. Six factors were considered in this model—customer acquisition, customer choice, alliances, customer service, financial dynamics, and societal results. The team responsible for this model reported that an aggressive strategy would be the best way to approach this new industry. This included installation of OnStar in every GM vehicle and free first year subscription service. This eliminated the high cost of dealer installation, but it carried with it a cost that was not recoverable if the buyer chose not to renew the OnStar subscription.

The implementation of this business strategy and subsequent growth progressed as indicated by the model. As of fall 2001, OnStar had an 80% market share with more than two million subscribers, and this number was growing rapidly. Update: As of the first quarter of 2013, OnStar is estimated to have over six million subscribers worldwide, revenues of $1.5 billion per year, and profit margins of over 30%.

Sources: Based on "A Multimethod Approach for Creating New Business Models: The General Motors OnStar Project," *Interfaces*, 32, 1 (January–February 2002): 20–34.
Based on General Motors quarterly earnings report released on May 2, 2013.

Simulated results can differ from analytical results in a short simulation.

It is interesting to note that the average demand of 3.9 tires in this 10-day simulation differs significantly from the *expected* daily demand, which we can compute from the data in Table 2:

$$\text{Expected daily demand} = \sum_{i=0}^{5} (\text{Probability of } i \text{ tires}) \times (\text{Demand of } i \text{ tires})$$

$$= (0.05)(0) + (0.10)(1) + (0.20)(2) + (0.30)(3)$$
$$+ (0.20)(4) + (0.15)(5)$$
$$= 2.95 \text{ tires}$$

If this simulation were repeated hundreds or thousands of times, it is much more likely that the average *simulated* demand would be nearly the same as the *expected* demand.

Naturally, it would be risky to draw any hard and fast conclusions regarding the operation of a firm from only a short simulation. However, this simulation by hand demonstrates the important principles involved. It helps us to understand the process of Monte Carlo simulation that is used in computerized simulation models.

TABLE 5

Ten-Day Simulation of Demand for Radial Tires

DAY	RANDOM NUMBER	SIMULATED DAILY DEMAND
1	52	3
2	37	3
3	82	4
4	69	4
5	98	5
6	96	5
7	33	2
8	50	3
9	88	5
10	90	5

39 = total 10-day demand

3.9 = average daily demand for tires

PROGRAM 1

QM for Windows Output Screen for Simulation of Harry's Auto Tire Example

Category name	Value	Frequency	Probability	Cumulative Probability	Value * Frequency	Occurrences	Percentage	Occurences * Value
Category 1	0	10	0.05	0.05	0	53	0.05	0
Category 2	1	20	0.1	0.15	0.1	113	0.11	113
Category 3	2	4		0.4	0.4	213	0.21	426
Category 4	3	6		0.9	0.9			73
Category 5	4	40	0.2	0.85	0.8			84
Category 6	5	30	0.15	1	0.75	134	0.13	670
Total		200	1	Expected	2.95	1000	1	2866
							Average	2.87

Number of trials: 1000 Seed: 0

Harry's Auto Tire Shop Solution

The expected value is calculated mathematically.

This is the output for this individual simulation run.

The simulation for Harry's Auto Tire involved only one variable. The true power of simulation is seen when several random variables are involved and the situation is more complex. In Section 4 we see a simulation of an inventory problem in which both the demand and the lead time may vary.

As you might expect, the computer can be a very helpful tool in carrying out the tedious work in larger simulation undertakings. In the next two sections, we demonstrate how QM for Windows and Excel can both be used for simulation.

Using QM for Windows for Simulation

Program 1 is a Monte Carlo simulation using the QM for Windows software. Inputs to this model are the possible values for the variable, the number of trials to be generated, and either the

PROGRAM 2

Using Excel 2013 to Simulate Tire Demand for Harry's Auto Tire Shop

	A	B	C	D	E	F	G	H	I
1	**Harry's Tire Shop**								
2		Probability	Probability Range (Lower)	Cumulative Probability	Tires Demand		Day	Random Number	Simulated Demand
3		0.05	0	0.05	0		1	0.437221	3
4		0.1	0.05	0.15	1		2	0.798398	4
5		0.2	0.15	0.35	2		3	0.187351	2
6		0.3	0.35	0.65	3		4	0.711124	4
7		0.2	0.65	0.85	4		5	0.348322	2
8		0.15	0.85	1	5		6	0.406072	3
9							7	0.750798	4
10							8	0.676279	4
11							9	0.592743	3
12							10	0.189257	2
13								Average	3.1
14		Results (Frequency table)							
15		Tires Demanded	Frequency	Percentage	Cum %				
16		0	0	0%	0%				
17		1	0	0%	0%				
18		2	3	30%	30%				
19		3	3	30%	60%				
20		4	4	40%	100%				
21		5	0	0%	100%				
22			10						

Key Formulas

I 13 =AVERAGE(I3:I12)	**C** 22 =SUM(C16:C21)
H 3 =RAND() **I** =VLOOKUP(H3,$C$3:$E$8,3,TRUE) **Copy H3:I3 to H4:I12**	**C** **D** 3 0 =B3 4 =D3 =D3+B4 **Copy C4:D4 to C5:D8**
C 16 =FREQUENCY($I$3:$I$12,$B$16:$B$21) **This entered as an array. Highlight C16:C21, type this formula, then press Ctrl-Shift-Enter.**	**D** **E** 16 =C16/$C$22 =D16 17 =C17/$C$22 =E16+D17 **Copy D17:E17 to D18:E21**

associated frequency or the probability for each value. If frequencies are input, QM for Windows will compute the probabilities as well as the cumulative probability distribution. We see that the expected value (2.95) is computed mathematically, and we can compare the actual sample average (2.87) with this. If another simulation is performed, the sample average may change.

Simulation with Excel Spreadsheets

The ability to generate random numbers and then "look up" these numbers in a table in order to associate them with a specific event makes spreadsheets excellent tools for conducting simulations. Program 2 illustrates an Excel simulation for Harry's Auto Tire.

The RAND() function is used to generate a random number between 0 and 1. The VLOOKUP function looks up the random number in the leftmost column of the defined lookup table ($C$3:$E$8). It moves downward through this column until it finds a cell that is bigger than the random number. It then goes to the previous row and gets the value from column E of the table.

In Program 2, for example, the first random number shown is 0.437. Excel looked down the left-hand column of the lookup table ($C$3:$E$8) of Program 2 until it found 0.65. From the previous row it retrieved the value in column E, which is 3. Pressing the F9 function key recalculates the random numbers and the simulation.

MODELING IN THE REAL WORLD Simulating Chips

Defining
the Problem

↓

Developing
a Model

↓

Acquiring
Input Data

↓

Developing
a Solution

↓

Testing the
Solution

↓

Analyzing
the Results

↓

Implementing
the Results

Defining the Problem:

The world's largest semiconductor manufacturer, Intel Corporation, has gross annual sales of over fifty billion dollars. To stay competitive, Intel spends over five billion dollars a year on new semiconductor fabrication equipment. Increasing lead times of fabrication equipment coupled with increasing variability in the global semiconductor chip market led to board room quandaries in capital equipment purchasing.

Developing a Model:

Analysts at Intel built a simulation model of the ordering, shipping, and installation of their capital equipment business process.

Acquiring Input Data:

These same analysts modeled and analyzed the current capital equipment procurement practices at Intel for several years.

Developing a Solution:

A two mode simulation model was developed. The model was named the Dual Mode Equipment Procedure (DMEP).

Testing the Solution:

In the first mode of DMEP, capital equipment was procured according to standard contracts and standard lead times. In the second mode, new capital equipment is purchased at slightly higher costs but with reduced lead times. The idea was that the reduced lead times in equipment meant Intel would reap the benefits of being the first to market with new products.

Analyzing the Results:

The DMEP model integrated common forecasting techniques with Monte Carlo simulation to procure capital equipment at higher costs but with shorter lead times as outlined above.

Implementing the Results:

Once implemented and in place, the DMEP decision engine saved Intel Corporation hundreds of millions of dollars.

Source: Based on K. G. Kempf, F. Erhun, E. F. Hertzler, T. R. Rosenberg, and C. Peng. "Optimizing Capital Investment Decisions at Intel Corporation," *Interfaces* 43, 1 (January–February 2013): 62–78.

The FREQUENCY function in Excel (column C in Program 2) is used to tabulate how often a value occurs in a set of data. This is an array function, so special procedures are required to enter it. First, highlight the entire range where this is to be located (C16:C21 in this example). Then enter the function, as illustrated in cell C16, and press Ctrl + Shift + Enter. This causes the formula to be entered as an array into all the cells that were highlighted (cells C16:C21).

Many problems exist in which the variable to be simulated is normally distributed and thus is a continuous variable. A function (NORMINV) in Excel makes generating normal random numbers very easy, as seen in Program 3. The mean is 40 and the standard deviation is 5. The format is

$$= \text{NORMINV} \ (probability, mean, standard\_deviation)$$

In Program 3, the 200 simulated values for the normal random variable are generated in Column A. A chart (cells C3:E19) was developed to show the distribution of the randomly generated numbers.

Excel QM has a simulation module that is very easy to use. When *Simulation* is selected from the Excel QM menu, an initialization window opens, and you enter the number of categories and the number of simulation trials you want to run. A spreadsheet will be developed, and you then enter the values and the frequencies, as shown in Program 4. The actual random numbers and their associated demand values are also displayed in the output, but they are not shown in Program 4.

PROGRAM 3

Generating Normal Random Numbers in Excel

	A	B	C	D	E
1	Generating Normal Random Numbers				
2					
3	Random number		Value	Frenquency	Percentage
4	48.33642948		26	1	0.5%
5	36.21820631		28	0	0.0%
6	34.78432388		30	1	0.5%
7	46.61361129		32	6	3.0%
8	38.63662756		34	9	4.5%
9	44.22026912		36	21	10.5%
10	41.97911359		38	24	12.0%
11	34.25168722		40	31	15.5%
12	41.25648029		42	30	15.0%
13	40.70042594		44	31	15.5%
14	40.04584085		46	17	8.5%
15	38.50150643		48	15	7.5%
16	39.84624169		50	8	4.0%
17	46.11687306		52	3	1.5%
18	48.01731698		54	2	1.0%
19	35.86007936		56	1	0.5%
20	38.18663076			200	
201	35.96608863		Rows 21-200 are hidden		
202	36.45899378				
203	45.67207291				

Key Formulas

A	E
4 =NORMINV(RAND(),40,5)	4 =D4/$D$20
Copy A4 to A5:A203	**Copy E4 to E5:E19**

D
4 =FREQUENCY(A4:A203,C4:C19)
This entered as an array. Highlight D4:D19, type this formula, then press Ctrl-Shift-Enter.

PROGRAM 4

Excel QM Simulation of Harry's Auto Tire Example

	A	B	C	D	E	F	G	H	I	J	K	L	M
1	Harry's Auto Tire												
2			Enter the values and the frequencies						other simulation. If				
3	Simulation		here. The probabilities and simulation						dom number".				
4			results will then appear.										
5													
6		Data				Expected Value				Simulation results			
7	Random Number Sorter	Category name	Value	Frequency		Probability	Cumulative Probability	Value * Frequency		Value	Simulation Occurrences	Percentage	Occurrences * Value
8	0	Category 1	0	10		0.05	0.05	0		0	8	0.04	0
9	5	Category 2	1	20		0.1	0.15	20		1	15	0.075	15
10	15	Category 3	2	40		0.2	0.35	80		2	35	0.175	70
11	35	Category 4	3	60		0.3	0.65	180		3	72	0.36	216
12	65	Category 5	4	40		0.2	0.85	160		4	39	0.195	156
13	85	Category 6	5	30		0.15	1	150		5	31	0.155	155
14		Total		200			Expected			Totals	200	1	612
15											Average		3.06

4 Simulation and Inventory Analysis

Simulation is useful when demand and lead time are probabilistic—in this case the inventory models like economic order quantity can't be used.

Commonly used models, such as "deterministic" inventory models, are based on the assumption that both product demand and reorder lead time are known, constant values. In many real-world inventory situations, though, demand and lead time are variables, and accurate analysis becomes extremely difficult to handle by any means other than simulation.

In this section we present an inventory problem with two decision variables and two probabilistic components. The owner of the hardware store described in the next section would like to establish *order quantity* and *reorder point* decisions for a particular product that has probabilistic (uncertain) daily demand and reorder lead time. He wants to make a series of simulation runs, trying out various order quantities and reorder points, to minimize his total inventory cost for the item. Inventory costs in this case include an ordering, holding, and stockout cost.

Simkin's Hardware Store

Mark Simkin, owner and general manager of Simkin Hardware, wants to find a good, low-cost inventory policy for one particular product: the Ace model electric drill. Due to the complexity of this situation, he has decided to use simulation to help with this. The first step in the simulation process seen in Figure 1 is to define the problem. Simkin specifies this to be finding a good inventory policy for the Ace electric drill.

In the second step of this process, Simkin identifies two types of variables: the controllable and uncontrollable inputs. The controllable inputs (or decision variables) are the order quantity and the reorder point. Simkin must specify the values that he wishes to consider. The other important variables are the uncontrollable inputs: the fluctuating daily demand and the variable lead time. Monte Carlo simulation is used to simulate the values for both of these.

Daily demand for the Ace model drill is relatively low but subject to some variability. Over the past 300 days, Simkin has observed the sales shown in column 2 of Table 6. He converts this historical frequency data into a probability distribution for the variable daily demand (column 3). A cumulative probability distribution is formed in column 4. Finally, Simkin establishes an interval of random numbers to represent each possible daily demand (column 5).

When Simkin places an order to replenish his inventory of Ace electric drills, there is a delivery lag of one to three days. This means that lead time can also be considered a probabilistic variable. The number of days it took to receive the past 50 orders is presented in Table 7. In a fashion similar to that for the demand variable, Simkin establishes a probability distribution for the lead time variable (column 3 of Table 7), computes the cumulative distribution (column 4), and assigns random number intervals for each possible time (column 5).

The third step in the simulation process is to develop the simulation model. A **flow diagram, or flowchart**, is helpful in the logical coding procedures for programming this simulation process (see Figure 3).

In flowcharts, special symbols are used to represent different parts of a simulation. The rectangular boxes represent actions that must be taken. The diamond shaped figures represent branching points where the next step depends on the answer to the question in the diamond. The beginning and ending points of the simulation are represented as ovals or rounded rectangles.

TABLE 6
Probabilities and Random Number Intervals for Daily Ace Drill Demand

(1) DEMAND FOR ACE DRILL	(2) FREQUENCY (DAYS)	(3) PROBABILITY	(4) CUMULATIVE PROBABILITY	(5) INTERVAL OF RANDOM NUMBERS
0	15	0.05	0.05	01 to 05
1	30	0.10	0.15	06 to 15
2	60	0.20	0.35	16 to 35
3	120	0.40	0.75	36 to 75
4	45	0.15	0.90	76 to 90
5	30	0.10	1.00	91 to 00
	300	1.00		

TABLE 7

Probabilities and Random Number Intervals for Reorder Lead Time

(1) LEAD TIME (DAYS)	(2) FREQUENCY (ORDERS)	(3) PROBABILITY	(4) CUMULATIVE PROBABILITY	(5) RANDOM NUMBER INTERVAL
1	10	0.20	0.20	01 to 20
2	25	0.50	0.70	21 to 70
3	<u>15</u>	<u>0.30</u>	1.00	71 to 00
	50	1.00		

FIGURE 3

Flow Diagram for Simkin's Inventory Example

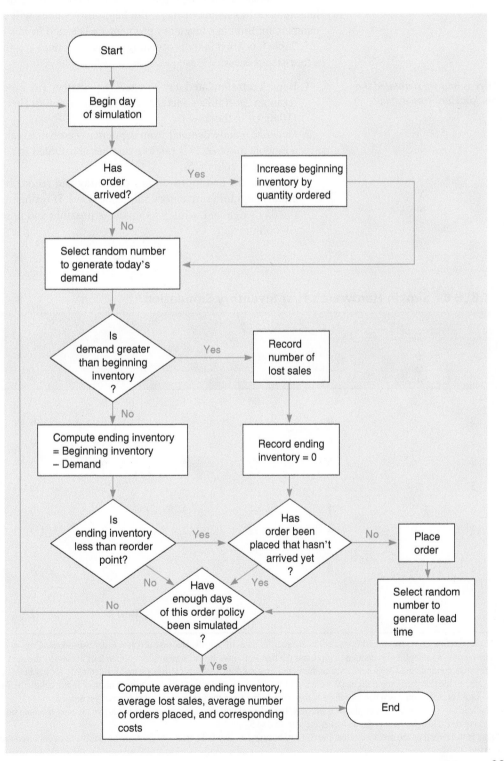

The fourth step of this simulation is to specify the values of the variables that we wish to test.

A delivery lag is the lead time in receiving an order—the time it was placed until it was received.

The first inventory policy that Simkin Hardware wants to simulate is an order quantity of 10 with a reorder point of 5. That is, every time the on-hand inventory level at the end of the day is 5 or less, Simkin will call his supplier and place an order for 10 more drills. If the lead time is one day, by the way, the order will not arrive the next morning but at the beginning of the following working day.

The fifth step of the simulation process is to actually conduct the simulation, and the Monte Carlo method is used for this. The entire process is simulated for a 10-day period in Table 8. We can assume that beginning inventory is 10 units on day 1. (Actually, it makes little difference in a long simulation what the initial inventory level is. Since we would tend in real life to simulate hundreds or thousands of days, the beginning values will tend to be averaged out.) Random numbers for Simkin's inventory problem are selected from the second column of Table 4.

Table 8 is filled in by proceeding one day (or line) at a time, working from left to right. It is a four-step process:

Here is how we simulated the Simkin Hardware example.

1. Begin each simulated day by checking whether any ordered inventory has just arrived (column 2). If it has, increase the current inventory (in column 3) by the quantity ordered (10 units, in this case).
2. Generate a daily demand from the demand probability distribution in Table 6 by selecting a random number. This random number is recorded in column 4. The demand simulated is recorded in column 5.
3. Compute the ending inventory every day and record it in column 6. Ending inventory equals beginning inventory minus demand. If on-hand inventory is insufficient to meet the day's demand, satisfy as much as possible and note the number of lost sales (in column 7).

TABLE 8   Simkin Hardware's First Inventory Simulation

	ORDER QUANTITY = 10 UNITS			REORDER POINT = 5 UNITS						
(1) DAY	(2) UNITS RECEIVED	(3) BEGINNING INVENTORY	(4) RANDOM NUMBER	(5) DEMAND	(6) ENDING INVENTORY	(7) LOST SALES	(8) ORDER	(9) RANDOM NUMBER	(10) LEAD TIME
1	...	10	06	1	9	0	No		
2	0	9	63	3	6	0	No		
3	0	6	57	3	③[a]	0	Yes	⑫[b]	1
4	0	3	㉙[c]	5	0	2	No[d]		
5	⑩[e]	10	52	3	7	0	No		
6	0	7	69	3	4	0	Yes	33	2
7	0	4	32	2	2	0	No		
8	0	2	30	2	0	0	No		
9	⑩[f]	10	48	3	7	0	No		
10	0	7	88	4	3	0	Yes	14	1
					Total 41	2			

[a] This is the first time inventory dropped below the reorder point of 5 drills. Because no prior order was outstanding, an order is placed.

[b] The random number 02 is generated to represent the first lead time. It was drawn from column 2 of Table 4 as the next number in the list being used. A separate column could have been used to draw lead time random numbers from if we had wanted to do so, but in this example we did not do so.

[c] Again, notice that the random digits 02 were used for lead time (see footnote b). So the next number in the column is 94.

[d] No order is placed on day 4 because there is one outstanding from the previous day that has not yet arrived.

[e] The lead time for the first order placed is one day, but as noted in the text, an order does not arrive the next morning but at the beginning of the following working day. Thus, the first order arrives at the start of day 5.

[f] This is the arrival of the order placed at the close of business on day 6. Fortunately for Simkin, no lost sales occurred during the 2-day lead time until the order arrived.

4. Determine whether the day's ending inventory has reached the reorder point (5 units). If it has and if there are no outstanding orders, place an order (column 8). Lead time for a new order is simulated by first choosing a random number from Table 4 and recording it in column 9. (We can continue down the same string of the random number table that we were using to generate numbers for the demand variable.) Finally, we convert this random number into a lead time by using the distribution set in Table 7.

Analyzing Simkin's Inventory Costs

Now that the simulation results have been generated, Simkin is ready to proceed to step 6 of this process—examining the results. Since the objective is to find a low-cost solution, Simkin must determine, given these results, what the costs would be. In doing this, Simkin finds some interesting results. The average daily ending inventory is

$$\text{Average ending inventory} = \frac{41 \text{ total units}}{10 \text{ days}} = 4.1 \text{ units per day}$$

We also note the average lost sales and number of orders placed per day:

$$\text{Average lost sales} = \frac{2 \text{ sales lost}}{10 \text{ days}} = 0.2 \text{ unit per day}$$

$$\text{Average number of orders placed} = \frac{3 \text{ orders}}{10 \text{ days}} = 0.3 \text{ order per day}$$

These data are useful in studying the inventory costs of the policy being simulated.

Simkin Hardware is open for business 200 days per year. Simkin estimates that the cost of placing each order for Ace drills is $10. The cost of holding a drill in stock is $6 per drill per year, which can also be viewed as 3 cents per drill per day (over a 200-day year). Finally, Simkin estimates that the cost of each shortage, or lost sale, is $8. What is Simkin's total daily inventory cost for the ordering policy of order quantity, $Q = 10$ and reorder point, ROP $= 5$?

Let us examine the three cost components:

$$\text{Daily order cost} = (\text{Cost of placing one order})$$
$$\times (\text{Number of orders placed per day})$$
$$= \$10 \text{ per order} \times 0.3 \text{ order per day} = \$3$$

$$\text{Daily holding cost} = (\text{Cost of holding one unit for one day})$$
$$\times (\text{Average ending inventory})$$
$$= \$0.03 \text{ per unit per day} \times 4.1 \text{ units per day}$$
$$= \$0.12$$

$$\text{Daily stockout cost} = (\text{Cost per lost sale})$$
$$\times (\text{Average number of lost sales per day})$$
$$= \$8 \text{ per lost sale} \times 0.2 \text{ lost sale per day}$$
$$= \$1.60$$

$$\text{Total Daily inventory cost} = \text{Daily order cost} + \text{Daily holding cost}$$
$$+ \text{Daily stockout cost} = \$4.72$$

Thus, the total daily inventory cost for this simulation is $4.72. Annualizing this daily figure to a 200-day working year suggests that this inventory policy's cost is approximately $944.

Now once again we want to emphasize something very important. This simulation should be extended many more days before we draw any conclusions as to the cost of the inventory policy being tested. If a hand simulation is being conducted, 100 days would provide a better representation. If a computer is doing the calculations, 1,000 days would be helpful in reaching accurate cost estimates.

It is important to remember that the simulation should be conducted for many, many days before it is legitimate to draw any solid conclusions.

IN ACTION Federal Aviation Administration Uses Simulation to Solve Assignment Problem

The Federal Aviation Administration (FAA) is responsible for managing transportation in the air. This typically involves the assignment of airline flights to particular air-traffic routes in real time. On the surface, this problem may seem rather mundane. However, as air traffic demand has grown in recent years, the number of available air-traffic routes has diminished at any given time. This can make the associated assignment problem very hard. Confounding the problem is the weather, as thunderstorms can wreak havoc on the availability of air-traffic routes at any given time.

In 2005, the FAA developed a simulation decision-making tool known as the Airspace Flow Program (AFP) at a total cost

of about $5 million. The AFP integrates upcoming and current flight data with impending storm weather data and simulates several different possible assignment decisions. All of these "look-ahead" simulations are then analyzed, allowing FAA decision makers to "pre-pick" a robust set of assignment solutions that minimize system-wide flight delays. The result is faster, more efficient flights for the traveler and hundreds of millions of dollars of annual savings for the airlines.

Source: Based on V. Sud, M. Tanino, J. Wetherly, M. Brennan, M. Lehky, K. Howard, and R. Oiesen. "Reducing Flight Delays Through Better Traffic Management," *Interfaces* 39, 1 (2009): 35–45.

Let's say that Simkin *does* complete a 1,000-day simulation of the policy that order quantity = 10 drills, reorder point = 5 drills. Does this complete his analysis? The answer is *no*—this is just the beginning! We should now verify that the model is correct and validate that the model truly represents the situation on which it is based. As indicated in Figure 1, once the results of the model are examined, we may want to go back and modify the model that we have developed. If we are satisfied that the model performed as we expected, then we can specify other values of the variables. Simkin must now compare *this* potential strategy to other possibilities. For example, what about $Q = 10$, ROP = 4; or $Q = 12$, ROP = 6; or $Q = 14$, ROP = 5? Perhaps every combination of values of Q from 6 to 20 drills and ROP from 3 to 10 should be simulated. After simulating all reasonable combinations of order quantities and reorder points, Simkin would go to step 7 of the simulation process and probably select the pair that yields the lowest total inventory cost.

5 Simulation of a Queuing Problem

An important area of simulation application has been in the analysis of waiting line problems. As mentioned earlier, the assumptions required for solving queuing problems analytically are quite restrictive. For most realistic queuing systems, simulation may actually be the only approach available. This section illustrates the simulation at a large unloading dock and its associated queue.

Port of New Orleans

Barge arrivals and unloading rates are both probabilistic variables. Unless they follow the queuing probability distributions, we must turn to a simulation approach.

Fully loaded barges arrive at night in New Orleans following their long trips down the Mississippi River from industrial midwestern cities. The number of barges docking on any given night ranges from 0 to 5. The probability of 0, 1, 2, 3, 4, or 5 arrivals is displayed in Table 9. In the same table, we establish cumulative probabilities and corresponding random number intervals for each possible value.

A study by the dock superintendent reveals that because of the nature of their cargo, the number of barges unloaded also tends to vary from day to day. The superintendent provides information from which we can create a probability distribution for the variable *daily unloading rate* (see Table 10). As we just did for the arrival variable, we can set up an interval of random numbers for the unloading rates.

Barges are unloaded on a first-in, first-out basis. Any barges that are not unloaded the day of arrival must wait until the following day. Tying up a barge in dock is an expensive proposition, and the superintendent cannot ignore the angry phone calls from barge line owners reminding him that "time is money!" He decides that before going to the Port of New Orleans's controller to request additional unloading crews, a simulation study of arrivals, unloadings, and delays should be conducted. A 100-day simulation would be ideal, but for purposes of illustration, the superintendent begins with a shorter 15-day analysis. Random numbers are drawn from the top row of Table 4 to generate daily arrival rates. They are drawn from the second row of Table 4 to create daily unloading rates. Table 11 shows the day-by-day port simulation.

TABLE 9
Overnight Barge Arrival Rates and Random Number Intervals

NUMBER OF ARRIVALS	PROBABILITY	CUMULATIVE PROBABILITY	RANDOM NUMBER INTERVAL
0	0.13	0.13	01 to 13
1	0.17	0.30	14 to 30
2	0.15	0.45	31 to 45
3	0.25	0.70	46 to 70
4	0.20	0.90	71 to 90
5	0.10	1.00	91 to 00

TABLE 10
Unloading Rates and Random Number Intervals

DAILY UNLOADING RATE	PROBABILITY	CUMULATIVE PROBABILITY	RANDOM NUMBER INTERVAL
1	0.05	0.05	01 to 05
2	0.15	0.20	06 to 20
3	0.50	0.70	21 to 70
4	0.20	0.90	71 to 90
5	0.10	1.00	91 to 00
	1.00		

TABLE 11 Queuing Simulation of Port of New Orleans Barge Unloadings

(1) DAY	(2) NUMBER DELAYED FROM PREVIOUS DAY	(3) RANDOM NUMBER	(4) NUMBER NIGHTLY ARRIVALS	(5) TOTAL TO BE UNLOADED	(6) RANDOM NUMBER	(7) NUMBER UNLOADED
1	—[a]	52	3	3	37	3
2	0	06	0	0	63	0[b]
3	0	50	3	3	28	3
4	0	88	4	4	02	1
5	3	53	3	6	74	4
6	2	30	1	3	35	3
7	0	10	0	0	24	0[c]
8	0	47	3	3	03	1
9	2	99	5	7	29	3
10	4	37	2	6	60	3
11	3	66	3	6	74	4
12	2	91	5	7	85	4
13	3	35	2	5	90	4
14	1	32	2	3	73	3[d]
15	0	00	5	5	59	3
	20		41			39
	Total delays		Total arrivals			Total unloadings

[a]We can begin with no delays from the previous day. In a long simulation, even if we started with 5 overnight delays, that initial condition would be averaged out.
[b]Three barges *could* have been unloaded on day 2. But because there were no arrivals and no backlog existed, zero unloadings took place.
[c]The same situation as noted in footnote b takes place.
[d]This time 4 barges could have been unloaded, but since only 3 were in the queue, the number unloaded is recorded as 3.

The superintendent will probably be interested in at least three useful and important pieces of information:

Here are the simulation results regarding average barge delays, average nightly arrivals, and average unloadings.

$$\text{Average number of barges delayed to the next day} = \frac{20 \text{ delays}}{15 \text{ days}}$$

$$= 1.33 \text{ barges delayed per day}$$

$$\text{Average number of nightly arrivals} = \frac{41 \text{ arrivals}}{15 \text{ days}} = 2.73 \text{ arrivals}$$

$$\text{Average number of barges unloaded each day} = \frac{39 \text{ unloadings}}{15 \text{ days}} = 2.60 \text{ unloadings}$$

When these data are analyzed in the context of delay costs, idle labor costs, and the cost of hiring extra unloading crews, it will be possible for the dock superintendent and port controller to make a better staffing decision. They may even elect to resimulate the process assuming different unloading rates that would correspond to increased crew sizes. Although simulation is a tool that cannot guarantee an optimal solution to problems such as this, it can be helpful in recreating a process and identifying good decision alternatives.

Using Excel to Simulate the Port of New Orleans Queuing Problem

Excel has been used to simulate the Port of New Orleans example, and the results are shown in Program 5. The VLOOKUP function is used as it was used in previous Excel simulations. Ten days of operation were simulated, and the results are displayed in rows 4 to 13 of the spreadsheet.

PROGRAM 5

Excel Model for Port of New Orleans Queuing Simulation

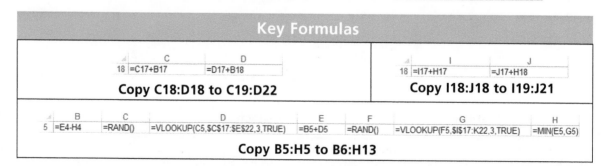

Port of New Orleans Barge Unloadings

Day	Previously delayed	Random number	Arrivals	Total to be unoaded	Random Number	Possibly unloaded	Unloaded
1	0	0.050665	0	0	0.610832	3	0
2	0	0.655742	3	3	0.647549	3	3
3	0	0.108456	0	0	0.621061	3	0
4	0	0.301333	2	2	0.212901	3	2
5	0	0.087923	0	0	0.82934	4	0
6	0	0.818649	4	4	0.278551	3	3
7	1	0.159061	1	2	0.684277	3	2
8	0	0.107859	0	0	0.711577	4	0
9	0	0.40093	2	2	0.889061	4	2
10	0	0.893377	4	4	0.900322	5	4

Barge Arrivals

Demand	Probability	Lower	Cumulative	Demand
0	0.13	0	0.13	0
1	0.17	0.13	0.3	1
2	0.15	0.3	0.45	2
3	0.25	0.45	0.7	3
4	0.2	0.7	0.9	4
5	0.1	0.9	1	5

Unloading rates

Number	Probability	Lower	Cumulative	Unloading
1	0.05		0.05	1
2	0.15	0.05	0.2	2
3	0.5	0.2	0.7	3
4	0.2	0.7	0.9	4
5	0.1	0.9	1	5

Key Formulas

	C	D
18	=C17+B17	=D17+B18

Copy C18:D18 to C19:D22

	I	J
18	=I17+H17	=J17+H18

Copy I18:J18 to I19:J21

	B	C	D	E	F	G	H
5	=E4-H4	=RAND()	=VLOOKUP(C5,$C$17:$E$22,3,TRUE)	=B5+D5	=RAND()	=VLOOKUP(F5,$I$17:K22,3,TRUE)	=MIN(E5,G5)

Copy B5:H5 to B6:H13

6 Simulation Model for a Maintenance Policy

Maintenance problems are an area in which simulation is widely used.

Simulation is a valuable technique for analyzing various maintenance policies before actually implementing them. A firm can decide whether to add more maintenance staff based on machine downtime costs and costs of additional labor. It can simulate replacing parts that have not yet failed in exploring ways to prevent future breakdowns. Many companies use computerized simulation models to decide if and when to shut down an entire plant for maintenance activities. This section provides an example of the value of simulation in setting maintenance policy.

Three Hills Power Company

The Three Hills Power Company provides electricity to a large metropolitan area through a series of almost 200 hydroelectric generators. Management recognizes that even a well-maintained generator will have periodic failures or breakdowns. Energy demands over the past three years have been consistently high, and the company is concerned over downtime of generators. It currently employs four highly skilled repairpersons at $30 per hour. Each works every fourth 8-hour shift. In this way there is a repairperson on duty 24 hours a day, 7 days a week.

As expensive as the maintenance staff salaries are, breakdown expenses are even more costly. For each hour that one of its generators is down, Three Hills loses approximately $75. This amount is the charge for reserve power that Three Hills must "borrow" from the neighboring utility company.

Stephanie Robbins has been assigned to conduct a management analysis of the break down problem. She determines that simulation is a workable tool because of the probabilistic nature of this problem. Stephanie decides her objective is to determine (1) the service maintenance cost, (2) the simulated machine breakdown cost, and (3) the total of these breakdown and maintenance costs (which gives the total cost of this system). Since the total downtime of the machines is needed to compute the breakdown cost, Stephanie must know when each machine breaks and when each machine returns to service. Therefore, a next event step simulation model must be used. In planning for this simulation, a flowchart, as seen in Figure 4, is developed.

Stephanie identifies two important maintenance system components. First, the time between successive generator breakdowns varies historically from as little as one-half hour to as much as three hours. For the past 100 breakdowns Stephanie tabulates the frequency of various times between machine failures (see Table 12). She also creates a probability distribution and assigns random number intervals to each expected time range.

Robbins then notes that the people who do repairs log their maintenance time in one-hour time blocks. Because of the time it takes to reach a broken generator, repair times are generally rounded to one, two, or three hours. In Table 13 she performs a statistical analysis of past repair times, similar to that conducted for breakdown times.

Robbins begins conducting the simulation by selecting a series of random numbers to generate simulated times between generator breakdowns and a second series to simulate repair times required. A simulation of 15 machine failures is presented in Table 14. We now examine the elements in the table, one column at a time.

Column 1: Breakdown Number.   This is just the count of breakdowns as they occur, going from 1 to 15.

Column 2: Random Number for Breakdowns.   This is a number used to simulate time between breakdowns. The numbers in this column have been selected from Table 4, from the second column from the right-hand side of the table.

Column 3: Time Between Breakdowns.   This number is generated from column 2 random numbers and the random number intervals defined in Table 12. The first random number, 57, falls in the interval 28 to 60, implying a time of 2 hours since the prior breakdown.

FIGURE 4

Three Hills Flow Diagram

Column 4: Time of Breakdown.   This converts the data in column 3 into an actual time of day for each breakdown. This simulation assumes that the first day begins at midnight (00:00 hours). Since the time between zero breakdowns and the first breakdown is 2 hours, the first recorded machine failure is at 02:00 on the clock. The second breakdown, you note, occurs 1.5 hours later, at a calculated clock time of 03:30 (or 3:30 A.M.).

Column 5: Time Repairperson Is Free to Begin Repair.   This is 02:00 hours for the first breakdown if we assume that the repairperson began work at 00:00 hours and was not tied up from a previous generator failure. Before recording this time on the second and all subsequent lines, however,

TABLE 12

Time Between Generator Breakdown at Three Hills Power

TIME BETWEEN RECORDED MACHINE FAILURES (HOURS)	NUMBER OF TIMES OBSERVED	PROBABILITY	CUMULATIVE PROBABILITY	RANDOM NUMBER INTERVAL
0.5	5	0.05	0.05	01 to 05
1.0	6	0.06	0.11	06 to 11
1.5	16	0.16	0.27	12 to 27
2.0	33	0.33	0.60	28 to 60
2.5	21	0.21	0.81	61 to 81
3.0	19	0.19	1.00	82 to 00
Total	100	1.00		

TABLE 13

Generator Repair Times Required

REPAIR TIME REQUIRED (HOURS)	NUMBER OF TIMES OBSERVED	PROBABILITY	CUMULATIVE PROBABILITY	RANDOM NUMBER INTERVAL
1	28	0.28	0.28	01 to 28
2	52	0.52	0.80	29 to 80
3	20	0.20	1.00	81 to 00
Total	100	1.00		

we must check column 8 to see what time the repairperson finishes the previous job. Look, for example, at the seventh breakdown. The breakdown occurs at 15:00 hours (or 3:00 P.M.). But the repairperson does not complete the previous job, the sixth breakdown, until 16:00 hours. Hence, the entry in column 5 is 16:00 hours.

One further assumption is made to handle the fact that each repairperson works only an 8-hour shift: When each person is replaced by the next shift, he or she simply hands the tools over to the new worker. The new repairperson continues working on the same broken generator until the job is completed. There is no lost time and no overlap of workers. Hence, labor costs for each 24-hour day are exactly 24 hours $\times$ \$30 per hour = \$720.

Column 6: Random Number for Repair Time. This is a number selected from the rightmost column of Table 4. It helps simulate repair times.

Column 7: Repair Time Required. This is generated from column 6's random numbers and Table 13's repair time distribution. The first random number, 07, represents a repair time of 1 hour since it falls in the random number interval 01 to 28.

Column 8: Time Repair Ends. This is the sum of the entry in column 5 (time repairperson is free to begin) plus the required repair time from column 7. Since the first repair begins at 02:00 and takes one hour to complete, the time repair ends is recorded in column 8 as 03:00.

Column 9: Number of Hours the Machine Is Down. This is the difference between column 4 (time of breakdown) and column 8 (time repair ends). In the case of the first breakdown, that difference is 1 hour (03:00 minus 02:00). In the case of the tenth breakdown, the difference is 23:00 hours minus 19:30 hours, or 3.5 hours.

Cost Analysis of the Simulation

The simulation of 15 generator breakdowns in Table 14 spans a time of 34 hours of operation. The clock began at 00:00 hours of day 1 and ran until the final repair at 10:00 hours of day 2.

TABLE 14 Simulation of Generator Breakdowns and Repairs

(1) BREAKDOWN NUMBER	(2) RANDOM NUMBER FOR BREAKDOWNS	(3) TIME BETWEEN BREAKDOWNS	(4) TIME OF BREAKDOWN	(5) TIME REPAIRPERSON IS FREE TO BEGIN THIS REPAIR	(6) RANDOM NUMBER FOR REPAIR TIME	(7) REPAIR TIME REQUIRED	(8) TIME REPAIR ENDS	(9) NUMBER OF HOURS MACHINE DOWN
1	57	2	02:00	02:00	07	1	03:00	1
2	17	1.5	03:30	03:30	60	2	05:30	2
3	36	2	05:30	05:30	77	2	07:30	2
4	72	2.5	08:00	08:00	49	2	10:00	2
5	85	3	11:00	11:00	76	2	13:00	2
6	31	2	13:00	13:00	95	3	16:00	3
7	44	2	15:00	16:00	51	2	18:00	3
8	30	2	17:00	18:00	16	1	19:00	2
9	26	1.5	18:30	19:00	14	1	20:00	1.5
10	09	1	19:30	20:00	85	3	23:00	3.5
11	49	2	21:30	23:00	59	2	01:00	3.5
12	13	1.5	23:00	01:00	85	3	04:00	5
13	33	2	01:00	04:00	40	2	06:00	5
14	89	3	04:00	06:00	42	2	08:00	4
15	13	1.5	05:30	08:00	52	2	10:00	4.5
								Total 44

IN ACTION   Simulating Jackson Memorial Hospital's Operating Rooms

Miami's Jackson Memorial Hospital, Florida's largest hospital, with 1,576 inpatient beds, is also one of the finest hospitals in the United States. In June 1996, it received the highest accreditation score of any public-sector hospital in the country. Jackson's Department of Management Systems Engineering is constantly seeking ways of increasing hospital efficiency, and the construction of new operating rooms (ORs) prompted the development of a simulation of the existing 31 ORs.

The OR boundary includes the Holding Area and the Recovery Area, both of which were experiencing problems due to ineffective scheduling of OR services. A simulation study, modeled using the ARENA software package, sought to maximize the current use of OR rooms and staff. Inputs to the model included (1) the amount of time a patient waits in holding, (2) the specific process the patient undergoes, (3) the staff schedule, (4) room availability, and (5) time of day.

The first hurdle that the research team had to deal with at Jackson was the vast number of records to scour to extract data for the probabilistic simulation model. The second hurdle was the *quality* of the data. A thorough analysis of the records determined which were good and which had to be discarded. In the end, Jackson's carefully screened databases led to a good set of model inputs. The simulation model then successfully developed five measures of OR performance: (1) number of procedures a day, (2) average case time, (3) staff utilization, (4) room utilization, and (5) average waiting time in the holding area.

Source: Based on M. A. Centeno, et al. "Challenges of Simulating Hospital Facilities," *Proceedings of the 12th Annual Conference of the Production and Operations Management Society*, Orlando, FL (March 2001): 50.

The critical factor that interests Robbins is the total number of hours that generators are out of service (from column 9). This is computed to be 44 hours. She also notes that toward the end of the simulation period, a backlog is beginning to appear. The thirteenth breakdown occurred at 01:00 hours but could not be worked on until 04:00 hours. The fourteenth and fifteenth breakdowns experienced similar delays. Robbins is determined to write a computer program to carry out a few hundred more simulated breakdowns but first wants to analyze the data she has collected thus far.

She measures her objectives as follows:

$$\text{Service maintenance cost} = 34 \text{ hours of worker service time} \times \$30 \text{ per hour}$$
$$= \$1,020$$

$$\text{Simulated machine breakdown cost} = 44 \text{ total hours of breakdown}$$
$$\times \$75 \text{ lost per hour of downtime}$$
$$= \$3,300$$

$$\text{Total simulated maintenance cost of the current system} = \text{Service cost} + \text{Breakdown cost}$$
$$= \$1,020 + \$3,300$$
$$= \$4,320$$

A total cost of $4,320 is reasonable only when compared with other more attractive or less attractive maintenance options. Should, for example, the Three Hills Power Company add a second full-time repairperson to each shift? Should it add just one more worker and let him or her come on duty every fourth shift to help catch up on any backlogs? These are two alternatives that Robbins may choose to consider through simulation. You can help by solving Problem 25 at the end of the chapter.

As mentioned at the outset of this section, simulation can also be used in other maintenance problems, including the analysis of *preventive maintenance*. Perhaps the Three Hills Power Company should consider strategies for replacing generator motors, valves, wiring, switches, and other miscellaneous parts that typically fail. It could (1) replace all parts after a certain type when one fails on any generator, or (2) repair or replace all parts after a certain length of service based on an estimated average service life. This would again be done by setting probability distributions for failure rates, selecting random numbers, and simulating past failures and their associated costs.

Preventive maintenance policies can also be simulated.

BUILDING AN EXCEL SIMULATION MODEL FOR THREE HILLS POWER COMPANY   Program 6 provides an Excel spreadsheet approach to simulating the Three Hills Power maintenance problem.

PROGRAM 6

Excel Model for Three Hills Power Company Maintenance Problem

	A	B	C	D	E	F	G	H
1	Three Hills Power Company							
2								
3	Breakdown number	Random number	Time between breakdowns	Time of breakdowns	Time repairperson is free	Random Number	Repair time	Repair ends
4	1	0.7267	2.5	2.5	2.5	0.9740	3	5.5
5	2	0.8303	3	5.5	5.5	0.9279	3	8.5
6	3	0.5993	2	7.5	8.5	0.6616	2	10.5
7	4	0.4673	2	9.5	10.5	0.1386	1	11.5
8	5	0.4184	2	11.5	11.5	0.2754	1	12.5
9	6	0.9412	3	14.5	14.5	0.7995	2	16.5
10	7	0.4346	2	16.5	16.5	0.3224	2	18.5
11	8	0.6600	2.5	19	19	0.2994	2	21
12	9	0.8929	3	22	22	0.9344	3	25
13	10	0.7589	2.5	24.5	25	0.7028	2	27

	A	B	C	D	E		G	H	I	J	K
15	Demand Table						Repair times				
16	Time between breakdowns	Probability	Lower	Cumulative	Demand		Time	Probability	Lower	Cumulative	Lead time
17	0.5	0.05	0	0.05	0.5		1	0.28	0.00	0.28	1
18	1.0	0.06	0.05	0.11	1		2	0.52	0.28	0.80	2
19	1.5	0.16	0.11	0.27	1.5		3	0.20	0.80	1.00	3
20	2.0	0.33	0.27	0.6	2						
21	2.5	0.21	0.6	0.81	2.5						
22	3.0	0.19	0.81	1	3						

Key Formulas

	C	D	E
18	=C17+B17	=D17+B18	=A18

Copy C18:E18 to C19:E22

	I	J	K
18	=I17+H17	=J17+H18	=G18

	B	C	D	E	F	G	H
5	=RAND()	=VLOOKUP(B5,$C$17:$E$22,3,TRUE)	=D4+C5	=MAX(D5,H4)	=RAND()	=VLOOKUP(F5,$I$17:$K$19,3,TRUE)	=E5+G5

Copy B5:H5 to B6:H13

7 Other Simulation Issues

Simulation is one of the most widely used tools in business. As we have seen in the earlier parts of this chapter, applications abound, as we are not restricted by the assumptions in some of the mathematical models. In this section, we look at a few other issues related to simulation, including some of the software tools available.

Two Other Types of Simulation Models

Simulation models are often broken into three categories. The first, the Monte Carlo method just discussed, uses the concepts of probability distribution and random numbers to evaluate system responses to various policies. The other two categories are operational gaming and systems simulation. Although in theory the three methods are distinctly different, the growth of computerized simulation has tended to create a common basis in procedures and blur these differences.*

OPERATIONAL GAMING **Operational gaming** refers to simulation involving two or more competing players. The best examples are military games and business games. Both allow participants to match their management and decision-making skills in hypothetical situations of conflict.

Military games are used worldwide to train a nation's top military officers, to test offensive and defensive strategies, and to examine the effectiveness of equipment and armies. Business games, first developed by the firm Booz, Allen, and Hamilton in the 1950s, are popular with both executives and business students. They provide an opportunity to test business skills and decision-making ability in a competitive environment. The person or team that performs best

---

*Theoretically, random numbers are used only in Monte Carlo simulation. However, in some complex gaming or systems simulation problems in which all relationships cannot be defined exactly, it may be necessary to use the probability concepts of the Monte Carlo method.

in the simulated environment is rewarded by knowing that his or her company has been most successful in earning the largest profit, grabbing a high market share, or perhaps increasing the firm's trading value on the stock exchange.

During each period of competition, be it a week, month, or quarter, teams respond to market conditions by coding their latest management decisions with respect to inventory, production, financing, investment, marketing, and research. The competitive business environment is simulated by computer, and a new printout summarizing current market conditions is presented to players. This allows teams to simulate years of operating conditions in a matter of days, weeks, or a semester.

SYSTEMS SIMULATION   **Systems simulation** is similar to business gaming in that it allows users to test various managerial policies and decisions to evaluate their effect on the operating environment. This variation of simulation models the dynamics of large *systems*. Such systems include corporate operations,* the national economy, a hospital, or a city government system.

In a *corporate operating system*, sales, production levels, marketing policies, investments, union contracts, utility rates, financing, and other factors are all related in a series of mathematical equations that are examined by simulation. In a simulation of an *urban government*, systems simulation can be employed to evaluate the impact of tax increases, capital expenditures for roads and buildings, housing availability, new garbage routes, immigration and out-migration, locations of new schools or senior citizen centers, birth and death rates, and many more vital issues. Simulations of *economic systems*, often called econometric models, are used by government agencies, bankers, and large organizations to predict inflation rates, domestic and foreign money supplies, and unemployment levels. Inputs and outputs of a typical economic system simulation are illustrated in Figure 5.

The value of systems simulation lies in its allowance of what-if? questions to test the effects of various policies. A corporate planning group, for example, can change the value of any input, such as an advertising budget, and examine the impact on sales, market share, or short-term costs. Simulation can also be used to evaluate different research and development projects or to determine long-range planning horizons.

Econometric models are huge simulations involving thousands of regression equations tied together by economic factors. They use what-if? questions to test out various policies.

Verification and Validation

In the development of a simulation model, it is important that the model be checked to see that it is working properly and providing a good representation of the real world situation. The **verification** process involves determining that the computer model is internally consistent and following the logic of the conceptual model.

Validation is the process of comparing a model to the real system that it represents to make sure that it is accurate. The assumptions of the model should be checked to see that the appropriate probability distribution is being used. An analysis of the inputs and outputs should be made to see that the results are reasonable. If we know what the actual outputs are for a specific set of inputs, we could use those inputs in the computer model to see that the outputs of the simulation are consistent with the real world system.

Verification relates to building the model right. Validation relates to building the right model.

It has been said that verification answers the question "Did we build the model right?" On the other hand, validation answers the question "Did we build the right model?" Only after we are convinced that the model is good should we feel comfortable in using the results.

FIGURE 5
Inputs and Outputs of a Typical Economic System Simulation

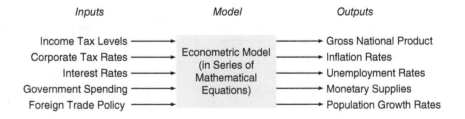

Inputs	Model	Outputs
Income Tax Levels		Gross National Product
Corporate Tax Rates	Econometric Model (in Series of Mathematical Equations)	Inflation Rates
Interest Rates		Unemployment Rates
Government Spending		Monetary Supplies
Foreign Trade Policy		Population Growth Rates

*This is sometimes referred to as *industrial dynamics*, a term coined by Jay Forrester. Forrester's goal was to find a way "to show how policies, decisions, structure, and delays are interrelated to influence growth and stability" in industrial systems. See J. W. Forrester. *Industrial Dynamics* (Cambridge, MA: MIT Press, 1961).

IN ACTION   Simulating a Tiger

What does it take to beat Tiger Woods on the golf course? Quantitative analysts studied that very question using a simulation model.

The simulation model was quite extensive. It was essentially a simulation based estimate of relative tournament difficulty. It included variables such as individual player skill, strength of the field (how good are the players at any particular tournament), depth of field (how many players are at any particular tournament), along with random variation in individual scoring. The model noted that when Tiger Woods wins, he wins by an average of 2.84 strokes per tournament.

This difference suggested that Tiger Woods wasn't just lucky and was, in fact, significantly better than everyone else in the field. Indeed, from the moment he became a professional golfer in 1996 he won 71 of the ensuing 239 PGA TOUR events that he entered. That's a staggering 29.7% winning percentage!

Source: Based on R. A. Connolly and R. J. Rendleman, Jr. "What It Takes to Win on the PGA TOUR (If Your Name Is "Tiger" or If It Isn't".) *Interfaces*, 42, 6 (November–December 2012): 554–576.

Role of Computers in Simulation

We recognize that computers are critical in simulating complex tasks. They can generate random numbers, simulate thousands of time periods in a matter of seconds or minutes, and provide management with reports that make decision making easier. As a matter of fact, a computer approach is almost a necessity for us to draw valid conclusions from a simulation. Because we require a very large number of simulations, it would be a real burden to rely on pencil and paper alone.

While general-purpose programming languages can be used for simulation, some special **simulation software tools** have been developed that make the simulation process much easier. Some of these tools are Arena, ProModel, SIMUL8, ExtendSim, Proof 5, and numerous others.* In addition to these stand-alone tools, there are several Excel add-ins, such as @Risk, Crystal Ball, RiskSim, and XLSim, which can make simulating with Excel very easy.

Summary

The purpose of this chapter is to discuss the concept and approach of simulation as a problem-solving tool. Simulation involves building a mathematical model that attempts to describe a real-world situation. The model's goal is to incorporate important variables and their interrelationships in such a way that we can study the impact of managerial changes on the total system. The approach has many advantages over other quantitative analysis techniques and is especially useful when a problem is too complex or difficult to solve by other means.

The Monte Carlo method of simulation is developed through the use of probability distributions and random numbers. Random number intervals are established to represent possible outcomes for each probabilistic variable in the model. Random numbers are then either selected from a random number table or generated by computer to simulate variable outcomes. The simulation procedure is conducted for many time periods to evaluate the long-term impact of each policy value being studied. Monte Carlo simulation by hand is illustrated on problems of inventory control, queuing, and machine maintenance.

Operational gaming and systems simulation, two other categories of simulation, are also presented in this chapter. The chapter concludes with a discussion of the important role of the computer in the simulation process.

Glossary

Flow Diagram, or Flowchart   A graphical means of presenting the logic of a simulation model. It is a tool that helps in writing a simulation computer program.

Monte Carlo Simulation   Simulations that experiment with probabilistic elements of a system by generating random numbers to create values for those elements.

Operational Gaming   The use of simulation in competitive situations such as military games and business or management games.

Prewritten Simulation Programs   Graphical programs that are prestructured to handle a variety of situations.

---

*For a list of simulation software products, see James J. Swain. "To Boldly Go," *OR/MS Today* 36, 5 (October 2009): 50–61.

Random Number   A number whose digits are selected completely at random.

Random Number Interval   A range of random numbers assigned to represent a possible simulation outcome.

Simulation   A quantitative analysis technique that involves building a mathematical model that represents a real-world situation. The model is then experimented with to estimate the effects of various actions and decisions.

Simulation Software Tools   Programming languages especially designed to be efficient in handling simulation problems.

Systems Simulation   Simulation models that deal with the dynamics of large organizational or governmental systems.

Validation   The process of comparing a model to the real system that it represents to make sure that it is accurate.

Verification   The process of determining that the computer model is internally consistent and follows the logic of the conceptual model.

Solved Problems

Solved Problem 1

Higgins Plumbing and Heating maintains a stock of 30-gallon hot water heaters that it sells to homeowners and installs for them. Owner Jerry Higgins likes the idea of having a large supply on hand to meet customer demand, but he also recognizes that it is expensive to do so. He examines hot water heater sales over the past 50 weeks and notes the following:

HOT WATER HEATER SALES PER WEEK	NUMBER OF WEEKS THIS NUMBER WAS SOLD
4	6
5	5
6	9
7	12
8	8
9	7
10	3
	Total 50

a. If Higgins maintains a constant supply of 8 hot water heaters in any given week, how many times will he be out of stock during a 20-week simulation? We use random numbers from the seventh column of Table 4, beginning with the random digits 10.

b. What is the average number of sales per week (including stockouts) over the 20-week period?

c. Using an analytic nonsimulation technique, what is the expected number of sales per week? How does this compare with the answer in part (b)?

Solution

The variable of interest is the number of sales per week.

HEATER SALES	PROBABILITY	RANDOM NUMBER INTERVALS
4	0.12	01 to 12
5	0.10	13 to 22
6	0.18	23 to 40
7	0.24	41 to 64
8	0.16	65 to 80
9	0.14	81 to 94
10	0.06	95 to 00
	1.00	

a.

WEEK	RANDOM NUMBER	SIMULATED SALES	WEEK	RANDOM NUMBER	SIMULATED SALES
1	10	4	11	08	4
2	24	6	12	48	7
3	03	4	13	66	8
4	32	6	14	97	10
5	23	6	15	03	4
6	59	7	16	96	10
7	95	10	17	46	7
8	34	6	18	74	8
9	34	6	19	77	8
10	51	7	20	44	7

With a supply of 8 heaters, Higgins will be out of stock three times during the 20-week period (in weeks 7, 14, and 16).

b. Average sales by simulation $= \dfrac{\text{Total sales}}{20 \text{ weeks}} = \dfrac{135}{20} = 6.75$ per week.

c. Using expected value,

$$E(\text{sales}) = 0.12(4 \text{ heaters}) + 0.10(5) + 0.18(6) + 0.24(7)$$
$$+ 0.16(8) + 0.14(9) + 0.06(10)$$
$$= 6.88 \text{ heaters}$$

With a longer simulation, these two approaches will lead to even closer values.

Solved Problem 2

The manager of a bank in Greensboro, North Carolina, is attempting to determine how many tellers are needed at the drive-in window during peak times. As a general policy, the manager wishes to offer service such that average customer waiting time does not exceed 2 minutes. Given the existing service level, as shown in the following data, does the drive-in window meet this criterion?

DATA FOR SERVICE TIME			
SERVICE TIME (MINUTES)	PROBABILITY (FREQUENCY)	CUMULATIVE PROBABILITY	RANDOM NUMBER INTERVAL
0	0.00	0.00	(impossible)
1.0	0.25	0.25	01 to 25
2.0	0.20	0.45	26 to 45
3.0	0.40	0.85	46 to 85
4.0	0.15	1.00	86 to 00

	DATA FOR CUSTOMER ARRIVALS		
TIME BETWEEN SUCCESSIVE CUSTOMER ARRIVALS	PROBABILITY (FREQUENCY)	CUMULATIVE PROBABILITY	RANDOM NUMBER INTERVAL
0	0.10	0.10	01 to 10
1.0	0.35	0.45	11 to 45
2.0	0.25	0.70	46 to 70
3.0	0.15	0.85	71 to 85
4.0	0.10	0.95	86 to 95
5.0	0.05	1.00	96 to 00

Solution

Average waiting time is a variable of concern.

(1) CUSTOMER NUMBER	(2) RANDOM NUMBER	(3) INTERVAL TO ARRIVAL	(4) TIME OF ARRIVAL	(5) RANDOM NUMBER	(6) SERVICE TIME	(7) START SERVICE	(8) END SERVICE	(9) WAIT TIME	(10) IDLE TIME
1	50	2	9:02	52	3	9:02	9:05	0	2
2	28	1	9:03	37	2	9:05	9:07	2	0
3	68	2	9:05	82	3	9:07	9:10	2	0
4	36	1	9:06	69	3	9:10	9:13	4	0
5	90	4	9:10	98	4	9:13	9:17	3	0
6	62	2	9:12	96	4	9:17	9:21	5	0
7	27	1	9:13	33	2	9:21	9:23	8	0
8	50	2	9:15	50	3	9:23	9:26	8	0
9	18	1	9:16	88	4	9:26	9:30	10	0
10	36	1	9:17	90	4	9:30	9:34	13	0
11	61	2	9:19	50	3	9:34	9:37	15	0
12	21	1	9:20	27	2	9:37	9:39	17	0
13	46	2	9:22	45	2	9:39	9:41	17	0
14	01	0	9:22	81	3	9:41	9:44	19	0
15	14	1	9:23	66	3	9:44	9:47	21	0

Read the data as in the following example for the first row:

Column 1: Number of customer.

Column 2: From third column of random number Table 4.

Column 3: Time interval corresponding to random number (random number of 50 implies a 2-minute interval).

Column 4: Starting at 9 A.M. the first arrival is at 9:02.

Column 5: From the first column of the random number Table 4.

Column 6: Teller time corresponding to random number 52 is 3 minutes.

Column 7: Teller is available and can start at 9:02.

Column 8: Teller completes work at 9:05 (9:02 + 0:03).

Column 9: Wait time for customer is 0 as the teller was available.

Column 10: Idle time for the teller was 2 minutes (9:00 to 9:02).

The drive-in window clearly does not meet the manager's criteria for an average wait time of 2 minutes. As a matter of fact, we can observe an increasing queue buildup after only a few customer simulations. This observation can be confirmed by expected value calculations on both arrival and service rates.

Self-Test

- Before taking the self-test, refer to the learning objectives at the beginning of the chapter, the notes in the margins, and the glossary at the end of the chapter.
- Use the key at the end of the chapter to correct your answers.
- Restudy pages that correspond to any questions that you answered incorrectly or material you feel uncertain about.

1. Simulation is a technique usually reserved for studying only the simplest and most straightforward of problems.
   a. True
   b. False

2. A simulation model is designed to arrive at a single specific numerical answer to a given problem.
   a. True
   b. False

3. Simulation typically requires a familiarity with statistics to evaluate the results.
   a. True
   b. False

4. The verification process involves making sure that
   a. the model adequately represents the real-world system.
   b. the model is internally consistent and logical.
   c. the correct random numbers are used.
   d. enough trial runs are simulated.

5. The validation process involves making sure that
   a. the model adequately represents the real-world system.
   b. the model is internally consistent and logical.
   c. the correct random numbers are used.
   d. enough trial runs are simulated.

6. Which of the following is an *advantage* of simulation?
   a. It allows time compression.
   b. It is always relatively simple and inexpensive.
   c. The results are usually transferable to other problems.
   d. It will always find the optimal solution to a problem.

7. Which of the following is a *disadvantage* of simulation?
   a. It is inexpensive even for the most complex problem.
   b. It always generates the optimal solution to a problem.
   c. The results are usually transferable to other problems.
   d. Managers must generate all of the conditions and constraints for solutions that they wish to examine.

8. A meteorologist was simulating the number of days that rain would occur in a month. The random number interval from 01 to 30 was used to indicate that rain occurred on a particular day, and the interval 31–00 indicated that rain did not occur. What is the probability that rain did occur?
   a. 0.30
   b. 0.31
   c. 1.00
   d. 0.70

9. Simulation is best thought of as a technique to
   a. give concrete numerical answers.
   b. increase understanding of a problem.
   c. provide rapid solutions to relatively simple problems.
   d. provide optimal solutions to complex problems.

10. When simulating the Monte Carlo experiment, the average simulated demand over the long run should approximate the
    a. real demand.
    b. expected demand.
    c. sample demand.
    d. daily demand.

11. The idea behind simulation is to
    a. imitate a real-world situation.
    b. study the properties and operating characteristics of a real-world situation.
    c. draw conclusions and make action decisions based on simulation results.
    d. all of the above.

12. Using simulation for a queuing problem would be appropriate if
    a. the arrival rate follows a Poisson distribution.
    b. the service rate is constant.
    c. the FIFO queue discipline is assumed.
    d. there is a 10% chance an arrival would leave before receiving service.

13. A probability distribution has been developed, and the probability of 2 arrivals in the next hour is 0.20. A random number interval is to be assigned to this. Which of the following would *not* be an appropriate interval?
    a. 01–20
    b. 21–40
    c. 00–20
    d. 00–19
    e. All of the above would be appropriate.

14. In a Monte Carlo simulation, a variable that we might want to simulate is
    a. lead time for inventory orders to arrive.
    b. times between machine breakdowns.
    c. times between arrivals at a service facility.
    d. number of employees absent from work each day.
    e. all of the above.

15. Use the following random numbers to simulate *yes* and *no* answers to 10 questions by starting in the first *row* and letting
    a. the double-digit numbers 00–49 represent *yes*, and 50–99 represent *no*.
    b. the double-digit even numbers represent *yes*, and the odd numbers represent *no*.
    Random numbers: 52 06 50 88 53 30 10 47 99 37 66 91 35 32 00 84 57 00

Discussion Questions and Problems

Discussion Questions

1 What are the advantages and limitations of simulation models?

2 Why might a manager be forced to use simulation instead of an analytical model in dealing with a problem of
(a) inventory ordering policy?
(b) ships docking in a port to unload?
(c) bank teller service windows?
(d) the U.S. economy?

3 What types of management problems can be solved more easily by quantitative analysis techniques other than simulation?

4 What are the major steps in the simulation process?

5 What is Monte Carlo simulation? What principles underlie its use, and what steps are followed in applying it?

6 List three ways in which random numbers may be generated for use in a simulation.

7 Discuss the concepts of verification and validation in simulation.

8 Give two examples of random variables that would be continuous and give two examples of random variables that would be discreet.

9 In the simulation of an order policy for drills at Simkin's Hardware, would the results (Table 8) change significantly if a longer period were simulated? Why is the 10-day simulation valid or invalid?

10 Why is a computer necessary in conducting a real-world simulation?

11 What is operational gaming? What is systems simulation? Give examples of how each may be applied.

12 Do you think the application of simulation will increase strongly in the next 10 years? Why or why not?

13 List five of the simulation software tools that are available today.

Problems*

The problems that follow involve simulations that are to be done by hand. You are aware that to obtain accurate and meaningful results, long periods must be simulated. This is usually handled by computer. If you are able to program some of the problems using a spreadsheet, or QM for Windows, we suggest that you try to do so. If not, the hand simulations will still help you in understanding the simulation process.

14 Clark Property Management is responsible for the maintenance, rental, and day-to-day operation of a large apartment complex on the east side of New Orleans. George Clark is especially concerned about the cost projections for replacing air conditioner compressors. He would like to simulate the number of compressor failures each year over the next 20 years. Using data from a similar apartment building he manages in a New Orleans suburb, Clark establishes a table of relative frequency of failures during a year as shown in the following table:

NUMBER OF A.C. COMPRESSOR FAILURES	PROBABILITY (RELATIVE FREQUENCY)
0	0.06
1	0.13
2	0.25
3	0.28
4	0.20
5	0.07
6	0.01

He decides to simulate the 20-year period by selecting two-digit random numbers from the third column of Table 4, starting with the random number 50.

Conduct the simulation for Clark. Is it common to have three or more consecutive years of operation with two or fewer compressor failures per year?

15 The number of cars arriving per hour at Lundberg's Car Wash during the past 200 hours of operation is observed to be the following:

NUMBER OF CARS ARRIVING	FREQUENCY
3 or fewer	0
4	20
5	30
6	50
7	60
8	40
9 or more	0
	Total 200

(a) Set up a probability and cumulative probability distribution for the variable of car arrivals.
(b) Establish random number intervals for the variable.

*Note: means the problem may be solved with QM for Windows; means the problem may be solved with Excel; and means the problem may be solved with QM for Windows and/or Excel.

(c) Simulate 15 hours of car arrivals and compute the average number of arrivals per hour. Select the random numbers needed from the first column of Table 4, beginning with the digits 52.

16 Compute the expected number of cars arriving in Problem 15 using the expected value formula. Compare this with the results obtained in the simulation.

17 Refer to the data in Solved Problem 1, which deals with Higgins Plumbing and Heating. Higgins has now collected 100 weeks of data and finds the following distribution for sales:

HOT WATER HEATER SALES PER WEEK	NUMBER OF WEEKS THIS NUMBER WAS SOLD
3	2
4	9
5	10
6	15
7	25
8	12
9	12
10	10
11	5

(a) Resimulate the number of stockouts incurred over a 20-week period (assuming Higgins maintains a constant supply of 8 heaters).

(b) Conduct this 20-week simulation two more times and compare your answers with those in part (a). Did they change significantly? Why or why not?

(c) What is the new expected number of sales per week?

18 An increase in the size of the barge unloading crew at the Port of New Orleans (see Section 5) has resulted in a new probability distribution for daily unloading rates. In particular, Table 10 may be revised as shown here:

DAILY UNLOADING RATE	PROBABILITY
1	0.03
2	0.12
3	0.40
4	0.28
5	0.12
6	0.05

(a) Resimulate 15 days of barge unloadings and compute the average number of barges delayed, average number of nightly arrivals, and average number of barges unloaded each day. Draw

random numbers from the leftmost value of the bottom row of Table 4 to generate daily arrivals and from the second-from-the-bottom row to generate daily unloading rates.

(b) How do these simulated results compare with those in the chapter?

19 Every home football game for the past eight years at Eastern State University has been sold out. The revenues from ticket sales are significant, but the sale of food, beverages, and souvenirs has contributed greatly to the overall profitability of the football program. One particular souvenir is the football program for each game. The number of programs sold at each game is described by the following probability distribution:

NUMBER (IN 100s) OF PROGRAMS SOLD	PROBABILITY
23	0.15
24	0.22
25	0.24
26	0.21
27	0.18

Historically, Eastern has never sold fewer than 2,300 programs or more than 2,700 programs at one game. Each program costs $0.80 to produce and sells for $2.00. Any programs that are not sold are donated to a recycling center and do not produce any revenue.

(a) Simulate the sales of programs at 10 football games. Use the last column in the random number table (Table 4) and begin at the top of the column.

(b) If the university decided to print 2,500 programs for each game, what would the average profits be for the 10 games simulated in part (a)?

(c) If the university decided to print 2,600 programs for each game, what would the average profits be for the 10 games simulated in part (a)?

20 Refer to Problem 19. Suppose the sale of football programs described by the probability distribution in that problem only applies to days when the weather is good. When poor weather occurs on the day of a football game, the crowd that attends the game is only half of capacity. When this occurs, the sales of programs decreases, and the total sales are given in the following table:

NUMBER (IN 100s) OF PROGRAMS SOLD	PROBABILITY
12	0.25
13	0.24
14	0.19
15	0.17
16	0.15

Programs must be printed two days prior to game day. The university is trying to establish a policy for determining the number of programs to print based on the weather forecast.

(a) If the forecast is for a 20% chance of bad weather, simulate the weather for ten games with this forecast. Use column 4 of Table 4.

(b) Simulate the demand for programs at 10 games in which the weather is bad. Use column 5 of the random number table (Table 4) and begin with the first number in the column.

(c) Beginning with a 20% chance of bad weather and an 80% chance of good weather, develop a flowchart that would be used to prepare a simulation of the demand for football programs for 10 games.

(d) Suppose there is a 20% chance of bad weather, and the university has decided to print 2,500 programs. Simulate the total profits that would be achieved for 10 football games.

21 Dumoor Appliance Center sells and services several brands of major appliances. Past sales for a particular model of refrigerator have resulted in the following probability distribution for demand:

DEMAND PER WEEK	0	1	2	3	4
Probability	0.20	0.40	0.20	0.15	0.05

The lead time, in weeks, is described by the following distribution:

LEAD TIME (WEEKS)	1	2	3
Probability	0.15	0.35	0.50

Based on cost considerations as well as storage space, the company has decided to order 10 of these each time an order is placed. The holding cost is $1 per week for each unit that is left in inventory at the end of the week. The stockout cost has been set at $40 per stockout. The company has decided to place an order whenever there are only two refrigerators left at the end of the week. Simulate 10 weeks of operation for Dumoor Appliance assuming there are currently 5 units in inventory. Determine what the weekly stockout cost and weekly holding cost would be for the problem.

22 Repeat the simulation in Problem 21, assuming that the reorder point is 4 units rather than 2. Compare the costs for these two situations.

23 Simkin's Hardware Store simulated an inventory ordering policy for Ace electric drills that involved an order quantity of 10 drills with a reorder point of 5. The first attempt to develop a cost-effective ordering strategy is illustrated in Table 8. The brief simulation resulted in a total daily inventory cost of $4.72. Simkin would now like to compare this strategy with

one in which he orders 12 drills, with a reorder point of 6. Conduct a 10-day simulation for him and discuss the cost implications.

24 Draw a flow diagram to represent the logic and steps of simulating barge arrivals and unloadings at the Port of New Orleans (see Section 5). For a refresher in flowcharts, see Figure 3.

25 Stephanie Robbins is the Three Hills Power Company management analyst assigned to simulate maintenance costs. In Section 6 we describe the simulation of 15 generator breakdowns and the repair times required when one repairperson is on duty per shift. The total simulated maintenance cost of the current system is $4,320.

Robbins would now like to examine the relative cost-effectiveness of adding one more worker per shift. Each new repairperson would be paid $30 per hour, the same rate as the first is paid. The cost per breakdown hour is still $75. Robbins makes one vital assumption as she begins—that repair times with two workers will be exactly one-half the times required with only one repairperson on duty per shift. Table 13 can then be restated as follows:

REPAIR TIME REQUIRED (HOURS)	PROBABILITY
0.5	0.28
1	0.52
1.5	0.20
	1.00

(a) Simulate this proposed maintenance system change over a 15-generator breakdown period. Select the random numbers needed for time between breakdowns from the second-from-the-bottom row of Table 4 (beginning with the digits 69). Select random numbers for generator repair times from the last row of the table (beginning with 37).

(b) Should Three Hills add a second repairperson each shift?

26 The Brennan Aircraft Division of TLN Enterprises operates a large number of computerized plotting machines. For the most part, the plotting devices are used to create line drawings of complex wing airfoils and fuselage part dimensions. The engineers operating the automated plotters are called loft lines engineers.

The computerized plotters consist of a minicomputer system connected to a 4- by 5-foot flat table with a series of ink pens suspended above it. When a sheet of clear plastic or paper is properly placed on the table, the computer directs a series of horizontal and vertical pen movements until the desired figure is drawn.

The plotting machines are highly reliable, with the exception of the four sophisticated ink pens that are built in. The pens constantly clog and jam in a raised or lowered position. When this occurs, the plotter is unusable.

Currently, Brennan Aircraft replaces each pen as it fails. The service manager has, however, proposed replacing all four pens every time one fails. This should cut down the frequency of plotter failures. At present, it takes one hour to replace one pen. All four pens could be replaced in two hours. The total cost of a plotter being unusable is $50 per hour. Each pen costs $8.

If only one pen is replaced each time a clog or jam occurs, the following breakdown data are thought to be valid:

HOURS BETWEEN PLOTTER FAILURES IF ONE PEN IS REPLACED DURING A REPAIR	PROBABILITY
10	0.05
20	0.15
30	0.15
40	0.20
50	0.20
60	0.15
70	0.10

Based on the service manager's estimates, if all four pens are replaced each time one pen fails, the probability distribution between failures is as follows:

HOURS BETWEEN PLOTTER FAILURES IF ALL FOUR PENS ARE REPLACED DURING A REPAIR	PROBABILITY
100	0.15
110	0.25
120	0.35
130	0.20
140	0.00

(a) Simulate Brennan Aircraft's problem and determine the best policy. Should the firm replace one pen or all four pens on a plotter each time a failure occurs?

(b) Develop a second approach to solving this problem, this time without simulation. Compare the results. How does it affect Brennan's policy decision using simulation?

27 Dr. Mark Greenberg practices dentistry in Topeka, Kansas. Greenberg tries hard to schedule appointments so that patients do not have to wait beyond their appointment time. His October 20 schedule is shown in the following table.

SCHEDULED APPOINTMENT AND TIME		EXPECTED TIME NEEDED
Adams	9:30 A.M.	15
Brown	9:45 A.M.	20
Crawford	10:15 A.M.	15
Dannon	10:30 A.M.	10
Erving	10:45 A.M.	30
Fink	11:15 A.M.	15
Graham	11:30 A.M.	20
Hinkel	11:45 A.M.	15

Unfortunately, not every patient arrives exactly on schedule, and expected times to examine patients are just that—*expected*. Some examinations take longer than expected, and some take less time.

Greenberg's experience dictates the following:

(a) 20% of the patients will be 20 minutes early.
(b) 10% of the patients will be 10 minutes early.
(c) 40% of the patients will be on time.
(d) 25% of the patients will be 10 minutes late.
(e) 5% of the patients will be 20 minutes late.

He further estimates that

(a) 15% of the time he will finish in 20% less time than expected.
(b) 50% of the time he will finish in the expected time.
(c) 25% of the time he will finish in 20% more time than expected.
(d) 10% of the time he will finish in 40% more time than expected.

Dr. Greenberg has to leave at 12:15 P.M. on October 20 to catch a flight to a dental convention in New York. Assuming that he is ready to start his workday at 9:30 A.M. and that patients are treated in order of their scheduled exam (even if one late patient arrives after an early one), will he be able to make the flight? Comment on this simulation.

28 The Pelnor Corporation is the nation's largest manufacturer of industrial-size washing machines. A main ingredient in the production process is 8- by 10-foot sheets of stainless steel. The steel is used for both interior washer drums and outer casings.

Steel is purchased weekly on a contractual basis from the Smith-Layton Foundry, which, because of limited availability and lot sizing, can ship either 8,000 or 11,000 square feet of stainless steel each week. When Pelnor's weekly order is placed, there is a 45% chance that 8,000 square feet will arrive and a 55% chance of receiving the larger size order.

Pelnor uses the stainless steel on a stochastic (nonconstant) basis. The probabilities of demand each week follow:

STEEL NEEDED PER WEEK (SQ FT)	PROBABILITY
6,000	0.05
7,000	0.15
8,000	0.20
9,000	0.30
10,000	0.20
11,000	0.10

Pelnor has a capacity to store no more than 25,000 square feet of steel at any time. Because of the contract, orders *must* be placed each week regardless of the on-hand supply.

(a) Simulate stainless steel order arrivals and use for 20 weeks. (Begin the first week with a starting inventory of 0 stainless steel.) If an end-of-week inventory is ever negative, assume that back orders are permitted and fill the demand from the next arriving order.

(b) Should Pelnor add more storage area? If so, how much? If not, comment on the system.

×: 29 Milwaukee's General Hospital has an emergency room that is divided into six departments: (1) the initial exam station, to treat minor problems or make diagnoses; (2) an x-ray department; (3) an operating room; (4) a cast-fitting room; (5) an observation room for recovery and general observation before final diagnoses or release; and (6) an out-processing department where clerks check patients out and arrange for payment or insurance forms.

The probabilities that a patient will go from one department to another are presented in the table below:

(a) Simulate the trail followed by 10 emergency room patients. Proceed one patient at a time from each one's entry at the initial exam station until he or she leaves through out-processing. You should be aware that a patient can enter the same department more than once.

(b) Using your simulation data, what are the chances that a patient enters the x-ray department twice?

×: 30 Management of the First Syracuse Bank is concerned about a loss of customers at its main office downtown. One solution that has been proposed is to add one or more drive-through teller stations to make it easier for customers in cars to obtain quick service without parking. Chris Carlson, the bank president, thinks the bank should only risk the cost of installing one drive-through. He is informed by his staff that the cost (amortized over a 20-year period) of building a drive-through is $12,000 per year. It also costs $16,000 per year in wages and benefits to staff each new teller window.

The director of management analysis, Beth Shader, believes that the following two factors encourage the immediate construction of two drive-through stations, however. According to a recent article in *Banking Research* magazine, customers who wait in long lines for drive-through teller service will cost banks an average of $1 per minute in loss of goodwill. Also, adding a second drive-through will cost an additional $16,000 in staffing, but amortized construction costs can be cut to a total of $20,000 per year if two drive-throughs are

Table for Problem 29

FROM	TO	PROBABILITY
Initial exam at emergency room entrance	X-ray department	0.45
	Operating room	0.15
	Observation room	0.10
	Out-processing clerk	0.30
X-ray department	Operating room	0.10
	Cast-fitting room	0.25
	Observation room	0.35
	Out-processing clerk	0.30
Operating room	Cast-fitting room	0.25
	Observation room	0.70
	Out-processing clerk	0.05
Cast-fitting room	Observation room	0.55
	X-ray department	0.05
	Out-processing clerk	0.40
Observation room	Operating room	0.15
	X-ray department	0.15
	Out-processing clerk	0.70

installed together instead of one at a time. To complete her analysis, Shader collected one month's arrival and service rates at a competing downtown bank's drive-through stations. These data are shown as observation analyses 1 and 2 in the following tables.

(a) Simulate a 1-hour time period, from 1 P.M. to 2 P.M., for a single-teller drive-through.
(b) Simulate a 1-hour time period, from 1 P.M. to 2 P.M., for a single line of people waiting for next available teller in a two-teller system.
(c) Conduct a cost analysis of the two options. Assume that the bank is open 7 hours per day and 200 days per year.

OBSERVATION ANALYSIS 1: INTERARRIVAL TIMES FOR 1,000 OBSERVATIONS

TIME BETWEEN ARRIVALS (MINUTES)	NUMBER OF OCCURRENCES
1	200
2	250
3	300
4	150
5	100

OBSERVATION ANALYSIS 2: CUSTOMER SERVICE TIME FOR 1,000 CUSTOMERS

SERVICE TIME (MINUTES)	NUMBER OF OCCURRENCES
1	100
2	150
3	350
4	150
5	150
6	100

Internet Homework Problems

See our Internet home page, at www.pearsonhighered.com/render, for additional homework problems 31 to 37.

Case Study

Alabama Airlines

Alabama Airlines opened its doors in June 1995 as a commuter service with its headquarters and only hub located in Birmingham. A product of airline deregulation, Alabama Air joined the growing number of successful short-haul, point-to-point airlines, including Lone Star, Comair, Atlantic Southeast, Skywest, and Business Express.

Alabama Air was started and managed by two former pilots, David Douglas (who had been with the defunct Eastern Airlines) and Savas Ozatalay (formerly with Pan Am). It acquired a fleet of 12 used prop-jet planes and the airport gates vacated by the 1994 downsizing of Delta Air Lines.

With business growing quickly, Douglas turned his attention to Alabama Air's toll-free reservations system. Between midnight and 6:00 A.M., only one telephone reservations agent had been on duty. The time between incoming calls during this period is distributed as shown in Table 15. Douglas carefully observed and timed the agent and estimated that the time taken

to process passenger inquiries is distributed as shown in Table 16.

All customers calling Alabama Air go on hold and are served in the order of the calls unless the reservations agent is

TABLE 15 Incoming Call Distribution

TIME BETWEEN CALLS (MINUTES)	PROBABILITY
1	0.11
2	0.21
3	0.22
4	0.20
5	0.16
6	0.10

TABLE 16 Service Time Distribution

TIME TO PROCESS CUSTOMER INQUIRIES (MINUTES)	PROBABILITY
1	0.20
2	0.19
3	0.18
4	0.17
5	0.13
6	0.10
7	0.03

TABLE 17 Incoming Call Distribution

TIME BETWEEN CALLS (MINUTES)	PROBABILITY
1	0.22
2	0.25
3	0.19
4	0.15
5	0.12
6	0.07

available for immediate service. Douglas is deciding whether a second agent should be on duty to cope with customer demand. To maintain customer satisfaction, Alabama Air does not want a customer on hold for more than 3 to 4 minutes and also wants to maintain a "high" operator utilization.

Further, the airline is planning a new TV advertising campaign. As a result, it expects an increase in toll-free-line phone inquiries. Based on similar campaigns in the past, the incoming call distribution from midnight to 6 A.M. is expected to be as shown in Table 17. (The same service time distribution will apply.)

Discussion Questions

1. What would you advise Alabama Air to do for the current reservation system based on the original call distribution? Create a simulation model to investigate the scenario. Describe the model carefully and justify the duration of the simulation, assumptions, and measures of performance.
2. What are your recommendations regarding operator utilization and customer satisfaction if the airline proceeds with the advertising campaign?

Source: Professor Zbigniew H. Przasnyski, Loyola Marymount University.

Case Study

Statewide Development Corporation

Statewide Development Corporation has built a very large apartment complex in Gainesville, Florida. As part of the student-oriented marketing strategy that has been developed, it is stated that if any problems with plumbing or air conditioning are experienced, a maintenance person will begin working on the problem within one hour. If a tenant must wait more than one hour for the repairperson to arrive, a $10 deduction from the monthly rent will be made for each additional hour of time waiting. An answering machine will take the calls and record the time of the call if the maintenance person is busy. Past experience at other complexes has shown that during the week when most occupants are at school, there is little difficulty in meeting the one hour guarantee. However, it is observed that weekends have been particularly troublesome during the summer months.

A study of the number of calls to the office on weekends concerning air conditioning and plumbing problems has resulted in the following distribution:

TIME BETWEEN CALLS (MINUTES)	PROBABILITY
30	0.15
60	0.30
90	0.30
120	0.25

The time required to complete a service call varies according to the difficulty of the problem. Parts needed for most repairs are kept in a storage room at the complex. However, for certain types of unusual problems, a trip to a local supply house is necessary. If a part is available on site, the maintenance person finishes one job before checking on the next complaint. If the part is not available on site and any other calls have been received, the maintenance person will stop by the other apartment(s) before going to the supply house. It takes approximately one hour to drive to the supply house, pick up a part, and return to the apartment complex. Past records indicate that, on approximately 10% of all calls, a trip must be made to the supply house.

The time required to resolve a problem if the part is available on site varies according to the following:

TIME FOR REPAIR (MINUTES)	PROBABILITY
30	0.45
60	0.30
90	0.20
120	0.05

It takes approximately 30 minutes to diagnose difficult problems for which parts are not on site. Once the part has been obtained from a supply house, it takes approximately one hour

to install the new part. If any new calls have been recorded while the maintenance person has been away picking up a new part, these new calls will wait until the new part has been installed.

The cost of salary and benefits for a maintenance person is $20 per hour. Management would like to determine whether two maintenance people should be working on weekends instead of just one. It can be assumed that each person works at the same rate.

Discussion Questions

1. Use simulation to help you analyze this problem. State any assumptions that you are making about this situation to help clarify the problem.
2. On a typical weekend day, how many tenants would have to wait more than an hour, and how much money would the company have to credit these tenants?

Case Study

FB Badpoore Aerospace

FB Badpoore Aerospace makes carbon brake discs for large airplanes with a proprietary "cross weave" of the carbon fibers. The brake discs are 4 feet in diameter but weigh significantly less than conventional ceramic brake discs making them attractive for airplane manufacturers as well as commercial airliners.

Processing the discs at FB Badpoore requires heat treating the discs in a sequence of 12 electric, high pressure, industrial grade furnaces (simply called Furnace A, Furnace B, Furnace C, . . . , Furnace L) each of them fed with a proprietary mixture of chemicals. All brake discs visit each of the 12 furnaces in the same order, Furnace A through Furnace L. These dozen furnaces each follow their own very specific set of simultaneous temperature and pressure profiles. An example of one such profile is depicted in Figure 6. All profiles are 12 hours in duration.

All 12 furnaces are top loading. Additionally, each of them are cylindrical in shape, 15 feet in diameter, and about 10 feet in depth. They are arranged in an "egg-carton-like" array (six on one side and six on the other), loaded and unloaded via their top facing round ends by three overhead ten ton bridge cranes, and located in part of the factory known as the *furnace deck.*

Each furnace can process seven stacks of 20 discs at a time. This equates to a batch size of 140 discs. Each batch is loaded onto a ceramic *furnace shelf* that is sturdy, round, and

14 feet in diameter. The furnace deck is said to be *fully loaded* when all 12 furnaces are processing discs.

Loading and unloading the discs is a labor intensive process requiring high level coordination of the three overhead bridge cranes. Bridge crane Alpha (BC-A) serves the incoming area, furnaces A, B, K, L, as well as the outgoing area where discs are stored when they have finished processing in all 12 furnaces. Bridge crane Beta (BC-B) serves furnaces C, D, I, and J while bridge crane Gamma (BC-G) serves furnaces E, F, G, and H. When discs travel within a service area, they are moved by the crane assigned to that area. When discs have to travel between service areas, they are first deposited in a waiting area before moved into the next service area. For example, discs being moved from Furnace D to Furnace E would be unloaded from Furnace D by BC-B, which would deposit them in the waiting area. Then BC-G would pick up the batch and load it into (an already empty) Furnace E.

Due to energy restrictions by the local electric utility company, all furnace processing must be performed at night between 8:00 P.M. and 10:00 A.M. daily. This, in turn, requires all loading and unloading operations to be performed during the day. Indeed, the main shift is from 1:00 P.M. (allowing the discs to cool after processing and before unloading) and 9:00 P.M. (allowing the shift to end by starting up all 12 furnaces after 8:00 P.M.).

FIGURE 6
Temperature and
Pressure Profile Example

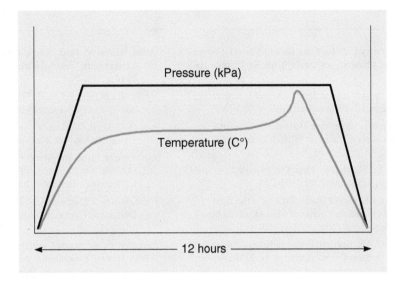

Each furnace has a known yield rate with no noticeable variation according to the following:

FURNACE	A	B	C	D	E	F	G	H	I	J	K	L
Yield	0.95	0.975	0.975	0.975	0.975	0.975	0.975	0.995	0.995	0.995	0.995	0.999

That is to say, one in twenty batches fail at Furnace A and must be scrapped whereas only one in a thousand fail at Furnace L. As one might expect, upstream batch failures are very disruptive to the downstream operations. Scrapping batches causes downstream furnaces to sit idle under the current "zero in queue" work in process (WIP) inventory policy as they wait for good batches to arrive from upstream operations.

Design, build, and perform a 1000 day simulation model study of the system described above in Excel incorporating the random number generator function, RAND(). Start your simulation with a fully loaded furnace deck.

Discussion Questions

1. Determine and comment on the overall yield (the number of batches that make it all the way through Furnace L divided by the number that started at Furnace A) of disc brakes at FB Badpoore.
2. Determine the utilization of Furnace L.
3. Suggest improvements to the system.

Bibliography

Banks, Jerry, John S. Carson, Barry L. Nelson, and David M. Nicol. *Discrete-Event System Simulation*, 4th ed. Upper Saddle River, NJ: Prentice Hall, 2005.

Evans, J. R., and D. L. Olson. *Introduction to Simulation and Risk Analysis*, 2nd ed. Upper Saddle River, NJ: Prentice Hall, 2002.

Fishman, G. S., and V. G. Kulkarni. "Improving Monte Carlo Efficiency by Increasing Variance," *Management Science* 38, 10 (October 1992): 1432–1444.

Fu, Michael C. "Optimization for Simulation: Theory vs. Practice," *INFORMS Journal on Computing* 14, 3 (Summer 2002): 192–215.

Gass, Saul I., and Arjang A. Assad. "Model World: Tales from the Time Line—The Definition of OR and the Origins of Monte Carlo Simulation," *Interfaces* 35, 5 (September–October 2005): 429–435.

Gavirneni, Srinagesh, Douglas J. Morrice, and Peter Mullarkey. "Simulation Helps Maxager Shorten Its Sales Cycle," *Interfaces* 34, 2 (March–April 2004): 87–96.

Hartvigsen, David. *SimQuick: Process Simulation with Excel*, 2nd ed. Upper Saddle River, NJ: Prentice Hall, 2004.

Lee, Dong-Eun. "Probability of Project Completion Using Stochastic Project Scheduling Simulation," *Journal of Construction Engineering & Management* 131, 3 (2005): 310–318.

Melão, N., and M. Pidd. "Use of Business Process Simulation: A Survey of Practitioners," *Journal of the Operational Research Society* 54, 1 (2003): 2–10.

Metropolis, N., and S. Ulam. "The Monte Carlo Method," *Journal of American Statistical Association* 44, 247 (1949): 335–341.

Pegden, C. D., R. E. Shannon, and R. P. Sadowski. *Introduction to Simulation Using SIMAN*. New York: McGraw-Hill, 1995.

Sabuncuoglu, Ihsan, and Ahmet Hatip. "The Turkish Army Uses Simulation to Model and Optimize Its Fuel-Supply System," *Interfaces* 35, 6 (November–December 2005): 474–482.

Smith, Jeffrey S. "Survey on the Use of Simulation for Manufacturing System Design and Operation," *Journal of Manufacturing Systems* 22, 2 (2003): 157–171.

Terzi, Sergio, and Sergio Cavalieri. "Simulation in the Supply Chain Context: A Survey," *Computers in Industry* 53, 1 (2004): 3–16.

Winston, Wayne L. *Simulation Modeling Using @Risk*. Pacific Grove, CA: Duxbury, 2001.

Zhang, H., C. M. Tam, and Jonathan J. Shi. "Simulation-Based Methodology for Project Scheduling," *Construction Management & Economics* 20, 8 (2002): 667–668.

Solutions to Selected Problems

14 No

16 Expected value 6.35 (using formula). The average number is 7 in Problem 13-15.

18 (b) Average number delayed = 0.40. Average number of arrivals = 2.07.

26 (a) Cost/hour is generally more expensive replacing 1 pen each time.
(b) Expected cost/hour with 1 pen policy = $1.38 (or $58/breakdown); expected cost/hour with 4-pen policy = $1.12 (or $132/breakdown).

Solutions to Self-Tests

1. b	**8.** a
2. b	**9.** b
3. a	**10.** b
4. b	**11.** d
5. a	**12.** d
6. a	**13.** c
7. d	

14. e

15. (a) no, yes, no, no, no, yes, yes, yes, no, yes
(b) yes, yes, yes, yes, no, yes, yes, no, no, no

1. Introduction to Database Management

Traditional business information systems were designed for record-keeping and they were characterized by many separate and unrelated files (**traditional file-systems**). Problems inherent in file systems make using a database system desirable. These problems include:
1) data redundancy, 2) data and structural dependence, 3) inadequate analytic capabilities, and 4) excessive programming requirements. Database Management Systems (DBMSs) were introduced to address these problems. Unlike file systems, DBMSs maintain logically related data in a single logical data repository (see the figure below). It is important to distinguish the database from the DBMS. A ***database*** is a shared, integrated computer structure that houses end user data (raw facts) and metadata (data about data) (Rob and Coronel,). On the other hand, a DBMS is a collection of programs that manages database structure and controls access to data. A DBMS is designed to support an integrated, centralized data structure, and therefore helps overcome the limitations of the traditional file-oriented systems.

A DBMS is designed to share data among multiple applications or users and makes data management more efficient. Its advantages include:
- Program-data independence and increased flexibility
- Minimal data redundancy
- Improved data consistency and data sharing
- Increased productivity of application development and enforcement of standards
- Improved data quality and accessibility
- Increased data security

In order to effectively manage databases, the database administrator(DBA) need to work with programmers and analysts to design and implement the database as well as with users and managers to establish database policies and Implement security features and access permissions.

2) Database Models

The evolution of databases covers three major database models: **1)** hierarchical **2)** network, and **3)** relational. New models, such as object oriented data models have also emerged recently. Our focus in this course is on the ***relational database model***, which revolutionalized the database management theory and practice.

2.1) Hierarchical Model

The hierarchical model organizes data in a top-down tree like manner, which assumes that all data relationship can be structured as hierarchies. This database model has a well-defined, predetermined data accessing paths. Any piece of data must be retrieved from the top downward. The hierarchical model can support only one-to-many relationships (we will discuss "relationships" later). The hierarchical model works well in the business environment where structured answers can be specified in advance, such as daily processing of business transactions. However, the model is not very flexible for ad-hoc queries.

2.2) Network Model

The network database model is quite similar to the hierarchical database structure, except that it supports many-to-many relationships, and therefore is more flexible in terms of data analysis. However, the access paths still have to be defined in advance.

1

2.3)   Relational Model

Developed by E.F. Codd (IBM) in 1970, the relational database structure is based on the organization of data in two-dimensional tables called *relations.* It is easier to understand than its hierarchical and network database predecessors, and has advantages of structural and data independence. It enables us to view data logically rather than physically. Relations can be "linked" through common data elements. Using these "links", users can easily extract and combine data from different tables.

3)   The Relational Database Concept:

The relational database model organizes and represents data in the form of *tables* or *relations*. *Relation* is a term that comes from Mathematics and represents a simple two-dimensional table, consisting of *rows* (or *records* or *entities*) and *columns* (or *fields* or *attributes*) of data. Below is an example of a relational database, consisting of three tables (or three relations).

WORKER Table

WORKER_ID	LNAME	FNAME	HOURLY_RATE	SKILL_TYPE
1235	Faraday	Mandy	12.50	Electric
1412	Nemo	Charles	13.75	Plumbing
2920	Garrett	Rob	10.00	Roofing
3231	Mason	Peter	17.40	Framing
1520	Rickover	Henry	11.75	Plumbing
1311	Coulomb	John	15.50	Electric
3001	Barrister	John	8.20	Framing

BUILDING Table

BLDG_ID	BLDG_ADDRESS	TYPE	QLTY_LEVEL	STATUS
312	123 Elm	Office	2	2
435	456 Maple	Retail	1	1
515	789 Oak	Residence	3	1
210	1011 Birch	Office	3	1
111	1213 Aspen	Office	4	1
460	1415 Beech	Warehouse	3	3

ASSIGNMENT Table

WORKER_ID	BLDG_ID	START_DATE	NUM_DAYS
1235	312	10/10	5
1412	312	10/01	10
1235	515	10/17	22
1412	460	12/08	18
1412	435	10/15	15
1412	515	11/05	8
1311	435	10/08	12

Question: Can you guess why some column headings are underlined?

3.1) Table (or Relation):

"Table" is the most fundamental component in a relational database, such as MS Access. Every MS Access database must have at least one table. Tables consist of rows and columns. Rows usually represent each entity of interest (e.g., employees, buildings, students, or computers), whereas columns represent attributes or characteristics of each individual object, e.g., Last Names, First Names, DOB, etc. See additional examples of "tables" below:

EMPLOYEES IN A DEPARTMENT

EMPLOYEE_ID	LNAME	FNAME	SALARY	POSITION
A091	Adams	Jane	45,368.00	Computer Associate
F014	Fuller	Kent	34,209.00	Executive Secretary
L002	Lynn	LeAnn	56,129.00	Lab Manager
...				

COMPUTERS IN A LAB

ID	MAKE	MODEL	PROCESSOR	SPEED
LAB01	Gateway	P5	Pentium	75
LAB03	Hewlett Packard	XL360	AMD	125
LAB12	Dell	DimensionPro	Celeron	99
...				

Question: Can you identify entities and attributes in each of the tables above?

3.2) Primary Key (or Key Fields):

The power of a relational database system such as MS Access comes from its ability to quickly find and bring together information stored in separate tables using queries, forms, and reports. In order to do this, each table must include a column or set of columns that uniquely identifies each record stored in the table. This unique information is called the **primary key** of the table (e.g., SIN for individuals). Once you designate a primary key for a table, most database applications will not allow any duplication in the primary key field(s). A primary key may have one attribute or more than one attribute. When a primary key is constructed using more than one column or field, it becomes a **Composite Primary Key**.

3.3 Foreign Key:

A *Foreign Key* is an attribute whose values must match primary key values in the related table. The foreign key is a common attribute that creates a relationship link between two tables. Two tables can be related in a *one-to-one, one-to-many*, or *many-to-many* relationships conceptually. To implement many-to-many relationships physically in a table, the relationship need to be converted into one-to-many relationships using a new table called BRIDGE or CROSS table. The Primary key of this bridge table is often constructed as a Composite Primary key consisting of the primary keys of the two original tables together.

Consider the above tables, WORKER, BUILDING, and ASSIGNMENT. All the underlined columns in the above tables are Primary keys. The combination of the WORKER_ID and BLDG_ID in the ASSIGNMENT table above is an example of a Composite Primary key. The ASSIGNMENT table is an example of a BRIDGE or CROSS table because it is used to convert the many-to-many relationship between the WORKER table and BUILDING table (a worker can work on many buildings and a building can have many workers assigned to it). If we directly

3

implement the many-to-many relationship without a bridge or cross table, it creates redundancies in both tables because we have to list all buildings for every worker in the WORKER table, and at the same time, we have to list every worker for every building in the BUILDING table.

The use of the ASSIGNMENT table allows the designer to list every worker uniquely in a WORKER table and every building uniquely in a BUILDING table. At the same time, the ASSIGNMENT table creates the link between the WORKER and BUILDING tables by showing who is working on which building. As a result of this modification, the conceptual many-to-many relationship between WORKER and BUILDING is indirectly converted into two one-to-many relationships. There is now a one-to-many relationship between WORKER and ASSIGNMENT because of the WORKER_ID in the ASSIGNMENT table. There is also a one-to-many relationship between BUILDING and ASSIGNMENT because of the BLDG_ID.

Therefore, the **WORKER_ID** and **BLDG_ID** together represent a Composite Primary key for the ASSIGNMENT table. Individually, they also represent foreign keys in the ASSIGNMENT table. Therefore, the ASSIGNMENT table has two foreign keys (WORKER_ID and BLDG_ID individually).

3.4   **Relationships:**

Let's look at relationships further. Relationships are rules set between two tables by the database designer to specify the maximum number of objects in one table that can be related to individual objects in the other table. As mentioned above, there are three basic types of relationships: **1)** one-to-one, **2)** one-to-many, and **3)** many-to-many. See the examples below. Can you think of other examples for each case?

To illustrate the **one-to-one relationship**, we'll consider the following two tables.
MARRIAGE CERTIFICATE DATABASE

HUSBAND Table

SIN#	NAME	BIRTHDATE	MARRIED_TO
858-30-1468	G. Chesterton	12/12/66	427-99-6754
022-11-4078	D. Pickwick	09/19/73	882-76-0544
156-25-0539	J. Diamonds	02/29/70	429-22-3772

WIFE Table

SIN#	NAME	BIRTHDATE
427-99-6754	G. Wells	01/05/68
882-76-0544	B. Hernandez	12/12/70
429-22-3772	L. Sawyer	11/11/69

In this example, a "husband" entity in the first table can be related to no more than one "wife" entity in the second table. The two tables are "linked" through a common data element, which is the **SIN#** of the wife. The column "MARRIED TO" is called a *Foreign Key* in the HUSBAND table because it refers to the primary key in the WIFE table. The two columns can have different names, but they should have similar data type to establish the relationships.

The one-to-many relationship is very common in most relational databases. It also takes advantage of foreign keys in order to link two tables. Consider the following example: AUTHOR-BOOK DATABASE (based on the assumption that a book is written by one and only one author)

AUTHOR Table

AUTHOR_ID	LNAME	BIRTHDATE
SA100	Sagan	10/23/54
HE231	Hesse	07/06/25
GI122	Gibran	05/11/02

BOOKS Table

BOOK_ID	AUTHOR_ID	NAME	CATEGORY
001	SA100	Contact	Sci-Fiction
002	HE231	Steppenwolf	Gen-Fiction
003	HE231	Narcissus&Goldmund	Gen-Fiction
004	GI122	Sand and Foam	Poem
005	SA100	Broca's Brain	Sci-Fiction
006	SA100	Comet	Sci-Fiction
007	GI122	A Tear and A Smile	Poem
008	HE231	Journey to the East	Gen-Fiction

Now, the AUTHRO_ID column in the BOOKS table behaves as a foreign key referring to the authors in the AUTHOR table. In this case, the AUTHOR table is called a **reference table**. The arrows above trace the Author_ID, SA100 to show one example.

If we assume that a book can be written by more than one authors (such as textbooks), then we would have a **many-to-many relationship**.

AUTHORS Table

AUTHOR_ID	LNAME	BIRTHDATE
HA112	Hansen	11/29/55
HA113	Elliott	09/03/60
HI955	Hickam	05/11/52
BA001	Bard	06/09/70
GL591	Globerson	02/19/68

"**CROSS**" Table

BOOK_ID	AUTHOR_ID
001	HA112
001	HA113
002	HA113
003	BA001
003	HA112
004	HA113
004	GL591
005	HI955
006	GL591
006	BA001
007	HA112
008	GL591
008	BA001

BOOKS Table

BOOK_ID	NAME
001	Managerial Economics
002	Macro-Economics
003	Micro-Economics
004	Project Management
005	Decision Support System
006	Learning SAS
007	Intro. To Economics
008	Inventory Management

As you see, this time we need to create an additional "CROSS" table or "BRIDGE" table in order to link AUTHORs and BOOKS tables. In the CROSS table, "BOOK_ID" and "AUTHOR_ID" separately are foreign keys, but they both are combined to make up a primary key for the CROSS table. When two or more columns make up a primary key, we call this **a composite primary key.** Let's look at how the authorship of the books is assigned:

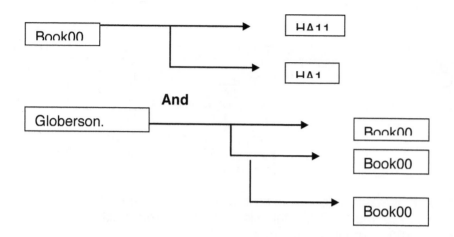

As you can see from this simple illustration, the structure of a relational database and its relationship (one-to-one, one-to-many, or –many-to-many) depends on the situations and assumptions made by the people who design the system. Database designers may use different data structures in order to solve the same problem. As much as possible, a one-to-one relationship is avoided, and when we encounter a many-to-many relationship, we convert it into one-to-many relationships using a CROSS table as illustrated above. This is because, if many-to-many relationship is implemented directly, the design will lead to data redundancy, which is contrary to the main purpose of the relational database design.

For further illustration on primary keys, foreign keys, and relationships, consider the following Mini University database tables and answer the questions with the help of your instructor.

6

STUDENT

udId	LastName	FirstName	Major	Credits
001	Smith	Tom	History	90
002	Chin	Ann	Math	36
005	Lee	Perry	History	3
010	Burns	Edward	Art	63
013	McCarthy	Owen	Math	0
015	Jones	Mary	Math	42

ENROLL

StudId	ClassNumber	Grade
S1001	ART103A	A
S1001	HST205A	C
S1002	ART103A	D
S1002	CSC201A	F
S1002	MTH103C	B
S1010	ART103A	
S1010	MTH103C	
S1020	CSC201A	B

CLASS

ClassNumber	Room	Schedule	ProfId
ART103A	H221	MWF9	P101
CSC201A	M110	TuThF10	P105
CSC203A	M110	MThF12	P105
HST205A	H221	MWF11	P115
MTH101B	H225	MTuTh9	P110
MTH103C	H225	MWF11	P110

PROFESSOR

ProfId	LName	Department	Rank
P101	Adams	Art	Professor
P105	Tanaka	CSC	Instructor
P110	Byrne	Math	Assistant
P115	Smith	History	Associate

1.   For each table in the above database, identify the **primary key** and **foreign key(s)**. Write "N/A" if a table does not have a foreign key.

Table	Primary Key	Foreign Key(s)
STUDENT		
PROFESSOR		
CLASS		
ENROLL		

2.   Describe the relationships that exist among the tables listed below.

Tables	Relationship Type (1:1 or 1:M or M:M)
STUDENT AND CLASS	
STUDENT AND ENROLL	
CLASS AND ENROLL	
PROFESSOR AND CLASS	

3.   What is the role of the **ENROLL** table in the above database?

4.   Which of the primary keys identified in question 1 is a composite primary key? Why?

5.   Explain why you do not see the relationship between STUDENT and CLASS directly in the above tables?

7

4) Database Design: Rules and Tools:

4.1. Physical and Logical Designs

Before we get into the details of database design, we need to know two key terms: **logical** and **physical** designs. The planning of a database system consists of two stages. The **logical design** is the presentation of data, as they would be perceived by end users. The **physical design** is the presentation of data as they are actually organized and structured on physical storage media. Examples of data and tables above are just simple illustrations. In reality, you will often find much more complicated situations, and thus designing a database system become a much more complex task. In this section, we'll introduce some basic tools that many database designers use to conceptualize, document, and carry out their database projects. They include: Entity Relationship Diagram (ERD) and Data Dictionary.

4.2. Entity Relationship Diagram (ERD)

ERD is a snapshot of relations and data structures. The purpose is to view the real world as a set of basic entities and relationships among these entities. Below is another example of the ER diagram, describing the authors and their books in a one-to-many relationship illustrated above. Draw the full ER diagram for the Mini University database illustrated above with the help of your instructor?

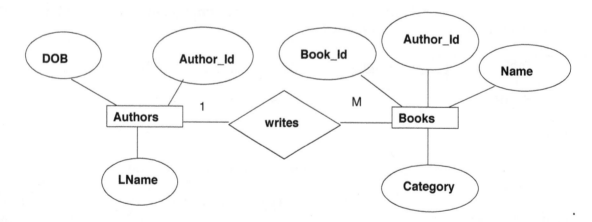

Figure: ER Diagram

4.3. Data Dictionary (also called Meta Data: data about data):

A data dictionary contains details about each piece of data and its association with others. Typically, the information maintained in the data dictionary includes entity names, sizes, formats, ownerships, relationships, security, and the processes in which the data are used. An example of data dictionary (or Meta Data) in MS Access is the table structure in its design view along with its property pane (see figure below).

Field Name	Data Type	Description
SalesRep_ID	Text	
Last_Name	Text	
First_Name	Text	
M_I	Text	
Date_Hired	Date/Time	
Vacation_Days	Number	
Gender	Text	
Base_Salary	Currency	
Social Insurance Number	Text	
EMP_TYPE	Text	
numbermm	Number	

Field Properties

General	Lookup	
Field Size	4	
Format		
Input Mask	>LLLL	
Caption	Sales Rep. ID	
Default Value		
Validation Rule		
Validation Text		
Required	No	
Allow Zero Length	No	
Indexed	Yes (No Duplicates)	
Unicode Compression	Yes	
IME Mode	No Control	
IME Sentence Mode	None	
Smart Tags		

Figure: Illustrating Meta data in Microsoft Access table design

In addition to using the ERD and Data Dictionary, there are certain rules that database designers must follow in order to keep their data organized and provide easy and flexible access. We'll discuss below the two fundamental rules of relational database design.

4.4. Integrity Rules

Entity Integrity: All records must be uniquely identified (no nulls or duplicates). This means that every table must have a primary key field.

Referential Integrity: Foreign key values must match field values in reference table (no dangling references). It should contain a value that refers to an existing valid tuple (row) in another relation. Look at the AUTHOR-BOOK database in the one-to-many relationship. The author IDs, acting as foreign keys in the BOOK table, must match the author IDs in the reference table. You can set the referential integrity rule in MS-Access using the relationship line's dialog box. Click on the relationship line and check the box for referential integrity.

4.5. Database Normalization

Normalization is a process for analyzing and reducing a relational table structure to its most streamlined form to minimize data redundancies and eliminate anomalies. It involves a series of stages called normal forms: The practical normalization stages (forms) include:

- **First Normal (1NF)**
- **Second Normal Form (2NF)**
- **Third Normal Form (3NF)**

9

In most business applications, 3NF is the highest stage maintained. Higher level Normal Forms are theoretical and do not arise commonly in applications. In this course, the First Normal Form (1NF) is illustrated because it is the most basic normal form which is the basis of all higher level normal forms. If a table is not in the 1NF, it is not relational table. Higher level normal forms are introduced in upper level courses. To illustrate the 1NF, let's consider the following example.

Table-1

EmployeeID	DepartmentID	Name	SkillType	BonusRate
JK01	MKT, FIN	John Kane	P	3.0
KR01	OPT	Linda Gravano	E	2.9
MR03	ACT, ISM	Mary Rowland	M	4.5
LP01	RAD	Luis Pettino	E	2.9

Problems | Repeating values | | Non-atomic entries |

First Normal Form (1NF): "No **repeating values** and all attribute values need to be **atomic**."

The above table (Table-1) is not in 1NF. E.g., John Kane belongs to two different departments, which may be fine and realistic in a real business setting. However, the data model for the DepartmentID should not show "MKT, FIN". In order to "normalize" this table into 1NF, "MKT, FIN" needs to be broken down into two different records. In other words, eliminate the **repeating values** and the **non-atomic** values. We also need to show last names and first names in individual columns. In addition, 1NF makes sure that all key attributes are defined and all attributes depend on the primary key in the table.

Table-2

EmployeeID	DepartmentID	Last_Name	First_Name	SkillType	BonusRate
JK01	MKT	Kane	John	P	3.0
JK01	FIN	Kane	John	P	3.0
KR01	OPT	Gravano	Linda	E	2.9
MR03	ACT	Rowland	Mary	M	4.5
MR03	ISM	Rowland	Mary	M	4.5
LP01	RAD	Pettino	Luis	E	2.9

Example-2:
Table-3

Dept_Number	Dept_MgrSIN	Dept_Location
5	123-456-789	{Toronto, St. Catharines, Burlington}
4	987-654-321	Toronto
1	124-569-876	St. Catharines

1NF: Repeating values eliminated in Table-4.
Table-4

Dept_Number	Dept_Location	Dept_MgrSIN
5	Toronto	123-456-789
5	St. Catharines	123-456-789
5	Burlington	123-456-789
4	Toronto	987-654-321
1	St. Catharines	124-569-876

10

5. New Developments: How Organizations Get the Most from Their Data:

Business Intelligence: refers to applications and technologies that are used to gather, provide access to, and analyze information to support decision making.

Data Mining: A method for better understanding data for trends, correlations, forecasting, and summary statistics. It includes:
- **Online Transaction Processing (OLTP):** Immediate automated responses to user requests.
- **Online Analytical Processing (OLAP):** Graphical software tools that provide complex analysis of data stored in a database or "data warehouse". It involves drills down to deeper levels of consolidation, time series and trend analysis, as well as "What if" and "why" questions.

Data Warehousing: Integrating multiple operational databases into a single repository. It involves multi-dimensional queries, analysis, and processing. Its main purpose is to put key business information into the hands of decision makers.

Data Marts: Instead of one large data warehouse, many organizations create multiple data marts each containing s a subset of the data, e.g., Finance, inventory, personnel. Each data mart is customized for particular decision support applications.

ADDITIONAL REFERENCES:

Jessup, L., Valacich, J., and Wade, M., Information Systems Today, Prentice-Hall, 2006.

Rob, P. and Coronel, C., Database Systems: Design, Implementation, & Management, Course Technology 2005.

Elmasri, R., and Navathe, S., Fundamentals of Database Systems. Addison-Wesley, 2000.

Hansen, G., and Hansen J., Database Management and Design. Prentice-Hall, 1996.

Laudon, K., and Laudon J., Information Systems and the Internet: A Problem Solving Approach. Dryden Press, 1998.

11

Appendices

From Appendices of *Quantitative Analysis for Management*, Twelfth Edition. Barry Render, Ralph M. Stair, Jr., Michael E. Hanna, and Trevor S. Hale. Copyright © 2015 by Pearson Education, Inc. All rights reserved.

Appendix: Areas Under the Standard Normal Curve

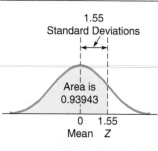

1.55
Standard Deviations

Area is
0.93943

0   1.55
Mean Z

Example: To find the area under the normal curve, you must know how many standard deviations that point is to the right of the mean. Then the area under the normal curve can be read directly from the normal table. For example, the total area under the normal curve for a point that is 1.55 standard deviations to the right of the mean is 0.93943.

	0.00	0.01	0.02	0.03	0.04	0.05	0.06	0.07	0.08	0.09
0.0	0.50000	0.50399	0.50798	0.51197	0.51595	0.51994	0.52392	0.52790	0.53188	0.53586
0.1	0.53983	0.54380	0.54776	0.55172	0.55567	0.55962	0.56356	0.56749	0.57142	0.57535
0.2	0.57926	0.58317	0.58706	0.59095	0.59483	0.59871	0.60257	0.60642	0.61026	0.61409
0.3	0.61791	0.62172	0.62552	0.62930	0.63307	0.63683	0.64058	0.64431	0.64803	0.65173
0.4	0.65542	0.65910	0.66276	0.66640	0.67003	0.67364	0.67724	0.68082	0.68439	0.68793
0.5	0.69146	0.69497	0.69847	0.70194	0.70540	0.70884	0.71226	0.71566	0.71904	0.72240
0.6	0.72575	0.72907	0.73237	0.73565	0.73891	0.74215	0.74537	0.74857	0.75175	0.75490
0.7	0.75804	0.76115	0.76424	0.76730	0.77035	0.77337	0.77637	0.77935	0.78230	0.78524
0.8	0.78814	0.79103	0.79389	0.79673	0.79955	0.80234	0.80511	0.80785	0.81057	0.81327
0.9	0.81594	0.81859	0.82121	0.82381	0.82639	0.82894	0.83147	0.83398	0.83646	0.83891
1.0	0.84134	0.84375	0.84614	0.84849	0.85083	0.85314	0.85543	0.85769	0.85993	0.86214
1.1	0.86433	0.86650	0.86864	0.87076	0.87286	0.87493	0.87698	0.87900	0.88100	0.88298
1.2	0.88493	0.88686	0.88877	0.89065	0.89251	0.89435	0.89617	0.89796	0.89973	0.90147
1.3	0.90320	0.90490	0.90658	0.90824	0.90988	0.91149	0.91309	0.91466	0.91621	0.91774
1.4	0.91924	0.92073	0.92220	0.92364	0.92507	0.92647	0.92785	0.92922	0.93056	0.93189
1.5	0.93319	0.93448	0.93574	0.93699	0.93822	0.93943	0.94062	0.94179	0.94295	0.94408
1.6	0.94520	0.94630	0.94738	0.94845	0.94950	0.95053	0.95154	0.95254	0.95352	0.95449
1.7	0.95543	0.95637	0.95728	0.95818	0.95907	0.95994	0.96080	0.96164	0.96246	0.96327
1.8	0.96407	0.96485	0.96562	0.96638	0.96712	0.96784	0.96856	0.96926	0.96995	0.97062
1.9	0.97128	0.97193	0.97257	0.97320	0.97381	0.97441	0.97500	0.97558	0.97615	0.97670
2.0	0.97725	0.97778	0.97831	0.97882	0.97932	0.97982	0.98030	0.98077	0.98124	0.98169
2.1	0.98214	0.98257	0.98300	0.98341	0.98382	0.98422	0.98461	0.98500	0.98537	0.98574
2.2	0.98610	0.98645	0.98679	0.98713	0.98745	0.98778	0.98809	0.98840	0.98870	0.98899
2.3	0.98928	0.98956	0.98983	0.99010	0.99036	0.99061	0.99086	0.99111	0.99134	0.99158
2.4	0.99180	0.99202	0.99224	0.99245	0.99266	0.99286	0.99305	0.99324	0.99343	0.99361
2.5	0.99379	0.99396	0.99413	0.99430	0.99446	0.99461	0.99477	0.99492	0.99506	0.99520
2.6	0.99534	0.99547	0.99560	0.99573	0.99585	0.99598	0.99609	0.99621	0.99632	0.99643
2.7	0.99653	0.99664	0.99674	0.99683	0.99693	0.99702	0.99711	0.99720	0.99728	0.99736
2.8	0.99744	0.99752	0.99760	0.99767	0.99774	0.99781	0.99788	0.99795	0.99801	0.99807
2.9	0.99813	0.99819	0.99825	0.99831	0.99836	0.99841	0.99846	0.99851	0.99856	0.99861
3.0	0.99865	0.99869	0.99874	0.99878	0.99882	0.99886	0.99889	0.99893	0.99896	0.99900
3.1	0.99903	0.99906	0.99910	0.99913	0.99916	0.99918	0.99921	0.99924	0.99926	0.99929
3.2	0.99931	0.99934	0.99936	0.99938	0.99940	0.99942	0.99944	0.99946	0.99948	0.99950

	0.00	0.01	0.02	0.03	0.04	0.05	0.06	0.07	0.08	0.09
3.3	0.99952	0.99953	0.99955	0.99957	0.99958	0.99960	0.99961	0.99962	0.99964	0.99965
3.4	0.99966	0.99968	0.99969	0.99970	0.99971	0.99972	0.99973	0.99974	0.99975	0.99976
3.5	0.99977	0.99978	0.99978	0.99979	0.99980	0.99981	0.99981	0.99982	0.99983	0.99983
3.6	0.99984	0.99985	0.99985	0.99986	0.99986	0.99987	0.99987	0.99998	0.99988	0.99989
3.7	0.99989	0.99990	0.99990	0.99990	0.99991	0.99991	0.99992	0.99992	0.99992	0.99992
3.8	0.99993	0.99993	0.99993	0.99994	0.99994	0.99994	0.99994	0.99995	0.99995	0.99995
3.9	0.99995	0.99995	0.99996	0.99996	0.99996	0.99996	0.99996	0.99996	0.99997	0.99997

Appendix: Binomial Probabilities

Probability of exactly r successes in n trials

n	r	P									
		0.05	0.10	0.15	0.20	0.25	0.30	0.35	0.40	0.45	0.50
1	0	0.9500	0.9000	0.8500	0.8000	0.7500	0.7000	0.6500	0.6000	0.5500	0.5000
	1	0.0500	0.1000	0.1500	0.2000	0.2500	0.3000	0.3500	0.4000	0.4500	0.5000
2	0	0.9025	0.8100	0.7225	0.6400	0.5625	0.4900	0.4225	0.3600	0.3025	0.2500
	1	0.0950	0.1800	0.2550	0.3200	0.3750	0.4200	0.4550	0.4800	0.4950	0.5000
	2	0.0025	0.0100	0.0225	0.0400	0.0625	0.0900	0.1225	0.1600	0.2025	0.2500
3	0	0.8574	0.7290	0.6141	0.5120	0.4219	0.3430	0.2746	0.2160	0.1664	0.1250
	1	0.1354	0.2430	0.3251	0.3840	0.4219	0.4410	0.4436	0.4320	0.4084	0.3750
	2	0.0071	0.0270	0.0574	0.0960	0.1406	0.1890	0.2389	0.2880	0.3341	0.3750
	3	0.0001	0.0010	0.0034	0.0080	0.0156	0.0270	0.0429	0.0640	0.0911	0.1250
4	0	0.8145	0.6561	0.5220	0.4096	0.3164	0.2401	0.1785	0.1296	0.0915	0.0625
	1	0.1715	0.2916	0.3685	0.4096	0.4219	0.4116	0.3845	0.3456	0.2995	0.2500
	2	0.0135	0.0486	0.0975	0.1536	0.2109	0.2646	0.3105	0.3456	0.3675	0.3750
	3	0.0005	0.0036	0.0115	0.0256	0.0469	0.0756	0.1115	0.1536	0.2005	0.2500
	4	0.0000	0.0001	0.0005	0.0016	0.0039	0.0081	0.0150	0.0256	0.0410	0.0625
5	0	0.7738	0.5905	0.4437	0.3277	0.2373	0.1681	0.1160	0.0778	0.0503	0.0313
	1	0.2036	0.3281	0.3915	0.4096	0.3955	0.3602	0.3124	0.2592	0.2059	0.1563
	2	0.0214	0.0729	0.1382	0.2048	0.2637	0.3087	0.3364	0.3456	0.3369	0.3125
	3	0.0011	0.0081	0.0244	0.0512	0.0879	0.1323	0.1811	0.2304	0.2757	0.3125
	4	0.0000	0.0005	0.0022	0.0064	0.0146	0.0284	0.0488	0.0768	0.1128	0.1563
	5	0.0000	0.0000	0.0001	0.0003	0.0010	0.0024	0.0053	0.0102	0.0185	0.0313
6	0	0.7351	0.5314	0.3771	0.2621	0.1780	0.1176	0.0754	0.0467	0.0277	0.0156
	1	0.2321	0.3543	0.3993	0.3932	0.3560	0.3025	0.2437	0.1866	0.1359	0.0938
	2	0.0305	0.0984	0.1762	0.2458	0.2966	0.3241	0.3280	0.3110	0.2780	0.2344
	3	0.0021	0.0146	0.0415	0.0819	0.1318	0.1852	0.2355	0.2765	0.3032	0.3125
	4	0.0001	0.0012	0.0055	0.0154	0.0330	0.0595	0.0951	0.1382	0.1861	0.2344
	5	0.0000	0.0001	0.0004	0.0015	0.0044	0.0102	0.0205	0.0369	0.0609	0.0938
	6	0.0000	0.0000	0.0000	0.0001	0.0002	0.0007	0.0018	0.0041	0.0083	0.0156
7	0	0.6983	0.4783	0.3206	0.2097	0.1335	0.0824	0.0490	0.0280	0.0152	0.0078
	1	0.2573	0.3720	0.3960	0.3670	0.3115	0.2471	0.1848	0.1306	0.0872	0.0547
	2	0.0406	0.1240	0.2097	0.2753	0.3115	0.3177	0.2985	0.2613	0.2140	0.1641
	3	0.0036	0.0230	0.0617	0.1147	0.1730	0.2269	0.2679	0.2903	0.2918	0.2734
	4	0.0002	0.0026	0.0109	0.0287	0.0577	0.0972	0.1442	0.1935	0.2388	0.2734
	5	0.0000	0.0002	0.0012	0.0043	0.0115	0.0250	0.0466	0.0774	0.1172	0.1641
	6	0.0000	0.0000	0.0001	0.0004	0.0013	0.0036	0.0084	0.0172	0.0320	0.0547
	7	0.0000	0.0000	0.0000	0.0000	0.0001	0.0002	0.0006	0.0016	0.0037	0.0078
8	0	0.6634	0.4305	0.2725	0.1678	0.1001	0.0576	0.0319	0.0168	0.0084	0.0039
	1	0.2793	0.3826	0.3847	0.3355	0.2670	0.1977	0.1373	0.0896	0.0548	0.0313
	2	0.0515	0.1488	0.2376	0.2936	0.3115	0.2965	0.2587	0.2090	0.1569	0.1094

n	r	0.05	0.10	0.15	0.20	0.25	0.30	0.35	0.40	0.45	0.50
						P					
	3	0.0054	0.0331	0.0839	0.1468	0.2076	0.2541	0.2786	0.2787	0.2568	0.2188
	4	0.0004	0.0046	0.0185	0.0459	0.0865	0.1361	0.1875	0.2322	0.2627	0.2734
	5	0.0000	0.0004	0.0026	0.0092	0.0231	0.0467	0.0808	0.1239	0.1719	0.2188
	6	0.0000	0.0000	0.0002	0.0011	0.0038	0.0100	0.0217	0.0413	0.0703	0.1094
	7	0.0000	0.0000	0.0000	0.0001	0.0004	0.0012	0.0033	0.0079	0.0164	0.0313
	8	0.0000	0.0000	0.0000	0.0000	0.0000	0.0001	0.0002	0.0007	0.0017	0.0039
9	0	0.6302	0.3874	0.2316	0.1342	0.0751	0.0404	0.0207	0.0101	0.0046	0.0020
	1	0.2985	0.3874	0.3679	0.3020	0.2253	0.1556	0.1004	0.0605	0.0339	0.0176
	2	0.0629	0.1722	0.2597	0.3020	0.3003	0.2668	0.2162	0.1612	0.1110	0.0703
	3	0.0077	0.0446	0.1069	0.1762	0.2336	0.2668	0.2716	0.2508	0.2119	0.1641
	4	0.0006	0.0074	0.0283	0.0661	0.1168	0.1715	0.2194	0.2508	0.2600	0.2461
	5	0.0000	0.0008	0.0050	0.0165	0.0389	0.0735	0.1181	0.1672	0.2128	0.2461
	6	0.0000	0.0001	0.0006	0.0028	0.0087	0.0210	0.0424	0.0743	0.1160	0.1641
	7	0.0000	0.0000	0.0000	0.0003	0.0012	0.0039	0.0098	0.0212	0.0407	0.0703
	8	0.0000	0.0000	0.0000	0.0000	0.0001	0.0004	0.0013	0.0035	0.0083	0.0176
	9	0.0000	0.0000	0.0000	0.0000	0.0000	0.0000	0.0001	0.0003	0.0008	0.0020
10	0	0.5987	0.3487	0.1969	0.1074	0.0563	0.0282	0.0135	0.0060	0.0025	0.0010
	1	0.3151	0.3874	0.3474	0.2684	0.1877	0.1211	0.0725	0.0403	0.0207	0.0098
	2	0.0746	0.1937	0.2759	0.3020	0.2816	0.2335	0.1757	0.1209	0.0763	0.0439
	3	0.0105	0.0574	0.1298	0.2013	0.2503	0.2668	0.2522	0.2150	0.1665	0.1172
	4	0.0010	0.0112	0.0401	0.0881	0.1460	0.2001	0.2377	0.2508	0.2384	0.2051
	5	0.0001	0.0015	0.0085	0.0264	0.0584	0.1029	0.1536	0.2007	0.2340	0.2461
	6	0.0000	0.0001	0.0012	0.0055	0.0162	0.0368	0.0689	0.1115	0.1596	0.2051
	7	0.0000	0.0000	0.0001	0.0008	0.0031	0.0090	0.0212	0.0425	0.0746	0.1172
	8	0.0000	0.0000	0.0000	0.0001	0.0004	0.0014	0.0043	0.0106	0.0229	0.0439
	9	0.0000	0.0000	0.0000	0.0000	0.0000	0.0001	0.0005	0.0016	0.0042	0.0098
	10	0.0000	0.0000	0.0000	0.0000	0.0000	0.0000	0.0000	0.0001	0.0003	0.0010
15	0	0.4633	0.2059	0.0874	0.0352	0.0134	0.0047	0.0016	0.0005	0.0001	0.0000
	1	0.3658	0.3432	0.2312	0.1319	0.0668	0.0305	0.0126	0.0047	0.0016	0.0005
	2	0.1348	0.2669	0.2856	0.2309	0.1559	0.0916	0.0476	0.0219	0.0090	0.0032
	3	0.0307	0.1285	0.2184	0.2501	0.2252	0.1700	0.1110	0.0634	0.0318	0.0139
	4	0.0049	0.0428	0.1156	0.1876	0.2252	0.2186	0.1792	0.1268	0.0780	0.0417
	5	0.0006	0.0105	0.0449	0.1032	0.1651	0.2061	0.2123	0.1859	0.1404	0.0916
	6	0.0000	0.0019	0.0132	0.0430	0.0917	0.1472	0.1906	0.2066	0.1914	0.1527
	7	0.0000	0.0003	0.0030	0.0138	0.0393	0.0811	0.1319	0.1771	0.2013	0.1964
	8	0.0000	0.0000	0.0005	0.0035	0.0131	0.0348	0.0710	0.1181	0.1647	0.1964
	9	0.0000	0.0000	0.0001	0.0007	0.0034	0.0116	0.0298	0.0612	0.1048	0.1527
	10	0.0000	0.0000	0.0000	0.0001	0.0007	0.0030	0.0096	0.0245	0.0515	0.0916
	11	0.0000	0.0000	0.0000	0.0000	0.0001	0.0006	0.0024	0.0074	0.0191	0.0417
	12	0.0000	0.0000	0.0000	0.0000	0.0000	0.0001	0.0004	0.0016	0.0052	0.0139
	13	0.0000	0.0000	0.0000	0.0000	0.0000	0.0000	0.0001	0.0003	0.0010	0.0032
	14	0.0000	0.0000	0.0000	0.0000	0.0000	0.0000	0.0000	0.0000	0.0001	0.0005
	15	0.0000	0.0000	0.0000	0.0000	0.0000	0.0000	0.0000	0.0000	0.0000	0.0000

						P					
n	r	0.05	0.10	0.15	0.20	0.25	0.30	0.35	0.40	0.45	0.50
20	0	0.3585	0.1216	0.0388	0.0115	0.0032	0.0008	0.0002	0.0000	0.0000	0.0000
	1	0.3774	0.2702	0.1368	0.0576	0.0211	0.0068	0.0020	0.0005	0.0001	0.0000
	2	0.1887	0.2852	0.2293	0.1369	0.0669	0.0278	0.0100	0.0031	0.0008	0.0002
	3	0.0596	0.1901	0.2428	0.2054	0.1339	0.0716	0.0323	0.0123	0.0040	0.0011
	4	0.0133	0.0898	0.1821	0.2182	0.1897	0.1304	0.0738	0.0350	0.0139	0.0046
	5	0.0022	0.0319	0.1028	0.1746	0.2023	0.1789	0.1272	0.0746	0.0365	0.0148
	6	0.0003	0.0089	0.0454	0.1091	0.1686	0.1916	0.1712	0.1244	0.0746	0.0370
	7	0.0000	0.0020	0.0160	0.0545	0.1124	0.1643	0.1844	0.1659	0.1221	0.0739
	8	0.0000	0.0004	0.0046	0.0222	0.0609	0.1144	0.1614	0.1797	0.1623	0.1201
	9	0.0000	0.0001	0.0011	0.0074	0.0271	0.0654	0.1158	0.1597	0.1771	0.1602
	10	0.0000	0.0000	0.0002	0.0020	0.0099	0.0308	0.0686	0.1171	0.1593	0.1762
	11	0.0000	0.0000	0.0000	0.0005	0.0030	0.0120	0.0336	0.0710	0.1185	0.1602
	12	0.0000	0.0000	0.0000	0.0001	0.0008	0.0039	0.0136	0.0355	0.0727	0.1201
	13	0.0000	0.0000	0.0000	0.0000	0.0002	0.0010	0.0045	0.0146	0.0366	0.0739
	14	0.0000	0.0000	0.0000	0.0000	0.0000	0.0002	0.0012	0.0049	0.0150	0.0370
	15	0.0000	0.0000	0.0000	0.0000	0.0000	0.0000	0.0003	0.0013	0.0049	0.0148
	16	0.0000	0.0000	0.0000	0.0000	0.0000	0.0000	0.0000	0.0003	0.0013	0.0046
	17	0.0000	0.0000	0.0000	0.0000	0.0000	0.0000	0.0000	0.0000	0.0002	0.0011
	18	0.0000	0.0000	0.0000	0.0000	0.0000	0.0000	0.0000	0.0000	0.0000	0.0002
	19	0.0000	0.0000	0.0000	0.0000	0.0000	0.0000	0.0000	0.0000	0.0000	0.0000
	20	0.0000	0.0000	0.0000	0.0000	0.0000	0.0000	0.0000	0.0000	0.0000	0.0000

						P					
n	r	0.55	0.60	0.65	0.70	0.75	0.80	0.85	0.90	0.95	
1	0	0.4500	0.4000	0.3500	0.3000	0.2500	0.2000	0.1500	0.1000	0.0500	
	1	0.5500	0.6000	0.6500	0.7000	0.7500	0.8000	0.8500	0.9000	0.9500	
2	0	0.2025	0.1600	0.1225	0.0900	0.0625	0.0400	0.0225	0.0100	0.0025	
	1	0.4950	0.4800	0.4550	0.4200	0.3750	0.3200	0.2550	0.1800	0.0950	
	2	0.3025	0.3600	0.4225	0.4900	0.5625	0.6400	0.7225	0.8100	0.9025	
3	0	0.0911	0.0640	0.0429	0.0270	0.0156	0.0080	0.0034	0.0010	0.0001	
	1	0.3341	0.2880	0.2389	0.1890	0.1406	0.0960	0.0574	0.0270	0.0071	
	2	0.4084	0.4320	0.4436	0.4410	0.4219	0.3840	0.3251	0.2430	0.1354	
	3	0.1664	0.2160	0.2746	0.3430	0.4219	0.5120	0.6141	0.7290	0.8574	
4	0	0.0410	0.0256	0.0150	0.0081	0.0039	0.0016	0.0005	0.0001	0.0000	
	1	0.2005	0.1536	0.1115	0.0756	0.0469	0.0256	0.0115	0.0036	0.0005	
	2	0.3675	0.3456	0.3105	0.2646	0.2109	0.1536	0.0975	0.0486	0.0135	
	3	0.2995	0.3456	0.3845	0.4116	0.4219	0.4096	0.3685	0.2916	0.1715	
	4	0.0915	0.1296	0.1785	0.2401	0.3164	0.4096	0.5220	0.6561	0.8145	
5	0	0.0185	0.0102	0.0053	0.0024	0.0010	0.0003	0.0001	0.0000	0.0000	
	1	0.1128	0.0768	0.0488	0.0283	0.0146	0.0064	0.0022	0.0004	0.0000	
	2	0.2757	0.2304	0.1811	0.1323	0.0879	0.0512	0.0244	0.0081	0.0011	
	3	0.3369	0.3456	0.3364	0.3087	0.2637	0.2048	0.1382	0.0729	0.0214	
	4	0.2059	0.2592	0.3124	0.3602	0.3955	0.4096	0.3915	0.3280	0.2036	
	5	0.0503	0.0778	0.1160	0.1681	0.2373	0.3277	0.4437	0.5905	0.7738	

						P				
n	r	0.55	0.60	0.65	0.70	0.75	0.80	0.85	0.90	0.95
6	0	0.0083	0.0041	0.0018	0.0007	0.0002	0.0001	0.0000	0.0000	0.0000
	1	0.0609	0.0369	0.0205	0.0102	0.0044	0.0015	0.0004	0.0001	0.0000
	2	0.1861	0.1382	0.0951	0.0595	0.0330	0.0154	0.0055	0.0012	0.0001
	3	0.3032	0.2765	0.2355	0.1852	0.1318	0.0819	0.0415	0.0146	0.0021
	4	0.2780	0.3110	0.3280	0.3241	0.2966	0.2458	0.1762	0.0984	0.0305
	5	0.1359	0.1866	0.2437	0.3025	0.3560	0.3932	0.3993	0.3543	0.2321
	6	0.0277	0.0467	0.0754	0.1176	0.1780	0.2621	0.3771	0.5314	0.7351
7	0	0.0037	0.0016	0.0006	0.0002	0.0001	0.0000	0.0000	0.0000	0.0000
	1	0.0320	0.0172	0.0084	0.0036	0.0013	0.0004	0.0001	0.0000	0.0000
	2	0.1172	0.0774	0.0466	0.0250	0.0115	0.0043	0.0012	0.0002	0.0000
	3	0.2388	0.1935	0.1442	0.0972	0.0577	0.0287	0.0109	0.0026	0.0002
	4	0.2918	0.2903	0.2679	0.2269	0.1730	0.1147	0.0617	0.0230	0.0036
	5	0.2140	0.2613	0.2985	0.3177	0.3115	0.2753	0.2097	0.1240	0.0406
	6	0.0872	0.1306	0.1848	0.2471	0.3115	0.3670	0.3960	0.3720	0.2573
	7	0.0152	0.0280	0.0490	0.0824	0.1335	0.2097	0.3206	0.4783	0.6983
8	0	0.0017	0.0007	0.0002	0.0001	0.0000	0.0000	0.0000	0.0000	0.0000
	1	0.0164	0.0079	0.0033	0.0012	0.0004	0.0001	0.0000	0.0000	0.0000
	2	0.0703	0.0413	0.0217	0.0100	0.0038	0.0011	0.0002	0.0000	0.0000
	3	0.1719	0.1239	0.0808	0.0467	0.0231	0.0092	0.0026	0.0004	0.0000
	4	0.2627	0.2322	0.1875	0.1361	0.0865	0.0459	0.0185	0.0046	0.0004
	5	0.2568	0.2787	0.2786	0.2541	0.2076	0.1468	0.0839	0.0331	0.0054
	6	0.1569	0.2090	0.2587	0.2965	0.3115	0.2936	0.2376	0.1488	0.0515
	7	0.0548	0.0896	0.1373	0.1977	0.2670	0.3355	0.3847	0.3826	0.2793
	8	0.0084	0.0168	0.0319	0.0576	0.1001	0.1678	0.2725	0.4305	0.6634
9	0	0.0008	0.0003	0.0001	0.0000	0.0000	0.0000	0.0000	0.0000	0.0000
	1	0.0083	0.0035	0.0013	0.0004	0.0001	0.0000	0.0000	0.0000	0.0000
	2	0.0407	0.0212	0.0098	0.0039	0.0012	0.0003	0.0000	0.0000	0.0000
	3	0.1160	0.0743	0.0424	0.0210	0.0087	0.0028	0.0006	0.0001	0.0000
	4	0.2128	0.1672	0.1181	0.0735	0.0389	0.0165	0.0050	0.0008	0.0000
	5	0.2600	0.2508	0.2194	0.1715	0.1168	0.0661	0.0283	0.0074	0.0006
	6	0.2119	0.2508	0.2716	0.2668	0.2336	0.1762	0.1069	0.0446	0.0077
	7	0.1110	0.1612	0.2162	0.2668	0.3003	0.3020	0.2597	0.1722	0.0629
	8	0.0339	0.0605	0.1004	0.1556	0.2253	0.3020	0.3679	0.3874	0.2985
	9	0.0046	0.0101	0.0207	0.0404	0.0751	0.1342	0.2316	0.3874	0.6302
10	0	0.0003	0.0001	0.0000	0.0000	0.0000	0.0000	0.0000	0.0000	0.0000
	1	0.0042	0.0016	0.0005	0.0001	0.0000	0.0000	0.0000	0.0000	0.0000
	2	0.0229	0.0106	0.0043	0.0014	0.0004	0.0001	0.0000	0.0000	0.0000
	3	0.0746	0.0425	0.0212	0.0090	0.0031	0.0008	0.0001	0.0000	0.0000
	4	0.1596	0.1115	0.0689	0.0368	0.0162	0.0055	0.0012	0.0001	0.0000
	5	0.2340	0.2007	0.1536	0.1029	0.0584	0.0264	0.0085	0.0015	0.0001
	6	0.2384	0.2508	0.2377	0.2001	0.1460	0.0881	0.0401	0.0112	0.0010
	7	0.1665	0.2150	0.2522	0.2668	0.2503	0.2013	0.1298	0.0574	0.0105
	8	0.0763	0.1209	0.1757	0.2335	0.2816	0.3020	0.2759	0.1937	0.0746
	9	0.0207	0.0403	0.0725	0.1211	0.1877	0.2684	0.3474	0.3874	0.3151
	10	0.0025	0.0060	0.0135	0.0282	0.0563	0.1074	0.1969	0.3487	0.5987

						P				
n	r	0.55	0.60	0.65	0.70	0.75	0.80	0.85	0.90	0.95
15	0	0.0000	0.0000	0.0000	0.0000	0.0000	0.0000	0.0000	0.0000	0.0000
	1	0.0001	0.0000	0.0000	0.0000	0.0000	0.0000	0.0000	0.0000	0.0000
	2	0.0010	0.0003	0.0001	0.0000	0.0000	0.0000	0.0000	0.0000	0.0000
	3	0.0052	0.0016	0.0004	0.0001	0.0000	0.0000	0.0000	0.0000	0.0000
	4	0.0191	0.0074	0.0024	0.0006	0.0001	0.0000	0.0000	0.0000	0.0000
	5	0.0515	0.0245	0.0096	0.0030	0.0007	0.0001	0.0000	0.0000	0.0000
	6	0.1048	0.0612	0.0298	0.0116	0.0034	0.0007	0.0001	0.0000	0.0000
	7	0.1647	0.1181	0.0710	0.0348	0.0131	0.0035	0.0005	0.0000	0.0000
	8	0.2013	0.1771	0.1319	0.0811	0.0393	0.0138	0.0030	0.0003	0.0000
	9	0.1914	0.2066	0.1906	0.1472	0.0917	0.0430	0.0132	0.0019	0.0000
	10	0.1404	0.1859	0.2123	0.2061	0.1651	0.1032	0.0449	0.0105	0.0006
	11	0.0780	0.1268	0.1792	0.2186	0.2252	0.1876	0.1156	0.0428	0.0049
	12	0.0318	0.0634	0.1110	0.1700	0.2252	0.2501	0.2184	0.1285	0.0307
	13	0.0090	0.0219	0.0476	0.0916	0.1559	0.2309	0.2856	0.2669	0.1348
	14	0.0016	0.0047	0.0126	0.0305	0.0668	0.1319	0.2312	0.3432	0.3658
	15	0.0001	0.0005	0.0016	0.0047	0.0134	0.0352	0.0874	0.2059	0.4633
20	0	0.0000	0.0000	0.0000	0.0000	0.0000	0.0000	0.0000	0.0000	0.0000
	1	0.0000	0.0000	0.0000	0.0000	0.0000	0.0000	0.0000	0.0000	0.0000
	2	0.0000	0.0000	0.0000	0.0000	0.0000	0.0000	0.0000	0.0000	0.0000
	3	0.0002	0.0000	0.0000	0.0000	0.0000	0.0000	0.0000	0.0000	0.0000
	4	0.0013	0.0003	0.0000	0.0000	0.0000	0.0000	0.0000	0.0000	0.0000
	5	0.0049	0.0013	0.0003	0.0000	0.0000	0.0000	0.0000	0.0000	0.0000
	6	0.0150	0.0049	0.0012	0.0002	0.0000	0.0000	0.0000	0.0000	0.0000
	7	0.0366	0.0146	0.0045	0.0010	0.0002	0.0000	0.0000	0.0000	0.0000
	8	0.0727	0.0355	0.0136	0.0039	0.0008	0.0001	0.0000	0.0000	0.0000
	9	0.1185	0.0710	0.0336	0.0120	0.0030	0.0005	0.0000	0.0000	0.0000
	10	0.1593	0.1171	0.0686	0.0308	0.0099	0.0020	0.0002	0.0000	0.0000
	11	0.1771	0.1597	0.1158	0.0654	0.0271	0.0074	0.0011	0.0001	0.0000
	12	0.1623	0.1797	0.1614	0.1144	0.0609	0.0222	0.0046	0.0004	0.0000
	13	0.1221	0.1659	0.1844	0.1643	0.1124	0.0545	0.0160	0.0020	0.0000
	14	0.0746	0.1244	0.1712	0.1916	0.1686	0.1091	0.0454	0.0089	0.0003
	15	0.0365	0.0746	0.1272	0.1789	0.2023	0.1746	0.1028	0.0319	0.0022
	16	0.0139	0.0350	0.0738	0.1304	0.1897	0.2182	0.1821	0.0898	0.0133
	17	0.0040	0.0123	0.0323	0.0716	0.1339	0.2054	0.2428	0.1901	0.0596
	18	0.0008	0.0031	0.0100	0.0278	0.0669	0.1369	0.2293	0.2852	0.1887
	19	0.0001	0.0005	0.0020	0.0068	0.0211	0.0576	0.1368	0.2702	0.3774
	20	0.0000	0.0000	0.0002	0.0008	0.0032	0.0115	0.0388	0.1216	0.3585

Appendix: Values of $e^{-\lambda}$ for Use in the Poisson Distribution

λ	$e^{-\lambda}$	λ	$e^{-\lambda}$
0.0	1.0000	3.1	0.0450
0.1	0.9048	3.2	0.0408
0.2	0.8187	3.3	0.0369
0.3	0.7408	3.4	0.0334
0.4	0.6703	3.5	0.0302
0.5	0.6065	3.6	0.0273
0.6	0.5488	3.7	0.0247
0.7	0.4966	3.8	0.0224
0.8	0.4493	3.9	0.0202
0.9	0.4066	4.0	0.0183
1.0	0.3679	4.1	0.0166
1.1	0.3329	4.2	0.0150
1.2	0.3012	4.3	0.0136
1.3	0.2725	4.4	0.0123
1.4	0.2466	4.5	0.0111
1.5	0.2231	4.6	0.0101
1.6	0.2019	4.7	0.0091
1.7	0.1827	4.8	0.0082
1.8	0.1653	4.9	0.0074
1.9	0.1496	5.0	0.0067
2.0	0.1353	5.1	0.0061
2.1	0.1225	5.2	0.0055
2.2	0.1108	5.3	0.0050
2.3	0.1003	5.4	0.0045
2.4	0.0907	5.5	0.0041
2.5	0.0821	5.6	0.0037
2.6	0.0743	5.7	0.0033
2.7	0.0672	5.8	0.0030
2.8	0.0608	5.9	0.0027
2.9	0.0550	6.0	0.0025
3.0	0.0498		

Appendix: F Distribution Values

F distribution table for the upper 5% probability ($\alpha = 0.05$).

df2	df1																
	1	2	3	4	5	6	7	8	9	10	12	15	20	24	30	120	∞
1	161.4	199.5	215.7	224.6	230.2	234.0	236.8	238.9	240.5	241.9	243.9	245.9	248.0	249.0	250.1	253.3	254.3
2	18.51	19.00	19.16	19.25	19.30	19.33	19.35	19.37	19.38	19.40	19.41	19.43	19.45	19.45	19.46	19.49	19.50
3	10.13	9.55	9.28	9.12	9.01	8.94	8.89	8.85	8.81	8.79	8.74	8.70	8.66	8.64	8.62	8.55	8.53
4	7.71	6.94	6.59	6.39	6.26	6.16	6.09	6.04	6.00	5.96	5.91	5.86	5.80	5.77	5.75	5.66	5.63
5	6.61	5.79	5.41	5.19	5.05	4.95	4.88	4.82	4.77	4.74	4.68	4.62	4.56	4.53	4.50	4.40	4.36
6	5.99	5.14	4.76	4.53	4.39	4.28	4.21	4.15	4.10	4.06	4.00	3.94	3.87	3.84	3.81	3.70	3.67
7	5.59	4.74	4.35	4.12	3.97	3.87	3.79	3.73	3.68	3.64	3.57	3.51	3.44	3.41	3.38	3.27	3.23
8	5.32	4.46	4.07	3.84	3.69	3.58	3.50	3.44	3.39	3.35	3.28	3.22	3.15	3.12	3.08	2.97	2.93
9	5.12	4.26	3.86	3.63	3.48	3.37	3.29	3.23	3.18	3.14	3.07	3.01	2.94	2.90	2.86	2.75	2.71
10	4.96	4.10	3.71	3.48	3.33	3.22	3.14	3.07	3.02	2.98	2.91	2.85	2.77	2.74	2.70	2.58	2.54
11	4.84	3.98	3.59	3.36	3.20	3.09	3.01	2.95	2.90	2.85	2.79	2.72	2.65	2.61	2.57	2.45	2.40
12	4.75	3.89	3.49	3.26	3.11	3.00	2.91	2.85	2.80	2.75	2.69	2.62	2.54	2.51	2.47	2.34	2.30
13	4.67	3.81	3.41	3.18	3.03	2.92	2.83	2.77	2.71	2.67	2.60	2.53	2.46	2.42	2.38	2.25	2.21
14	4.60	3.74	3.34	3.11	2.96	2.85	2.76	2.70	2.65	2.60	2.53	2.46	2.39	2.35	2.31	2.18	2.13
15	4.54	3.68	3.29	3.06	2.90	2.79	2.71	2.64	2.59	2.54	2.48	2.40	2.33	2.29	2.25	2.11	2.07
16	4.49	3.63	3.24	3.01	2.85	2.74	2.66	2.59	2.54	2.49	2.42	2.35	2.28	2.24	2.19	2.06	2.01
17	4.45	3.59	3.20	2.96	2.81	2.70	2.61	2.55	2.49	2.45	2.38	2.31	2.23	2.19	2.15	2.01	1.96
18	4.41	3.55	3.16	2.93	2.77	2.66	2.58	2.51	2.46	2.41	2.34	2.27	2.19	2.15	2.11	1.97	1.92
19	4.38	3.52	3.13	2.90	2.74	2.63	2.54	2.48	2.42	2.38	2.31	2.23	2.16	2.11	2.07	1.93	1.88
20	4.35	3.49	3.10	2.87	2.71	2.60	2.51	2.45	2.39	2.35	2.28	2.20	2.12	2.08	2.04	1.90	1.84
24	4.26	3.40	3.01	2.78	2.62	2.51	2.42	2.36	2.30	2.25	2.18	2.11	2.03	1.98	1.94	1.79	1.73
30	4.17	3.32	2.92	2.69	2.53	2.42	2.33	2.27	2.21	2.16	2.09	2.01	1.93	1.89	1.84	1.68	1.62
40	4.08	3.23	2.84	2.61	2.45	2.34	2.25	2.18	2.12	2.08	2.00	1.92	1.84	1.79	1.74	1.58	1.51
60	4.00	3.15	2.76	2.53	2.37	2.25	2.17	2.10	2.04	1.99	1.92	1.84	1.75	1.70	1.65	1.47	1.39
120	3.92	3.07	2.68	2.45	2.29	2.18	2.09	2.02	1.96	1.91	1.83	1.75	1.66	1.61	1.55	1.35	1.25
∞	3.84	3.00	2.60	2.37	2.21	2.10	2.01	1.94	1.88	1.83	1.75	1.67	1.57	1.52	1.46	1.22	1.00

F distribution table for the upper 1% probability ($\alpha = 0.01$).

df2 \ df1	1	2	3	4	5	6	7	8	9	10	12	15	20	24	30	120	∞
1	4052	5000	5403	5625	5764	5859	5928	5982	6022.5	6056	6106	6157	6209	6235	6261	6339	6366
2	98.50	99.00	99.17	99.25	99.30	99.33	99.36	99.37	99.39	99.40	99.42	99.43	99.45	99.46	99.47	99.49	99.50
3	34.12	30.82	29.46	28.71	28.24	27.91	27.67	27.49	27.35	27.23	27.05	26.87	26.69	26.60	26.50	26.22	26.13
4	21.20	18.00	16.69	15.98	15.52	15.21	14.98	14.80	14.66	14.55	14.37	14.20	14.02	13.93	13.84	13.56	13.46
5	16.26	13.27	12.06	11.39	10.97	10.67	10.46	10.29	10.16	10.05	9.89	9.72	9.55	9.47	9.38	9.11	9.02
6	13.75	10.92	9.78	9.15	8.75	8.47	8.26	8.10	7.98	7.87	7.72	7.56	7.40	7.31	7.23	6.97	6.88
7	12.25	9.55	8.45	7.85	7.46	7.19	6.99	6.84	6.72	6.62	6.47	6.31	6.16	6.07	5.99	5.74	5.65
8	11.26	8.65	7.59	7.01	6.63	6.37	6.18	6.03	5.91	5.81	5.67	5.52	5.36	5.28	5.20	4.95	4.86
9	10.56	8.02	6.99	6.42	6.06	5.80	5.61	5.47	5.35	5.26	5.11	4.96	4.81	4.73	4.65	4.40	4.31
10	10.04	7.56	6.55	5.99	5.64	5.39	5.20	5.06	4.94	4.85	4.71	4.56	4.41	4.33	4.25	4.00	3.91
11	9.65	7.21	6.22	5.67	5.32	5.07	4.89	4.74	4.63	4.54	4.40	4.25	4.10	4.02	3.94	3.69	3.60
12	9.33	6.93	5.95	5.41	5.06	4.82	4.64	4.50	4.39	4.30	4.16	4.01	3.86	3.78	3.70	3.45	3.36
13	9.07	6.70	5.74	5.21	4.86	4.62	4.44	4.30	4.19	4.10	3.96	3.82	3.66	3.59	3.51	3.25	3.17
14	8.86	6.51	5.56	5.04	4.69	4.46	4.28	4.14	4.03	3.94	3.80	3.66	3.51	3.43	3.35	3.09	3.00
15	8.68	6.36	5.42	4.89	4.56	4.32	4.14	4.00	3.89	3.80	3.67	3.52	3.37	3.29	3.21	2.96	2.87
16	8.53	6.23	5.29	4.77	4.44	4.20	4.03	3.89	3.78	3.69	3.55	3.41	3.26	3.18	3.10	2.84	2.75
17	8.40	6.11	5.18	4.67	4.34	4.10	3.93	3.79	3.68	3.59	3.46	3.31	3.16	3.08	3.00	2.75	2.65
18	8.29	6.01	5.09	4.58	4.25	4.01	3.84	3.71	3.60	3.51	3.37	3.23	3.08	3.00	2.92	2.66	2.57
19	8.18	5.93	5.01	4.50	4.17	3.94	3.77	3.63	3.52	3.43	3.30	3.15	3.00	2.92	2.84	2.58	2.49
20	8.10	5.85	4.94	4.43	4.10	3.87	3.70	3.56	3.46	3.37	3.23	3.09	2.94	2.86	2.78	2.52	2.42
24	7.82	5.61	4.72	4.22	3.90	3.67	3.50	3.36	3.26	3.17	3.03	2.89	2.74	2.66	2.58	2.31	2.21
30	7.56	5.39	4.51	4.02	3.70	3.47	3.30	3.17	3.07	2.98	2.84	2.70	2.55	2.47	2.39	2.11	2.01
40	7.31	5.18	4.31	3.83	3.51	3.29	3.12	2.99	2.89	2.80	2.66	2.52	2.37	2.29	2.20	1.92	1.80
60	7.08	4.98	4.13	3.65	3.34	3.12	2.95	2.82	2.72	2.63	2.50	2.35	2.20	2.12	2.03	1.73	1.60
120	6.85	4.79	3.95	3.48	3.17	2.96	2.79	2.66	2.56	2.47	2.34	2.19	2.03	1.95	1.86	1.53	1.38
∞	6.63	4.61	3.78	3.32	3.02	2.80	2.64	2.51	2.41	2.32	2.18	2.04	1.88	1.79	1.70	1.32	1.00

Appendix: Using POM-QM for Windows

Welcome to POM-QM for Windows. Along with its companion Excel QM (see Appendix: Using Excel QM and Excel Add-Ins), it makes available to you the most user-friendly software available for the field of quantitative analysis/quantitative methods (QA/QM). This software may also be used for the field of production/operations management (POM). It is possible to display all of the modules, only the QM modules, or only the POM modules. Because this text is about quantitative methods, only the QM modules are shown throughout the textbook, and this software is referenced as QM for Windows. QM for Windows is a package that has been designed to help you to better learn and understand this field. The software can be used to either solve problems or check answers that have been derived by hand. You will find that this software is exceptionally friendly due to the following features:

- Anyone familiar with any standard spreadsheet or word processor in Windows will easily be able to use QM for Windows. All modules have help screens that can be accessed at any time.

- The screens for every module are consistent, so that when you become accustomed to using one module, you will have an easy time with the other modules.

- The spreadsheet-type data editor allows full screen editing.

- Files are opened and saved in the usual Windows fashion, and in addition, files are named by module, which makes it easy to find files saved previously.

- It is easy to change from one solution method to another to compare methods and answers.

- Graphs are easily displayed and printed.

Installing POM-QM for Windows

Go to the Companion Website for this text to download and install the POM-QM for Windows software. Instructions are provided on how to download, install, and register the software.

After the installation and registration is complete, you will have a program group added to your Program Manager. The group will be called POM-QM for Windows 3. In addition, a shortcut to the program will be placed on the desktop. To use the QM for Windows program, double-click on the shortcut on the desktop or use Start, POM-QM for Windows 3, POM-QM for Windows.

When you use QM for Windows for the first time, you should select Help from the menu bar, and then select PDF Manual or Word Manual to obtain complete instructions on using the software. Brief instructions will be provided in this appendix.

The first screen that is displayed in QM for Windows contains the assorted components that are available on most screens. The top of that screen is the standard Windows title bar. Below the title bar is a standard Windows menu bar. The details of the eight menu options File, Edit, View, Module, Format, Tools, Window, and Help are explained in this appendix. Upon starting QM for Windows, some of the menu options such as Edit and Format may not be available. They will become available when a module is selected or when a problem is entered.

Below the menu are two toolbars: a standard toolbar and a format toolbar. The toolbars contain standard shortcuts for several of the menu commands. If you move the mouse over the button for about two seconds, an explanation of the button will be displayed on the screen.

The next bar contains an instruction. There is always an instruction here trying to help you to figure out what to do or what to enter. Currently, the instruction indicates to select a module or open a file. When data are to be entered into the data table, this instruction will explain what type of data (integer, real, positive, etc.) are to be entered.

Solving a problem
There are several ways to solve a problem. The easiest way is to press the Solve button on the standard toolbar. Alternatively, the function key F9 may be used. Finally, if you press the enter key after the last piece of data is entered, the problem will be solved. After solving a problem, to return to editing the data press the Edit button, which has replaced the Solve button on the standard toolbar, or use F9.

Creating a New Problem

To enter a new problem, select Module to see the list of available techniques. Click the module you wish to use based on the type of problem to be solved. Next you either click the icon to enter a new problem or open a previously saved problem, or you select **File** and then **New** or **Open**. In some modules, when New is selected, there will be a menu of submodules. Where this is the case, one of these must be selected before the problem is entered.

The top line of the creation screen contains a text box in which the title of the problem can be entered. For many modules it is necessary to enter the number of rows in the problem. Rows will have different names depending on the modules. For example, in linear programming, rows are constraints, whereas in forecasting, rows are past periods. The number of rows can be chosen with either the scroll bar or the text box.

POM-QM for Windows has the capability to allow you different options for the default row and column names. Select one of the radio buttons to indicate which style of default naming should be used. In most modules the row names are not used for computations, but you should be careful because in some modules (most notably, Project Management) the names might relate to precedences.

Many modules require you to enter the number of columns. This is given in the same way as the number of rows. All row and column names can be changed in the data table.

Some modules will have an extra option box, such as for choosing minimize or maximize or selecting whether distances are symmetric. Select one of these options. In most cases this option can later be changed on the data screen.

When you are satisfied with your choices, click on the **OK** button or press the **Enter** key. At this point, a blank data screen will be displayed. Screens will differ from module to module.

Entering and Editing Data

Enter

This key moves from cell to cell in the order from left to right, from top to bottom, skipping the first column (which usually contains names). Therefore, when entering a table of data, if you start at the upper left and work your way to the lower right row by row, this key is exceptionally useful.

After a new data set has been created or an existing data set has been loaded, the data can be edited. Every entry is in a row and column position. You navigate through the spreadsheet using the cursor movement keys. These keys function in a regular way with one exception—the **Enter** key.

The instruction bar on the screen will contain a brief instruction describing what is to be done. There are essentially three types of cells in the data table. One type is a regular data cell into which you enter either a name or a number. A second type is a cell that cannot be changed. A third type is a cell that contains a drop-down box. For example, the signs in a linear programming constraint are chosen from this type of box. To see all of the options, press the box with the arrow.

There is one more aspect to the data screen that needs to be considered. Some modules need extra data above that in the table. In most of these cases the data are contained in text/scrollbar combinations that appear on top of the data table.

Solution Displays

Numerical Formatting

Formatting is handled by the program automatically. For example, in most cases the number 1000 will automatically be formatted as 1,000. Do not type the comma. The program will prevent you from doing so!

At this point you can press the **Solve** button to begin the solution process. A new screen will be displayed.

An important thing to notice is that there is more solution information available. This can be seen by the icons given at the bottom. Click on these to view the information. Alternatively, notice that the Window option in the main menu is now enabled. It is always enabled at solution time. Even if the icons are covered by a window, the Window option will always allow you to view the other solution windows.

Now that we have examined how to create and solve a problem we explain all of the Menu options that are available.

File

File contains the usual options that one finds in Windows:

New   As demonstrated before, this is chosen to begin a new problem/file.

Open   This is used to open/load a previously saved file. File selection is the standard Windows common dialog type. Notice that the extension for files in the QM for Windows system is given by the first three letters of the module name. For example, all linear programming files have the extension *.lin. When you go to the open dialog, the default value is for the program to look for files of the type in this module. This can be changed at the bottom left where it says "Files of Type."

Deleting Files

It is not possible to delete a file using QM for Windows. Use the Windows file manager to do so.

The names that are legal are standard file names. Case (upper or lower) does not matter. You may type them in as uppercase, lowercase, or mixed. In all of the examples, QM for Windows will add the three-letter extension to the end of the file name. For example, linear programming problem will become *linear programming problem.lin* (assuming that it is indeed a linear programming problem).

Save   Save will replace the file without asking you if you care about overwriting the previous version of this file. If you try to save and have not previously named the file, you will be asked to name this file.

Save as Save as will prompt you for a file name before saving. This option is very similar to the option to load a data file. When you choose this option, the Save As Dialog Box for Files will be displayed.

Save as Excel File Save as Excel File saves a file as an Excel file with both the data and appropriate formulas for the solutions and is available for some but not all of the modules.

Save as HTML Save as HTML saves the tables as an HTML formatted file that can immediately be placed on the Internet.

Print Print will display a print menu screen with four tabs. The Information tab allows you to select which of the output tables should be printed. The Page Header tab allows you to control the information displayed at the top of the page. The Layout tab controls the printing style. Information may be printed as plain ASCII text or as a table (grid) resembling the table on the screen. Try both types of printing and see which one you/your instructor prefers. The Print tab allows certain print settings to be changed.

Exit the Program The last option on the File menu is Exit. This will exit the program if you are on the data screen or exit the solution screen and return to the data screen if you are on the solution screen. This can also be achieved by pressing the Edit command button on the solution screen.

Edit

The commands under Edit have three purposes. The first four commands are used to insert or delete rows or columns. The next command is used to copy an entry from one cell to all cells below it in the column. This is not often useful, but when it is useful it saves a great deal of work. The last two entries can be used to copy the data table to other Windows programs.

View

View has several options that enable you to customize the appearance of the screen. The toolbar can be displayed or not. The Instruction bar can be displayed at its default location above the data or below the data, as a floating window, or not at all. The status bar can be displayed or not.

Colors can be set to monochrome (black and white) or from this state to their original colors.

Module

The module selection contains a list of programs available with this text.

Format

Format also has several options for the display. The colors for the entire screen can be set, and the font type and size for the table can be set. Zeros can be set to display as blanks rather than zeros. The problem title that is displayed in the data table and was created at the creation screen can be changed. The table can be squeezed or expanded. That is, the column widths can be decreased or increased. The input can be checked or not.

Tools

The Tools menu option is an area available to annotate problems. If you want to write a note to yourself about the problem, select annotation; the note will be saved with the file if you save the file.

A calculator is available for simple calculations, including square root. There is a normal distribution calculator that can be used for finding confidence intervals and the like.

A normal distribution calculator is found in the Tools menu option.

Window

The Window menu option is enabled only at the solution screen. Additional output is available under Window. The type of output depends on the module being used.

Help

The Help menu option provides information about the software in general as well as about the individual modules. The first time you run POM-QM for Windows, you should select Help and choose Program Update to ensure that your software has the latest updates.

Help also contains a manual with further details about the program, a link to a program update and a link for e-mail support. If you send mail, be sure to include the name of the program (POM-QM for Windows), the version of the program (from Help, About), the module in which the problem is occurring, and a detailed explanation of the problem, and to attach the data file for which the problem occurs.

Appendix: Using Excel QM and Excel Add-Ins

Excel QM

Excel QM has been designed to help you to better learn and understand both quantitative analysis and Excel. Even though the software contains many modules and submodules, the screens for every module are consistent and easy to use.

Excel QM is an add-in to Excel, so you must have Excel on your PC. To install Excel QM, go to the Companion Website for instructions and the free download. An Excel QM icon will be placed on your desktop.

To run Excel QM, click the icon on the desktop and Excel will start with the Excel QM add-in available. In addition to the usual Excel tabs, a tab for Excel QM will appear. Click this to see the Excel QM ribbon. There are two items on this ribbon that can be used to access the available techniques. The first way is to select **By Chapter**, which will show the techniques arranged by chapter number. The second way is to select **Alphabetical**, which will display the techniques in alphabetical order. Using either of these, select the appropriate technique based on the problem you want to enter. A window will open for you to input information about the problem, such as the number of variables or the number of observations. When you click **OK**, a spreadsheet that has been initialized will appear. Instructions are included in a text box that appears just below the title that has been given to that problem. These instructions typically indicate what you must enter on the worksheet and, for certain methods, what other steps are necessary to obtain the final solution. For many of the modules, no further steps are necessary. For others, such as linear programming, Excel QM will have provided the inputs and made the necessary selections for the use of Solver.

Excel QM serves two purposes in the learning process. First, it can simply help you solve homework problems. You enter the appropriate data, and the program provides numerical solutions. QM for Windows operates on the same principle. But Excel QM allows for a second approach, that is, noting the Excel *formulas* used to develop solutions and modifying them to deal with a wider variety of problems. This "open" approach allows you to observe, understand, and even change the formulas underlying the Excel calculations, conveying Excel's power as a quantitative analysis tool.

Technical Support for Excel QM

If you have technical problems with either POM-QM for Windows or Excel QM that your instructor cannot answer, send an e-mail to the address found at the www.prenhall.com/weiss website. If you send e-mail, be sure to include the name of the program (POM-QM for Windows or Excel QM), the version of the program (from Help, About in POM-QM for Windows; from QM About in Excel QM), the module in which the problem is occurring, and a detailed explanation of the problem, and to attach the data file for which the problem occurs (if appropriate).

Activating Excel Add-Ins in Excel 2013 and 2010

Two important Excel add-ins are Solver and Analysis ToolPak. Both of these are a part of Excel but must be activated or loaded before you can use them the first time. To load these add-ins, follow these steps:

1. For Excel 2013 and 2010, click the **File** tab, click **Options**, and then click **Add-Ins**.
2. In the Manage box, select **Excel Add-Ins** and click **Go**.
3. Check the boxes next to Analysis ToolPak and Solver Add-In, and then click **OK**.

The Data tab now displays Solver and Data Analysis every time Excel is started.

Appendix

Tables

Table 1 Binomial Probabilities

								p							
n	x	.01	.05	.10	.20	.30	.40	.50	.60	.70	.80	.90	.95	.99	x
2	0	.980	.902	.810	.640	.490	.360	.250	.160	.090	.040	.010	.002	0+	0
	1	.020	.095	.180	.320	.420	.480	.500	.480	.420	.320	.180	.095	.020	1
	2	0+	.002	.010	.040	.090	.160	.250	.360	.490	.640	.810	.902	.980	2
3	0	.970	.857	.729	.512	.343	.216	.125	.064	.027	.008	.001	0+	0+	0
	1	.029	.135	.243	.384	.441	.432	.375	.288	.189	.096	.027	.007	0+	1
	2	0+	.007	.027	.096	.189	.288	.375	.432	.441	.384	.243	.135	.029	2
	3	0+	0+	.001	.008	.027	.064	.125	.216	.343	.512	.729	.857	.970	3
4	0	.961	.815	.656	.410	.240	.130	.062	.026	.008	.002	0+	0+	0+	0
	1	.039	.171	.292	.410	.412	.346	.250	.154	.076	.026	.004	0+	0+	1
	2	.001	.014	.049	.154	.265	.346	.375	.346	.265	.154	.049	.014	.001	2
	3	0+	0+	.004	.026	.076	.154	.250	.346	.412	.410	.292	.171	.039	3
	4	0+	0+	0+	.002	.008	.026	.062	.130	.240	.410	.656	.815	.961	4
5	0	.951	.774	.590	.328	.168	.078	.031	.010	.002	0+	0+	0+	0+	0
	1	.048	.204	.328	.410	.360	.259	.156	.077	.028	.006	0+	0+	0+	1
	2	.001	.021	.073	.205	.309	.346	.312	.230	.132	.051	.008	.001	0+	2
	3	0+	.001	.008	.051	.132	.230	.312	.346	.309	.205	.073	.021	.001	3
	4	0+	0+	0+	.006	.028	.077	.156	.259	.360	.410	.328	.204	.048	4
	5	0+	0+	0+	0+	.002	.010	.031	.078	.168	.328	.590	.774	.951	5
6	0	.941	.735	.531	.262	.118	.047	.016	.004	.001	0+	0+	0+	0+	0
	1	.057	.232	.354	.393	.303	.187	.094	.037	.010	.002	0+	0+	0+	1
	2	.001	.031	.098	.246	.324	.311	.234	.138	.060	.015	.001	0+	0+	2
	3	0+	.002	.015	.082	.185	.276	.312	.276	.185	.082	.015	.002	0+	3
	4	0+	0+	.001	.015	.060	.138	.234	.311	.324	.246	.098	.031	.001	4
	5	0+	0+	0+	.002	.010	.037	.094	.187	.303	.393	.354	.232	.057	5
	6	0+	0+	0+	0+	.001	.004	.016	.047	.118	.262	.531	.735	.941	6
7	0	.932	.698	.478	.210	.082	.028	.008	.002	0+	0+	0+	0+	0+	0
	1	.066	.257	.372	.367	.247	.131	.055	.017	.004	0+	0+	0+	0+	1
	2	.002	.041	.124	.275	.318	.261	.164	.077	.025	.004	0+	0+	0+	2
	3	0+	.004	.023	.115	.227	.290	.273	.194	.097	.029	.003	0+	0+	3
	4	0+	0+	.003	.029	.097	.194	.273	.290	.227	.115	.023	.004	0+	4
	5	0+	0+	0+	.004	.025	.077	.164	.261	.318	.275	.124	.041	.002	5
	6	0+	0+	0+	0+	.004	.017	.055	.131	.247	.367	.372	.257	.066	6
	7	0+	0+	0+	0+	0+	.002	.008	.028	.082	.210	.478	.698	.932	7
8	0	.923	.663	.430	.168	.058	.017	.004	.001	0+	0+	0+	0+	0+	0
	1	.075	.279	.383	.336	.198	.090	.031	.008	.001	0+	0+	0+	0+	1
	2	.003	.051	.149	.294	.296	.209	.109	.041	.010	.001	0+	0+	0+	2
	3	0+	.005	.033	.147	.254	.279	.219	.124	.047	.009	0+	0+	0+	3
	4	0+	0+	.005	.046	.136	.232	.273	.232	.136	.046	.005	0+	0+	4
	5	0+	0+	0+	.009	.047	.124	.219	.279	.254	.147	.033	.005	0+	5
	6	0+	0+	0+	.001	.010	.041	.109	.209	.296	.294	.149	.051	.003	6
	7	0+	0+	0+	0+	.001	.008	.031	.090	.198	.336	.383	.279	.075	7
	8	0+	0+	0+	0+	0+	.001	.004	.017	.058	.168	.430	.663	.923	8

NOTE: 0+ represents a positive probability less than 0.0005.
From Frederick C. Mosteller, Robert E. K. Rourke, and George B. Thomas, Jr., *Probability with Statistical Applications,* 2nd ed., © 1970. Reprinted and electronically reproduced by permission of Pearson Education, Inc., Upper Saddle River, New Jersey.

NEGATIVE *z* Scores

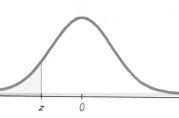

Table 2 Standard Normal (*z*) Distribution: Cumulative Area from the LEFT

z	.00	.01	.02	.03	.04	.05	.06	.07	.08	.09
−3.50 and lower	.0001									
−3.4	.0003	.0003	.0003	.0003	.0003	.0003	.0003	.0003	.0003	.0002
−3.3	.0005	.0005	.0005	.0004	.0004	.0004	.0004	.0004	.0004	.0003
−3.2	.0007	.0007	.0006	.0006	.0006	.0006	.0006	.0005	.0005	.0005
−3.1	.0010	.0009	.0009	.0009	.0008	.0008	.0008	.0008	.0007	.0007
−3.0	.0013	.0013	.0013	.0012	.0012	.0011	.0011	.0011	.0010	.0010
−2.9	.0019	.0018	.0018	.0017	.0016	.0016	.0015	.0015	.0014	.0014
−2.8	.0026	.0025	.0024	.0023	.0023	.0022	.0021	.0021	.0020	.0019
−2.7	.0035	.0034	.0033	.0032	.0031	.0030	.0029	.0028	.0027	.0026
−2.6	.0047	.0045	.0044	.0043	.0041	.0040	.0039	.0038	.0037	.0036
−2.5	.0062	.0060	.0059	.0057	.0055	.0054	.0052	.0051 *	.0049	.0048
−2.4	.0082	.0080	.0078	.0075	.0073	.0071	.0069	.0068	.0066	.0064
−2.3	.0107	.0104	.0102	.0099	.0096	.0094	.0091	.0089	.0087	.0084
−2.2	.0139	.0136	.0132	.0129	.0125	.0122	.0119	.0116	.0113	.0110
−2.1	.0179	.0174	.0170	.0166	.0162	.0158	.0154	.0150	.0146	.0143
−2.0	.0228	.0222	.0217	.0212	.0207	.0202	.0197	.0192	.0188	.0183
−1.9	.0287	.0281	.0274	.0268	.0262	.0256	.0250	.0244	.0239	.0233
−1.8	.0359	.0351	.0344	.0336	.0329	.0322	.0314	.0307	.0301	.0294
−1.7	.0446	.0436	.0427	.0418	.0409	.0401	.0392	.0384	.0375	.0367
−1.6	.0548	.0537	.0526	.0516	.0505 *	.0495	.0485	.0475	.0465	.0455
−1.5	.0668	.0655	.0643	.0630	.0618	.0606	.0594	.0582	.0571	.0559
−1.4	.0808	.0793	.0778	.0764	.0749	.0735	.0721	.0708	.0694	.0681
−1.3	.0968	.0951	.0934	.0918	.0901	.0885	.0869	.0853	.0838	.0823
−1.2	.1151	.1131	.1112	.1093	.1075	.1056	.1038	.1020	.1003	.0985
−1.1	.1357	.1335	.1314	.1292	.1271	.1251	.1230	.1210	.1190	.1170
−1.0	.1587	.1562	.1539	.1515	.1492	.1469	.1446	.1423	.1401	.1379
−0.9	.1841	.1814	.1788	.1762	.1736	.1711	.1685	.1660	.1635	.1611
−0.8	.2119	.2090	.2061	.2033	.2005	.1977	.1949	.1922	.1894	.1867
−0.7	.2420	.2389	.2358	.2327	.2296	.2266	.2236	.2206	.2177	.2148
−0.6	.2743	.2709	.2676	.2643	.2611	.2578	.2546	.2514	.2483	.2451
−0.5	.3085	.3050	.3015	.2981	.2946	.2912	.2877	.2843	.2810	.2776
−0.4	.3446	.3409	.3372	.3336	.3300	.3264	.3228	.3192	.3156	.3121
−0.3	.3821	.3783	.3745	.3707	.3669	.3632	.3594	.3557	.3520	.3483
−0.2	.4207	.4168	.4129	.4090	.4052	.4013	.3974	.3936	.3897	.3859
−0.1	.4602	.4562	.4522	.4483	.4443	.4404	.4364	.4325	.4286	.4247
−0.0	.5000	.4960	.4920	.4880	.4840	.4801	.4761	.4721	.4681	.4641

NOTE: For values of *z* below −3.49, use 0.0001 for the area.
*Use these common values that result from interpolation:

z Score	Area
−1.645	0.0500
−2.575	0.0050

(*continued*)

POSITIVE z Scores

Table 2 *(continued)* Cumulative Area from the LEFT

z	.00	.01	.02	.03	.04	.05	.06	.07	.08	.09
0.0	.5000	.5040	.5080	.5120	.5160	.5199	.5239	.5279	.5319	.5359
0.1	.5398	.5438	.5478	.5517	.5557	.5596	.5636	.5675	.5714	.5753
0.2	.5793	.5832	.5871	.5910	.5948	.5987	.6026	.6064	.6103	.6141
0.3	.6179	.6217	.6255	.6293	.6331	.6368	.6406	.6443	.6480	.6517
0.4	.6554	.6591	.6628	.6664	.6700	.6736	.6772	.6808	.6844	.6879
0.5	.6915	.6950	.6985	.7019	.7054	.7088	.7123	.7157	.7190	.7224
0.6	.7257	.7291	.7324	.7357	.7389	.7422	.7454	.7486	.7517	.7549
0.7	.7580	.7611	.7642	.7673	.7704	.7734	.7764	.7794	.7823	.7852
0.8	.7881	.7910	.7939	.7967	.7995	.8023	.8051	.8078	.8106	.8133
0.9	.8159	.8186	.8212	.8238	.8264	.8289	.8315	.8340	.8365	.8389
1.0	.8413	.8438	.8461	.8485	.8508	.8531	.8554	.8577	.8599	.8621
1.1	.8643	.8665	.8686	.8708	.8729	.8749	.8770	.8790	.8810	.8830
1.2	.8849	.8869	.8888	.8907	.8925	.8944	.8962	.8980	.8997	.9015
1.3	.9032	.9049	.9066	.9082	.9099	.9115	.9131	.9147	.9162	.9177
1.4	.9192	.9207	.9222	.9236	.9251	.9265	.9279	.9292	.9306	.9319
1.5	.9332	.9345	.9357	.9370	.9382	.9394	.9406	.9418	.9429	.9441
1.6	.9452	.9463	.9474	.9484	.9495 *	.9505	.9515	.9525	.9535	.9545
1.7	.9554	.9564	.9573	.9582	.9591	.9599	.9608	.9616	.9625	.9633
1.8	.9641	.9649	.9656	.9664	.9671	.9678	.9686	.9693	.9699	.9706
1.9	.9713	.9719	.9726	.9732	.9738	.9744	.9750	.9756	.9761	.9767
2.0	.9772	.9778	.9783	.9788	.9793	.9798	.9803	.9808	.9812	.9817
2.1	.9821	.9826	.9830	.9834	.9838	.9842	.9846	.9850	.9854	.9857
2.2	.9861	.9864	.9868	.9871	.9875	.9878	.9881	.9884	.9887	.9890
2.3	.9893	.9896	.9898	.9901	.9904	.9906	.9909	.9911	.9913	.9916
2.4	.9918	.9920	.9922	.9925	.9927	.9929	.9931	.9932	.9934	.9936
2.5	.9938	.9940	.9941	.9943	.9945	.9946	.9948	.9949 *	.9951	.9952
2.6	.9953	.9955	.9956	.9957	.9959	.9960	.9961	.9962	.9963	.9964
2.7	.9965	.9966	.9967	.9968	.9969	.9970	.9971	.9972	.9973	.9974
2.8	.9974	.9975	.9976	.9977	.9977	.9978	.9979	.9979	.9980	.9981
2.9	.9981	.9982	.9982	.9983	.9984	.9984	.9985	.9985	.9986	.9986
3.0	.9987	.9987	.9987	.9988	.9988	.9989	.9989	.9989	.9990	.9990
3.1	.9990	.9991	.9991	.9991	.9992	.9992	.9992	.9992	.9993	.9993
3.2	.9993	.9993	.9994	.9994	.9994	.9994	.9994	.9995	.9995	.9995
3.3	.9995	.9995	.9995	.9996	.9996	.9996	.9996	.9996	.9996	.9997
3.4	.9997	.9997	.9997	.9997	.9997	.9997	.9997	.9997	.9997	.9998
3.50 and up	.9999									

NOTE: For values of *z* above 3.49, use 0.9999 for the area.

*Use these common values that result from interpolation:

z Score	Area
1.645	0.9500
2.575	0.9950

Common Critical Values

Confidence Level	Critical Value
0.90	1.645
0.95	1.96
0.99	2.575

Table 3 *t* Distribution: Critical *t* Values

Degrees of Freedom	Area in One Tail				
	0.005	0.01	0.025	0.05	0.10
	Area in Two Tails				
	0.01	0.02	0.05	0.10	0.20
1	63.657	31.821	12.706	6.314	3.078
2	9.925	6.965	4.303	2.920	1.886
3	5.841	4.541	3.182	2.353	1.638
4	4.604	3.747	2.776	2.132	1.533
5	4.032	3.365	2.571	2.015	1.476
6	3.707	3.143	2.447	1.943	1.440
7	3.499	2.998	2.365	1.895	1.415
8	3.355	2.896	2.306	1.860	1.397
9	3.250	2.821	2.262	1.833	1.383
10	3.169	2.764	2.228	1.812	1.372
11	3.106	2.718	2.201	1.796	1.363
12	3.055	2.681	2.179	1.782	1.356
13	3.012	2.650	2.160	1.771	1.350
14	2.977	2.624	2.145	1.761	1.345
15	2.947	2.602	2.131	1.753	1.341
16	2.921	2.583	2.120	1.746	1.337
17	2.898	2.567	2.110	1.740	1.333
18	2.878	2.552	2.101	1.734	1.330
19	2.861	2.539	2.093	1.729	1.328
20	2.845	2.528	2.086	1.725	1.325
21	2.831	2.518	2.080	1.721	1.323
22	2.819	2.508	2.074	1.717	1.321
23	2.807	2.500	2.069	1.714	1.319
24	2.797	2.492	2.064	1.711	1.318
25	2.787	2.485	2.060	1.708	1.316
26	2.779	2.479	2.056	1.706	1.315
27	2.771	2.473	2.052	1.703	1.314
28	2.763	2.467	2.048	1.701	1.313
29	2.756	2.462	2.045	1.699	1.311
30	2.750	2.457	2.042	1.697	1.310
31	2.744	2.453	2.040	1.696	1.309
32	2.738	2.449	2.037	1.694	1.309
33	2.733	2.445	2.035	1.692	1.308
34	2.728	2.441	2.032	1.691	1.307
35	2.724	2.438	2.030	1.690	1.306
36	2.719	2.434	2.028	1.688	1.306
37	2.715	2.431	2.026	1.687	1.305
38	2.712	2.429	2.024	1.686	1.304
39	2.708	2.426	2.023	1.685	1.304
40	2.704	2.423	2.021	1.684	1.303
45	2.690	2.412	2.014	1.679	1.301
50	2.678	2.403	2.009	1.676	1.299
60	2.660	2.390	2.000	1.671	1.296
70	2.648	2.381	1.994	1.667	1.294
80	2.639	2.374	1.990	1.664	1.292
90	2.632	2.368	1.987	1.662	1.291
100	2.626	2.364	1.984	1.660	1.290
200	2.601	2.345	1.972	1.653	1.286
300	2.592	2.339	1.968	1.650	1.284
400	2.588	2.336	1.966	1.649	1.284
500	2.586	2.334	1.965	1.648	1.283
1000	2.581	2.330	1.962	1.646	1.282
2000	2.578	2.328	1.961	1.646	1.282
Large	2.576	2.326	1.960	1.645	1.282

Left tail

α

Critical *t* value
(negative)

Right tail

α

Critical *t* value
(positive)

Two tails

$\alpha/2$ $\alpha/2$

Critical *t* value   Critical *t* value
(negative)   (positive)

Table 4 Chi-Square (χ^2) Distribution

Degrees of Freedom	Area to the Right of the Critical Value									
	0.995	0.99	0.975	0.95	0.90	0.10	0.05	0.025	0.01	0.005
1	—	—	0.001	0.004	0.016	2.706	3.841	5.024	6.635	7.879
2	0.010	0.020	0.051	0.103	0.211	4.605	5.991	7.378	9.210	10.597
3	0.072	0.115	0.216	0.352	0.584	6.251	7.815	9.348	11.345	12.838
4	0.207	0.297	0.484	0.711	1.064	7.779	9.488	11.143	13.277	14.860
5	0.412	0.554	0.831	1.145	1.610	9.236	11.071	12.833	15.086	16.750
6	0.676	0.872	1.237	1.635	2.204	10.645	12.592	14.449	16.812	18.548
7	0.989	1.239	1.690	2.167	2.833	12.017	14.067	16.013	18.475	20.278
8	1.344	1.646	2.180	2.733	3.490	13.362	15.507	17.535	20.090	21.955
9	1.735	2.088	2.700	3.325	4.168	14.684	16.919	19.023	21.666	23.589
10	2.156	2.558	3.247	3.940	4.865	15.987	18.307	20.483	23.209	25.188
11	2.603	3.053	3.816	4.575	5.578	17.275	19.675	21.920	24.725	26.757
12	3.074	3.571	4.404	5.226	6.304	18.549	21.026	23.337	26.217	28.299
13	3.565	4.107	5.009	5.892	7.042	19.812	22.362	24.736	27.688	29.819
14	4.075	4.660	5.629	6.571	7.790	21.064	23.685	26.119	29.141	31.319
15	4.601	5.229	6.262	7.261	8.547	22.307	24.996	27.488	30.578	32.801
16	5.142	5.812	6.908	7.962	9.312	23.542	26.296	28.845	32.000	34.267
17	5.697	6.408	7.564	8.672	10.085	24.769	27.587	30.191	33.409	35.718
18	6.265	7.015	8.231	9.390	10.865	25.989	28.869	31.526	34.805	37.156
19	6.844	7.633	8.907	10.117	11.651	27.204	30.144	32.852	36.191	38.582
20	7.434	8.260	9.591	10.851	12.443	28.412	31.410	34.170	37.566	39.997
21	8.034	8.897	10.283	11.591	13.240	29.615	32.671	35.479	38.932	41.401
22	8.643	9.542	10.982	12.338	14.042	30.813	33.924	36.781	40.289	42.796
23	9.260	10.196	11.689	13.091	14.848	32.007	35.172	38.076	41.638	44.181
24	9.886	10.856	12.401	13.848	15.659	33.196	36.415	39.364	42.980	45.559
25	10.520	11.524	13.120	14.611	16.473	34.382	37.652	40.646	44.314	46.928
26	11.160	12.198	13.844	15.379	17.292	35.563	38.885	41.923	45.642	48.290
27	11.808	12.879	14.573	16.151	18.114	36.741	40.113	43.194	46.963	49.645
28	12.461	13.565	15.308	16.928	18.939	37.916	41.337	44.461	48.278	50.993
29	13.121	14.257	16.047	17.708	19.768	39.087	42.557	45.722	49.588	52.336
30	13.787	14.954	16.791	18.493	20.599	40.256	43.773	46.979	50.892	53.672
40	20.707	22.164	24.433	26.509	29.051	51.805	55.758	59.342	63.691	66.766
50	27.991	29.707	32.357	34.764	37.689	63.167	67.505	71.420	76.154	79.490
60	35.534	37.485	40.482	43.188	46.459	74.397	79.082	83.298	88.379	91.952
70	43.275	45.442	48.758	51.739	55.329	85.527	90.531	95.023	100.425	104.215
80	51.172	53.540	57.153	60.391	64.278	96.578	101.879	106.629	112.329	116.321
90	59.196	61.754	65.647	69.126	73.291	107.565	113.145	118.136	124.116	128.299
100	67.328	70.065	74.222	77.929	82.358	118.498	124.342	129.561	135.807	140.169

Source: Donald B. Owen, *Handbook of Statistical Tables.*

Degrees of Freedom

$n - 1$	**Confidence interval or hypothesis test** for a standard deviation σ or variance σ^2
$k - 1$	**Goodness-of-fit** with k categories
$(r - 1)(c - 1)$	**Contingency table** with r rows and c columns
$k - 1$	**Kruskal-Wallis test** with k samples

Linear Correlation

Table 5 Critical Values of the Pearson Correlation Coefficient r

n	$\alpha = .05$	$\alpha = .01$
4	.950	.990
5	.878	.959
6	.811	.917
7	.754	.875
8	.707	.834
9	.666	.798
10	.632	.765
11	.602	.735
12	.576	.708
13	.553	.684
14	.532	.661
15	.514	.641
16	.497	.623
17	.482	.606
18	.468	.590
19	.456	.575
20	.444	.561
25	.396	.505
30	.361	.463
35	.335	.430
40	.312	.402
45	.294	.378
50	.279	.361
60	.254	.330
70	.236	.305
80	.220	.286
90	.207	.269
100	.196	.256

NOTE: To test H_0: $\rho = 0$ against H_1: $\rho \neq 0$, reject H_0 if the absolute value of r is greater than the critical value in the table.

Rank Correlation

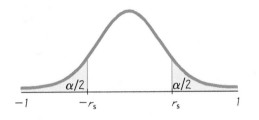

Table 6 Critical Values of Spearman's Rank Correlation Coefficient r_s

n	$\alpha = 0.10$	$\alpha = 0.05$	$\alpha = 0.02$	$\alpha = 0.01$
5	.900	—	—	—
6	.829	.886	.943	—
7	.714	.786	.893	.929
8	.643	.738	.833	.881
9	.600	.700	.783	.833
10	.564	.648	.745	.794
11	.536	.618	.709	.755
12	.503	.587	.678	.727
13	.484	.560	.648	.703
14	.464	.538	.626	.679
15	.446	.521	.604	.654
16	.429	.503	.582	.635
17	.414	.485	.566	.615
18	.401	.472	.550	.600
19	.391	.460	.535	.584
20	.380	.447	.520	.570
21	.370	.435	.508	.556
22	.361	.425	.496	.544
23	.353	.415	.486	.532
24	.344	.406	.476	.521
25	.337	.398	.466	.511
26	.331	.390	.457	.501
27	.324	.382	.448	.491
28	.317	.375	.440	.483
29	.312	.368	.433	.475
30	.306	.362	.425	.467

NOTES:
1. For $n > 30$ use $r_s = \pm z/\sqrt{n-1}$, where z corresponds to the level of significance. For example, if $\alpha = 0.05$, then $z = 1.96$.
2. If the absolute value of the test statistic r_s exceeds the positive critical value, then reject $H_0\colon \rho_s = 0$ and conclude that there is a correlation.

Based on data from *Biostatistical Analysis*, 4th edition © 1999, by Jerrold Zar, Prentice Hall, Inc., Upper Saddle River, New Jersey, and "Distribution of Sums of Squares of Rank Differences to Small Numbers with Individuals," *The Annals of Mathematical Statistics*, Vol. 9, No. 2.

Index